أطلس القرآن

أماكن، أقوام، أعلام

Atlas of
The Qur'ân

Places . Nations . Landmarks

© **Maktaba Dar-us-Salam, 2003**
King Fahd National Library Cataloging-in-Publication Data

Abu Khalil, Shawqi
Atlas of the Quran./ Shawqi Abu Khalil - Riyadh, 2003
392 p.; 17x25 cm
ISBN: 9960-897-54-0
1- Qur'ân - Indexes   I - Title
221.3 dc   1424/5483

Legal Deposit no. 1424/5483
ISBN: 9960-897-54-0

A Unique Publication for the First Time

Atlas of
The Qur'ân

Places . Nations . Landmarks

An Authentic Collection of the Qur'ânic Information
with Maps, Tables and Pictures

Compiled by
Dr. Shawqi Abu Khalil

DARUSSALAM
GLOBAL LEADER IN ISLAMIC BOOKS

Riyadh, Jeddah, Sharjah, Lahore
London, Houston, New York

First Edition: October 2003

Supervised by:

ABDUL MALIK MUJAHID

Headquarters:
P.O. Box: 22743, Riyadh 11416, KSA
Tel: 00966-1-4033962/4043432
Fax: 00966-1-4021659
E-mail: darussalam@awalnet.net.sa
Website: www.dar-us-salam.com
Bookshop: Tel: 00966-1-4614483
Fax: 00966-1-4644945

Branches & Agents:

K.S.A. Darussalam Showrooms Riyadh

• Olyah branch: Tel 00966-1-4614483
Fax: 4644945

• Malaz branch: Tel 4735220 Fax: 4735221

• Jeddah: Tel & Fax: 00966-2-6807752

• Al-Khobar: Tel: 00966-3-8692900
Fax: 00966-3-8691551

U.A.E.

• Tel: 00971-6-5632623 Fax: 5632624

PAKISTAN

• Lower Mall, Lahore
50-Lower Mall, Lahore
Tel: 0092-42-7240024 Fax: 7354072

• Rahman Market, Ghazni Street
Urdu Bazar, Lahore
Tel: 0092-42-7120054 Fax: 7320703

U. S. A.

• Houston: P.O. Box: 79194 Tx 77279
Tel: 001-713-722 0419
Fax: 001-713-722 0431
E-mail: sales @ dar-us-salam.com
Website: http:// www.dar-us-salam.com

• New York: 572 Atlantic Ave, Brooklyn
New York-11217
Tel: 001-718-625 5925

AUSTRALIA

• Lakemba NSW: ICIS: Ground Floor 165-171, Haldon St. Tel & Fax: (61-2) 9758 4040, 9758 4030

U.K.

• London: Darussalam International Publications Ltd., 226 High Street, Walthamstow, London E17 7JH U.K.
Tel: 0044-208 520 2666
Mobile: 0044-794 730 6706
Fax: 0044-208 521 7645

• Darussalam International Publications Limited, Regent Park Mosque,
146 Park Road, London NW8 7RG,
Tel: 0044-207 724 3363

FRANCE

• Editions & Libairie Essalam
135, Bd de Menilmontant 75011
Paris (France)
Tel: 01 43 381956/4483 - Fax 01 43 574431
Website: http: www.Essalam.com
E-mail: essalam@essalam.com

MALAYSIA

• E&D BOOKS SDN. BHD. - 321 B 3rd Floor, Suria Klcc Kuala Lumpur City Center 50088
Tel & Fax: 00603-21663433, 459 2032

SINGAPORE

• Muslim Converts Association of Singapore
Singapore- 424484 Tel: 440 6924, 348 8344
Fax: 440 6724

SRILANKA

• Darul Kitab 6, Nirmal Road, Colombo-4
Tel: 0094-1-589 038 Fax: 0094-74 722433

KUWAIT

• Islam Presentation Committee
Enlightenment Book Shop, P.O. Box: 1613 Safat 13017 Kuwait
Tel: 00965-244 7526 Fax: 240 0057

INDIA

• Islamic Dimensions 56/58 Tandel Street (North) Dongri, Mumbai 4000 009, India
Tel: 0091-22-3736875, Fax: 3730689

A Note From The Publisher

The Noble Qur'ân is the last Divine Book which has been revealed by Allâh for the guidance of mankind up to the Day of Resurrection. One of the bright sides of this Book is that it is read and recited much more than any other book of the world. In a real sense this very Book has encircled into it the evershining pearls of all the visible and invisible knowledge and the wisdom, the world needs for survival and eternal success. Hence the reading of the Qur'ân, understanding of its meanings and interpretations is important and obligatory on all the followers of Islam.

Muslim Community should be proud for having the last Divine Book in a well-preserved form. This blessed opportunity has not been provided to any other heavenly religion. Before the revelation of the Qur'ân, hundred of Scriptures including the three former heavenly Books as well have been annihilated. Whatever they have at hand as they disclose are nothing but only the Collections of narratives and sayings of spiritual guides. On the other hand, today the Noble Qur'ân has its originality as it was, in the hearts of lakhs of the memorizers (*Huffaz*) of the Qur'ân. As regards to its manuscripts written from time to time in various periods, their samples are available even today and found in museums, government under-taken libraries as well as many of the private libraries and various publication institutes at large scales.

After revelation of the Qur'ân, various artifice skills developed. Besides its modulation forms, some of them pertained to its literal terms – explanatory points, religious decrees, themes, topic and issue discussions etc. But along with these skills, other techniques and arts such as calligraphy, designing, printing, binding, etc., also developed.

Later on the reference of the Qur'ânic geography, descriptions of the Prophets, the Qur'ânic habitations, the Qur'ânic landmarks etc., were described in scores of the books, by the end of 20th century. But in the third millenium of the world civilization, these descriptions appeared on surface in the form of a new way of 'understanding the Qur'ân'. For the first time an effort has been made to bring out the places, personalities and nations etc., as indicated in the Qur'ân, in the form of a unique presentation comprising maps, photographs and tables. This great endeavor is *Atlas of the Qur'ân* by a prominent research scholar of geography and an Arabian renowned figure, Dr Shawqi Abu Khalil.

For the interpretation and explanation of the religious books, the ancient and modern orientalists have done a notable work, and whatever work they did, it is of course a landmark for other research scholars. The habitations and personalities mentioned in Torah, or the land marks, places and personalities mentioned in four books of New Testament are available (in a beautiful manner) in more than a dozen geographical books with maps, known as atlas. But in various chapters of the Qur'ân, the descriptions replete with the events of the Hijaz, Arab nations, places, personalities, oceans, rivers, gulfs, lakes, mountains, forests, caves, cities etc., are available and hundreds of the writers, scholars and authors have also gone through their details, and many of the research books have also been compiled on these topics, but on the other hand, all this fruitful information has yet not been presented in the form of a book (atlas) consisting of maps, photographs and tables. These concerned contents or literary camposi-tions containing the Qur'ânic maps and tables were not before me so that a reciter of the Qur'ân may think of the details of the indications found in the Qur'ân while reciting it.

Since the dawn of the establishment of Darussalam, the multilingual institution for the publication of the Qur'ân and the Qur'ânic sciences and ideologies, we have been on the line of our objectives, i.e., the circulation & publication of the Qur'ân in various languages with its ideologies in scientific manner. In this regard, we keeping in view the modern opportunities, are applying all kinds of modern scientific means and techniques in the teaching & the publication of the Qur'ân. Being an ordinary student of the Qur'ân, it has been my sincere effort to bring out the books (published in Arabic language) on teaching of the Qur'ân, teaching of *Hadith*, biography of the Messenger ﷺ into the Urdu, English and other languages. Then after two and half years ago, when I went through the great work: (اطلس القرآن: أماكن، أقوام، اعلام) (*Atlas of the Qur'ân*: Places, Nations, Landmarks) by the distinguished author of Arabic language, Dr Shawqi Abu Khalil, I found it adorned with colored maps besides the Qur'ânic topics and Verses. I was happily surprised and impressed after looking through its pages, and then at the same time, I decided, considering it a valuable presentation, that our institution, Darussalam, would certainly bring out its Urdu and English editions.

So, a contact was made with Dar Al-Fikr, Damascus - the publisher of *Atlas of the Qur'ân*, but they refused. Then some common friends were asked to do something in this regard, and the publisher was addressed through a letter also, but nothing could be finalized. Last year, Mr. Hasan Salim, the son of Mr. Muhammad Adnan Salim, owner of Dar Al-Fikr, came to Riyadh. He visited the offices of Darussalam and was very much impressed after knowing about the aims and objects of Darussalam and its efforts for the spread of Islamic knowledge, he promised to have a talk with his father regarding the publication of the *Atlas of the Qur'ân*.

In the beginning of the year 2003, I specially went to Damascus, which is like a second home to me. In the past ten or twelve years, I must have gone there at least 30 or 35 times. In Damascus, the second name of Darussalam is Darul Fiha'. Its owner, Mr. Muhammad Yasir Tabba' is dear to me like a younger brother. After reaching Damascus, I informed my hosts that the only purpose of my visit is to have a conversation with Dar Al-Fikr regarding the books *Atlas of the Qur'ân* and the *Atlas on the Prophet's Biography*. The next day we were at the offices of Dar Al-Fikr. Mr. Hasan Salim greeted me heartily. I started talking him about the books again. He proposed to have a talk with his father who was a very busy person. I asked for a few minutes talk with him. His secretary agreed to allow us time for a short talk reminding about the appointments previously assigned.

The meeting that was scheduled to be of a short duration, exceeded one hour and a half until the secretary of Mr. Muhammad Adnan Salim interrupted to remind about the visitors that were waiting.

Dar Al-Fikr was established 50 years ago. Mr. Muhammad Adnan Salim has passed 70 years of life, having a very good health by the grace of Allāh and running the organization with full enthusiasm. He told me about the visit of Maulana Maudoodi to Damascus in 1960 and that the Maulana paid a visit to his house for a social call. Mr. Muhammad Adnan Salim had arranged a dinner for his reception and invited prominent scholars and writers in it. We were engrossed in the past memories. He has a wide experience of publishing books and is well known in the Islamic world. He provided me valuable guidance as regards the publishing field.

However, this meeting ended upon the permission to print both of the books. It was decided that Darussalam will pay regular royalty on them and some money will be paid as advance. Thanks are to Allâh that after some weeks when he visited Riyadh to participate in a conference of writers, an agreement was signed between us, and so I was able to fulfill the wish I was most eager of. I am thankful to Mr. Muhammad Adnan Salim for his cooperation and permission to publish the translations of the books.

It may be perceived that the compilation of the Qur'ânic Atlas consisting of personalities, nations, events and landmarks, places etc., as mentioned in the Qur'ân, was not an easier task. Certainly the author might have made a journey toward the passed period, and imaginarily perceived the pictures of the events mentioned in the Noble Qur'ân. It seems in the journey to the past, other heavenly books, history, narratives and the modern archaeological studies were also proved helpful to this great writer. Certainly this journey in the back direction consisting of several periods would have been a typical and unique experience of his life, but this experience itself is one of the best rewards of the struggles the author did. Having a dip in the ocean of this beautiful experience, the writer has compiled both of his atlases. I am sure that both of them would open for the readers the channel of intelligence and spiritual journey which the author found.

Now the work on the other valuable presentation: (أطلس السيرة النبوية) *Atlas on the Prophet's Biography* is under process, and *In sha Allâh* with high standards of printing and designing, it will soon be in the hands of the readers.

The readers are humbly requested to accept from us this unique presentation, and pray to Allâh for us to be more active in the struggle towards the multilingual publications of much needed books, treatises etc., based on Islam.

May Allâh bless us with splendid success.

Abdul-Malik Mujahid
General Manager
Darussalam, Riyadh

Contents

11

Preface

All praise is for Allâh, Lord of all that exists. O Allâh, send prayers and salutations upon our Prophet Muhammad, his family, his Companions, and all those who follow his way until the Last Day.

This atlas consists of pictures and maps of places, peoples, and important figures that are mentioned in Allâh's Book. The idea to produce this atlas first took root in my mind in the year 1990, when I looked at a map of the Arabian Peninsula and saw a small dot on it, beside which was written, 'The grave of Prophet Hûd.' It was located in the eastern part of the city of Taryam, in Hadramawt. When I saw this, I asked myself: When a Muslim reads the Noble Qur'ân and when he comes across the story of Hûd ﷺ, does he know where Hûd ﷺ actually lived? And when he reads the Chapter Al-Ahqâf (Curved Sand Hills), does he know where the intended sand hills are actually situated?

Without taking any definite shape, the idea continued to grow in my mind until I visited the city of Baku, wherein I came across a temple that used to be frequented by fire worshipers. It was there that I asked myself: in Allâh's Book, a Muslim reads about the Magians (Majus), but does he know where they lived and whether there are any remnants of them today?

The idea continued to grow and take form in my mind until it finally became ripe and complete. Since the way has already been paved for me through the many atlases that have been produced on various topics, I knew exactly what I had to do and what steps I needed to take in order to produce this atlas. I began the project, seeking help from Allâh and placing my complete trust upon Him. The project seemed formidable to say the least, for no book of this kind has ever been produced in the Islamic world. True, some historians have written about the places and peoples that are mentioned in the Noble Qur'ân, but their efforts have been restricted to a written description of those places and peoples, and even that written description is not comprehensive. They made no effort to present pictures and maps. Such history books include the likes of *Mountains, Places, and Waters*, by Az-Zamakhshari; and, *Important Figures in the Noble Qur'ân*, by Yahya 'Abdullah Al-Mu'allimi.

I began my efforts with an in-depth reading of Allâh's Book, looking for Verses that mentioned places, peoples, and important persons. Then came the research part of this endeavor, a stage that led to the drawing of the pictures and maps in this book, and the writing of the brief explanations that are written alongside them.

This does not mean that I did not face any obstacles during the course of this endeavor; to the contrary, I faced many obstacles, the least of which had to do with places and peoples of the Hereafter or of the unseen world – such as *Sidratul-Muntaha*, the people of *A'râf*, *Al-Kauthar*, the Devil, and so on. It goes without saying that we cannot now associate such places, peoples, and beings with a map or a picture. The unseen world is just that – unseen. But one of the bigger obstacles that I was continually faced with had to do with certain books that expand on and explain the stories of the Qur'ân as well as certain *Tafsir* books. The problem is that some of those books rely heavily on Israelite narrations, narrations that for the most part are taken from the Torah. Should we rely on such narrations?

To be sure, the answer to this question became clear to me immediately: No, we cannot rely on them. Instead we must rely on our trustworthy sources, for to rely on the Torah to explain the Qur'ân is at once dangerous and wrong. But if we find an Israelite narration that is not in conflict with our beliefs, we mention it alongside other opinions; it represents a possibility among possibilities but not the clear-cut truth, for there is no way to authenticate such narrations. When there are a number of views concerning any given issue, I mention them all and then, if there is proof to give greater credence to one of those views, I point that out.

Another obstacle I faced was in the ordering of this book: where should I begin and what sequence should I follow? I decided to proceed according to the chronology of the events that are mentioned in the Qur'ân. So of course I began with Adam ﷺ and ended with our Prophet, Muhammad ﷺ. And even when it came to the events of our Prophet's biography, at least those of which that are mentioned in the Noble Qur'ân, I proceeded according to the chronology of those events. Since I followed this methodology, and since there is a helpful index at the back of this Atlas, the reader should have no difficulty in finding what he is looking for.

The reader must bear in mind that this *Atlas of the Qur'ân* is not meant as a book that explains the stories of the Prophets or the events that are mentioned in the Noble Qur'ân; neither is it a book of *Tafsir*. There are many good and valuable books on each of those topics. This book is an atlas: a collection of maps, charts, pictures, and illustrations – all of which have to do with the places, peoples, and important persons that are mentioned in the Noble Qur'ân. To each chart, map, illustration, or picture I added only that amount of explanation that is necessary to explain each of the above.

To add to the benefit of this atlas, I added tables that mention how many times each topic is mentioned in the Qur'ân; and in addition to that, I included those Verses of the Qur'ân that are related to each picture and map.

On most of the maps, when I mention oceans and cities, I use the names that they are known by today, so that the reader can have a clear idea of where a given place is actually located. I also mention historical places with the names they were known by centuries ago. In doing so, I mainly relied on *The Arab and the Islamic History Atlas*. I even included a map of the Arabian Peninsula as it was 5000 years ago, so that the reader can compare the cities of that time with present-day cities and borders. At times, I refer the reader to a map on a previous page, particularly when there is no additional benefit in drawing it again.

That is a basic summary of what I have done in this *Atlas of the Qur'ân*, and at least according to my knowledge, no one has preceded me in this endeavor. And so I ask Allâh ﷻ to guide me to what is right. It is sufficient honor for one to be guided by Allâh to serve His Noble Book.

I cannot forget to extend my thanks to the people at Dar Al-Fikr, who have supported me and encouraged me from the time that I first had the idea to produce this work. Whenever I needed help along the way, they did their best to provide me with the support and help I needed to do make this atlas a work of superior quality the kind of superior quality that we have come to expect from Dar Al-Fikr's books.

And first and last, all praise is for Allâh ﷻ.

Damascus, Syria:
22nd of Jumada Al-Akhirah, 1421 H,
Or the 21st of September 2001
Dr. Shawqi Abu Khalil.

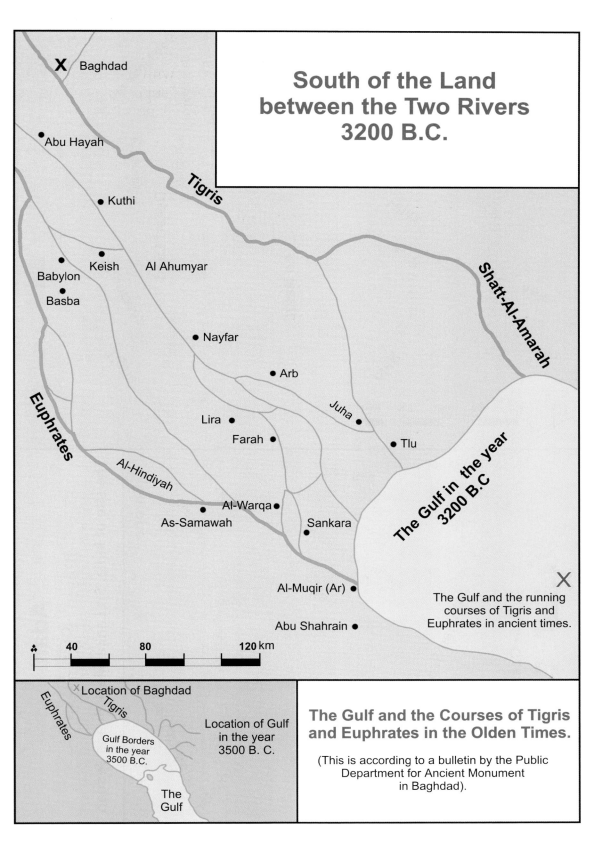

South of the Land between the Two Rivers 3200 B.C.

X Baghdad

• Abu Hayah

Tigris

• Kuthi

• Keish   Al Ahumyar

• Babylon

• Basba

• Nayfar

• Arb

Juha •

Lira •

Farah •

• Tlu

Euphrates

Al-Hindiyah

• Al-Warqa

As-Samawah •

Sankara •

Shatt-Al-Amarah

The Gulf in the year 3200 B.C

Al-Muqir (Ar) •

X

The Gulf and the running courses of Tigris and Euphrates in ancient times.

Abu Shahrain •

| 40 | 80 | 120 km |

X Location of Baghdad

Euphrates

Tigris

Gulf Borders in the year 3500 B.C.

Location of Gulf in the year 3500 B. C.

The Gulf

The Gulf and the Courses of Tigris and Euphrates in the Olden Times.

(This is according to a bulletin by the Public Department for Ancient Monument in Baghdad).

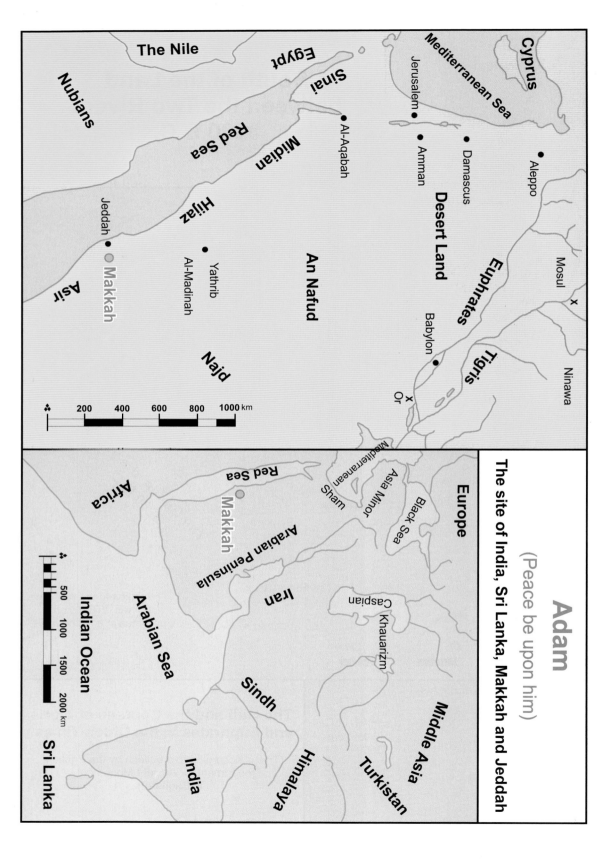

Adam
(Peace be upon him)

The site of India, Sri Lanka, Makkah and Jeddah

Adam عليه السلام

Adam عليه السلام is mentioned in the Qur'ân a total of 25 times, in a total of 25 Verses, which are:

Chapter Name (Sûrah)	Number of Chapter (Sûrah)	Verse Numbers
Al-Baqarah	2	31, 33, 34, 35, 37
Āl-'Imrân	3	33, 59
Al-Mâ'idah	5	27
Al-A'râf	7	11, 19, 26, 27, 31, 35, 172
Al-Isra'	17	61, 70
Al-Kahf	18	50
Maryam	19	58
Ta-Ha	20	115, 116, 117, 120, 121
Ya-Sin	36	60

۞ وَإِذْ قَالَ رَبُّكَ لِلْمَلَٰٓئِكَةِ إِنِّي جَاعِلٌ فِي ٱلْأَرْضِ خَلِيفَةً قَالُوٓاْ أَتَجْعَلُ فِيهَا مَن يُفْسِدُ فِيهَا وَيَسْفِكُ ٱلدِّمَآءَ وَنَحْنُ نُسَبِّحُ بِحَمْدِكَ وَنُقَدِّسُ لَكَّ قَالَ إِنِّيٓ أَعْلَمُ مَا لَا تَعْلَمُونَ ﴿٣٠﴾ وَعَلَّمَ ءَادَمَ ٱلْأَسْمَآءَ كُلَّهَا ثُمَّ عَرَضَهُمْ عَلَى ٱلْمَلَٰٓئِكَةِ فَقَالَ أَنۢبِـُٔونِي بِأَسْمَآءِ هَٰٓؤُلَآءِ إِن كُنتُمْ صَٰدِقِينَ ﴿٣١﴾ قَالُواْ سُبْحَٰنَكَ لَا عِلْمَ لَنَآ إِلَّا مَا عَلَّمْتَنَآ إِنَّكَ أَنتَ ٱلْعَلِيمُ ٱلْحَكِيمُ ﴿٣٢﴾ قَالَ يَٰٓـَٔادَمُ أَنۢبِئْهُم بِأَسْمَآئِهِمْ فَلَمَّآ أَنۢبَأَهُم بِأَسْمَآئِهِمْ قَالَ أَلَمْ أَقُل لَّكُمْ إِنِّيٓ أَعْلَمُ غَيْبَ ٱلسَّمَٰوَٰتِ وَٱلْأَرْضِ وَأَعْلَمُ مَا تُبْدُونَ وَمَا كُنتُمْ تَكْتُمُونَ ﴿٣٣﴾ وَإِذْ قُلْنَا لِلْمَلَٰٓئِكَةِ ٱسْجُدُواْ لِءَادَمَ فَسَجَدُوٓاْ إِلَّآ إِبْلِيسَ أَبَىٰ وَٱسْتَكْبَرَ وَكَانَ مِنَ ٱلْكَٰفِرِينَ ﴿٣٤﴾ وَقُلْنَا يَٰٓـَٔادَمُ ٱسْكُنْ أَنتَ

وَزَوْجُكَ ٱلْجَنَّةَ وَكُلَا مِنْهَا رَغَدًا حَيْثُ شِئْتُمَا وَلَا تَقْرَبَا هَٰذِهِ ٱلشَّجَرَةَ فَتَكُونَا مِنَ ٱلظَّٰلِمِينَ ﴿٣٥﴾ فَأَزَلَّهُمَا ٱلشَّيْطَٰنُ عَنْهَا فَأَخْرَجَهُمَا مِمَّا كَانَا فِيهِ ۖ وَقُلْنَا ٱهْبِطُوا۟ بَعْضُكُمْ لِبَعْضٍ عَدُوٌّ ۖ وَلَكُمْ فِى ٱلْأَرْضِ مُسْتَقَرٌّ وَمَتَٰعٌ إِلَىٰ حِينٍ ﴿٣٦﴾ فَتَلَقَّىٰٓ ءَادَمُ مِن رَّبِّهِۦ كَلِمَٰتٍ فَتَابَ عَلَيْهِ ۚ إِنَّهُۥ هُوَ ٱلتَّوَّابُ ٱلرَّحِيمُ ﴿٣٧﴾ قُلْنَا ٱهْبِطُوا۟ مِنْهَا جَمِيعًا ۖ فَإِمَّا يَأْتِيَنَّكُم مِّنِّى هُدًى فَمَن تَبِعَ هُدَاىَ فَلَا خَوْفٌ عَلَيْهِمْ وَلَا هُمْ يَحْزَنُونَ ﴿٣٨﴾ ۞

And (remember) when your Lord said to the angels: "Verily, I am going to place (mankind) generations after generations on earth." They said: "Will You place therein those who will make mischief therein and shed blood, — while we glorify You with praises and thanks and sanctify You." He (Allāh) said: "I know that which you do not know." And He taught Adam all the names (of everything), then He showed them to the angels and said, "Tell Me the names of these if you are truthful." They (angels) said: "Glorified are You, we have no knowledge except what you have taught us. Verily, it is You, the All-Knower, the All-Wise." He said: "O Adam! Inform them of their names," and when he had informed them of their names, He said: "Did I not tell you that I know the *Ghaib* (Unseen) in the heavens and the earth, and I know what you reveal and what you have been concealing?" And (remember) when We said to the angels: "Prostrate yourselves before Adam." And they prostrated except *Iblīs* (Satan), he refused and was proud and was one of the disbelievers (disobedient to Allāh). And We said: "O Adam! Dwell you and your wife in Paradise and eat both of you freely with pleasure and delight, of things therein as wherever you will, but come not near this tree or you both will be of the *Zālimūn* (wrong doers)." Then the *Shaitān* (Satan) made them slip therefrom (Paradise), and got them out from that in which they were. We said: "Get you down, all, with enmity between yourselves. On earth will be a dwelling place for you and an enjoyment for a time." Then Adam received from his Lord Words. And his Lord pardoned him (accepted his repentance). Verily, He is the One Who forgives (accepts repentance), the Most Merciful. We said: "Get down all of you from this place (the Paradise), then whenever there comes to you Guidance from Me, and whoever follows My Guidance, there shall be no fear on them, nor shall they grieve.

(Qur'ân 2: 30-38)

وَلَقَدْ عَهِدْنَآ إِلَىٰٓ ءَادَمَ مِن قَبْلُ فَنَسِىَ وَلَمْ نَجِدْ لَهُۥ عَزْمًا ۞ وَإِذْ قُلْنَا لِلْمَلَـٰٓئِكَةِ ٱسْجُدُوا۟ لِأَدَمَ فَسَجَدُوٓا۟ إِلَّآ إِبْلِيسَ أَبَىٰ ۞ فَقُلْنَا يَـٰٓـَٔادَمُ إِنَّ هَـٰذَا عَدُوٌّ لَّكَ وَلِزَوْجِكَ فَلَا يُخْرِجَنَّكُمَا مِنَ ٱلْجَنَّةِ فَتَشْقَىٰٓ ۞ إِنَّ لَكَ أَلَّا تَجُوعَ فِيهَا وَلَا تَعْرَىٰ ۞ وَأَنَّكَ لَا تَظْمَؤُا۟ فِيهَا وَلَا تَضْحَىٰ ۞ فَوَسْوَسَ إِلَيْهِ ٱلشَّيْطَـٰنُ قَالَ يَـٰٓـَٔادَمُ هَلْ أَدُلُّكَ عَلَىٰ شَجَرَةِ ٱلْخُلْدِ وَمُلْكٍ لَّا يَبْلَىٰ ۞ فَأَكَلَا مِنْهَا فَبَدَتْ لَهُمَا سَوْءَٰتُهُمَا وَطَفِقَا يَخْصِفَانِ عَلَيْهِمَا مِن وَرَقِ ٱلْجَنَّةِ وَعَصَىٰٓ ءَادَمُ رَبَّهُۥ فَغَوَىٰ ۞ ثُمَّ ٱجْتَبَـٰهُ رَبُّهُۥ فَتَابَ عَلَيْهِ وَهَدَىٰ ۞ قَالَ ٱهْبِطَا مِنْهَا جَمِيعًۢا بَعْضُكُمْ لِبَعْضٍ عَدُوٌّ فَإِمَّا يَأْتِيَنَّكُم مِّنِّى هُدًى فَمَنِ ٱتَّبَعَ هُدَاىَ فَلَا يَضِلُّ وَلَا يَشْقَىٰ ۞

And indeed We made a covenant with Adam before, but he forgot, and We found on his part no firm willpower. And (remember) when We said to the angels: "Prostrate yourselves to Adam." They prostrated themselves (all) except *Iblīs* (Satan); he refused. Then We said: "O Adam! Verily, this is an enemy to you and to your wife. So, let him not get you both out of Paradise, so that you will be distressed. Verily, you have (a promise from Us) that you will never be hungry therein nor naked. And you (will) suffer not from thirst therein nor from the sun's heat. Then *Shaitān* (Satan) whispered to him, saying: "O Adam! Shall I lead you to the Tree of Eternity and to a kingdom that will never waste away?" Then they both ate of the tree, and so their private parts became manifest to them, and they began to cover themselves with the leaves of Paradise for their covering. Thus did Adam disobey his Lord, so he went astray. Then his Lord chose him, and turned to him with forgiveness, and gave him guidance. He (Allāh) said: "Get you down (from Paradise to the earth), both of you together, some of you are an enemy to some others. Then if there comes to you guidance from Me, then whoever follows My Guidance he shall neither go astray nor shall be distressed.

(Qur'ân 20: 115-123)

Allâh ﷻ said:

"Get you down, all, with enmity between yourselves. On earth will be a dwelling place for you and an enjoyment for a time."

The question then arises, where was it that Adam ﷺ and Hawwaah landed when they descended to the earth. In *Ad-Dur Al-Manthur*, it is related from Ibn 'Abbas ﷺ that Adam ﷺ, Hawwa, Iblīs, and the snake landed in a place called Dajnah, which is situated somewhere between Makkah and At-Tâ'if. It is also said that Adam ﷺ landed at As-Safa (a well-known mountain in Makkah) and that Hawwaah landed at Al-Marwah (another well-known mountain in Makkah). In another narration from Ibn 'Abbâs ﷺ, it is mentioned that Adam ﷺ landed somewhere in India.

In that narration, which is related by Ibn Sa'ad and Ibn Asâkir from Ibn 'Abbâs ﷺ, it is mentioned that Adam ﷺ landed in India while Hawwaah landed in Jeddah; and that Adam ﷺ then searched out for her until he reached Muzdalifah; to this very day, pilgrims gather during *Hajj* at Muzdalifah. The word Muzdalifah is derived from the verb *Izdalafah*, which means to approach. Some believe that Muzdalifah was given its name because it is there that Hawwaah approached Adam ﷺ and met up with him.

At-Tabarâni, Abu Nu'aim, and Ibn Asâkir all related from Abu Hurairah ﷺ that the Messenger of Allâh ﷺ said, "Adam ﷺ descended in India." And At-Tabarâni related the following narration from 'Abdullah ibn 'Umar ﷺ: When Allâh made Adam ﷺ descend, He made him descend in the land of India. He then went to Makkah and afterwards went to Ash-Sham (Syria and surrounding regions), which is where he died."

From these and other narrations, we learn the following: Adam ﷺ descended to earth in India, on a mountain that is called Baudh, on the island of Sri Lanka (Serendib/Ceylon), just below the Indian Subcontinent. Ibn Batutah recorded in his journals that he landed on that island, the inhabitants of which, he reported, still remembered Adam ﷺ by the name "father" and Hawwa by the name "mother."

As for his grave, it is said that Adam ﷺ was buried in the mountain of Abu Qubais; according to a different view, it is maintained that he was buried on Mount Baudh, which is where he landed in the first place when he descended to earth. It is mentioned in some narrations that, after the flood, Noah ﷺ had to bury him for a second time, and that he buried him in Jerusalem.

Of the various narrations on the topic, I deem certain narrations of At-Tabari, Ibn Al-Athir, and Al-Ya'qubi to be the strongest. They indicate that, after Allâh ﷻ forgave Adam ﷺ, Jibreel ﷺ carried Adam ﷺ to Mount Arafat, where Jibreel ﷺ taught him the rites of *Hajj*; those narrations also indicate that it was at the foot of Mount Abu Qubais that Adam ﷺ died and was subsequently buried.

- Ad-Durr Al-Manthur Fit-Tafsir Bil-Ma'thur: 1/55
- Raihlah Ibn Battutah: 584, 585
- Qisas Al-Anbiya, by Ibn Kathir: 34
- Qisas Al-Anbiya (well-known by the name, Al-'Arais), by Tha'labi: 36
- Qisas Al-Anbiya, by At-Tabari: 38
- Al-Qâmus Al-Islami: 1/56
- Mukhtasir Taarikh Damashq, by Ibn 'Asaakir: 4/224
- Mo'jam Al-Buldan: 2/163 and 3/215
- Al-Mo'jam Al-Mufahris Li-Alfadh Al-Qur'ân Al-Karim: 24
- Al-Mo'jam Al-Mufahris Li-Ma'âni Al-Qur'ân Al-Karim: 38

The Two Sons Of Adam العليهلا: Qâbil and Hâbil

Their story is related in *Sûratul-Mā'idah*:

﴿وَٱتْلُ عَلَيْهِمْ نَبَأَ ٱبْنَىْ ءَادَمَ بِٱلْحَقِّ إِذْ قَرَّبَا قُرْبَانًا فَتُقُبِّلَ مِنْ أَحَدِهِمَا وَلَمْ يُتَقَبَّلْ مِنَ ٱلْآخَرِ قَالَ لَأَقْتُلَنَّكَ قَالَ إِنَّمَا يَتَقَبَّلُ ٱللَّهُ مِنَ ٱلْمُتَّقِينَ ۝ لَئِنۢ بَسَطتَ إِلَىَّ يَدَكَ لِتَقْتُلَنِى مَآ أَنَا۠ بِبَاسِطٍ يَدِىَ إِلَيْكَ لِأَقْتُلَكَ إِنِّىٓ أَخَافُ ٱللَّهَ رَبَّ ٱلْعَـٰلَمِينَ ۝ إِنِّىٓ أُرِيدُ أَن تَبُوٓأَ بِإِثْمِى وَإِثْمِكَ فَتَكُونَ مِنْ أَصْحَـٰبِ ٱلنَّارِ وَذَٰلِكَ جَزَٰٓؤُا۟ ٱلظَّـٰلِمِينَ ۝ فَطَوَّعَتْ لَهُۥ نَفْسُهُۥ قَتْلَ أَخِيهِ فَقَتَلَهُۥ فَأَصْبَحَ مِنَ ٱلْخَـٰسِرِينَ ۝ فَبَعَثَ ٱللَّهُ غُرَابًا يَبْحَثُ فِى ٱلْأَرْضِ لِيُرِيَهُۥ كَيْفَ يُوَٰرِى سَوْءَةَ أَخِيهِ قَالَ يَـٰوَيْلَتَىٰٓ أَعَجَزْتُ أَنْ أَكُونَ مِثْلَ هَـٰذَا ٱلْغُرَابِ فَأُوَٰرِىَ سَوْءَةَ أَخِى فَأَصْبَحَ مِنَ ٱلنَّـٰدِمِينَ ۝﴾

And (O Muhammad ﷺ) recite to them (the Jews) the story of the two sons of Adam (Hābīl and Qābīl — Abel and Cain) in truth; when each offered a sacrifice (to Allāh), it was accepted from the one but not from the other. The latter said to the former: "I will surely, kill you." The former said: "Verily, Allāh accepts only from those who are *Al-Muttaqūn* (the pious). If you do stretch your hand against me to kill me, I shall never stretch my hand against you to kill you: for I fear Allāh, the Lord of the *ʿĀlamīn* (mankind, jinn, and all that exists). Verily, I intend to let you draw my sin on yourself as well as yours, then you will be one of the dwellers of the Fire; and that is the recompense of the *Zālimūn* (wrong doers)." So, the *Nafs* (self) of the other (latter one) encouraged him and made fair-seeming to him the murder of his brother; he murdered him and became one of the losers. Then Allāh sent a crow who scratched the ground to show him how to hide the dead body of his brother. He (the murderer) said: "Woe to me! Am I not even able to be as this crow and to hide the dead body of my brother?" Then he became one of those who regretted.

(Qur'ân 5: 27-31)

It seems likeliest that the events of this story took place in Makkah, for that is where Adam ﷺ and Hawwaah lived. One narration mentions that after he killed his brother, Hâbil, Qâbil fled to Yemen. A narration from At-Tabari supports the view that the events of the story took place in Makkah, where Adam ﷺ lived. The wording of that narration is as follows: "And he fled from his father, Adam ﷺ, and headed towards Yemen."

For a long time now, the commoners of Syria have believed that Qâbil killed his brother at Mount Qâsyun, which overlooks the northern part of Damascus. At one of the entrances of that mountain there is a cave that the commoners call, The Cave of Blood, because, they say, that is where the murder took place. On the right side of the road that leads from Damascus to Az-Zabdâni and Baludân, there is a mountain that overlooks the valley of the Burdi River; the mountain is situated in the area of At-Takiyyah. There is a grave thereabouts that measures 15 m long; some believe that it is the grave of Hâbil.

- Qisas Al-Anbiya, by Ibn Kathir: 52
- Qisas Al-Anbiya, by Ath-Tha'labi: 44
- Qisas Al-Anbiya, by At-Tabari: 74
- Qisas Al-Anbiya, by An-Najjâr: 22

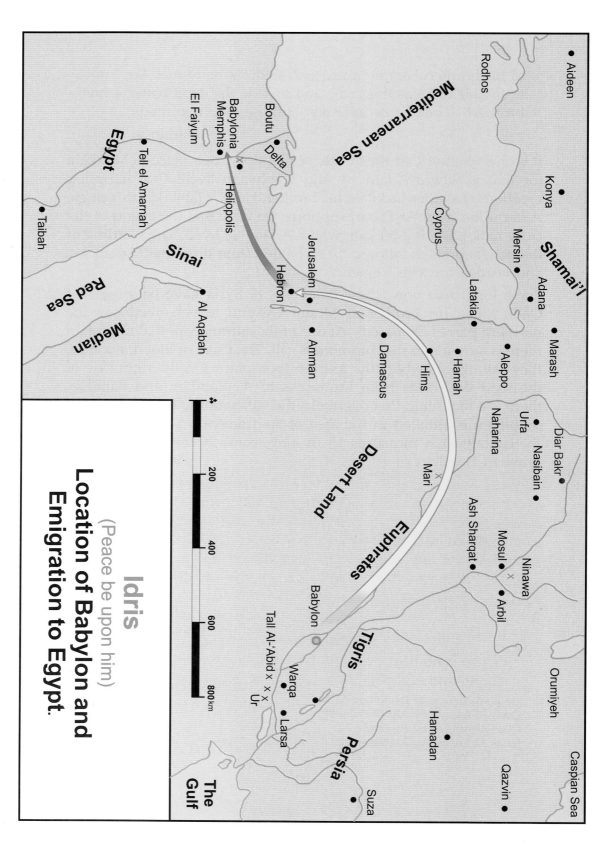

Idris
(Peace be upon him)

Location of Babylon and Emigration to Egypt.

Idris عليه السلام

Idris عليه السلام is twice mentioned by name in the Noble Qur'ân:

﴿وَٱذْكُرْ فِي ٱلْكِتَٰبِ إِدْرِيسَ إِنَّهُۥ كَانَ صِدِّيقًا نَّبِيًّا ٥٦ وَرَفَعْنَٰهُ مَكَانًا عَلِيًّا ٥٧﴾

And mention in the Book (the Qur'ân) Idrīs. Verily, he was a man of truth, (and) a Prophet. And We raised him to a high station.

(Qur'ân 19: 56, 57)

﴿وَإِسْمَٰعِيلَ وَإِدْرِيسَ وَذَا ٱلْكِفْلِ كُلٌّ مِّنَ ٱلصَّٰبِرِينَ ٨٥ وَأَدْخَلْنَٰهُمْ فِي رَحْمَتِنَآ إِنَّهُم مِّنَ ٱلصَّٰلِحِينَ ٨٦﴾

And (remember) Isma'īl (Ishmael), Idrīs and Dhul-Kifl (Isaiah): all were from among *As-Sābirūn* (the patient). And We admitted them to Our Mercy. Verily, they were of the righteous.

(Qur'ân 21: 85, 86)

Born in Egypt, in the city of Memphis (Minf), Idris عليه السلام was first given the name Hirmis Al-Harâmisah. According to another report, however, he was born in Babylon (Bâbil) and then later migrated to Egypt. When he first saw the Nile River, he said, *"Babilyun,"* which means: a river like your river, a large river, a blessed river. It is said that 188 cities were built during his era, the smallest of which was Ar-Ruha. Idris عليه السلام is the first to have studied wisdom and astronomy, and some wise sayings are still credited to him, among which the following are examples:

- There is no better way to thank Allâh عز وجل for His favors than to be kind and generous to His creation.

- When you invoke Allâh عز وجل, make your intention sincere and pure.

- Wisdom is the life of the soul.

- Do not be jealous of people for the things they have, for their enjoyment of those things is short-lived.

- Nothing can make one feel rich when one seeks to have more than the bare necessities.

- Qisas Al-Anbiyâ, by Ibn Kathir: 63
- Qisas Al-Anbiyâ', by Ath-Tha'labi: 50
- Qisas Al-Anbiyâ', by At-Tabari: 80
- Qisas Al-Anbiyâ', by An-Najjâr: 24

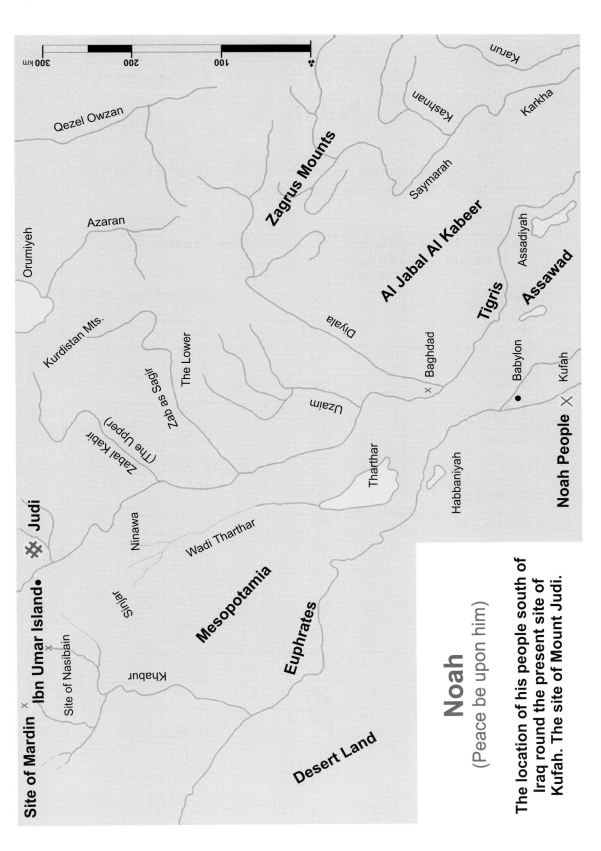

Noah
(Peace be upon him)

The location of his people south of Iraq round the present site of Kufah. The site of Mount Judi.

Site of Mardin × Ibn Umar Island ● �֍ Judi

Site of Nasibain

Orumiyeh

Qezel Owzan

Azaran

Kurdistan Mts.

Zab as Sagir

Zabal Kabir (The Upper)

The Lower

Ninawa

Sinjar

Khabur

Wadi Tharthar

Mesopotamia

Euphrates

Desert Land

Tharthar

Habbaniyah

Uzaim

Zagrus Mounts

Al Jabal Al Kabeer

Diyala

Saymarah

Baghdad ×

Tigris

Assadiyah

Assawad

Babylon ●

Kufah ×

Noah People ×

Kashnan

Karkha

Karun

300 Km
200
100

Noah السلام عليه

Noah السلام عليه is mentioned `43 times in the Noble Qur'ân; he is mentioned in the following Chapters and Verses:

Chapter Name (Sûrah)	Number of Chapter (Sûrah)	Verse Numbers
Āl-'Imrân	3	22
An-Nisa'	4	163
Al-An'âm	6	84
Al-A'râf	7	59, 69
At-Taubah	9	70
Yûnus	10	71
Hûd	11	25, 32, 36, 42, 45, 46, 48, 89
Ibrâhim	14	9
Al-Isra'	17	17, 3
Maryam	19	58
Al-Anbiya'	21	86
Al-Hajj	22	42
Al-Mu'minûn	23	23
Al-Furqân	25	37
Ash-Shu'arâ	26	105, 106, 116
Al-'Ankabût	29	14

Chapter Name (Sûrah)	Number of Chapter (Sûrah)	Verse Numbers
Al-Ahzâb	33	7
As-Sâffât	37	75, 79
Sâd	38	12
Ghâfir	40	5, 31
Ash-Shûra	42	13
Qâf	50	12
Adh-Dhâriyât	51	46
An-Najm	53	52
Al-Qamr	54	9
Al-Hadid	57	26
At-Tahrim	66	10
Nûh	71	1, 21, 16

۞ وَلَقَدۡ أَرۡسَلۡنَا نُوحًا إِلَىٰ قَوۡمِهِۦ إِنِّي لَكُمۡ نَذِيرٞ مُّبِينٌ ۝ أَن لَّا تَعۡبُدُوٓاۡ إِلَّا ٱللَّهَۖ إِنِّيٓ أَخَافُ عَلَيۡكُمۡ عَذَابَ يَوۡمٍ أَلِيمٖ ۝ فَقَالَ ٱلۡمَلَأُ ٱلَّذِينَ كَفَرُواۡ مِن قَوۡمِهِۦ مَا نَرَىٰكَ إِلَّا بَشَرٗا مِّثۡلَنَا وَمَا نَرَىٰكَ ٱتَّبَعَكَ إِلَّا ٱلَّذِينَ هُمۡ أَرَاذِلُنَا بَادِيَ ٱلرَّأۡيِ وَمَا نَرَىٰ لَكُمۡ عَلَيۡنَا مِن فَضۡلٍۭ بَلۡ نَظُنُّكُمۡ كَٰذِبِينَ ۝ قَالَ يَٰقَوۡمِ أَرَءَيۡتُمۡ إِن كُنتُ عَلَىٰ بَيِّنَةٖ مِّن رَّبِّي وَءَاتَىٰنِي رَحۡمَةٗ مِّنۡ عِندِهِۦ فَعُمِّيَتۡ عَلَيۡكُمۡ أَنُلۡزِمُكُمُوهَا وَأَنتُمۡ لَهَا كَٰرِهُونَ ۝ وَيَٰقَوۡمِ لَآ أَسۡـَٔلُكُمۡ عَلَيۡهِ مَالًاۖ إِنۡ أَجۡرِيَ إِلَّا عَلَى ٱللَّهِۚ وَمَآ أَنَا۠ بِطَارِدِ ٱلَّذِينَ ءَامَنُوٓاۚ إِنَّهُم مُّلَٰقُواۡ رَبِّهِمۡ وَلَٰكِنِّيٓ أَرَىٰكُمۡ قَوۡمٗا تَجۡهَلُونَ ۝ وَيَٰقَوۡمِ مَن يَنصُرُنِي مِنَ ٱللَّهِ إِن طَرَدتُّهُمۡۚ أَفَلَا تَذَكَّرُونَ ۝ وَلَآ أَقُولُ لَكُمۡ عِندِي خَزَآئِنُ ٱللَّهِ وَلَآ أَعۡلَمُ ٱلۡغَيۡبَ وَلَآ أَقُولُ إِنِّي مَلَكٞ وَلَآ أَقُولُ لِلَّذِينَ تَزۡدَرِيٓ أَعۡيُنُكُمۡ لَن يُؤۡتِيَهُمُ ٱللَّهُ خَيۡرًاۖ ٱللَّهُ أَعۡلَمُ بِمَا فِيٓ أَنفُسِهِمۡ إِنِّيٓ إِذٗا لَّمِنَ ٱلظَّٰلِمِينَ

قَالُوا۟ يَٰنُوحُ قَدْ جَٰدَلْتَنَا فَأَكْثَرْتَ جِدَٰلَنَا فَأْتِنَا بِمَا تَعِدُنَآ إِن كُنتَ مِنَ ٱلصَّٰدِقِينَ (٣١) قَالَ إِنَّمَا يَأْتِيكُم بِهِ ٱللَّهُ إِن شَآءَ وَمَآ أَنتُم بِمُعْجِزِينَ (٣٢) وَلَا يَنفَعُكُمْ نُصْحِىٓ إِنْ أَرَدتُّ أَنْ أَنصَحَ لَكُمْ إِن كَانَ ٱللَّهُ يُرِيدُ أَن يُغْوِيَكُمْ هُوَ رَبُّكُمْ وَإِلَيْهِ تُرْجَعُونَ (٣٤) أَمْ يَقُولُونَ ٱفْتَرَىٰهُ قُلْ إِنِ ٱفْتَرَيْتُهُۥ فَعَلَىَّ إِجْرَامِى وَأَنَا۠ بَرِىٓءٌ مِّمَّا تُجْرِمُونَ (٣٥) وَأُوحِىَ إِلَىٰ نُوحٍ أَنَّهُۥ لَن يُؤْمِنَ مِن قَوْمِكَ إِلَّا مَن قَدْ ءَامَنَ فَلَا تَبْتَئِسْ بِمَا كَانُوا۟ يَفْعَلُونَ (٣٦) وَٱصْنَعِ ٱلْفُلْكَ بِأَعْيُنِنَا وَوَحْيِنَا وَلَا تُخَٰطِبْنِى فِى ٱلَّذِينَ ظَلَمُوٓا۟ إِنَّهُم مُّغْرَقُونَ (٣٧) وَيَصْنَعُ ٱلْفُلْكَ وَكُلَّمَا مَرَّ عَلَيْهِ مَلَأٌ مِّن قَوْمِهِۦ سَخِرُوا۟ مِنْهُ قَالَ إِن تَسْخَرُوا۟ مِنَّا فَإِنَّا نَسْخَرُ مِنكُمْ كَمَا تَسْخَرُونَ (٣٨) فَسَوْفَ تَعْلَمُونَ مَن يَأْتِيهِ عَذَابٌ يُخْزِيهِ وَيَحِلُّ عَلَيْهِ عَذَابٌ مُّقِيمٌ (٣٩) حَتَّىٰٓ إِذَا جَآءَ أَمْرُنَا وَفَارَ ٱلتَّنُّورُ قُلْنَا ٱحْمِلْ فِيهَا مِن كُلٍّ زَوْجَيْنِ ٱثْنَيْنِ وَأَهْلَكَ إِلَّا مَن سَبَقَ عَلَيْهِ ٱلْقَوْلُ وَمَنْ ءَامَنَ وَمَآ ءَامَنَ مَعَهُۥٓ إِلَّا قَلِيلٌ (٤٠) وَقَالَ ٱرْكَبُوا۟ فِيهَا بِسْمِ ٱللَّهِ مَجْر۪ىٰهَا وَمُرْسَىٰهَآ إِنَّ رَبِّى لَغَفُورٌ رَّحِيمٌ (٤١) وَهِىَ تَجْرِى بِهِمْ فِى مَوْجٍ كَٱلْجِبَالِ وَنَادَىٰ نُوحٌ ٱبْنَهُۥ وَكَانَ فِى مَعْزِلٍ يَٰبُنَىَّ ٱرْكَب مَّعَنَا وَلَا تَكُن مَّعَ ٱلْكَٰفِرِينَ (٤٢) قَالَ سَـَٔاوِىٓ إِلَىٰ جَبَلٍ يَعْصِمُنِى مِنَ ٱلْمَآءِ قَالَ لَا عَاصِمَ ٱلْيَوْمَ مِنْ أَمْرِ ٱللَّهِ إِلَّا مَن رَّحِمَ وَحَالَ بَيْنَهُمَا ٱلْمَوْجُ فَكَانَ مِنَ ٱلْمُغْرَقِينَ (٤٣) وَقِيلَ يَٰٓأَرْضُ ٱبْلَعِى مَآءَكِ وَيَٰسَمَآءُ أَقْلِعِى وَغِيضَ ٱلْمَآءُ وَقُضِىَ ٱلْأَمْرُ وَٱسْتَوَتْ عَلَى ٱلْجُودِىِّ وَقِيلَ بُعْدًا لِّلْقَوْمِ ٱلظَّٰلِمِينَ (٤٤) وَنَادَىٰ نُوحٌ رَّبَّهُۥ فَقَالَ رَبِّ إِنَّ ٱبْنِى مِنْ أَهْلِى وَإِنَّ وَعْدَكَ ٱلْحَقُّ وَأَنتَ أَحْكَمُ ٱلْحَٰكِمِينَ (٤٥) قَالَ يَٰنُوحُ إِنَّهُۥ لَيْسَ مِنْ أَهْلِكَ إِنَّهُۥ عَمَلٌ غَيْرُ صَٰلِحٍ فَلَا تَسْـَٔلْنِ مَا لَيْسَ لَكَ بِهِۦ عِلْمٌ إِنِّىٓ أَعِظُكَ أَن تَكُونَ مِنَ ٱلْجَٰهِلِينَ (٤٦) قَالَ رَبِّ إِنِّىٓ أَعُوذُ بِكَ أَنْ أَسْـَٔلَكَ مَا لَيْسَ لِى بِهِۦ عِلْمٌ وَإِلَّا تَغْفِرْ لِى وَتَرْحَمْنِىٓ أَكُن مِّنَ ٱلْخَٰسِرِينَ (٤٧) قِيلَ يَٰنُوحُ ٱهْبِطْ بِسَلَٰمٍ مِّنَّا وَبَرَكَٰتٍ عَلَيْكَ وَعَلَىٰٓ أُمَمٍ مِّمَّن مَّعَكَ وَأُمَمٌ سَنُمَتِّعُهُمْ ثُمَّ يَمَسُّهُم مِّنَّا عَذَابٌ أَلِيمٌ (٤٨)

And indeed We sent Nūh (Noah) to his people (and he said): "I have come to you as a plain warner. That you worship none but Allāh; surely, I fear for you the torment of a painful Day." The chiefs who disbelieved among his people said: "We see you but a man like ourselves, nor do we see any follow you but the meanest among us and they (too) followed you without thinking. And we do not see in you any merit above us, in fact we think you are liars." He said: "O my people! Tell me, if I have a clear proof from my Lord, and a mercy (Prophethood) has come to me from Him, but that (mercy) has been obscured from your sight. Shall we compel you to accept it (Islamic Monotheism) when you have a strong hatred for it? And O my people! I ask of you no wealth for it, my reward is from none but Allāh. I am not going to drive away those who have believed. Surely, they are going to meet their Lord, but I see that you are a people that are ignorant. And O my people! Who will help me against Allāh, if I drove them away? Will you not then give a thought? And I do not say to you that with me are the Treasures of Allāh, nor that I know the *Ghaib* (Unseen); nor do I say I am an angel, and I do not say of those whom your eyes look down upon that Allāh will not bestow any good on them. Allāh knows what is in their inner selves (as regards belief). In that case, I should, indeed be one of the *Zālimūn* (wrong doers, oppressors)." They said: "O Nūh (Noah)! You have disputed with us and much have you prolonged the dispute with us, now bring upon us what you threaten us with, if you are of the truthful." He said: "Only Allāh will bring it (the punishment) on you, if He wills, and then you will escape not. And my advice will not profit you, even if I wish to give you good counsel, if Allāh's Will is to keep you astray. He is your Lord! and to Him you shall return." Or they (the pagans of Makkah) say: "He (Muham-mad ﷺ) has fabricated it (the Qur'ān)." Say: "If I have fabricated it, upon me be my crimes, but I am innocent of (all) those crimes which you commit." And it was revealed to Nūh (Noah): "None of your people will believe except those who have believed already. So be not sad because of what they used to do. And construct the ship under Our Eyes and with Our Revelation, and call not upon Me on behalf of those who did wrong; they are surely to be drowned." And as he was constructing the ship, whenever the chiefs of his people passed by him, they mocked at him. He said: "If you mock at us, so do we mock at you likewise for your mocking. And you will know who it is on whom will come a torment that will cover him with disgrace and on whom will fall a lasting torment." (So it was) till when Our Command came and the oven gushed forth (water like fountains from the earth). We said: "Embark therein, of each kind two (male and female), and your family — except him against whom the Word has already gone forth — and those who believe. And none believed with him, except a few." And he [Nūh (Noah) ﷺ] said: "Embark therein: in the Name of Allāh will be its (moving) course and its (resting) anchorage. Surely, my Lord is Oft-Forgiving, Most Merciful." (*Tafsir At-Tabarī*) So it (the ship) sailed with them amidst waves like mountains, and Nūh (Noah) called out to his son, who had separated himself (apart): "O my son! Embark with us and be not with the disbelievers." The son replied: "I will betake myself to some mountain, it will save me from the water." Nūh (Noah) said: "This day there is no saviour from the Decree of Allāh except him on whom He has mercy." And waves came in between them, so he (the son) was among the drowned. And it was said: "O earth! Swallow up your water, and O sky! Withhold (your rain)." And the water was made to subside and the Decree (of Allāh) was fulfilled (i.e. the destruction of the people of Nūh (Noah). And it (the ship) rested on (Mount) Judi, and it was said: "Away with the people who are *Zalimūn* (polytheists and wrong-doers)!" And Nūh (Noah) called upon his Lord and said, "O my Lord! Verily, my son is of my family! And certainly, Your Promise is true, and You are the Most Just of the judges." He said: "O Nūh (Noah)! Surely, he is not of your family; verily, his work is unrighteous, so ask not of Me that of which you have no knowledge! I admonish you, lest you should be one of the ignorant." Nūh (Noah) said: "O my Lord! I seek refuge with You from asking You that of which I have no knowledge. And unless You forgive me and have mercy on me, I would indeed be one of the losers." It was said: "O Nūh (Noah)! Come down (from the ship) with peace from Us and blessings on you and on the people who are with you (and on some of their offspring), but (there will be other) people to whom We shall grant their pleasures (for a time), but in the end a painful torment will reach them from Us.''

﴿ كَذَّبَتْ قَبْلَهُمْ قَوْمُ نُوحٍ فَكَذَّبُوا عَبْدَنَا وَقَالُوا مَجْنُونٌ وَازْدُجِرَ ۞ فَدَعَا رَبَّهُۥ أَنِّي مَغْلُوبٌ فَانتَصِرْ ۞ فَفَتَحْنَا أَبْوَٰبَ ٱلسَّمَآءِ بِمَآءٍ مُّنْهَمِرٍ ۞ وَفَجَّرْنَا ٱلْأَرْضَ عُيُونًا فَٱلْتَقَى ٱلْمَآءُ عَلَىٰٓ أَمْرٍ قَدْ قُدِرَ ۞ وَحَمَلْنَٰهُ عَلَىٰ ذَاتِ أَلْوَٰحٍ وَدُسُرٍ ۞ تَجْرِى بِأَعْيُنِنَا جَزَآءً لِّمَن كَانَ كُفِرَ ۞ وَلَقَد تَّرَكْنَٰهَآ ءَايَةً فَهَلْ مِن مُّدَّكِرٍ ۞ فَكَيْفَ كَانَ عَذَابِى وَنُذُرِ ۞ ﴾

The people of Nûh (Noah) denied (their Messenger) before them. They rejected Our slave, and said: "A madman!" and he was insolently rebuked and threatened. Then he invoked his Lord (saying): "I have been overcome, so help (me)!" So, We opened the gates of the heaven with water pouring forth. And We caused springs to gush forth from the earth. So, the waters (of the heaven and the earth) met for a matter predestined. And We carried him on a (ship) made of planks and nails, Floating under Our Eyes, a reward for him who had been rejected! And indeed, We have left this as a sign. Then is there any that will remember (or receive admonition)? Then how (terrible) was My torment and My Warnings?

﴿ إِنَّآ أَرْسَلْنَا نُوحًا إِلَىٰ قَوْمِهِۦٓ أَنْ أَنذِرْ قَوْمَكَ مِن قَبْلِ أَن يَأْتِيَهُمْ عَذَابٌ أَلِيمٌ ۞ قَالَ يَٰقَوْمِ إِنِّى لَكُمْ نَذِيرٌ مُّبِينٌ ۞ أَنِ ٱعْبُدُوا ٱللَّهَ وَٱتَّقُوهُ وَأَطِيعُونِ ۞ يَغْفِرْ لَكُم مِّن ذُنُوبِكُمْ وَيُؤَخِّرْكُمْ إِلَىٰٓ أَجَلٍ مُّسَمًّى إِنَّ أَجَلَ ٱللَّهِ إِذَا جَآءَ لَا يُؤَخَّرُ لَوْ كُنتُمْ تَعْلَمُونَ ۞ قَالَ رَبِّ إِنِّى دَعَوْتُ قَوْمِى لَيْلًا وَنَهَارًا ۞ فَلَمْ يَزِدْهُمْ دُعَآءِىٓ إِلَّا فِرَارًا ۞ وَإِنِّى كُلَّمَا دَعَوْتُهُمْ لِتَغْفِرَ لَهُمْ جَعَلُوٓا أَصَٰبِعَهُمْ فِىٓ ءَاذَانِهِمْ وَٱسْتَغْشَوْا ثِيَابَهُمْ وَأَصَرُّوا وَٱسْتَكْبَرُوا ٱسْتِكْبَارًا ۞ ثُمَّ إِنِّى دَعَوْتُهُمْ جِهَارًا ۞ ثُمَّ إِنِّىٓ أَعْلَنتُ لَهُمْ وَأَسْرَرْتُ لَهُمْ إِسْرَارًا ۞ فَقُلْتُ ٱسْتَغْفِرُوا رَبَّكُمْ إِنَّهُۥ كَانَ غَفَّارًا ۞ يُرْسِلِ ٱلسَّمَآءَ عَلَيْكُم مِّدْرَارًا ۞ وَيُمْدِدْكُم بِأَمْوَٰلٍ وَبَنِينَ وَيَجْعَل لَّكُمْ جَنَّٰتٍ وَيَجْعَل لَّكُمْ أَنْهَٰرًا ۞ مَّا لَكُمْ لَا تَرْجُونَ لِلَّهِ وَقَارًا ۞ وَقَدْ خَلَقَكُمْ أَطْوَارًا ۞ أَلَمْ تَرَوْا كَيْفَ خَلَقَ ٱللَّهُ سَبْعَ سَمَٰوَٰتٍ طِبَاقًا ۞ وَجَعَلَ ٱلْقَمَرَ فِيهِنَّ نُورًا وَجَعَلَ ٱلشَّمْسَ سِرَاجًا ۞ وَٱللَّهُ أَنۢبَتَكُم مِّنَ ۞

ٱلۡأَرۡضِ نَبَاتًا ۝ ثُمَّ يُعِيدُكُمۡ فِيهَا وَيُخۡرِجُكُمۡ إِخۡرَاجًا ۝ وَٱللَّهُ جَعَلَ لَكُمُ ٱلۡأَرۡضَ بِسَاطًا ۝ لِّتَسۡلُكُوا۟ مِنۡهَا سُبُلًا فِجَاجًا ۝ قَالَ نُوحٌ رَّبِّ إِنَّهُمۡ عَصَوۡنِي وَٱتَّبَعُوا۟ مَن لَّمۡ يَزِدۡهُ مَالُهُۥ وَوَلَدُهُۥٓ إِلَّا خَسَارًا ۝ وَمَكَرُوا۟ مَكۡرًا كُبَّارًا ۝ وَقَالُوا۟ لَا تَذَرُنَّ ءَالِهَتَكُمۡ وَلَا تَذَرُنَّ وَدًّا وَلَا سُوَاعًا وَلَا يَغُوثَ وَيَعُوقَ وَنَسۡرًا ۝ وَقَدۡ أَضَلُّوا۟ كَثِيرًا وَلَا تَزِدِ ٱلظَّـٰلِمِينَ إِلَّا ضَلَـٰلًا ۝ مِّمَّا خَطِيٓـَٰتِهِمۡ أُغۡرِقُوا۟ فَأُدۡخِلُوا۟ نَارًا فَلَمۡ يَجِدُوا۟ لَهُم مِّن دُونِ ٱللَّهِ أَنصَارًا ۝ وَقَالَ نُوحٌ رَّبِّ لَا تَذَرۡ عَلَى ٱلۡأَرۡضِ مِنَ ٱلۡكَـٰفِرِينَ دَيَّارًا ۝ إِنَّكَ إِن تَذَرۡهُمۡ يُضِلُّوا۟ عِبَادَكَ وَلَا يَلِدُوٓا۟ إِلَّا فَاجِرًا كَفَّارًا ۝ رَّبِّ ٱغۡفِرۡ لِي وَلِوَٰلِدَيَّ وَلِمَن دَخَلَ بَيۡتِيَ مُؤۡمِنًا وَلِلۡمُؤۡمِنِينَ وَٱلۡمُؤۡمِنَـٰتِ وَلَا تَزِدِ ٱلظَّـٰلِمِينَ إِلَّا تَبَارًا ۝

Verily, We sent Nūh (Noah) to his people (saying): "Warn your people before there comes to them a painful torment." He said: "O my people! Verily, I am a plain warner to you, that you should worship Allāh (Alone), fear (be dutiful to) Him, and obey me, He (Allāh) will forgive you of your sins and respite you to an appointed term. Verily, the term of Allāh when it comes, cannot be delayed, if you but know." He said: "O my Lord! Verily, I have called to my people night and day (i.e. secretly and openly to accept the doctrine of Islamic Monotheism), but all my calling added nothing but to (their) flight (from the truth). And verily, every time I called to them that You might forgive them, they thrust their fingers into their ears, covered themselves up with their garments, and persisted (in their refusal), and magnified themselves in pride. Then verily, I called to them openly (aloud). Then verily, I proclaimed to them in public, and I have appealed to them in private. I said (to them): "Ask forgiveness from your Lord, verily, He is Oft-Forgiving; He will send rain to you in abundance, and give you increase in wealth and children, and bestow on you gardens and bestow on you rivers." What is the matter with you, that [you fear not Allāh (His punishment), and] you hope not for reward (from Allāh or you believe not in His Oneness). While He has created you in (different) stages [i.e. first *Nutfah*, then *'Alaqah* and then *Mudghah*]. See you not how Allāh has created the seven heavens one above another? And has made the moon a light therein, and made the sun a lamp? And Allāh has brought you forth from the (dust of) earth. (*Tafsir At-Tabarī*) Afterwards He will return you into it (the earth), and bring you forth (again on the Day of Resurrection). And Allāh has made for you the earth a wide expanse. That you may go about therein in broad roads. Nūh (Noah) said: "My Lord! They have disobeyed me, and followed one whose wealth and children give him no increase but loss. And they have plotted a mighty plot. And they have said: 'You shall not leave your gods, nor shall you leave *Wadd*, nor *Suwā'*, nor *Yaghūth*, nor *Ya'ūq*, nor *Nasr*' (these are the names of their idols).' And indeed they have led many astray. And (O Allāh): 'Grant no increase to the *Zālimūn* (polytheists, wrong doers, and disbelievers) except error.' Because of their sins they were drowned, then were made to enter the Fire. And they found none to help them instead of Allāh. And Nūh (Noah) said: "My Lord! Leave not one of the disbelievers on the earth! If You leave them, they will mislead Your slaves, and they will beget none but wicked disbelievers. My Lord! Forgive me, and my parents, and him who enters my home as a believer, and all the believing men and women. And to the *Zālimūn* (polytheists, wrong doers, and disbelievers) grant You no increase but destruction!"

(Qur'ân 71: 1-28)

The people of Noah ﷺ lived in southern Iraq, not too far from where the city of Kufah is situated today.

Al-Judi is a mountain facing Ibn 'Umar Island at the junction of the Syrian and Turkish borders, on the eastern bank of Tigris River. This mountain could easily be seen from the Syrian town of Ain Dewar.

Historically it was mentioned that the land between the two rivers passed the following ages:

(1) The Old Stone Age: Mr. Sawyli (a scientist) discovered ancient remains of the stone age in 1954.

37

(2) New Stone age: (Grumu Civilization)

Mr. Bred Wood discovered in 1948 an important center of this age in Grumu village west of As-Sulaimaniyah city. Scientists believe that, the center was built around 6500 BC, which was little after the appearance of rural societies.

In the New stone age, there appeared also Tall Hassouna which is situated south of Mosul city. Its age goes back to round the year 5750 BC

Mr. Malwan found in 1931 similar pattern to (Tall Hassouna civilization) in Ninawa near Mosul city, and discovered other models of this civilization at different places in Iraq.

In (Tall Halafa) near the Syrian town Rasul-Ain the source of Khabur River, a German scientist called Bayron (Vaughn Uben-hiem), discovered similar patterns of the New Stone age civilization.

(3) The Copper-stone Age in the fertile plain surrounding the Tigris and Euphrates Rivers.

The civilization of this age is manifest in three important sites:

a- (The Slaves Mount) near Ur old city, south the land of the two rivers. This was discovered by the British Museum Expedition that was headed by Dr. Hall. The work of Dr. Hall was succeeded by the Historian Leonard Wooly who found in the old city of Ur, dolls made out of clay and that they have a religious significance.

b- The civilization of Auruk Age (Warqa).

This was explored by a German mission.

c- The civilization of Jamdat Nassur age:

The monuments of this age were discovered in 1920 by the archeologist Lankdon in a small hill called (Jamdat Nassur) that lies near the old city of Kish.

Towards the end of this age, according to history books, the great flood took place and inundated the land between the two rivers. The excavations that had been carried out in Ur, Uruk Kish and

Shurback revealed that a great flood had taken place between the Slave Age and Jamad Nassur Age.

Another archeologist, Mr. Wooly, found thick layers of mud two and a half meters deep in Ur city.

Mr. Wooly found ancient remains of human residing on top of these mud layers as well as below them. He concluded that this mud was brought about by the flood of Tigris and Euphrates.

> [It may be that the story of the flood mentioned in the holy books is older than this one by several ages, for Mr. Kountnu (Quoting from De Morgan) referred it to the rainy age, which followed the Ice Age at the end of the fourth stage when a large number of people perished. The Inscriptions that were discovered in the library of (Ashur Banib'al) commemorated this flood.]

Almost all the News Agencies through satellites reported on Wednesday Sept. 13, 2000 the following: Whole cities have been discovered at the bottom of the Black Sea. The team of scientists who discovered these cities said that this prove the flood that was mentioned in the holy books. The British Broadcasting Corporation (BBC) in London, broadcast this news on Thursday Sept. 14, 2000 in its program (*The World This Morning*) after TV channels broadcast the news the night before.

- Ash-Sharq Al-Adna Al-Qadim, by 'Abdul-'Aziz 'Uthmân: 213
- Qisas Al-Anbiyâ, by Ibn Kathir: 65
- Qisas Al-Anbiyâ, by Ath-Tha'labi: 55
- Qisas Al-Anbiyâ, by At-Tabari: 86
- Qisas Al-Anbiyâ, by An-Najjâr: 30
- Al-Mo'jam Al-Mufahris Li-Ma'âni Al-Qur'ân Al-Karim: 1268
- Wakâlât Al-Anbâ Al-'Alamiyyah Masa; dated: 13/9/2000

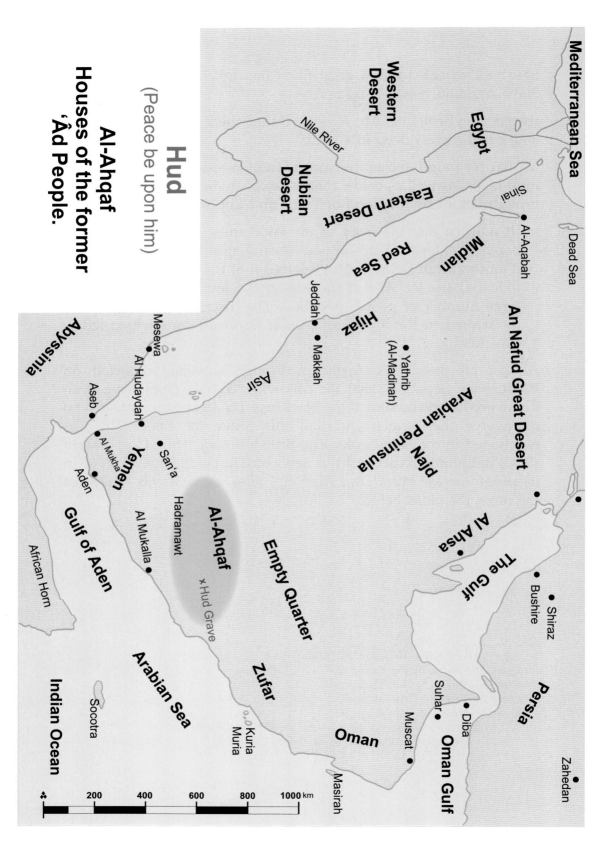

Hud
(Peace be upon him)

Al-Ahqaf
Houses of the former 'Ād People.

Mediterranean Sea

Egypt

Western Desert

Nile River

Nubian Desert

Eastern Desert

Sinai

Dead Sea

Al-Aqabah

Midian

An Nafud Great Desert

Red Sea

Hijaz

Jeddah

Makkah

Yathrib
(Al-Madinah)

Arabian Peninsula

Najd

Asir

Al Ahsa

The Gulf

Bushire

Shiraz

Persia

Zahedan

Abyssinia

Mesewa

Al Hudaydah

Aseb

Al Mukha

Aden

San'a

Yemen

Hadramawt

Al Mukalla

Al-Ahqaf

× Hud Grave

Empty Quarter

Zufar

Oman

Suhar

Muscat

Diba

Oman Gulf

Masirah

African Horn

Socotra

Kuria
Muria

Arabian Sea

Gulf of Aden

Indian Ocean

200 400 600 800 1000 km

Hûd عليه السلام

Prophet Hûd عليه السلام is mentioned seven times in the Noble Qur'ân, namely, in the following Chapters and Verses:

Chapter Name (Sûrah)	Number of Chapter (Sûrah)	Verse Numbers
Al-A'râf	7	65
Hûd	11	50, 53, 58, 60, 89
Ash-Shu'arâ'	26	124

﴿وَإِلَىٰ عَادٍ أَخَاهُمْ هُودًا قَالَ يَٰقَوْمِ ٱعْبُدُواْ ٱللَّهَ مَا لَكُم مِّنْ إِلَٰهٍ غَيْرُهُۥٓ إِنْ أَنتُمْ إِلَّا مُفْتَرُونَ ٥٠ يَٰقَوْمِ لَآ أَسْـَٔلُكُمْ عَلَيْهِ أَجْرًا إِنْ أَجْرِىَ إِلَّا عَلَى ٱلَّذِى فَطَرَنِىٓ أَفَلَا تَعْقِلُونَ ٥١ وَيَٰقَوْمِ ٱسْتَغْفِرُواْ رَبَّكُمْ ثُمَّ تُوبُوٓاْ إِلَيْهِ يُرْسِلِ ٱلسَّمَآءَ عَلَيْكُم مِّدْرَارًا وَيَزِدْكُمْ قُوَّةً إِلَىٰ قُوَّتِكُمْ وَلَا تَتَوَلَّوْاْ مُجْرِمِينَ ٥٢ قَالُواْ يَٰهُودُ مَا جِئْتَنَا بِبَيِّنَةٍ وَمَا نَحْنُ بِتَارِكِىٓ ءَالِهَتِنَا عَن قَوْلِكَ وَمَا نَحْنُ لَكَ بِمُؤْمِنِينَ ٥٣ إِن نَّقُولُ إِلَّا ٱعْتَرَىٰكَ بَعْضُ ءَالِهَتِنَا بِسُوٓءٍ قَالَ إِنِّىٓ أُشْهِدُ ٱللَّهَ وَٱشْهَدُوٓاْ أَنِّى بَرِىٓءٌ مِّمَّا تُشْرِكُونَ ٥٤ مِن دُونِهِۦ فَكِيدُونِى جَمِيعًا ثُمَّ لَا تُنظِرُونِ ٥٥ إِنِّى تَوَكَّلْتُ عَلَى ٱللَّهِ رَبِّى وَرَبِّكُم مَّا مِن دَآبَّةٍ إِلَّا هُوَ ءَاخِذٌۢ بِنَاصِيَتِهَآ إِنَّ رَبِّى عَلَىٰ صِرَٰطٍ مُّسْتَقِيمٍ ٥٦ فَإِن تَوَلَّوْاْ فَقَدْ أَبْلَغْتُكُم مَّآ أُرْسِلْتُ بِهِۦٓ إِلَيْكُمْ وَيَسْتَخْلِفُ رَبِّى قَوْمًا غَيْرَكُمْ وَلَا تَضُرُّونَهُۥ شَيْـًٔا إِنَّ رَبِّى عَلَىٰ كُلِّ شَىْءٍ حَفِيظٌ ٥٧ وَلَمَّا جَآءَ أَمْرُنَا نَجَّيْنَا هُودًا وَٱلَّذِينَ ءَامَنُواْ مَعَهُۥ بِرَحْمَةٍ مِّنَّا وَنَجَّيْنَٰهُم مِّنْ عَذَابٍ غَلِيظٍ ٥٨ وَتِلْكَ عَادٌ جَحَدُواْ بِـَٔايَٰتِ رَبِّهِمْ وَعَصَوْاْ رُسُلَهُۥ وَٱتَّبَعُوٓاْ أَمْرَ كُلِّ جَبَّارٍ عَنِيدٍ ٥٩ وَأُتْبِعُواْ فِى هَٰذِهِ ٱلدُّنْيَا لَعْنَةً وَيَوْمَ ٱلْقِيَٰمَةِ أَلَآ إِنَّ عَادًا كَفَرُواْ رَبَّهُمْ أَلَا بُعْدًا لِّعَادٍ قَوْمِ هُودٍ ٦٠﴾

And to the 'Ād (people We sent) their brother Hūd. He said,

"O my people! Worship Allāh! You have no other *ilāh* (god) but Him. Certainly, you do nothing but invent lies! O my people! I ask of you no reward for it (the Message). My reward is only from Him Who created me. Will you not then understand? And O my people! Ask forgiveness of your Lord and then repent to Him, He will send you (from the sky) abundant rain, and add strength to your strength, so do not turn away as *Mujrimūn* (criminals, disbelievers in the Oneness of Allāh)." They said: "O Hūd! No evidence have you brought us, and we shall not leave our gods for your (mere) saying! And we are not believers in you. All that we say is that some of our gods (false deities) have seized you with evil (madness)." He said: "I call Allāh to witness and bear you witness that I am free from that which you ascribe as partners in worship with Him (Allāh). So plot against me, all of you, and give me no respite. I put my trust in Allāh, my Lord and your Lord! There is not a moving (living) creature but He has the grasp of its forelock. Verily, my Lord is on a Straight Path (the truth). So if you turn away, still I have conveyed the Message with which I was sent to you. My Lord will make another people succeed you, and you will not harm Him in the least. Surely, my Lord is Guardian over all things." And when Our Commandment came, We saved Hūd and those who believed with him by a mercy from Us, and We saved them from a severe torment. Such were 'Ād (people). They rejected the *Ayāt* (proofs, evidences, Verses, lessons, signs, revelations, etc.) of their Lord and disobeyed His Messengers, and followed the command of every proud, obstinate (oppressor of the truth from their leaders). And they were pursued by a curse in this world and (so they will be) on the Day of Resurrection. No doubt! Verily, 'Ād disbelieved in their Lord. So, away with 'Ād, the people of Hūd.

(Qur'ân 11: 50-60)

﴾ كَذَّبَتْ عَادٌ الْمُرْسَلِينَ ۝ إِذْ قَالَ لَهُمْ أَخُوهُمْ هُودٌ أَلَا تَتَّقُونَ ۝ إِنِّي لَكُمْ رَسُولٌ أَمِينٌ ۝ فَاتَّقُوا اللَّهَ وَأَطِيعُونِ ۝ وَمَا أَسْأَلُكُمْ عَلَيْهِ مِنْ أَجْرٍ إِنْ أَجْرِيَ إِلَّا عَلَى رَبِّ الْعَالَمِينَ

42

أَتَبْنُونَ بِكُلِّ رِيعٍ ءَايَةً تَعْبَثُونَ ۝ وَتَتَّخِذُونَ مَصَانِعَ لَعَلَّكُمْ تَخْلُدُونَ ۝ وَإِذَا بَطَشْتُم بَطَشْتُمْ جَبَّارِينَ ۝ فَاتَّقُوا اللَّهَ وَأَطِيعُونِ ۝ وَاتَّقُوا الَّذِىٓ أَمَدَّكُم بِمَا تَعْلَمُونَ ۝ أَمَدَّكُم بِأَنْعَٰمٍ وَبَنِينَ ۝ وَجَنَّٰتٍ وَعُيُونٍ ۝ إِنِّىٓ أَخَافُ عَلَيْكُمْ عَذَابَ يَوْمٍ عَظِيمٍ ۝ قَالُوا سَوَآءٌ عَلَيْنَآ أَوَعَظْتَ أَمْ لَمْ تَكُن مِّنَ الْوَٰعِظِينَ ۝ إِنْ هَٰذَآ إِلَّا خُلُقُ الْأَوَّلِينَ ۝ وَمَا نَحْنُ بِمُعَذَّبِينَ ۝ فَكَذَّبُوهُ فَأَهْلَكْنَٰهُمْ إِنَّ فِى ذَٰلِكَ لَأَيَةً وَمَا كَانَ أَكْثَرُهُم مُّؤْمِنِينَ ۝ وَإِنَّ رَبَّكَ لَهُوَ الْعَزِيزُ الرَّحِيمُ ۝ ۞

'Ād (people) denied the Messengers. When their brother Hūd said to them: "Will you not fear Allāh and obey Him? Verily, I am a trustworthy Messenger to you. So fear Allāh, keep your duty to Him, and obey me. No reward do I ask of you for it (my Message of Islamic Monotheism); my reward is only from the Lord of the *'Ālamīn* (mankind, jinn, and all that exists). Do you build high palaces on every high place, while you do not live in them? And do you get for yourselves palaces (fine buildings) as if you will live therein forever? And when you seize (somebody), seize you (him) as tyrants? So fear Allāh, keep your duty to Him, and obey me. And keep your duty to Him, fear Him Who has aided you with all (good things) that you know. He has aided you with cattle and children. And gardens and springs. Verily, I fear for you the torment of a Great Day." They said: "It is the same to us whether you preach or be not of those who preach. This is no other than the false tales and religion of the ancients (*Tafsir At-Tabarī*). And we are not going to be punished." So they denied him, and We destroyed them. Verily, in this is indeed a sign, yet most of them are not believers. And verily your Lord, He is truly the All-Mighty, the Most Merciful.

(Qur'ân 26: 123-140)

Ibn 'Abbâs ؓ is reported to have said, "Verily, Hûd was the first to speak the Arabic language." The people of Ãd, to whom Hûd ﷺ had been sent, lived in an area of curved sand hills in the southern part of the Arabian Peninsula. They worshiped a number of idols:

43

Wudd, Suwa', Yaghuth, Ya'uq, and Nasr [refer to the map that shows the places of idols and images in the Arabian Peninsula]. Ibn 'Abbâs ﷺ said, "They [also] took to worshiping an idol that was called Al-Hattar.

The people of Ād that were destroyed are referred to as the 'first people of Ād'; as for the 'second people of Ād,' they are the inhabitants of Yemen from Qahtan, Saba, and their descendents. But it is also said that the 'second people of Ād' are none other than the people of Thamûd.

The people of Hadramawt say that, after Ād was destroyed, Hûd ﷺ lived in the land of Hadramawt, until he died in the western part of their land, not too far from the city of Taryam, which is near the Valley of Barhut. It is worth mentioning here that there is a grave in Palestine that is erroneously said to be his.

- Qisas Al-Anbiya, by Ibn Kathir: 93
- Qisas Al-Anbiya, by Ath-Tha'labi: 62
- Qisas Al-Anbiya, by At-Tabari: 118
- Qisas Al-Anbiya, by An-Najjaar: 49
- Al-Mo'jam Al-Mufahris Li-Alfadh Al-Qur'ân Al-Karim: 739
- Al-Mo'jam Al-Mufahris Li-Ma'âni Al-Qur'ân Al-Karim: 1294

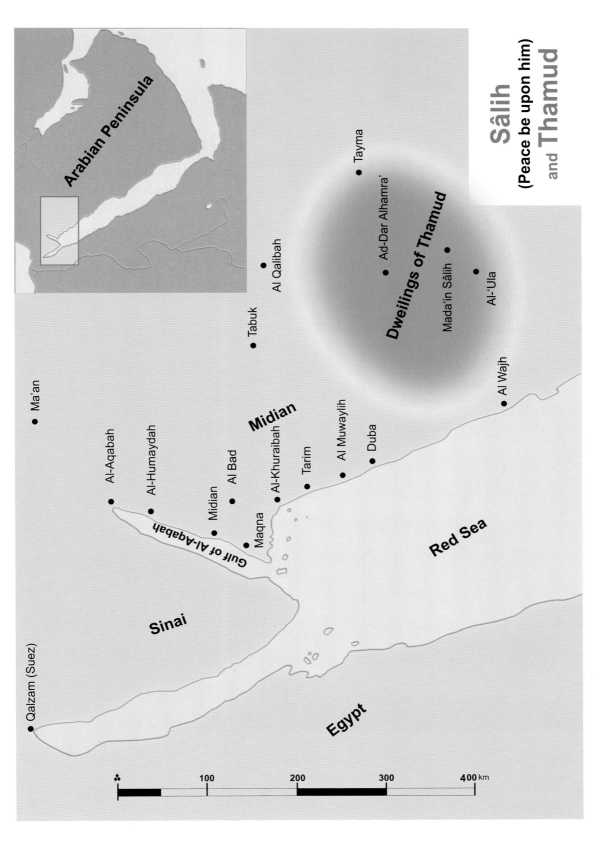

Sâlih
(Peace be upon him)
and Thamud

Arabian Peninsula

Ma'an

Qalzam (Suez)

Al-Aqabah

Al-Humaydah

Midian

Al Bad

Al-Khuraibah

Maqna

Tarim

Al Muwaylih

Duba

Gulf of Al-Aqabah

Midian

Sinai

Egypt

Red Sea

Tabuk

Al Qalibah

Tayma

Ad-Dar Alhamra'

Dweilings of Thamud

Mada'in Sâlih

Al-'Ula

Al Wajh

100   200   300   400 km

Sâlih الْعَلَيْهِ‌السَّلَام
And The Dwellings
Places Of Thamûd

Sâlih الْعَلَيْهِ‌السَّلَام is mentioned by name nine times in the Noble Qur'ân:

Chapter Name (Sûrah)	Number of Chapter (Sûrah)	Verse Numbers
Al-A'râf	7	73, 75, 77
Hûd	11	61, 62, 66, 89
Ash-Shu'arâ	26	142
An-Naml	27	45

﴿وَإِلَىٰ ثَمُودَ أَخَاهُمْ صَٰلِحًا قَالَ يَٰقَوْمِ ٱعْبُدُوا۟ ٱللَّهَ مَا لَكُم مِّنْ إِلَٰهٍ غَيْرُهُ قَدْ جَآءَتْكُم بَيِّنَةٌ مِّن رَّبِّكُمْ هَٰذِهِۦ نَاقَةُ ٱللَّهِ لَكُمْ ءَايَةً فَذَرُوهَا تَأْكُلْ فِىٓ أَرْضِ ٱللَّهِ وَلَا تَمَسُّوهَا بِسُوٓءٍ فَيَأْخُذَكُمْ عَذَابٌ أَلِيمٌ ۝ وَٱذْكُرُوٓا۟ إِذْ جَعَلَكُمْ خُلَفَآءَ مِنۢ بَعْدِ عَادٍ وَبَوَّأَكُمْ فِى ٱلْأَرْضِ تَتَّخِذُونَ مِن سُهُولِهَا قُصُورًا وَتَنْحِتُونَ ٱلْجِبَالَ بُيُوتًا فَٱذْكُرُوٓا۟ ءَالَآءَ ٱللَّهِ وَلَا تَعْثَوْا۟ فِى ٱلْأَرْضِ مُفْسِدِينَ ۝ قَالَ ٱلْمَلَأُ ٱلَّذِينَ ٱسْتَكْبَرُوا۟ مِن قَوْمِهِۦ لِلَّذِينَ ٱسْتُضْعِفُوا۟ لِمَنْ ءَامَنَ مِنْهُمْ أَتَعْلَمُونَ أَنَّ صَٰلِحًا مُّرْسَلٌ مِّن رَّبِّهِۦ قَالُوٓا۟ إِنَّا بِمَآ أُرْسِلَ بِهِۦ مُؤْمِنُونَ ۝ قَالَ ٱلَّذِينَ ٱسْتَكْبَرُوٓا۟ إِنَّا بِٱلَّذِىٓ ءَامَنتُم بِهِۦ كَٰفِرُونَ ۝ فَعَقَرُوا۟ ٱلنَّاقَةَ وَعَتَوْا۟ عَنْ أَمْرِ رَبِّهِمْ وَقَالُوا۟ يَٰصَٰلِحُ ٱئْتِنَا بِمَا تَعِدُنَآ إِن كُنتَ مِنَ ٱلْمُرْسَلِينَ ۝ فَأَخَذَتْهُمُ ٱلرَّجْفَةُ فَأَصْبَحُوا۟ فِى دَارِهِمْ جَٰثِمِينَ ۝ فَتَوَلَّىٰ عَنْهُمْ وَقَالَ يَٰقَوْمِ لَقَدْ أَبْلَغْتُكُمْ رِسَالَةَ رَبِّى وَنَصَحْتُ لَكُمْ وَلَٰكِن لَّا تُحِبُّونَ ٱلنَّٰصِحِينَ ۝﴾

46

And to Thamūd (people, We sent) their brother Sālih. He said: "O my people! Worship Allāh! You have no other *Ilāh* (God) but Him. (*Lā ilāha illallāh*: none has the right to be worshipped but Allāh.) Indeed there has come to you a clear sign (the miracle of the coming out of a huge she-camel from the midst of a rock) from your Lord. This she-camel of Allāh is a sign to you; so you leave her to graze in Allāh's earth, and touch her not with harm, lest a painful torment should seize you. And remember when He made you successors after 'Ād (people) and gave you habitations in the land, you build for yourselves palaces in plains, and carve out homes in the mountains. So remember the graces (bestowed upon you) from Allāh, and do not go about making mischief on the earth." The leaders of those who were arrogant among his people said to those who were counted weak — to such of them as believed: "Know you that Sālih is one sent from his Lord." They said: "We indeed believe in that with which he has been sent." Those who were arrogant said: "Verily, we disbelieve in that which you believe in." So they killed the she-camel and insolently defied the Commandment of their Lord, and said: "O Sālih! Bring about your threats if you are indeed one of the Messengers (of Allāh)." So the earthquake seized them, and they lay (dead), prostrate in their homes. Then he (Sālih) turned from them, and said: "O my people! I have indeed conveyed to you the Message of my Lord, and have given you good advice but you like not good advisers."

(Qur'ân 7: 73-79)

﴿وَإِلَىٰ ثَمُودَ أَخَاهُمْ صَـٰلِحًا قَالَ يَـٰقَوْمِ ٱعْبُدُواْ ٱللَّهَ مَا لَكُم مِّنْ إِلَـٰهٍ غَيْرُهُۥ هُوَ أَنشَأَكُم مِّنَ ٱلْأَرْضِ وَٱسْتَعْمَرَكُمْ فِيهَا فَٱسْتَغْفِرُوهُ ثُمَّ تُوبُوٓاْ إِلَيْهِ إِنَّ رَبِّى قَرِيبٌ مُّجِيبٌ ۝ قَالُواْ يَـٰصَـٰلِحُ قَدْ كُنتَ فِينَا مَرْجُوًّا قَبْلَ هَـٰذَآ أَتَنْهَىٰنَآ أَن نَّعْبُدَ مَا يَعْبُدُ ءَابَآؤُنَا وَإِنَّنَا لَفِى شَكٍّ مِّمَّا تَدْعُونَآ إِلَيْهِ مُرِيبٍ ۝ قَالَ يَـٰقَوْمِ أَرَءَيْتُمْ إِن كُنتُ عَلَىٰ بَيِّنَةٍ مِّن رَّبِّى وَءَاتَىٰنِى مِنْهُ رَحْمَةً فَمَن يَنصُرُنِى مِنَ ٱللَّهِ إِنْ عَصَيْتُهُۥ فَمَا تَزِيدُونَنِى غَيْرَ تَخْسِيرٍ ۝ وَيَـٰقَوْمِ هَـٰذِهِۦ نَاقَةُ ٱللَّهِ لَكُمْ ءَايَةً فَذَرُوهَا تَأْكُلْ فِىٓ أَرْضِ ٱللَّهِ وَلَا تَمَسُّوهَا بِسُوٓءٍ فَيَأْخُذَكُمْ عَذَابٌ قَرِيبٌ

47

٦٤ فَعَقَرُوهَا فَقَالَ تَمَتَّعُواْ فِى دَارِكُمْ ثَلَٰثَةَ أَيَّامٍ ذَٰلِكَ وَعْدٌ غَيْرُ مَكْذُوبٍ

٦٥ فَلَمَّا جَآءَ أَمْرُنَا نَجَّيْنَا صَٰلِحًا وَالَّذِينَ ءَامَنُواْ مَعَهُ بِرَحْمَةٍ مِّنَّا وَمِنْ خِزْىِ يَوْمِئِذٍ

إِنَّ رَبَّكَ هُوَ الْقَوِىُّ الْعَزِيزُ ٦٦ وَأَخَذَ الَّذِينَ ظَلَمُواْ الصَّيْحَةُ فَأَصْبَحُواْ فِى دِيَٰرِهِمْ

جَٰثِمِينَ ٦٧ كَأَن لَّمْ يَغْنَوْاْ فِيهَآ أَلَآ إِنَّ ثَمُودَاْ كَفَرُواْ رَبَّهُمْ أَلَا بُعْدًا لِّثَمُودَ ٦٨ ۞

And to Thamūd (people We sent) their brother Sālih . He said:
"O my people! Worship Allāh: you have no other *ilāh* (god) but
Him. He brought you forth from the earth and settled you
therein, then ask forgiveness of Him and turn to Him in
repentance. Certainly, my Lord is Near (to all by His
Knowledge), Responsive." They said: "O Sālih! You have
been among us as a figure of good hope (and we wished for
you to be our chief) till this [new thing which you have
brought that we leave our gods and worship your God (Allāh)
Alone]! Do you (now) forbid us the worship of what our
fathers have worshipped? But we are really in grave doubt as
to that to which you invite us (monotheism)." He said: "O my
people! Tell me, if I have a clear proof from my Lord, and there
has come to me a mercy (Prophethood) from Him, who then
can help me against Allāh, if I were to disobey Him? Then you
increase me not but in loss. "And O my people! This she-camel
of Allāh is a sign to you, so leave her to feed (graze) in Allāh's
land, and touch her not with evil, lest a near torment should
seize you." But they killed her. So he said: "Enjoy yourselves in
your homes for three days. This is a promise (i.e. a threat) that
will not be belied." So when Our Commandment came, We
saved Sālih and those who believed with him by a mercy from
Us, and from the disgrace of that Day. Verily, your Lord — He
is the All-Strong, the All-Mighty. And *As-Saihah* (torment —
awful cry) overtook the wrong doers, so they lay (dead),
prostrate in their homes, As if they had never lived there. No
doubt! Verily, Thamūd disbelieved in their Lord. So away with
Thamūd!

(Qur'ân 11: 61-68)

Mada'in Salih

بِسْمِ ﴿ كَذَّبَتْ ثَمُودُ ٱلْمُرْسَلِينَ ۝ إِذْ قَالَ لَهُمْ أَخُوهُمْ صَٰلِحٌ أَلَا تَتَّقُونَ ۝ إِنِّى لَكُمْ رَسُولٌ أَمِينٌ ۝ فَٱتَّقُوا۟ ٱللَّهَ وَأَطِيعُونِ ۝ وَمَآ أَسْـَٔلُكُمْ عَلَيْهِ مِنْ أَجْرٍ إِنْ أَجْرِىَ إِلَّا عَلَىٰ رَبِّ ٱلْعَٰلَمِينَ ۝ أَتُتْرَكُونَ فِى مَا هَٰهُنَآ ءَامِنِينَ ۝ فِى جَنَّٰتٍ وَعُيُونٍ ۝ وَزُرُوعٍ وَنَخْلٍ طَلْعُهَا هَضِيمٌ ۝ وَتَنْحِتُونَ مِنَ ٱلْجِبَالِ بُيُوتًا فَٰرِهِينَ ۝ فَٱتَّقُوا۟ ٱللَّهَ وَأَطِيعُونِ ۝ وَلَا تُطِيعُوٓا۟ أَمْرَ ٱلْمُسْرِفِينَ ۝ ٱلَّذِينَ يُفْسِدُونَ فِى ٱلْأَرْضِ وَلَا يُصْلِحُونَ ۝ قَالُوٓا۟ إِنَّمَآ أَنتَ مِنَ ٱلْمُسَحَّرِينَ ۝ مَآ أَنتَ إِلَّا بَشَرٌ مِّثْلُنَا فَأْتِ بِـَٔايَةٍ إِن كُنتَ مِنَ ٱلصَّٰدِقِينَ ۝ قَالَ هَٰذِهِۦ نَاقَةٌ لَّهَا شِرْبٌ وَلَكُمْ شِرْبُ يَوْمٍ مَّعْلُومٍ ۝ وَلَا تَمَسُّوهَا بِسُوٓءٍ فَيَأْخُذَكُمْ عَذَابُ يَوْمٍ عَظِيمٍ ۝ فَعَقَرُوهَا فَأَصْبَحُوا۟ نَٰدِمِينَ ۝ فَأَخَذَهُمُ ٱلْعَذَابُ إِنَّ فِى ذَٰلِكَ لَءَايَةً وَمَا كَانَ أَكْثَرُهُم مُّؤْمِنِينَ ۝ وَإِنَّ رَبَّكَ لَهُوَ ٱلْعَزِيزُ ٱلرَّحِيمُ ۝ ﴾

Thamūd (people) denied the Messenger. When their brother Sālih said to them: "Will you not fear Allāh and obey Him? I am a trustworthy Messenger to you. So fear Allāh, keep your duty to Him, and obey me. No reward do I ask of you for it (my Message of Islamic Monotheism); my reward is only from the Lord of the ʿĀlamīn (mankind, jinn and all that exists). Will you be left secure in that which you have here? In gardens and springs. And green crops (field) and date palms with soft spadix. And you hew out in the mountains, houses with great skill. So fear Allāh, keep your duty to Him, and obey me. And follow not the command of Al-Musrifūn (i.e. their chiefs, leaders who were polytheists, criminals and sinners), who make mischief in the land, and reform not.'' They said: You are only of those bewitched! You are but a human being like us. Then bring us a sign if you are of the truthful.'' He said: "Here is a she-camel: it has a right to drink (water), and you have a right to drink (water) (each) on a day, known. And touch her not with harm, lest the torment of a Great Day should seize you.'' But they killed her, and then they became regretful. So, the torment overtook them. Verily, in this is indeed a sign, yet most of them are not believers. And verily your Lord, He is truly the All-Mighty, the Most Merciful.

(Qur'ân 26: 141-159)

The dwelling places of Sâlih's people, Thamûd, are situated somewhere between Al-Hijaz and Ash-Sham (Syria and surrounding regions), in the southeastern part of Midian (Madyan), which is situated east of the Gulf of Al-'Aqabah. Chiseled out of stone, their dwellings are still preserved.

The people of Thamûd worshiped idols. Then Allâh sent Sâlih ﷺ to them, to both advise and remind them about their duties towards Allâh ﷻ. The miracle Sâlih ﷺ came with was the she-camel that came out of a stone. Though they were warned not to, they slaughtered that camel, and as a result of their disbelief and disobedience, they were destroyed. The only ones who were saved among them were Sâlih ﷺ and those who believed in his Prophethood. After their people were destroyed, those survivors traveled to Ramlah in Palestine. That they traveled there is the strongest of the various views regarding where they went, for it was the closest fertile land to them. And it is known that Arabs would give great importance to land that was situated near water and plentiful pasture, for they relied in their livelihood on the grazing of their livestock.

Nonetheless, the people of Hadramawt say that Sâlih ﷺ and his followers traveled to Hadramawt and settled there, because that is where they were originally from. There is a grave there that they say belongs to Sâlih ﷺ. Others have said that Sâlih ﷺ and his followers remained in their dwellings even after their people were destroyed. And yet others say that they traveled to Makkah and remained there until they died and that their graves are situated west of the Ka'bah.

- Qisas Al-Anbiya, by Ibn Kathir: 106
- Qisas Al-Anbiya, by Ath-Tha'labi: 68
- Qisas Al-Anbiya, by At-Tabari: 126
- Qisas Al-Anbiya, by An-Najjâr: 58
- Al-Mo'jam Al-Mufahris Li-Alfâdh Al-Qur'ân Al-Karim: 410
- Al-Mo'jam Al-Mufahris Li-Ma'âni Al-Qur'ân Al-Karim: 657

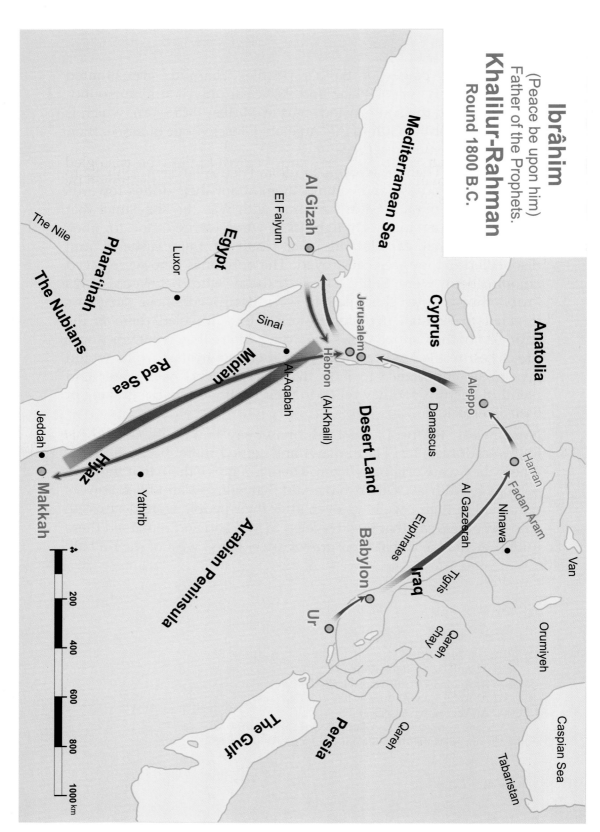

Ibrâhim
(Peace be upon him)
Father of the Prophets.

Khalilur-Rahman
Round 1800 B.C.

Ibrâhim ﷺ

He is the father of the Prophets, and the *Khalil* (one who is singled out for extra love) of the Most Merciful. Ibrâhim ﷺ is mentioned by name 69 times in the Noble Qur'ân:

Chapter Name (Sûrah)	Number of Chapter (Sûrah)	Verse Numbers
Al-Baqarah	2	124, 125 (twice), 126, 127, 130, 132, 133, 135, 136, 140, 258 (twice), 260
Āl-'Imrân	3	33, 65, 67, 84, 95, 97
An-Nisa'	4	54, 125 (twice), 163
Al-An'âm	6	74, 75, 83, 161
At-Taubah	9	70, 114 (twice)
Hûd	11	69, 74, 75, 76
Yusuf	12	6, 38
Ibrâhim	14	35
Al-Hijr	15	51
An-Nahl	16	120, 123
Maryam	19	41, 46, 58
Al-Anbiya'	21	51, 60, 62, 69
Al-Hajj	22	26, 43, 78
Ash-Shu'arâ	26	69
Al-'Ankabût	29	16, 31
Al-Ahzâb	33	7

As-Sâffât	37	83, 104, 109
Sâd	38	45
Ash-Shûra	42	13
Az-Zukhruf	43	26
Adh-Dhâriyât	51	24
An-Najm	53	37
Al-Hadid	57	26
Al-Mumtahinah	60	4 (twice)
Al-A'lâ	87	19

﴿وَلَقَدْ ءَاتَيْنَآ إِبْرَٰهِيمَ رُشْدَهُۥ مِن قَبْلُ وَكُنَّا بِهِۦ عَٰلِمِينَ ٥١ إِذْ قَالَ لِأَبِيهِ وَقَوْمِهِ مَا هَٰذِهِ التَّمَاثِيلُ الَّتِيٓ أَنتُمْ لَهَا عَٰكِفُونَ ٥٢ قَالُواْ وَجَدْنَآ ءَابَآءَنَا لَهَا عَٰبِدِينَ ٥٣ قَالَ لَقَدْ كُنتُمْ أَنتُمْ وَءَابَآؤُكُمْ فِى ضَلَٰلٍ مُّبِينٍ ٥٤ قَالُوٓاْ أَجِئْتَنَا بِالْحَقِّ أَمْ أَنتَ مِنَ اللَّٰعِبِينَ ٥٥ قَالَ بَل رَّبُّكُمْ رَبُّ السَّمَٰوَٰتِ وَالْأَرْضِ الَّذِى فَطَرَهُنَّ وَأَنَا۠ عَلَىٰ ذَٰلِكُم مِّنَ الشَّٰهِدِينَ ٥٦ وَتَاللَّهِ لَأَكِيدَنَّ أَصْنَٰمَكُم بَعْدَ أَن تُوَلُّواْ مُدْبِرِينَ ٥٧ فَجَعَلَهُمْ جُذَٰذًا إِلَّا كَبِيرًا لَّهُمْ لَعَلَّهُمْ إِلَيْهِ يَرْجِعُونَ ٥٨ قَالُواْ مَن فَعَلَ هَٰذَا بِـَٔالِهَتِنَآ إِنَّهُۥ لَمِنَ الظَّٰلِمِينَ ٥٩ قَالُواْ سَمِعْنَا فَتًى يَذْكُرُهُمْ يُقَالُ لَهُۥٓ إِبْرَٰهِيمُ ٦٠ قَالُواْ فَأْتُواْ بِهِۦ عَلَىٰٓ أَعْيُنِ النَّاسِ لَعَلَّهُمْ يَشْهَدُونَ ٦١ قَالُوٓاْ ءَأَنتَ فَعَلْتَ هَٰذَا بِـَٔالِهَتِنَا يَٰٓإِبْرَٰهِيمُ ٦٢ قَالَ بَلْ فَعَلَهُۥ كَبِيرُهُمْ هَٰذَا فَسْـَٔلُوهُمْ إِن كَانُواْ يَنطِقُونَ ٦٣ فَرَجَعُوٓاْ إِلَىٰٓ أَنفُسِهِمْ فَقَالُوٓاْ إِنَّكُمْ أَنتُمُ الظَّٰلِمُونَ ٦٤ ثُمَّ نُكِسُواْ عَلَىٰ رُءُوسِهِمْ لَقَدْ عَلِمْتَ مَا هَٰٓؤُلَآءِ يَنطِقُونَ ٦٥ قَالَ أَفَتَعْبُدُونَ مِن دُونِ اللَّهِ مَا لَا يَنفَعُكُمْ شَيْـًٔا وَلَا يَضُرُّكُمْ ٦٦ أُفٍّ لَّكُمْ وَلِمَا تَعْبُدُونَ مِن دُونِ اللَّهِ أَفَلَا تَعْقِلُونَ ٦٧ قَالُواْ حَرِّقُوهُ وَانصُرُوٓاْ ءَالِهَتَكُمْ إِن كُنتُمْ فَٰعِلِينَ ٦٨ قُلْنَا يَٰنَارُ كُونِى بَرْدًا وَسَلَٰمًا عَلَىٰٓ إِبْرَٰهِيمَ ٦٩ وَأَرَادُواْ بِهِۦ كَيْدًا فَجَعَلْنَٰهُمُ الْأَخْسَرِينَ ٧٠ وَنَجَّيْنَٰهُ وَلُوطًا إِلَى الْأَرْضِ الَّتِى بَٰرَكْنَا فِيهَا لِلْعَٰلَمِينَ ٧١ وَوَهَبْنَا لَهُۥٓ إِسْحَٰقَ وَيَعْقُوبَ نَافِلَةً وَكُلًّا جَعَلْنَا صَٰلِحِينَ ٧٢﴾

And indeed We bestowed aforetime on Ibrāhīm (Abraham) his (portion of) guidance, and We were All-Knower of him (as to his belief in the Oneness of Allāh). When he said to his father and his people: "What are these images to which you are devoted?" They said: "We found our fathers worshipping them." He said: "Indeed you and your fathers have been in manifest error." They said: "Have you brought us the Truth, or are you one of those who play about?" He said: "Nay, your Lord is the Lord of the heavens and the earth, Who created them and to that I am one of the witnesses. And by Allāh, I shall plot a plan (to destroy) your idols after you have gone away and turned your backs." So he broke them to pieces, (all) except the biggest of them, that they might turn to it. They said: "Who has done this to our *ālihah* (gods)? He must indeed be one of the *Zālimun* (wrong doers)." They said: "We heard a young man talking against them, who is called Ibrāhīm (Abraham)." They said: "Then bring him before the eyes of the people, that they may testify." They said: "Are you the one who has done this to our gods, O Ibrāhīm (Abraham)?" [Ibrāhīm (Abraham)] said: "Nay, this one, the biggest of them (idols) did it. Ask them, if they can speak!" So they turned to themselves and said: "Verily, you are the *Zālimūn* (polytheists and wrong doers)." Then they turned to themselves (their first thought and said): "Indeed you [Ibrāhīm (Abraham)] know well that these (idols) speak not!" [Ibrāhīm (Abraham)] said: "Do you then worship besides Allāh, things that can neither profit you nor harm you? Fie upon you, and upon that which you worship besides Allāh! Have you then no sense?" They said: "Burn him and help your *ālihah* (gods), if you will be doing." We (Allāh) said: "O fire! Be you coolness and safety for Ibrāhīm (Abraham)!" And they wanted to harm him, but We made them the worst losers. And We rescued him and Lūt (Lot) to the land which We have blessed for the *'Ālamīn* (mankind and jinn). And We bestowed upon him Ishāq (Isaac), and (a grandson) Ya'qūb (Jacob). Each one We made righteous.

(Qur'ân 21: 51-72)

﴿وَإِذْ قَالَ إِبْرَٰهِيمُ لِأَبِيهِ ءَازَرَ أَتَتَّخِذُ أَصْنَامًا ءَالِهَةً إِنِّىٓ أَرَىٰكَ وَقَوْمَكَ فِى ضَلَٰلٍ مُّبِينٍ ٧٤ وَكَذَٰلِكَ نُرِىٓ إِبْرَٰهِيمَ مَلَكُوتَ ٱلسَّمَٰوَٰتِ وَٱلْأَرْضِ وَلِيَكُونَ مِنَ ٱلْمُوقِنِينَ ٧٥ فَلَمَّا جَنَّ عَلَيْهِ ٱلَّيْلُ رَءَا كَوْكَبًا قَالَ هَٰذَا رَبِّى فَلَمَّآ أَفَلَ قَالَ لَآ أُحِبُّ ٱلْءَافِلِينَ ٧٦ فَلَمَّا رَءَا ٱلْقَمَرَ بَازِغًا قَالَ هَٰذَا رَبِّى فَلَمَّآ أَفَلَ قَالَ لَئِن لَّمْ يَهْدِنِى رَبِّى لَأَكُونَنَّ مِنَ ٱلْقَوْمِ ٱلضَّآلِّينَ ٧٧ فَلَمَّا رَءَا ٱلشَّمْسَ بَازِغَةً قَالَ هَٰذَا رَبِّى هَٰذَآ أَكْبَرُ فَلَمَّآ أَفَلَتْ قَالَ يَٰقَوْمِ إِنِّى بَرِىٓءٌ مِّمَّا تُشْرِكُونَ ٧٨ إِنِّى وَجَّهْتُ وَجْهِىَ لِلَّذِى فَطَرَ ٱلسَّمَٰوَٰتِ وَٱلْأَرْضَ حَنِيفًا وَمَآ أَنَا۠ مِنَ ٱلْمُشْرِكِينَ ٧٩ وَحَآجَّهُۥ قَوْمُهُۥ قَالَ أَتُحَٰٓجُّوٓنِّى فِى ٱللَّهِ وَقَدْ هَدَىٰنِ وَلَآ أَخَافُ مَا تُشْرِكُونَ بِهِۦٓ إِلَّآ أَن يَشَآءَ رَبِّى شَيْـًٔا وَسِعَ رَبِّى كُلَّ شَىْءٍ عِلْمًا أَفَلَا تَتَذَكَّرُونَ ٨٠ وَكَيْفَ أَخَافُ مَآ أَشْرَكْتُمْ وَلَا تَخَافُونَ أَنَّكُمْ أَشْرَكْتُم بِٱللَّهِ مَا لَمْ يُنَزِّلْ بِهِۦ عَلَيْكُمْ سُلْطَٰنًا فَأَىُّ ٱلْفَرِيقَيْنِ أَحَقُّ بِٱلْأَمْنِ إِن كُنتُمْ تَعْلَمُونَ ٨١ ٱلَّذِينَ ءَامَنُوا۟ وَلَمْ يَلْبِسُوٓا۟ إِيمَٰنَهُم بِظُلْمٍ أُو۟لَٰٓئِكَ لَهُمُ ٱلْأَمْنُ وَهُم مُّهْتَدُونَ ٨٢ وَتِلْكَ حُجَّتُنَآ ءَاتَيْنَٰهَآ إِبْرَٰهِيمَ عَلَىٰ قَوْمِهِۦ نَرْفَعُ دَرَجَٰتٍ مَّن نَّشَآءُ إِنَّ رَبَّكَ حَكِيمٌ عَلِيمٌ ٨٣ ﴾

And (remember) when Ibrāhīm (Abraham) said to his father Āzar: "Do you take idols as *ālihā* (gods)? Verily, I see you and your people in manifest error." Thus did we show Ibrāhīm (Abraham) the kingdom of the heavens and the earth that he be one of those who have Faith with certainty. When the night covered him over with darkness he saw a star. He said: "This is my lord." But when it set, he said: "I like not those that set." When he saw the moon rising up, he said: "This is my lord." But when it set, he said: "Unless my Lord guides me, I shall surely be among the people who went astray." When he saw the sun rising up, he said: "This is my lord. This is greater." But when it set, he said: "O my people! I am indeed free from all that you join as partners (in worship with Allāh). Verily, I have turned my face towards Him Who has created the heavens and the earth *Hanīfa* (Islamic Monotheism, i.e. worshipping none but Allāh Alone), and I am not of *Al-Mushrikūn*." His people disputed with him. He said: "Do you dispute with me concerning Allāh while He has guided me, and I fear not those whom you associate with Him (Allāh) in worship. (Nothing can happen to me) except when my Lord (Allāh) wills something. My Lord comprehends in His Knowledge all things. Will you not then remember? And how should I fear those whom you associate in worship with Allāh (though they can neither benefit nor harm), while you fear not that you have joined in worship with Allāh things for which He has not sent down to you any authority. (So) which of the two parties has more right to be in security? If you but know.'' It is those who believe (in the Oneness of Allāh and worship none but Him Alone) and confuse not their Belief with *Zulm* (wrong, i.e. by worshipping others besides Allāh), for them (only) there is security and they are the guided. And that was Our Proof which We gave Ibrāhīm (Abraham) against his people. We raise whom We will in degrees. Certainly your Lord is All-Wise, All-Knowing.

(Qur'ân 6: 74-83)

﴿وَٱتْلُ عَلَيْهِمْ نَبَأَ إِبْرَٰهِيمَ ۝ إِذْ قَالَ لِأَبِيهِ وَقَوْمِهِۦ مَا تَعْبُدُونَ ۝ قَالُوا۟ نَعْبُدُ أَصْنَامًا فَنَظَلُّ لَهَا عَٰكِفِينَ ۝ قَالَ هَلْ يَسْمَعُونَكُمْ إِذْ تَدْعُونَ ۝ أَوْ يَنفَعُونَكُمْ أَوْ يَضُرُّونَ ۝ قَالُوا۟ بَلْ وَجَدْنَآ ءَابَآءَنَا كَذَٰلِكَ يَفْعَلُونَ ۝ قَالَ أَفَرَءَيْتُم مَّا كُنتُمْ تَعْبُدُونَ ۝ أَنتُمْ وَءَابَآؤُكُمُ ٱلْأَقْدَمُونَ ۝ فَإِنَّهُمْ عَدُوٌّ لِّى إِلَّا رَبَّ ٱلْعَٰلَمِينَ ۝ ٱلَّذِى خَلَقَنِى فَهُوَ يَهْدِينِ ۝ وَٱلَّذِى هُوَ يُطْعِمُنِى وَيَسْقِينِ ۝ وَإِذَا مَرِضْتُ فَهُوَ يَشْفِينِ ۝ وَٱلَّذِى يُمِيتُنِى ثُمَّ يُحْيِينِ ۝ وَٱلَّذِىٓ أَطْمَعُ أَن يَغْفِرَ لِى خَطِيٓـَٔتِى يَوْمَ ٱلدِّينِ ۝ رَبِّ هَبْ لِى حُكْمًا وَأَلْحِقْنِى بِٱلصَّٰلِحِينَ ۝ وَٱجْعَل لِّى لِسَانَ صِدْقٍ فِى ٱلْءَاخِرِينَ ۝ وَٱجْعَلْنِى مِن وَرَثَةِ جَنَّةِ ٱلنَّعِيمِ ۝ وَٱغْفِرْ لِأَبِىٓ إِنَّهُۥ كَانَ مِنَ ٱلضَّآلِّينَ ۝ وَلَا تُخْزِنِى يَوْمَ يُبْعَثُونَ ۝ يَوْمَ لَا يَنفَعُ مَالٌ وَلَا بَنُونَ ۝ إِلَّا مَنْ أَتَى ٱللَّهَ بِقَلْبٍ سَلِيمٍ ۝ ﴾

And recite to them the story of Ibrāhīm (Abraham). When he said to his father and his people: "What do you worship?'' They said: "We worship idols, and to them we are ever devoted.'' He said: "Do they hear you when you call on (them)? Or do they benefit you or do they harm (you)?'' They said: "(Nay) but we found our fathers doing so." He said: "Do you observe that which you have been worshipping – you and your ancient fathers? Verily, they are enemies to me, except the Lord of the 'Ālamīn (mankind, jinn and all that exists), Who has created me, and it is He Who guides me. And it is He Who feeds me and gives me to drink. And when I am ill, it is He Who cures me. And Who will cause me to die, and then will bring me to life (again). And Who, I hope, will forgive me my faults on the Day of Recompense (the Day of Resurrection)." My Lord! Bestow *Hukm* (religious knowledge, right judgement of the affairs and Prophethood) on me, and join me with the righteous. And grant me an honorable mention in later generations. And make me one of the inheritors of the Paradise of Delight. And forgive my father, verily, he is of the erring. And disgrace me not on the Day when (all the creatures) will be resurrected. The Day whereon neither wealth nor sons will avail, Except him who comes to Allāh with a clean heart [clean from *Shirk* (polytheism) and *Nifāq* (hypocrisy)]."

(Qur'ân 26: 69-89)

﴿وَإِذْ قَالَ إِبْرَٰهِيمُ رَبِّ ٱجْعَلْ هَٰذَا ٱلْبَلَدَ ءَامِنًا وَٱجْنُبْنِى وَبَنِىَّ أَن نَّعْبُدَ ٱلْأَصْنَامَ ٣٥ رَبِّ إِنَّهُنَّ أَضْلَلْنَ كَثِيرًا مِّنَ ٱلنَّاسِ فَمَن تَبِعَنِى فَإِنَّهُۥ مِنِّى وَمَنْ عَصَانِى فَإِنَّكَ غَفُورٌ رَّحِيمٌ ٣٦ رَّبَّنَآ إِنِّىٓ أَسْكَنتُ مِن ذُرِّيَّتِى بِوَادٍ غَيْرِ ذِى زَرْعٍ عِندَ بَيْتِكَ ٱلْمُحَرَّمِ رَبَّنَا لِيُقِيمُوا۟ ٱلصَّلَوٰةَ فَٱجْعَلْ أَفْـِٔدَةً مِّنَ ٱلنَّاسِ تَهْوِىٓ إِلَيْهِمْ وَٱرْزُقْهُم مِّنَ ٱلثَّمَرَٰتِ لَعَلَّهُمْ يَشْكُرُونَ ٣٧ رَبَّنَآ إِنَّكَ تَعْلَمُ مَا نُخْفِى وَمَا نُعْلِنُ وَمَا يَخْفَىٰ عَلَى ٱللَّهِ مِن شَىْءٍ فِى ٱلْأَرْضِ وَلَا فِى ٱلسَّمَآءِ ٣٨ ٱلْحَمْدُ لِلَّهِ ٱلَّذِى وَهَبَ لِى عَلَى ٱلْكِبَرِ إِسْمَٰعِيلَ وَإِسْحَٰقَ إِنَّ رَبِّى لَسَمِيعُ ٱلدُّعَآءِ ٣٩ رَبِّ ٱجْعَلْنِى مُقِيمَ ٱلصَّلَوٰةِ وَمِن ذُرِّيَّتِى رَبَّنَا وَتَقَبَّلْ دُعَآءِ ٤٠ رَبَّنَا ٱغْفِرْ لِى وَلِوَٰلِدَىَّ وَلِلْمُؤْمِنِينَ يَوْمَ يَقُومُ ٱلْحِسَابُ ٤١ ﴾

And (remember) when Ibrāhīm (Abraham) said: "O my Lord! Make this city (Makkah) one of peace and security, and keep me and my sons away from worshipping idols. O my Lord! They have indeed led astray many among mankind. But whoso follows me, he verily, is of me. And whoso disobeys me, still You are indeed Oft-Forgiving, Most Merciful. O our Lord! I have made some of my offspring to dwell in an uncultivable valley by Your Sacred House (the Ka'bah at Makkah) in order, O our Lord, that they may perform *As-Salāt* (the prayers). So fill some hearts among men with love towards them, and (O Allāh) provide them with fruits so that they may give thanks. O our Lord! Certainly, You know what we conceal and what we reveal. Nothing on the earth or in the heaven is hidden from Allāh. All praise and thanks are Allāh's, Who has given me in old age Ismā'īl (Ishmael) and Ishāq (Isaac). Verily, my Lord is indeed the All-Hearer of invocations. O my Lord! Make me one who performs *As-Salāt* (the prayers), and (also) from my offspring, our Lord! And accept my invocation. Our Lord! Forgive me and my parents, and (all) the believers on the Day when the reckoning will be established."

(Qur'ân 14: 35-41)

﴿وَلَقَدْ جَآءَتْ رُسُلُنَآ إِبْرَٰهِيمَ بِٱلْبُشْرَىٰ قَالُوا۟ سَلَٰمًا قَالَ سَلَٰمٌ فَمَا لَبِثَ أَن جَآءَ بِعِجْلٍ حَنِيذٍ ۝ فَلَمَّا رَءَآ أَيْدِيَهُمْ لَا تَصِلُ إِلَيْهِ نَكِرَهُمْ وَأَوْجَسَ مِنْهُمْ خِيفَةً قَالُوا۟ لَا تَخَفْ إِنَّآ أُرْسِلْنَآ إِلَىٰ قَوْمِ لُوطٍ ۝ وَٱمْرَأَتُهُۥ قَآئِمَةٌ فَضَحِكَتْ فَبَشَّرْنَٰهَا بِإِسْحَٰقَ وَمِن وَرَآءِ إِسْحَٰقَ يَعْقُوبَ ۝ قَالَتْ يَٰوَيْلَتَىٰٓ ءَأَلِدُ وَأَنَا۠ عَجُوزٌ وَهَٰذَا بَعْلِى شَيْخًا إِنَّ هَٰذَا لَشَىْءٌ عَجِيبٌ ۝ قَالُوٓا۟ أَتَعْجَبِينَ مِنْ أَمْرِ ٱللَّهِ رَحْمَتُ ٱللَّهِ وَبَرَكَٰتُهُۥ عَلَيْكُمْ أَهْلَ ٱلْبَيْتِ إِنَّهُۥ حَمِيدٌ مَّجِيدٌ ۝ فَلَمَّا ذَهَبَ عَنْ إِبْرَٰهِيمَ ٱلرَّوْعُ وَجَآءَتْهُ ٱلْبُشْرَىٰ يُجَٰدِلُنَا فِى قَوْمِ لُوطٍ ۝ إِنَّ إِبْرَٰهِيمَ لَحَلِيمٌ أَوَّٰهٌ مُّنِيبٌ ۝ يَٰٓإِبْرَٰهِيمُ أَعْرِضْ عَنْ هَٰذَآ إِنَّهُۥ قَدْ جَآءَ أَمْرُ رَبِّكَ وَإِنَّهُمْ ءَاتِيهِمْ عَذَابٌ غَيْرُ مَرْدُودٍ ۝﴾

And verily, there came Our messengers to Ibrāhīm (Abraham) with glad tidings. They said: "*Salām* (greetings or peace!)." He answered, "*Salām* (greetings or peace!)," and he hastened to entertain them with a roasted calf. But when he saw their hands went not towards it (the meal), he mistrusted them, and conceived a fear of them. They said: "Fear not, we have been sent against the people of Lūt (Lot)." And his wife was standing (there), and she laughed [either, because the messengers did not eat their food or for being glad for the destruction of the people of Lūt (Lot)]. But We gave her glad tidings of Ishāq (Isaac), and after Ishāq, of Ya'qūb (Jacob). She said (in astonishment): "Woe to me! Shall I bear a child while I am an old woman, and here is my husband an old man? Verily, this is a strange thing!" They said: "Do you wonder at the Decree of Allāh? The Mercy of Allāh and His Blessings be on you, O the family [of Ibrāhīm (Abraham)]. Surely, He (Allāh) is All-Praiseworthy, All-Glorious." Then when the fear had gone away from (the mind of) Ibrāhīm (Abraham), and the glad tidings had reached him, he began to plead with Us (Our messengers) for the people of Lūt (Lot). Verily, Ibrāhīm (Abraham) was without doubt forbearing, used to invoke Allāh with humility, and was repentant (to Allāh all the time, again and again). "O Ibrāhīm (Abraham)! Forsake this. Indeed, the Commandment of your Lord has gone forth. Verily, there will come a torment for them which cannot be turned back."

(Qur'ân 11: 69-76)

Born in southern Iraq, Ibrâhim ﷺ settled in the city of Ur Al-Kaldâniyyah. His father was Azar bin Nâhur, though it is said that Azar was his uncle. The confusion perhaps stems from the custom of addressing one's uncle (uncle here referring only to the brother of one's father) with the word 'father.' Azar was from the people of Kutha, which is a village on the outskirts of Kufah. And it was in Kutha that the infamous attempt was made to burn Ibrâhim ﷺ. After the attempt to burn him failed, Ibrâhim ﷺ traveled to Harran, which is situated in the northern part of the Arabian Peninsula. He then traveled to Palestine, taking with him his wife, Sarah, and his nephew Lot ﷺ; and Lot's wife was also traveling with them. Due to a drought that afflicted the lands, Ibrâhim ﷺ had to travel to Egypt during the era of the shepherd kings.

Later on, Ibrâhim ﷺ returned with Lot ﷺ to southern Palestine, but they had to part from one another in order to preserve the mutual love and compassion that they shared. The reason they had to part was that there just wasn't enough fertile land for both of their herds of livestock. So Ibrâhim ﷺ settled in B'ir Sheva (As-Saba'), while Lot ﷺ settled down south of the Dead Sea.

Ibrâhim ﷺ then traveled with his second wife, Hâjar, to Makkah, and she took her son, Ismâ'il ﷺ, along with her. After Ibrâhim ﷺ left them in Makkah, which at the time was a forsaken and barren place, the well of Zamzam gushed forth. Now that water was found in Makkah, it became a desirable place to live; and so when the tribe of Jurhum was passing through the area and found out about the well, they settled down alongside Hâjar. As for Ibrâhim's death, he died in Palestine and was buried there in the city of Hebron.

Some historians mention that there are two kinds of Arabs:

1) Arab tribes and peoples that are extinct, such as the early Jurhums, and the peoples of Âd, Thamûd, and Jadis.

2) Arab peoples and tribes that are still around today. Historians erroneously trace their roots back to two kinds of Arabs:

   a) The pure Arabs, or the Al-Qahtâniyyun, who originally dwelled in Yemen. Their most famous tribes are the Jurhum and the Ya'rob. Many tribes branched off from the Ya'rub tribe, the biggest and most significant of them being the Kahlân and the Himyar tribes. The most famous sub-tribe of the Kahlân is the Al-Azd, from whom many important tribes descended: such as Al-Aus and Al-Khazraj, both of which settled in Yathrib (later known as Al-Madinah); and Al-Ghasâsinah, Tai, Madhhij, An-Nakh, 'Ans, Hamdân, Kindah, and Lakhm. These are all tribes that branched out from Kahlân; as for Himyar, it branched out into Qudâ'ah, which branched out into many other tribes, such as Baliy, Juhainah, Kalb, and Bharâ'.

   b) Non-Arabs who assimilated themselves into Arab culture. They are known as the Al-'Adnâniyyun. Some historians say that they are given that name because Ismâ'il ﷺ used to speak Assyrian or Hebrew. Then when Jurhum (from the Al-Qahtâniyyun) settled down in Makkah, Ismâ'il ﷺ and his mother lived alongside them. When he grew up, Ismâ'il ﷺ married from their tribe, and he as well as his children learned Arabic, which is why they are called 'the assimilated Arabs.' From them are descended the majority of Bedouin and city-dwelling Arabs that live in the Arabian Peninsula and in the lands of Al-Hijaz, until the deserts of Ash-Sham. After the collapse of the Ma'rib Dam, the pure Arabs of Yemen migrated and lived alongside the 'assimilated Arabs.'

One of 'Adnân's sons was Mu'id, from whom descended all of the descendents of 'Adnân. Mu'id had four children: Iyâd, Nizâr, Qanas, and Anmâr, and it is from Nizâr that two very important tribes branched off Rabi'ah and Mudar.

Rabi'ah settled down in the lands of Najd, from Al-Ghaur until Tihâmah. The children of Mudar settled down in Al-Hijaz, and they increased in numbers so rapidly that they ended up representing the majority in many of the lands of Najd as well. They eventually became the leaders of the inviolable city of Makkah.

It began with Mudar, who had two sons: Qais 'Ailân and Ilyâs. From Qais 'Ailân the tribes of Hawâzin, Sulaim, and Thaqif branched off. Ilyâs, on the other hand, had three children, from whom many tribes branched off – such as Aslam, Khuzâ'ah, Muzainah, Tamim, Khuzaimah, Al-Haun, Asad, and Kinânah. From Kinânah came An-Nadr; from An-Nadr came Mâlik; and from Mâlik came Fihr, which is the Quraish tribe of Makkah.

The notion of 'assimilated Arabs' is a mere fable and not factual history; some historians mentioned it, and then after a while, people simply took it as being true. The fact is that the era of Ibrâhim ﷺ and his son, Ismâ'il ﷺ, is an era in which the Arabic language thrived, and it is an era that has nothing to do with Assyrian or Hebrew. Through clear proofs, the distinction is now clear between the people of Ibrâhim, the people of Ya'qoob (Israel), the people of Musa ﷺ, the Jews, and the Hebrews. This point requires further explanation.

The term 'Hebrew' (Abri) was used approximately 2000 years before the start of the Christian calendar. But it was also used before that for Arab tribes that lived in the northern part of the Arabian Peninsula, in the deserts of Ash-Sham; it was also used for other Arab tribes that were settled in the surrounding area. The term

'Hebrew' was a synonym for a Bedouin or anyone who lived in the desert. That is why one finds the terms 'Ibri,' or, 'Hubairi,' or, 'Al-'Abiru,' or, 'Al-Khabiru,' in the ancient writings of the pharaohs, in a time when the Israelites, the followers of Musa صلى الله عليه وسلم, and the Jews had not yet come into the world.

The term Hebrew is not mentioned in the Noble Qur'ân at all; instead the terms, the 'Children of Israel,' 'the people of Musa صلى الله عليه وسلم,' and the 'Jews' are used. Only the rabbis in Palestine recently began to use the word Hebrew to refer to Jews.

It is noteworthy to mention here that Palestine was the land of exile for Ibrâhim صلى الله عليه وسلم, his son Ishâq صلى الله عليه وسلم, and his grandson Ya'qub صلى الله عليه وسلم, a fact that is established in the Torah itself. They were strangers in Palestine, living among its native dwellers, the Al-Kan'âniyyin. This is particularly the case for the Children of Israel (Israel is one of the names of Ya'qub), who were all born and raised in Harrân. This stage for them ended when the family of Ya'qub migrated to Egypt, where they joined up with Yusuf صلى الله عليه وسلم. Then they became assimilated into the culture and environment of Egypt.

Thus the term 'Israel' is supposed to refer to Ya'qoob – the grandson of Ibrâhim صلى الله عليه وسلم – and to his children. Their lives were spent mainly in the area of Harrân; as for Palestine, it was a place of exile for them.

As for the people of Musa صلى الله عليه وسلم, they followed the religion of Pure Monotheism. Their religion is different from the religion of the Jews, which calls for the worship of 'Yahwa,' who was their particular god, based on their description of themselves as being 'The Chosen People.' The actual teachings and *Shari'ah* (set of laws) of Musa صلى الله عليه وسلم were written in hieroglyphics, and no trace of those writings can now be found. Then the descendents of Musa's people embraced the language, culture, and customs of Kan'ân; those descendents deviated from the teachings and *Shari'ah* of Musa صلى الله عليه وسلم, and it is they who, from that time onward, became known as Jews.

The word 'Jew' was used for those who remained from the people of Yahudha, those who were taken as captives and led to Babel, 586 years before the beginning of the Christian calendar. As captives who were mixing in a new culture, they developed a new dialect that was based on Aramaic, and it is with that dialect that they wrote the Torah that is with us now; they had composed it while they were prisoners in Babel, approximately 800 years after the time of Musa ﷺ. That is why their dialect became known as the Aramaic of the Torah. Without a doubt, the Torah they composed does not contain the same *Shari'ah* (set of laws) that was revealed to Musa ﷺ. Therefore, we can call their book, 'The Torah of the Jews,' in order to distinguish it from, 'The Torah of Musa ﷺ.'

When the Jews composed their Torah, they had two main goals in mind: First, to glorify their history and to make themselves come off as the best of peoples – 'The Chosen People' – who were chosen and preferred by the Lord over all other peoples. And to give credence to their claim, they traced their roots back to a very significant historical figure, namely, Ibrâhim ﷺ, who was renowned during that time in all corners of the world. And so they set about recording their history, writing it based not on factual events, but on what their desires dictated.

Hence they traced their history back to Ibrâhim ﷺ and to his grandson, Ya'qub (Israel). They called the people of Musa ﷺ the Children of Israel, despite the fact that they lived 600 years after the life of Israel (i.e., Ya'qub ﷺ).

Their second goal was to make it seem as if Palestine was their home country, despite the fact that the Torah even mentions that Palestine was a land of exile for Ibrâhim ﷺ, Ishâq ﷺ, Ya'qub ﷺ, and Ya'qub's sons, who were born and raised in Harraan.

In point of fact, Ibrâhim ﷺ and his son Ismâ'il ﷺ belonged to Aramaic, Arabic tribes, which existed a number of centuries before the arrival of the Israelites, the followers of Mûsa ﷺ, and the Jews. And that is why I stated earlier that the era of Ibrâhim ﷺ is one in which Arabic thrived and is one that has nothing to do with the era of the Jews. The Qur'ân points to these issues in the following Verses:

﴿يَٰٓأَهْلَ ٱلْكِتَٰبِ لِمَ تُحَآجُّونَ فِىٓ إِبْرَٰهِيمَ وَمَآ أُنزِلَتِ ٱلتَّوْرَىٰةُ وَٱلْإِنجِيلُ إِلَّا مِنۢ بَعْدِهِۦٓ أَفَلَا تَعْقِلُونَ ۝ هَٰٓأَنتُمْ هَٰٓؤُلَآءِ حَٰجَجْتُمْ فِيمَا لَكُم بِهِۦ عِلْمٌ فَلِمَ تُحَآجُّونَ فِيمَا لَيْسَ لَكُم بِهِۦ عِلْمٌ وَٱللَّهُ يَعْلَمُ وَأَنتُمْ لَا تَعْلَمُونَ ۝ مَا كَانَ إِبْرَٰهِيمُ يَهُودِيًّا وَلَا نَصْرَانِيًّا وَلَٰكِن كَانَ

حَنِيفًا مُّسْلِمًا وَمَا كَانَ مِنَ ٱلْمُشْرِكِينَ ۝٦٧ ۞

O people of the Scripture (Jews and Christians)! Why do you dispute about Ibrāhīm (Abraham), while the Taurāt (Torah) and the Injīl (Gospel) were not revealed till after him? Have you then no sense? Verily, you are those who have disputed about that of which you have knowledge. Why do you then dispute concerning that of which you have no knowledge? It is Allāh Who knows, and you know not. Ibrāhīm (Abraham) was neither a Jew nor a Christian, but he was a true Muslim Hanīfa (Islamic Monotheism — to worship none but Allāh Alone) and he was not of Al-Mushrikūn (polytheists).

(Qur'ân 3:65-67)

- Bulugh Al-Arab Fi Ma'rifati Ahwâlul-'Arab: 1/8
- Târikh Al-Islam: 1:8
- Dâiratul-Ma'ârif Al-Britâniyyah: 11/379 (from the 1970 edition)
- Qisas Al-Anbiyâ, by Ibn Kathir: 117
- Qisas Al-Anbiyâ, by Ath-Tha'labi: 74
- Qisas Al-Anbiyâ, by At-Tabari: 134
- Qisas Al-Anbiyâ, by An-Najjâr: 70
- Al-Mo'jam Al-Mufahris Li-Alfâz Al-Qur'ân Al-Karim: 1
- Al-Mo'jam Al-Mufahris Li-Ma'âni Al-Qur'ân Al-Karim: 59
- Mufassal Al-'Arab Wal-Yahud Fit-Tarikh: pg. 86 and what comes after it.

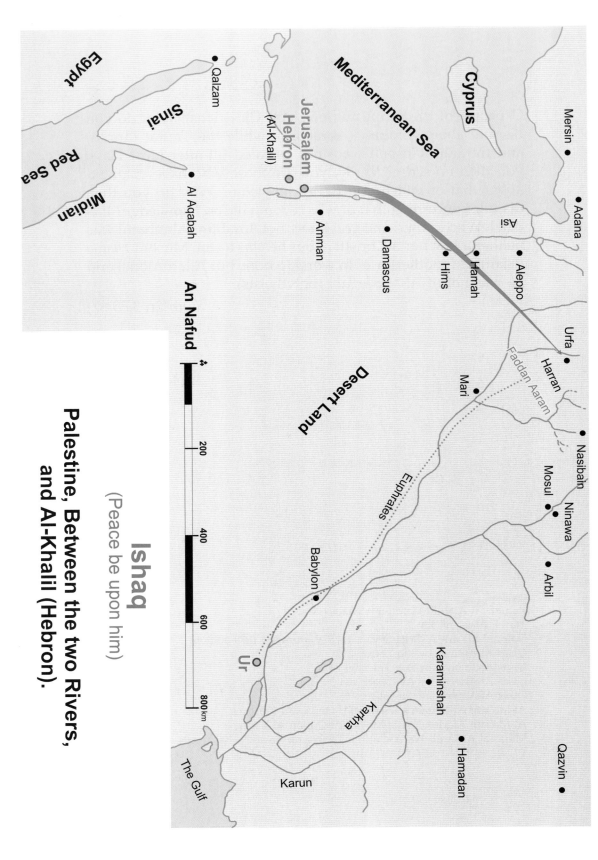

Ishaq
(Peace be upon him)
Palestine, Between the two Rivers, and Al-Khalil (Hebron).

Ishâq العليهلا and Ismâ'il العليهلا

In the Noble Qur'ân, Ishâq العليه is mentioned by name 17 times, in the following Verses:

Chapter Name (Sûrah)	Number of Chapter (Sûrah)	Verse Numbers
Al-Baqarah	2	133, 136, 140
Âl-'Imrân	3	84
An-Nisa'	4	163
Al-An'âm	6	84
Hûd	11	71 (twice)
Yusuf	12	6, 38
Ibrâhim	14	39
Maryam	19	49
Al-Anbiya'	21	72
Al-'Ankabût	29	29
As-Sâffât	37	112, 113
Sâd	38	48

﴿وَوَهَبْنَا لَهُ إِسْحَقَ وَيَعْقُوبَ كُلًّا هَدَيْنَا وَنُوحًا هَدَيْنَا مِن قَبْلُ وَمِن ذُرِّيَّتِهِ دَاوُدَ وَسُلَيْمَانَ وَأَيُّوبَ وَيُوسُفَ وَمُوسَىٰ وَهَارُونَ وَكَذَلِكَ نَجْزِى الْمُحْسِنِينَ ۞﴾

And We bestowed upon him Ishāq (Isaac) and Ya'qūb (Jacob), each of them We guided, and before him, We guided Nūh (Noah), and among his progeny Dāwūd (David), Sulaimān (Solomon), Ayyub (Job), Yūsuf (Joseph), Mūsā (Moses), and

City of Hebron (Al-Khalil)

Hārūn (Aaron). Thus do We reward *Al-Muhsinūn* (the good-doers.)

(Qur'ân 6:84)

﴿وَٱمْرَأَتُهُ قَآئِمَةٌ فَضَحِكَتْ فَبَشَّرْنَـٰهَا بِإِسْحَـٰقَ وَمِن وَرَآءِ إِسْحَـٰقَ يَعْقُوبَ ٧١﴾

And his wife was standing (there), and she laughed [either, because the messengers did not eat their food or for being glad for the destruction of the people of Lūt (Lot)]. But We gave her glad tidings of Ishāq (Isaac), and after Ishāq, of Ya'qūb (Jacob).

(Qur'ân 11:71)

﴿وَكَذَٰلِكَ يَجْتَبِيكَ رَبُّكَ وَيُعَلِّمُكَ مِن تَأْوِيلِ ٱلْأَحَادِيثِ وَيُتِمُّ نِعْمَتَهُ عَلَيْكَ وَعَلَىٰٓ ءَالِ يَعْقُوبَ كَمَآ أَتَمَّهَا عَلَىٰٓ أَبَوَيْكَ مِن قَبْلُ إِبْرَٰهِيمَ وَإِسْحَـٰقَ إِنَّ رَبَّكَ عَلِيمٌ حَكِيمٌ ٦﴾

"Thus will your Lord choose you and teach you the interpretation of dreams (and other things) and perfect His Favour on you and on the offspring of Ya'qūb (Jacob), as He perfected it on your fathers, Ibrāhīm (Abraham) and Ishāq (Isaac) aforetime! Verily, your Lord is All-Knowing, All-Wise."

(Qur'ân 12:6)

﴿ٱلْحَمْدُ لِلَّهِ ٱلَّذِى وَهَبَ لِى عَلَى ٱلْكِبَرِ إِسْمَـٰعِيلَ وَإِسْحَـٰقَ إِنَّ رَبِّى لَسَمِيعُ ٱلدُّعَآءِ ٣٩﴾

"All praise and thanks are Allāh's, Who has given me in old age Ismā'īl (Ishmael) and Ishāq (Isaac). Verily, my Lord is indeed the All-Hearer of invocations.

(Qur'ân 14:39)

Ishâq عليه السلام lived with his father, Ibrâhim عليه السلام. Some sources mention that Ishâq عليه السلام once sent a slave of his from Palestine to Faddân Aaram, in the northern part of Iraq. That slave returned with a female fellow traveler, whom Ishâq عليه السلام then married. When Ishâq عليه السلام died, he was buried in Hebron (Al-Khalil), in the Al-Makfilah cave.

***

And Ismâ'il ﷺ is mentioned by name 12 times in the Noble Qur'ân:

Chapter Name (Sûrah)	Number of Chapter (Sûrah)	Verse Numbers
Al-Baqarah	2	125, 127, 133, 136, 140
Āl-'Imrân	3	84
An-Nisa'	4	163
Al-An'âm	6	86
Ibrâhim	14	39
Maryam	19	54
Al-Anbiya'	21	85
Sâd	38	48

۞ فَأَرَادُوا بِهِۦ كَيْدًا فَجَعَلْنَٰهُمُ ٱلْأَسْفَلِينَ ۝ وَقَالَ إِنِّى ذَاهِبٌ إِلَىٰ رَبِّى سَيَهْدِينِ ۝ رَبِّ هَبْ لِى مِنَ ٱلصَّٰلِحِينَ ۝ فَبَشَّرْنَٰهُ بِغُلَٰمٍ حَلِيمٍ ۝ فَلَمَّا بَلَغَ مَعَهُ ٱلسَّعْىَ قَالَ يَٰبُنَىَّ إِنِّى أَرَىٰ فِى ٱلْمَنَامِ أَنِّى أَذْبَحُكَ فَٱنظُرْ مَاذَا تَرَىٰ قَالَ يَٰٓأَبَتِ ٱفْعَلْ مَا تُؤْمَرُ سَتَجِدُنِى إِن شَآءَ ٱللَّهُ مِنَ ٱلصَّٰبِرِينَ ۝ فَلَمَّآ أَسْلَمَا وَتَلَّهُۥ لِلْجَبِينِ ۝ وَنَٰدَيْنَٰهُ أَن يَٰٓإِبْرَٰهِيمُ ۝ قَدْ صَدَّقْتَ ٱلرُّءْيَآ إِنَّا كَذَٰلِكَ نَجْزِى ٱلْمُحْسِنِينَ ۝ إِنَّ هَٰذَا لَهُوَ ٱلْبَلَٰٓؤُا۟ ٱلْمُبِينُ ۝ وَفَدَيْنَٰهُ بِذِبْحٍ عَظِيمٍ ۝ وَتَرَكْنَا عَلَيْهِ فِى ٱلْءَاخِرِينَ ۝ سَلَٰمٌ عَلَىٰٓ إِبْرَٰهِيمَ ۝ كَذَٰلِكَ نَجْزِى ٱلْمُحْسِنِينَ ۝ ۞

So, they plotted a plot against him, but We made them the lowest. And he said (after his rescue from the fire): "Verily, I am going to my Lord. He will guide me!" "My Lord! Grant me (offspring) from the righteous." So, We gave him the glad tidings of a forbearing boy. And, when he (his son) was old enough to walk with him, he said: "O my son! I have seen in a dream that I am slaughtering you (offering you in sacrifice to Allāh). So look what you think!" He said: "O my father! Do that which you are commanded, *In shā' Allāh* (if Allāh wills), you shall find me of *As-Sābirūn* (the patient)." Then, when they

Maqam Ibrahim

had both submitted themselves (to the Will of Allāh), and he had laid him prostrate on his forehead (or on the side of his forehead for slaughtering); We called out to him: "O Ibrāhīm (Abraham)! You have fulfilled the dream!" Verily, thus do We reward the *Muhsinūn* (good-doers). Verily, that indeed was the manifest trial. And We ransomed him with a great sacrifice (i.e. کبش – a ram); And We left for him (a goodly remembrance) among the later generations. "*Salām* (peace) be upon Ibrāhīm (Abraham)!" Thus indeed do We reward the *Muhsinūn* (good-doers).

(Qur'ân 37: 98-110)

﴿وَإِذْ جَعَلْنَا ٱلْبَيْتَ مَثَابَةً لِّلنَّاسِ وَأَمْنًا وَٱتَّخِذُواْ مِن مَّقَامِ إِبْرَٰهِـۧمَ مُصَلًّى وَعَهِدْنَآ إِلَىٰٓ إِبْرَٰهِـۧمَ وَإِسْمَٰعِيلَ أَن طَهِّرَا بَيْتِيَ لِلطَّآئِفِينَ وَٱلْعَٰكِفِينَ وَٱلرُّكَّعِ ٱلسُّجُودِ ۝ وَإِذْ قَالَ إِبْرَٰهِـۧمُ رَبِّ ٱجْعَلْ هَٰذَا بَلَدًا ءَامِنًا وَٱرْزُقْ أَهْلَهُۥ مِنَ ٱلثَّمَرَٰتِ مَنْ ءَامَنَ مِنْهُم بِٱللَّهِ وَٱلْيَوْمِ ٱلْءَاخِرِ قَالَ وَمَن كَفَرَ فَأُمَتِّعُهُۥ قَلِيلًا ثُمَّ أَضْطَرُّهُۥٓ إِلَىٰ عَذَابِ ٱلنَّارِ وَبِئْسَ ٱلْمَصِيرُ ۝ وَإِذْ يَرْفَعُ إِبْرَٰهِـۧمُ ٱلْقَوَاعِدَ مِنَ ٱلْبَيْتِ وَإِسْمَٰعِيلُ رَبَّنَا تَقَبَّلْ مِنَّآ إِنَّكَ أَنتَ ٱلسَّمِيعُ ٱلْعَلِيمُ ۝ رَبَّنَا وَٱجْعَلْنَا مُسْلِمَيْنِ لَكَ وَمِن ذُرِّيَّتِنَآ أُمَّةً مُّسْلِمَةً لَّكَ وَأَرِنَا مَنَاسِكَنَا وَتُبْ عَلَيْنَآ إِنَّكَ أَنتَ ٱلتَّوَّابُ ٱلرَّحِيمُ ۝﴾

And (remember) when We made the House (the Ka'bah at Makkah) a place of resort for mankind and a place of safety. And take you (people) the *Maqām* (place) of Ibrāhīm (Abraham) [or the stone on which Ibrāhīm (Abraham) عليه السلام stood while he was building the Ka'bah] as a place of prayer (for some of your prayers, e.g. two *Rak'at* after the *Tawāf* of the Ka'bah at Makkah), and We commanded Ibrāhīm (Abraham) and Ismā'īl (Ishmael) that they should purify My House (the Ka'bah at Makkah) for those who are circumambulating it, or staying (*I'tikāf*), or bowing or prostrating themselves (there, in prayer). And (remember) when Ibrāhīm (Abraham) said, "My Lord, make this city (Makkah) a place of security and provide its people with fruits, such of them as believe in Allāh and the Last Day." He (Allāh) answered: "As for him who disbelieves, I shall leave him in contentment for a while, then I shall compel him to the torment of the Fire, and worst indeed is that destination!" And (remember) when Ibrāhīm (Abraham) and (his son) Ismā'īl (Ishmael) were raising the foundations of the House (the Ka'bah at Makkah), (saying), "Our Lord! Accept (this service) from us. Verily, You are the All-Hearer, the All-Knower. Our Lord! And make us submissive to You and of our offspring a nation submissive to You, and show us our *Manāsik* (all the ceremonies of pilgrimage — *Hajj* and *'Umrah*), and accept our repentance. Truly, You are the One Who accepts repentance, the Most Merciful.

(Qur'ân 2: 125-128)

The lives of Ismâ'il ﷺ and Ibrâhim ﷺ are closely linked to one another through important events:

- The famous slaughtering and sacrifice, which is why Ismâ'il is called, *Adh-Dhabih* (the sacrificed one)."

- In an important journey that is mentioned in the Qur'ân, Ismâ'il ﷺ migrated to Makkah with his mother and father.

- Ibrâhim ﷺ often visited Makkah, and on one of those visits, Allâh ﷻ ordered him and Ismâ'il ﷺ to build the Ka'bah, which of course they then built.

Ismâ'il ﷺ died in Makkah and was buried there, and it is believed that both he and his mother were buried near the Ka'bah.

- Qisas Al-Anbiya, by Ibn Kathir: 133
- Qisas Al-Anbiya, by Ath-Tha'labi: 81
- Qisas Al-Anbiya, by At-Tabari: 167
- Qisas Al-Anbiya, by An-Najjâr: 98, 103
- Al-Mo'jam Al-Mufahris Li-Alfâz Al-Qur'ân Al-Karim: 33, 347
- Al-Mo'jam Al-Mufahris Li-Ma'âni Al-Qur'ân Al-Karim: 103, 126

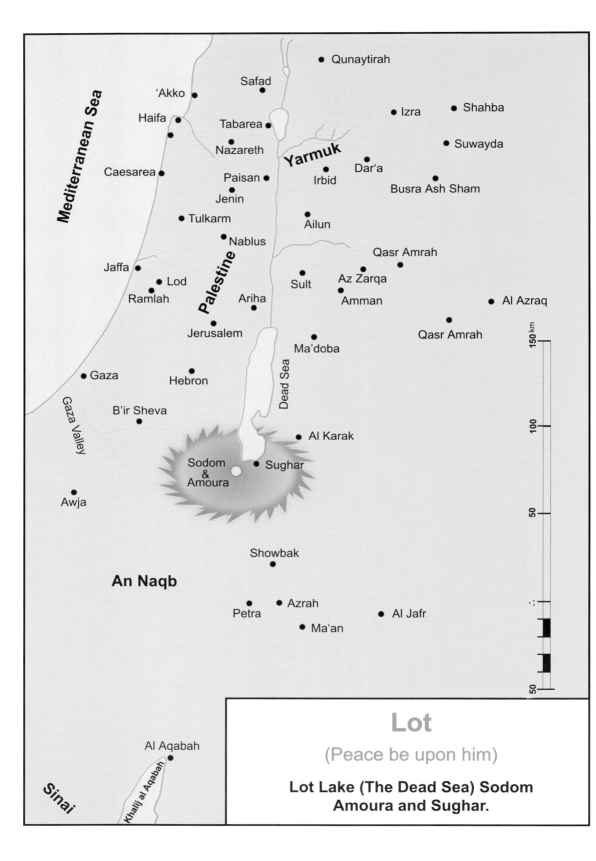

Mediterranean Sea

Qunaytirah

Safad

'Akko

Haifa

Tabarea

Izra

Shahba

Nazareth

Yarmuk

Suwayda

Caesarea

Paisan

Dar'a

Jenin

Irbid

Busra Ash Sham

Tulkarm

Ailun

Nablus

Qasr Amrah

Jaffa

Palestine

Sult

Az Zarqa

Lod

Amman

Al Azraq

Ramlah

Ariha

Qasr Amrah

Jerusalem

Ma'doba

Dead Sea

Gaza

Hebron

B'ir Sheva

Al Karak

Gaza Valley

Sodom & Amoura

Sughar

Awja

Showbak

An Naqb

Petra

Azrah

Al Jafr

Ma'an

150 km

100

50

50

Al Aqabah

Khalij al Aqabah

Sinai

Lot

(Peace be upon him)

Lot Lake (The Dead Sea) Sodom Amoura and Sughar.

Lot السَّلام

Lot السَّلام is mentioned by name 17 times in the Noble Qur'ân:

Chapter Name (Sûrah)	Number of Chapter (Sûrah)	Verse Numbers
Al-An'âm	6	86
Al-A'râf	7	80
Hûd	11	70, 74, 77, 81, 89
Al-Hijr	15	59, 61
Al-Anbiya'	21	71, 74
Al-Hajj	22	43
Ash-Shu'arâ	26	160, 161, 167
An-Naml	27	54, 56
Al-'Ankabût	29	26, 28, 32, 33
As-Sâffât	37	133
Sâd	38	13
Qâf	50	13
Al-Qamar	54	33, 34
At-Tahrim	66	10

وَلُوطًا إِذْ قَالَ لِقَوْمِهِ أَتَأْتُونَ ٱلْفَٰحِشَةَ مَا سَبَقَكُم بِهَا مِنْ أَحَدٍ مِّنَ ٱلْعَٰلَمِينَ ۝ إِنَّكُمْ لَتَأْتُونَ ٱلرِّجَالَ شَهْوَةً مِّن دُونِ ٱلنِّسَآءِ بَلْ أَنتُمْ قَوْمٌ مُّسْرِفُونَ ۝ وَمَا كَانَ جَوَابَ قَوْمِهِ إِلَّا أَن قَالُوٓا۟ أَخْرِجُوهُم مِّن قَرْيَتِكُمْ إِنَّهُمْ أُنَاسٌ يَتَطَهَّرُونَ ۝ فَأَنجَيْنَٰهُ وَأَهْلَهُ إِلَّا ٱمْرَأَتَهُۥ كَانَتْ مِنَ ٱلْغَٰبِرِينَ ۝ وَأَمْطَرْنَا عَلَيْهِم مَّطَرًا فَٱنظُرْ

And (remember) Lūt (Lot), when he said to his people: "Do you commit the worst sin such as none preceding you has committed in the *'Ālamīn* (mankind and jinn)? "Verily, you practise your lusts on men instead of women. Nay, but you are a people transgressing beyond bounds (by committing great sins)." And the answer of his people was only that they said: "Drive them out of your town, these are indeed men who want to be pure (from sins)!" Then We saved him and his family, except his wife; she was of those who remained behind (in the torment). And We rained down on them a rain (of stones). Then see what was the end of the *Mujrimūn* (criminals, polytheists and sinners).

(Qur'ân 7: 80-84)

﴿قَالُوا۟ يَٰلُوطُ إِنَّا رُسُلُ رَبِّكَ لَن يَصِلُوٓا۟ إِلَيْكَ فَأَسْرِ بِأَهْلِكَ بِقِطْعٍ مِّنَ ٱلَّيْلِ وَلَا يَلْتَفِتْ مِنكُمْ أَحَدٌ إِلَّا ٱمْرَأَتَكَ إِنَّهُۥ مُصِيبُهَا مَآ أَصَابَهُمْ إِنَّ مَوْعِدَهُمُ ٱلصُّبْحُ أَلَيْسَ ٱلصُّبْحُ بِقَرِيبٍ ﴿٨١﴾ فَلَمَّا جَآءَ أَمْرُنَا جَعَلْنَا عَٰلِيَهَا سَافِلَهَا وَأَمْطَرْنَا عَلَيْهَا حِجَارَةً مِّن سِجِّيلٍ مَّنضُودٍ ﴿٨٢﴾ مُّسَوَّمَةً عِندَ رَبِّكَ وَمَا هِىَ مِنَ ٱلظَّٰلِمِينَ بِبَعِيدٍ ﴿٨٣﴾ ﴾

They (messengers) said: "O Lūt (Lot)! Verily, we are the messengers from your Lord! They shall not reach you! So travel with your family in a part of the night, and let not any of you look back; but your wife (will remain behind), verily, the punishment which will afflict them, will afflict her. Indeed, morning is their appointed time. Is not the morning near?" So when Our Commandment came, We turned (the towns of Sodom in Palestine) upside down, and rained on them stones of baked clay, in a well-arranged manner one after another; Marked from your Lord; and they are not ever far from the *Zālimūn* (polytheists, evildoers).

(Qur'ân 11: 81-83)

﴿فَلَمَّا جَآءَ ءَالَ لُوطٍ ٱلْمُرْسَلُونَ ﴿٦١﴾ قَالَ إِنَّكُمْ قَوْمٌ مُّنكَرُونَ ﴿٦٢﴾ قَالُوا۟ بَلْ جِئْنَٰكَ بِمَا

76

كَانُوا۟ فِيهِ يَمْتَرُونَ ۝٦٣ وَأَتَيْنَـٰكَ بِٱلْحَقِّ وَإِنَّا لَصَـٰدِقُونَ ۝٦٤ فَأَسْرِ بِأَهْلِكَ بِقِطْعٍ مِّنَ ٱلَّيْلِ وَٱتَّبِعْ أَدْبَـٰرَهُمْ وَلَا يَلْتَفِتْ مِنكُمْ أَحَدٌ وَٱمْضُوا۟ حَيْثُ تُؤْمَرُونَ ۝٦٥ وَقَضَيْنَآ إِلَيْهِ ذَٰلِكَ ٱلْأَمْرَ أَنَّ دَابِرَ هَـٰٓؤُلَآءِ مَقْطُوعٌ مُّصْبِحِينَ ۝٦٦ وَجَآءَ أَهْلُ ٱلْمَدِينَةِ يَسْتَبْشِرُونَ ۝٦٧ قَالَ إِنَّ هَـٰٓؤُلَآءِ ضَيْفِى فَلَا تَفْضَحُونِ ۝٦٨ وَٱتَّقُوا۟ ٱللَّهَ وَلَا تُخْزُونِ ۝٦٩ قَالُوٓا۟ أَوَلَمْ نَنْهَكَ عَنِ ٱلْعَـٰلَمِينَ ۝٧٠ قَالَ هَـٰٓؤُلَآءِ بَنَاتِىٓ إِن كُنتُمْ فَـٰعِلِينَ ۝٧١ لَعَمْرُكَ إِنَّهُمْ لَفِى سَكْرَتِهِمْ يَعْمَهُونَ ۝٧٢ فَأَخَذَتْهُمُ ٱلصَّيْحَةُ مُشْرِقِينَ ۝٧٣ فَجَعَلْنَا عَـٰلِيَهَا سَافِلَهَا وَأَمْطَرْنَا عَلَيْهِمْ حِجَارَةً مِّن سِجِّيلٍ ۝٧٤ إِنَّ فِى ذَٰلِكَ لَـَٔايَـٰتٍ لِّلْمُتَوَسِّمِينَ ۝٧٥ وَإِنَّهَا لَبِسَبِيلٍ مُّقِيمٍ ۝٧٦ إِنَّ فِى ذَٰلِكَ لَـَٔايَةً لِّلْمُؤْمِنِينَ ۝٧٧ ۞

Then when the messengers (the angels) came to the family of Lūt (Lot). He said: "Verily, you are people unknown to me." They said: "Nay, we have come to you with that (torment) which they have been doubting. And we have brought you the truth (the news of the destruction of your nation) and certainly we tell the truth. Then travel in a part of the night with your family, and you go behind them in the rear, and let no one amongst you look back, but go on to where you are ordered." And We made known this decree to him that the root of those (sinners) was to be cut off in the early morning. And the inhabitants of the city came rejoicing (at the news of the young men's arrival). [Lūt (Lot)] said: "Verily, these are my guests, so shame me not. And fear Allāh and disgrace me not." They (people of the city) said: "Did we not forbid you from entertaining (or protecting) any of the ʾĀlamīn (people, foreigners and strangers from us)?" [Lūt (Lot)] said: "These (the girls of the nation) are my daughters (to marry lawfully), if you must act (so)." Verily, by your life (O Muhammad ﷺ), in their wild intoxication, they were wandering blindly. So As-Saihah (torment — awful cry) overtook them at the time of sunrise. And We turned (the towns of Sodom in Palestine) upside down and rained down on them stones of baked clay. Surely, in this are signs for those who see (or understand or learn the lessons from the Signs of Allāh). And verily, they (the cities) were right on the highroad (from Makkah to Syria, i.e.

the place where the Dead Sea is now). Surely, therein is indeed a sign for the believers.

(Qur'ân 15: 61-77)

بِسْمِ ٱللَّهِ وَبِسْمِ كَذَّبَتۡ قَوۡمُ لُوطٍ ٱلۡمُرۡسَلِينَ ١٦٠ إِذۡ قَالَ لَهُمۡ أَخُوهُمۡ لُوطٌ أَلَا تَتَّقُونَ ١٦١ إِنِّي لَكُمۡ رَسُولٌ أَمِينٌ ١٦٢ فَٱتَّقُوا۟ ٱللَّهَ وَأَطِيعُونِ ١٦٣ وَمَآ أَسۡـَٔلُكُمۡ عَلَيۡهِ مِنۡ أَجۡرٍ إِنۡ أَجۡرِیَ إِلَّا عَلَىٰ رَبِّ ٱلۡعَٰلَمِينَ ١٦٤ أَتَأۡتُونَ ٱلذُّكۡرَانَ مِنَ ٱلۡعَٰلَمِينَ ١٦٥ وَتَذَرُونَ مَا خَلَقَ لَكُمۡ رَبُّكُم مِّنۡ أَزۡوَٰجِكُم بَلۡ أَنتُمۡ قَوۡمٌ عَادُونَ ١٦٦ قَالُوا۟ لَئِن لَّمۡ تَنتَهِ يَٰلُوطُ لَتَكُونَنَّ مِنَ ٱلۡمُخۡرَجِينَ ١٦٧ قَالَ إِنِّي لِعَمَلِكُم مِّنَ ٱلۡقَالِينَ ١٦٨ رَبِّ نَجِّنِي وَأَهۡلِي مِمَّا يَعۡمَلُونَ ١٦٩ فَنَجَّيۡنَٰهُ وَأَهۡلَهُۥٓ أَجۡمَعِينَ ١٧٠ إِلَّا عَجُوزًا فِي ٱلۡغَٰبِرِينَ ١٧١ ثُمَّ دَمَّرۡنَا ٱلۡأٓخَرِينَ ١٧٢ وَأَمۡطَرۡنَا عَلَيۡهِم مَّطَرًا فَسَآءَ مَطَرُ ٱلۡمُنذَرِينَ ١٧٣ إِنَّ فِي ذَٰلِكَ لَأٓيَةً وَمَا كَانَ أَكۡثَرُهُم مُّؤۡمِنِينَ ١٧٤ وَإِنَّ رَبَّكَ لَهُوَ ٱلۡعَزِيزُ ٱلرَّحِيمُ ١٧٥

The people of Lūt (Lot) (— who dwelt in the towns of Sodom in Palestine) denied the Messengers. When their brother Lūt (Lot) said to them: "Will you not fear Allāh and obey Him? Verily, I am a trustworthy Messenger to you. So fear Allāh, keep your duty to Him, and obey me. No reward do I ask of you for it (my Message of Islamic Monotheism); my reward is only from the Lord of the 'Ālamīn (mankind, jinn and all that exists). Go you into the males of the 'Ālamīn (mankind), and leave those whom Allāh has created for you to be your wives? Nay, you are a trespassing people!" They said: "If you cease not. O Lūt (Lot)! Verily, you will be one of those who are driven out!" He said: "I am indeed of those who disapprove with severe anger and fury your (this evil) action (of sodomy). My Lord! Save me and my family from what they do." So, We saved him and his family, all, except an old woman (his wife) among those who remained behind. Then afterward We destroyed the others. And We rained on them a rain (of torment). And how evil was the rain of those who had been warned! Verily, in this is indeed a sign, yet most of them are not believers. And verily your Lord, He is truly the All-Mighty, the Most Merciful.

(Qur'ân 26: 160-175)

﴿ وَلُوطًا إِذْ قَالَ لِقَوْمِهِ إِنَّكُمْ لَتَأْتُونَ الْفَاحِشَةَ مَا سَبَقَكُم بِهَا مِنْ أَحَدٍ مِّنَ الْعَالَمِينَ ﴿٢٨﴾ أَئِنَّكُمْ لَتَأْتُونَ الرِّجَالَ وَتَقْطَعُونَ السَّبِيلَ وَتَأْتُونَ فِى نَادِيكُمُ الْمُنكَرَ فَمَا كَانَ جَوَابَ قَوْمِهِ إِلَّا أَن قَالُوا ائْتِنَا بِعَذَابِ اللَّهِ إِن كُنتَ مِنَ الصَّادِقِينَ ﴿٢٩﴾ قَالَ رَبِّ انصُرْنِى عَلَى الْقَوْمِ الْمُفْسِدِينَ ﴿٣٠﴾ وَلَمَّا جَاءَتْ رُسُلُنَا إِبْرَاهِيمَ بِالْبُشْرَىٰ قَالُوا إِنَّا مُهْلِكُوا أَهْلِ هَٰذِهِ الْقَرْيَةِ إِنَّ أَهْلَهَا كَانُوا ظَالِمِينَ ﴿٣١﴾ قَالَ إِنَّ فِيهَا لُوطًا قَالُوا نَحْنُ أَعْلَمُ بِمَن فِيهَا لَنُنَجِّيَنَّهُ وَأَهْلَهُ إِلَّا امْرَأَتَهُ كَانَتْ مِنَ الْغَابِرِينَ ﴿٣٢﴾ وَلَمَّا أَن جَاءَتْ رُسُلُنَا لُوطًا سِيءَ بِهِمْ وَضَاقَ بِهِمْ ذَرْعًا وَقَالُوا لَا تَخَفْ وَلَا تَحْزَنْ إِنَّا مُنَجُّوكَ وَأَهْلَكَ إِلَّا امْرَأَتَكَ كَانَتْ مِنَ الْغَابِرِينَ ﴿٣٣﴾ إِنَّا مُنزِلُونَ عَلَىٰ أَهْلِ هَٰذِهِ الْقَرْيَةِ رِجْزًا مِّنَ السَّمَاءِ بِمَا كَانُوا يَفْسُقُونَ ﴿٣٤﴾ وَلَقَد تَّرَكْنَا مِنْهَا آيَةً بَيِّنَةً لِّقَوْمٍ يَعْقِلُونَ ﴿٣٥﴾ ﴾

And (remember) Lūt (Lot), when he said to his people: "You commit *Al-Fāhishah* (sodomy — the worst sin) which none has preceded you in (committing) it in the *'Ālamīn* (mankind and jinn). Verily, you practise sodomy with men, and rob the wayfarer (travellers)! And practise *Al-Munkar* (disbelief and polytheism and every kind of evil wicked deed) in your meetings." But his people gave no answer except that they said: "Bring Allāh's torment upon us if you are one of the truthful." He said: "My Lord! Give me victory over the people who are *Mufsidūn* (those who commit great crimes and sins, oppressors, tyrants, mischief-makers, corrupters). And when Our messengers came to Ibrāhīm (Abraham) with the glad tidings they said: "Verily, we are going to destroy the people of this [Lūt (Lot's)] town (i.e. the town of Sodom in Palestine); truly, its people have been *Zālimūn* [wrong doers, polytheists disobedient to Allāh, and who denied their Messenger Lūt (Lot)]." Ibrāhīm (Abraham) said: "But there is Lūt (Lot) in it." They said: "We know better who is there. We will verily save him [Lūt (Lot)] and his family — except his wife, she will be of those who remain behind (i.e. she will be destroyed along with those who will be destroyed from her folk)." And when Our messengers came to Lūt (Lot), he was grieved because of them, and felt straitened on their account. They said: "Have no fear, and do not grieve! Truly, we shall save you and your family, — except your wife, she will be of those who remain behind (i.e. she will be destroyed along with those who will be destroyed from her folk). Verily, we are about to bring down on the people of this town a great torment from the sky, because they have been rebellious (against Allāh's Command)." And indeed We have left thereof an evident *Ayāh* (a lesson and a warning and a sign — the place where the Dead Sea is now in Palestine) for a folk who understand.

(Qur'ân 29: 28-35)

Lot ﷺ went to Ibrâhim ﷺ and believed in him. They returned together from Egypt, but the land they returned to was not spacious enough for both of their herds, for each of them was blessed with a great quantity of livestock. They then parted on the best of terms, Ibrâhim ﷺ staying where he was, and Lot ﷺ settling down south of the Dead Sea, where Sodom and Gomorrah were situated. Because of the wickedness and disbelief of the inhabitants of those two towns, Allâh ﷻ destroyed them with a violent earthquake. The nearby town of Sughar went unscathed, and that is where Lot ﷺ then took refuge.

- Qisas Al-Anbiya, by Ibn Kathir: 132
- Qisas Al-Anbiya, by Ath-Thalabi: 105
- Qisas Al-Anbiya, by At-Tabari: 186
- Qisas Al-Anbiya, by An-Najjâr: 112
- Al-Mo'jam Al-Mufahris Li-Alfâz Al-Qur'ân Al-Karim: 654
- Al-Mo'jam Al-Mufahris Li-Ma'âni Al-Qur'ân Al-Karim: 1047

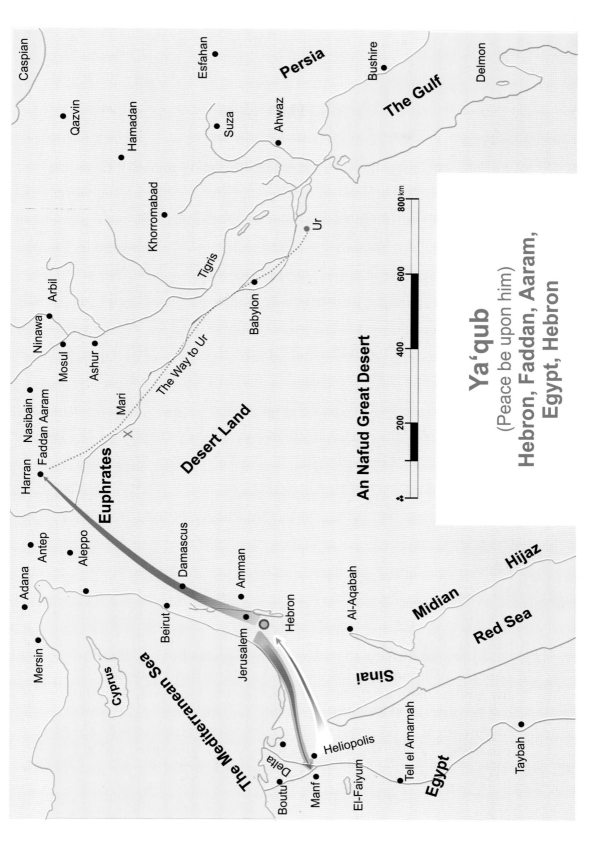

Caspian

Esfahan

Persia

Bushire

The Gulf

Delmon

Qazvin

Hamadan

Suza

Ahwaz

Khorromabad

Tigris

Ur

An Nafud Great Desert

Ninawa

Arbil

Mosul

Ashur

Babylon

The Way to Ur

Harran

Nasibain

Faddan Aaram

Mari

Euphrates

Desert Land

800 km

600

400

200

Adana

Antep

Aleppo

Damascus

Amman

Hebron

Al-Aqabah

Hijaz

Mersin

Beirut

Midian

Cyprus

Jerusalem

Red Sea

Sinai

The Mediterranean Sea

Tell el Amarnah

Egypt

Heliopolis

Taybah

Delta

Manf

El-Faiyum

Boutu

Ya'qub
(Peace be upon him)
Hebron, Faddan, Aaram, Egypt, Hebron

Ya'qûb ﷺ

Ya'qûb ibn Ishâq ibn Ibrâhim ﷺ is mentioned by name 16 times in the Noble Qur'ân:

Chapter Name (Sûrah)	Number of Chapter (Sûrah)	Verse Numbers
Al-Baqarah	2	132, 133, 136, 140
Âl-'Imrân	3	84
An-Nisa'	4	163
Al-An'âm	6	84
Hûd	11	71
Yusuf	12	6, 38, 68
Maryam	19	6, 49
Al-Anbiya'	21	72
Al-'Ankabût	29	27
Sâd	38	45

﴿وَوَصَّىٰ بِهَآ إِبْرَٰهِمُ بَنِيهِ وَيَعْقُوبُ يَٰبَنِىَّ إِنَّ ٱللَّهَ ٱصْطَفَىٰ لَكُمُ ٱلدِّينَ فَلَا تَمُوتُنَّ إِلَّا وَأَنتُم مُّسْلِمُونَ ۝ أَمْ كُنتُمْ شُهَدَآءَ إِذْ حَضَرَ يَعْقُوبَ ٱلْمَوْتُ إِذْ قَالَ لِبَنِيهِ مَا تَعْبُدُونَ مِنۢ بَعْدِى قَالُوا۟ نَعْبُدُ إِلَٰهَكَ وَإِلَٰهَ ءَابَآئِكَ إِبْرَٰهِمَ وَإِسْمَٰعِيلَ وَإِسْحَٰقَ إِلَٰهًا وَٰحِدًا وَنَحْنُ لَهُ مُسْلِمُونَ ۝﴾

And this (submission to Allāh, Islam) was enjoined by Ibrāhīm (Abraham) upon his sons and by Ya'qūb (Jacob) (saying), "O my sons! Allāh has chosen for you the (true) religion, then die not except in the Faith of Islam (as Muslims — Islamic Monotheism)." Or were you witnesses when death approached Ya'qūb (Jacob)? When he said to his sons, "What will you worship after me?'' They said, "We shall worship your *Ilāh* (God — Allāh) the *Ilāh* (God) of your fathers, Ibrāhīm (Abraham), Ismā'īl (Ishmael), Ishāq (Isaac), One *Ilāh* (God), and to Him we submit (in Islam).'' (Qur'ân 2: 132, 133)

وَتِلْكَ حُجَّتُنَآ ءَاتَيْنَٰهَآ إِبْرَٰهِيمَ عَلَىٰ قَوْمِهِۦ نَرْفَعُ دَرَجَٰتٍ مَّن نَّشَآءُ إِنَّ رَبَّكَ حَكِيمٌ عَلِيمٌ ۝ وَوَهَبْنَا لَهُۥٓ إِسْحَٰقَ وَيَعْقُوبَ كُلًّا هَدَيْنَا وَنُوحًا هَدَيْنَا مِن قَبْلُ وَمِن ذُرِّيَّتِهِۦ دَاوُۥدَ وَسُلَيْمَٰنَ وَأَيُّوبَ وَيُوسُفَ وَمُوسَىٰ وَهَٰرُونَ وَكَذَٰلِكَ نَجْزِى ٱلْمُحْسِنِينَ ۝ وَزَكَرِيَّا وَيَحْيَىٰ وَعِيسَىٰ وَإِلْيَاسَ كُلٌّ مِّنَ ٱلصَّٰلِحِينَ ۝ وَإِسْمَٰعِيلَ وَٱلْيَسَعَ وَيُونُسَ وَلُوطًا وَكُلًّا فَضَّلْنَا عَلَى ٱلْعَٰلَمِينَ

And that was Our Proof which We gave Ibrāhīm (Abraham) against his people. We raise whom We will in degrees. Certainly your Lord is All-Wise, All-Knowing. And We bestowed upon him Ishāq (Isaac) and Ya'qūb (Jacob), each of them We guided, and before him, We guided Nūh (Noah), and among his progeny Dāwūd (David), Sulaimān (Solomon), Ayyub (Job), Yūsuf (Joseph), Mūsā (Moses), and Hārūn (Aaron). Thus do We reward *Al-Muhsinūn* (the good-doers). And Zakariyyā (Zechariah), and Yahyā (John) and 'Īsā (Jesus) and Ilyās (Elias), each one of them was of the righteous. And Ismā'īl (Ishmael) and Alyasaa' (Elisha), and Yūnus (Jonah) and Lūt (Lot), and each one of them We preferred to the *'Ālamīn* [mankind and jinn (of their times)]. (Qur'ân 6: 83-86)

Having traveled to Faddaan Aaram in northern Iraq, Ya'qoob عليه السلام later returned to Palestine. And, as is mentioned in *Sûrat Yusuf*, he afterwards traveled to Egypt, where he joined up with his son, Yusuf عليه السلام. He lived there until his death when, as per his instructions, his body was preserved and transported to Palestine, where he was buried. He was buried in the cave of Al-Makfilah, in the city of Hebron (Al-Khalil).

- Qisas Al-Anbiya, by Ibn Kathir: 188
- Qisas Al-Anbiya, by Ath-Tha'labi: 110
- Qisas Al-Anbiya, by At-Tabari: 209
- Qisas Al-Anbiya, by An-Najjâr: 119
- Al-Mo'jam Al-Mufahris Li-Alfâz Al-Qur'ân Al-Karim: 773
- Al-Mo'jam Al-Mufahris Li-Ma'âni Al-Qur'ân Al-Karim: 1332

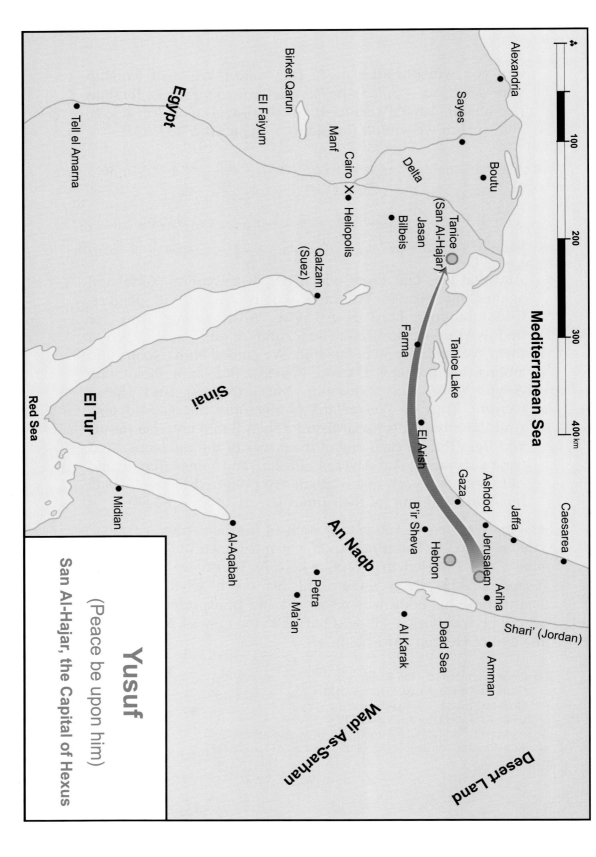

Yusuf
(Peace be upon him)
San Al-Hajar, the Capital of Hexus

Mediterranean Sea

Alexandria

Sayes

Boutu

Tanice
(San Al-Hajar)

Tanice Lake

Ashdod

Jaffa

Caesarea

Gaza

El Arish

B'ir Sheva

Jerusalem

Ariha

Hebron

Shari' (Jordan)

Dead Sea

Amman

Al Karak

Ma'an

Petra

An Naqb

Wadi As-Sarhan

Desert Land

Farma

Sinai

El Tur

Red Sea

Midian

Al-Aqabah

Qalzam
(Suez)

Heliopolis

Cairo X

Bilbeis

Jasan

Delta

Manf

El Faiyum

Birket Qarun

Egypt

Tell el Amarna

100

200

300

400 km

Yusuf العليه

Yusuf العليه is mentioned by name 27 times in the Noble Qur'ân:

Chapter Name (Sûrah)	Number of Chapter (Sûrah)	Verse Numbers
Al-An'aam	6	84
Yusuf	12	4, 7, 8, 9, 10, 11, 17, 21, 29, 46, 51, 56, 58, 69, 76, 77, 80, 84, 85, 87, 89, 90 (twice), 94, 99
Ghâfir	40	34

﴿إِذْ قَالَ يُوسُفُ لِأَبِيهِ يَٰٓأَبَتِ إِنِّى رَأَيْتُ أَحَدَ عَشَرَ كَوْكَبًا وَٱلشَّمْسَ وَٱلْقَمَرَ رَأَيْتُهُمْ لِى سَٰجِدِينَ ۝ قَالَ يَٰبُنَىَّ لَا تَقْصُصْ رُءْيَاكَ عَلَىٰٓ إِخْوَتِكَ فَيَكِيدُواْ لَكَ كَيْدًا إِنَّ ٱلشَّيْطَٰنَ لِلْإِنسَٰنِ عَدُوٌّ مُّبِينٌ ۝ وَكَذَٰلِكَ يَجْتَبِيكَ رَبُّكَ وَيُعَلِّمُكَ مِن تَأْوِيلِ ٱلْأَحَادِيثِ وَيُتِمُّ نِعْمَتَهُۥ عَلَيْكَ وَعَلَىٰٓ ءَالِ يَعْقُوبَ كَمَآ أَتَمَّهَا عَلَىٰٓ أَبَوَيْكَ مِن قَبْلُ إِبْرَٰهِيمَ وَإِسْحَٰقَ إِنَّ رَبَّكَ عَلِيمٌ حَكِيمٌ ۝﴾

(Remember) when Yūsuf (Joseph) said to his father: "O my father! Verily, I saw (in a dream) eleven stars and the sun and the moon — I saw them prostrating themselves to me." He (the father) said: "O my son! Relate not your vision to your brothers, lest they should arrange a plot against you. Verily, *Shaitān* (Satan) is to man an open enemy! Thus will your Lord choose you and teach you the interpretation of dreams (and other things) and perfect His Favour on you and on the offspring of Ya'qūb (Jacob), as He perfected it on your fathers, Ibrāhīm (Abraham) and Ishāq (Isaac) aforetime! Verily, your Lord is All-Knowing, All-Wise."

(Qur'ân 12: 4-6)

﴿وَجَاءَتْ سَيَّارَةٌ فَأَرْسَلُوا وَارِدَهُمْ فَأَدْلَىٰ دَلْوَهُ قَالَ يَٰبُشْرَىٰ هَٰذَا غُلَٰمٌ وَأَسَرُّوهُ بِضَٰعَةً وَٱللَّهُ عَلِيمٌ بِمَا يَعْمَلُونَ ۝ وَشَرَوْهُ بِثَمَنٍ بَخْسٍ دَرَٰهِمَ مَعْدُودَةٍ وَكَانُوا فِيهِ مِنَ ٱلزَّٰهِدِينَ ۝﴾

And there came a caravan of travellers and they sent their water-drawer, and he let down his bucket (into the well). He said: "What a good news! Here is a boy." So they hid him as merchandise (a slave). And Allāh was All-Knower of what they did. And they sold him for a low price, — for a few dirhams (i.e. for a few silver coins). And they were of those who regarded him insignificant. (Qur'ân 12: 19, 20)

﴿فَٱسْتَجَابَ لَهُ رَبُّهُ فَصَرَفَ عَنْهُ كَيْدَهُنَّ إِنَّهُ هُوَ ٱلسَّمِيعُ ٱلْعَلِيمُ ۝ ثُمَّ بَدَا لَهُم مِّن بَعْدِ مَا رَأَوُا ٱلْآيَٰتِ لَيَسْجُنُنَّهُ حَتَّىٰ حِينٍ ۝﴾

So his Lord answered his invocation and turned away from him their plot. Verily, He is the All-Hearer, the All-Knower. Then it occurred to them, after they had seen the proofs (of his innocence), to imprison him for a time. (Qur'ân 12: 34, 35)

﴿يُوسُفُ أَيُّهَا ٱلصِّدِّيقُ أَفْتِنَا فِي سَبْعِ بَقَرَٰتٍ سِمَانٍ يَأْكُلُهُنَّ سَبْعٌ عِجَافٌ وَسَبْعِ سُنۢبُلَٰتٍ خُضْرٍ وَأُخَرَ يَٰبِسَٰتٍ لَّعَلِّي أَرْجِعُ إِلَى ٱلنَّاسِ لَعَلَّهُمْ يَعْلَمُونَ ۝ قَالَ تَزْرَعُونَ سَبْعَ سِنِينَ دَأَبًا فَمَا حَصَدتُّمْ فَذَرُوهُ فِي سُنۢبُلِهِ إِلَّا قَلِيلًا مِّمَّا تَأْكُلُونَ ۝ ثُمَّ يَأْتِي مِنۢ بَعْدِ ذَٰلِكَ سَبْعٌ شِدَادٌ يَأْكُلْنَ مَا قَدَّمْتُمْ لَهُنَّ إِلَّا قَلِيلًا مِّمَّا تُحْصِنُونَ ۝ ثُمَّ يَأْتِي مِنۢ بَعْدِ ذَٰلِكَ عَامٌ فِيهِ يُغَاثُ ٱلنَّاسُ وَفِيهِ يَعْصِرُونَ ۝﴾

(He said): "O Yūsuf (Joseph), the man of truth! Explain to us (the dream) of seven fat cows whom seven lean ones were devouring, and of seven green ears of corn, and (seven) others dry, that I may return to the people, and that they may know." [Yūsuf (Joseph)] said: "For seven consecutive years, you shall sow as usual and that (the harvest) which you reap you shall leave it in the ears, (all) except a little of it which you may eat. Then will come after that, seven hard (years), which will devour what you have laid by in advance for them, (all) except a little of that which you have guarded (stored). Then thereafter will come a year in which people will have abundant rain and in which they will press (wine and oil)."

(Qur'ân 12: 46-49)

﴿وَقَالَ ٱلْمَلِكُ ٱئْتُونِي بِهِۦ أَسْتَخْلِصْهُ لِنَفْسِى فَلَمَّا كَلَّمَهُ قَالَ إِنَّكَ ٱلْيَوْمَ لَدَيْنَا مَكِينٌ أَمِينٌ ٥٤ قَالَ ٱجْعَلْنِى عَلَىٰ خَزَآئِنِ ٱلْأَرْضِ إِنِّى حَفِيظٌ عَلِيمٌ ٥٥ ﴾

And the king said: "Bring him to me that I may attach him to my person." Then, when he spoke to him, he said: "Verily, this day, you are with us high in rank and fully trusted." [Yūsuf (Joseph)] said: "Set me over the store-houses of the land; I will indeed guard them with full knowledge (as a minister of finance in Egypt)." (Qur'ân 12: 54, 55)

﴿قَالَ هَلْ عَلِمْتُم مَّا فَعَلْتُم بِيُوسُفَ وَأَخِيهِ إِذْ أَنتُمْ جَٰهِلُونَ ٨٩ قَالُوٓاْ أَءِنَّكَ لَأَنتَ يُوسُفُ قَالَ أَنَا۠ يُوسُفُ وَهَٰذَآ أَخِي قَدْ مَنَّ ٱللَّهُ عَلَيْنَآ إِنَّهُۥ مَن يَتَّقِ وَيَصْبِرْ فَإِنَّ ٱللَّهَ لَا يُضِيعُ أَجْرَ ٱلْمُحْسِنِينَ ٩٠ قَالُواْ تَٱللَّهِ لَقَدْ ءَاثَرَكَ ٱللَّهُ عَلَيْنَا وَإِن كُنَّا لَخَٰطِئِينَ ٩١ قَالَ لَا تَثْرِيبَ عَلَيْكُمُ ٱلْيَوْمَ يَغْفِرُ ٱللَّهُ لَكُمْ وَهُوَ أَرْحَمُ ٱلرَّٰحِمِينَ ٩٢ ٱذْهَبُواْ بِقَمِيصِي هَٰذَا فَأَلْقُوهُ عَلَىٰ وَجْهِ أَبِي يَأْتِ بَصِيرًا وَأْتُونِي بِأَهْلِكُمْ أَجْمَعِينَ ٩٣ ﴾

He said: "Do you know what you did with Yūsuf (Joseph) and his brother, when you were ignorant?" They said: "Are you indeed Yūsuf (Joseph)?" He said: "I am Yūsuf (Joseph), and this is my brother (Benjamin). Allāh has indeed been gracious to us. Verily, he who fears Allāh with obedience to Him (by abstaining from sins and evil deeds, and by performing righteous good deeds), and is patient, then surely, Allāh makes not the reward of the *Muhsinūn* (good-doers) to be lost." They said: "By Allāh! Indeed Allāh has preferred you to us, and we certainly have been sinners." He said: "No reproach on you this day; may Allāh forgive you, and He is the Most Merciful of those who show mercy! Go with this shirt of mine, and cast it over the face of my father, he will become clear-sighted, and bring to me all your family."

(Qur'ân 12: 89-93)

﴿فَلَمَّا دَخَلُواْ عَلَىٰ يُوسُفَ ءَاوَىٰٓ إِلَيْهِ أَبَوَيْهِ وَقَالَ ٱدْخُلُواْ مِصْرَ إِن شَآءَ ٱللَّهُ ءَامِنِينَ ٩٩ وَرَفَعَ أَبَوَيْهِ عَلَى ٱلْعَرْشِ وَخَرُّواْ لَهُۥ سُجَّدًا وَقَالَ يَٰٓأَبَتِ هَٰذَا تَأْوِيلُ رُءْيَٰيَ مِن قَبْلُ قَدْ جَعَلَهَا رَبِّى حَقًّا وَقَدْ أَحْسَنَ بِىٓ إِذْ أَخْرَجَنِى مِنَ ٱلسِّجْنِ وَجَآءَ بِكُم مِّنَ ٱلْبَدْوِ مِنۢ بَعْدِ أَن نَّزَغَ ٱلشَّيْطَٰنُ بَيْنِى وَبَيْنَ إِخْوَتِىٓ إِنَّ رَبِّى لَطِيفٌ لِّمَا يَشَآءُ إِنَّهُۥ هُوَ ٱلْعَلِيمُ ٱلْحَكِيمُ ١٠٠﴾

Then, when they came in before Yūsuf (Joseph), he took his parents to himself and said: "Enter Egypt, if Allāh wills, in security." And he raised his parents to the throne and they fell down before him prostrate. And he said: "O my father! This is the interpretation of my dream aforetime! My Lord has made it come true! He was indeed good to me, when He took me out of the prison, and brought you (all here) out of the bedouin life, after *Shaitān* (Satan) had sown enmity between me and my brothers. Certainly, my Lord is the Most Courteous and Kind to whom He wills. Truly, He! Only He is the All-Knowing, the All-Wise. (Qur'ân 12: 99, 100)

The story of Yusuf عليه السلام is well-known, and a detailed account of it is given in *Sûrat Yusuf*. He fell into a well in Jerusalem, and was afterwards saved but then taken to Egypt, where he was sold as a slave. After a life replete with tests and trials, Allâh ﷻ honored him with authority and stability in Egypt. He then provided a place of dwelling for his father, Ya'qûb عليه السلام, as well as for his brothers in the land of Jâsân or Jâshân, which is in northern Bilbis (the site of present-day Saft Al-Hannah). After his death, Yusuf عليه السلام was transported to Hebron, where he was buried in the cave of Al-Makfilah. A monument was built for him in Nabalus (Shakim), and another was built near An-Nabk, in Al-Qilmun, Syria.

-   Qisas Al-Anbiya, by Ibn Kathir: 185 - Qisas Al-Anbiya, by Ath-Tha'labi: 110
-   Qisas Al-Anbiya, by At-Tabari: 228 - Qisas Al-Anbiya, by An-Najjâr: 120
-   Al-Mo'jam Al-Mufahris Li-Alfâz Al-Qur'ân Al-Karim: 773
-   Al-Mo'jam Al-Mufahris Li-Ma'âni Al-Qur'ân Al-Karim: 1355

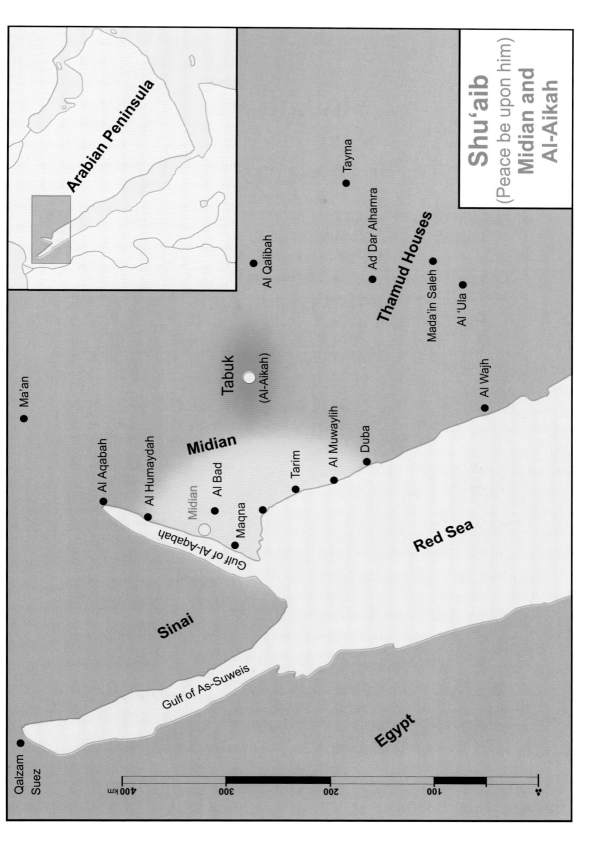

Shu'aib
(Peace be upon him)
Midian and
Al-Aikah

Arabian Peninsula

Tayma

Ad Dar Alhamra

Al Qalibah

Thamud Houses

Mada'in Saleh

Al 'Ula

Ma'an

Tabuk

(Al-Aikah)

Al Wajh

Al Aqabah

Al Humaydah

Midian

Al Bad

Midian

Tarim

Al Muwaylih

Maqna

Duba

Gulf of Al-Aqabah

Sinai

Red Sea

Gulf of As-Suweis

Qalzam
Suez

Egypt

400 km
300
200
100

Shu'aib ﷺ

Shu'aib ﷺ is mentioned by name a total of 11 times in the Noble Qur'ân:

Chapter Name (Sûrah)	Number of Chapter (Sûrah)	Verse Numbers
Al-A'râf	7	85, 88, 90, 92 (twice)
Hûd	11	84, 87, 91, 94
Ash-Shu'arâ	26	177
Al-'Ankabût	29	36

۞وَإِلَىٰ مَدْيَنَ أَخَاهُمْ شُعَيْبًا قَالَ يَٰقَوْمِ ٱعْبُدُوا۟ ٱللَّهَ مَا لَكُم مِّنْ إِلَٰهٍ غَيْرُهُۥ قَدْ جَآءَتْكُم بَيِّنَةٌ مِّن رَّبِّكُمْ فَأَوْفُوا۟ ٱلْكَيْلَ وَٱلْمِيزَانَ وَلَا تَبْخَسُوا۟ ٱلنَّاسَ أَشْيَآءَهُمْ وَلَا تُفْسِدُوا۟ فِى ٱلْأَرْضِ بَعْدَ إِصْلَٰحِهَا ذَٰلِكُمْ خَيْرٌ لَّكُمْ إِن كُنتُم مُّؤْمِنِينَ ۝ وَلَا تَقْعُدُوا۟ بِكُلِّ صِرَٰطٍ تُوعِدُونَ وَتَصُدُّونَ عَن سَبِيلِ ٱللَّهِ مَنْ ءَامَنَ بِهِۦ وَتَبْغُونَهَا عِوَجًا وَٱذْكُرُوٓا۟ إِذْ كُنتُمْ قَلِيلًا فَكَثَّرَكُمْ وَٱنظُرُوا۟ كَيْفَ كَانَ عَٰقِبَةُ ٱلْمُفْسِدِينَ ۝ وَإِن كَانَ طَآئِفَةٌ مِّنكُمْ ءَامَنُوا۟ بِٱلَّذِىٓ أُرْسِلْتُ بِهِۦ وَطَآئِفَةٌ لَّمْ يُؤْمِنُوا۟ فَٱصْبِرُوا۟ حَتَّىٰ يَحْكُمَ ٱللَّهُ بَيْنَنَا وَهُوَ خَيْرُ ٱلْحَٰكِمِينَ ۝ ۞ قَالَ ٱلْمَلَأُ ٱلَّذِينَ ٱسْتَكْبَرُوا۟ مِن قَوْمِهِۦ لَنُخْرِجَنَّكَ يَٰشُعَيْبُ وَٱلَّذِينَ ءَامَنُوا۟ مَعَكَ مِن قَرْيَتِنَآ أَوْ لَتَعُودُنَّ فِى مِلَّتِنَا قَالَ أَوَلَوْ كُنَّا كَٰرِهِينَ ۝ قَدِ ٱفْتَرَيْنَا عَلَى ٱللَّهِ كَذِبًا إِنْ عُدْنَا فِى مِلَّتِكُم بَعْدَ إِذْ نَجَّىٰنَا ٱللَّهُ مِنْهَا وَمَا يَكُونُ لَنَآ أَن نَّعُودَ فِيهَآ إِلَّآ أَن يَشَآءَ ٱللَّهُ رَبُّنَا وَسِعَ رَبُّنَا كُلَّ شَىْءٍ عِلْمًا عَلَى ٱللَّهِ تَوَكَّلْنَا رَبَّنَا ٱفْتَحْ بَيْنَنَا وَبَيْنَ قَوْمِنَا بِٱلْحَقِّ وَأَنتَ خَيْرُ ٱلْفَٰتِحِينَ ۝ وَقَالَ ٱلْمَلَأُ ٱلَّذِينَ كَفَرُوا۟ مِن قَوْمِهِۦ لَئِنِ ٱتَّبَعْتُمْ شُعَيْبًا إِنَّكُمْ إِذًا لَّخَٰسِرُونَ ۝ فَأَخَذَتْهُمُ ٱلرَّجْفَةُ فَأَصْبَحُوا۟ فِى دَارِهِمْ جَٰثِمِينَ ۝ ٱلَّذِينَ كَذَّبُوا۟ شُعَيْبًا كَأَن لَّمْ يَغْنَوْا۟

فِيهَا ٱلَّذِينَ كَذَّبُوا۟ شُعَيْبًا كَانُوا۟ هُمُ ٱلْخَـٰسِرِينَ ﴿٩٢﴾ فَتَوَلَّىٰ عَنْهُمْ وَقَالَ يَـٰقَوْمِ لَقَدْ أَبْلَغْتُكُمْ رِسَـٰلَـٰتِ رَبِّى وَنَصَحْتُ لَكُمْ ۖ فَكَيْفَ ءَاسَىٰ عَلَىٰ قَوْمٍ كَـٰفِرِينَ ﴿٩٣﴾ ۞

And to (the people of) Madyan (Midian), (We sent) their brother Shu'aib. He said: "O my people! Worship Allāh! You have no other *Ilāh* (God) but Him. [*Lā ilāha illallāh* (none has the right to be worshipped but Allāh).] Verily, a clear proof (sign) from your Lord has come to you; so give full measure and full weight and wrong not men in their things, and do not do mischief on the earth after it has been set in order, that will be better for you, if you are believers. And sit not on every road, threatening, and hindering from the path of Allāh those who believe in Him, and seeking to make it crooked. And remember when you were but few, and He multiplied you. And see what was the end of the *Mufsidūn* (mischief-makers, corrupters, liars). And if there is a party of you who believe in that with which I have been sent and a party who do not believe, so be patient until Allāh judges between us, and He is the Best of judges." The chiefs of those who were arrogant among his people said: "We shall certainly drive you out, O Shu'aib, and those who have believed with you from our town, or else you (all) shall return to our religion." He said: "Even though we hate it? We should have invented a lie against Allāh if we returned to your religion, after Allāh has rescued us from it. And it is not for us to return to it unless Allāh, our Lord, should will. Our Lord comprehends all things in His Knowledge. In Allāh (Alone) we put our trust. Our Lord! Judge between us and our people in truth, for You are the Best of those who give judgment." The chiefs of those who disbelieved among his people said (to their people): "If you follow Shu'aib, be sure then you will be the losers!" So the earthquake seized them and they lay (dead), prostrate in their homes. Those who denied Shu'aib, became as if they had never dwelt there (in their homes). Those who denied Shu'aib, they were the losers. Then he (Shu'aib) turned from them and said: "O my people! I have indeed conveyed my Lord's Messages to

91

you and I have given you good advice. Then how can I grieve for a disbelieving people's (destruction)."

(Qur'ân 7: 85-93)

﴿وَإِلَىٰ مَدۡيَنَ أَخَاهُمۡ شُعَيۡبًا قَالَ يَٰقَوۡمِ ٱعۡبُدُواْ ٱللَّهَ مَا لَكُم مِّنۡ إِلَٰهٍ غَيۡرُهُۥ وَلَا تَنقُصُواْ ٱلۡمِكۡيَالَ وَٱلۡمِيزَانَ إِنِّيٓ أَرَىٰكُم بِخَيۡرٍ وَإِنِّيٓ أَخَافُ عَلَيۡكُمۡ عَذَابَ يَوۡمٍ مُّحِيطٍ ٨٤ وَيَٰقَوۡمِ أَوۡفُواْ ٱلۡمِكۡيَالَ وَٱلۡمِيزَانَ بِٱلۡقِسۡطِ وَلَا تَبۡخَسُواْ ٱلنَّاسَ أَشۡيَآءَهُمۡ وَلَا تَعۡثَوۡاْ فِى ٱلۡأَرۡضِ مُفۡسِدِينَ ٨٥ بَقِيَّتُ ٱللَّهِ خَيۡرٌ لَّكُمۡ إِن كُنتُم مُّؤۡمِنِينَ وَمَآ أَنَا۠ عَلَيۡكُم بِحَفِيظٍ ٨٦ قَالُواْ يَٰشُعَيۡبُ أَصَلَوٰتُكَ تَأۡمُرُكَ أَن نَّتۡرُكَ مَا يَعۡبُدُ ءَابَآؤُنَآ أَوۡ أَن نَّفۡعَلَ فِىٓ أَمۡوَٰلِنَا مَا نَشَٰٓؤُاْۖ إِنَّكَ لَأَنتَ ٱلۡحَلِيمُ ٱلرَّشِيدُ ٨٧ قَالَ يَٰقَوۡمِ أَرَءَيۡتُمۡ إِن كُنتُ عَلَىٰ بَيِّنَةٍ مِّن رَّبِّى وَرَزَقَنِى مِنۡهُ رِزۡقًا حَسَنًاۚ وَمَآ أُرِيدُ أَنۡ أُخَالِفَكُمۡ إِلَىٰ مَآ أَنۡهَىٰكُمۡ عَنۡهُۚ إِنۡ أُرِيدُ إِلَّا ٱلۡإِصۡلَٰحَ مَا ٱسۡتَطَعۡتُۚ وَمَا تَوۡفِيقِىٓ إِلَّا بِٱللَّهِۚ عَلَيۡهِ تَوَكَّلۡتُ وَإِلَيۡهِ أُنِيبُ ٨٨ وَيَٰقَوۡمِ لَا يَجۡرِمَنَّكُمۡ شِقَاقِىٓ أَن يُصِيبَكُم مِّثۡلُ مَآ أَصَابَ قَوۡمَ نُوحٍ أَوۡ قَوۡمَ هُودٍ أَوۡ قَوۡمَ صَٰلِحٍۚ وَمَا قَوۡمُ لُوطٍ مِّنكُم بِبَعِيدٍ ٨٩ وَٱسۡتَغۡفِرُواْ رَبَّكُمۡ ثُمَّ تُوبُوٓاْ إِلَيۡهِۚ إِنَّ رَبِّى رَحِيمٌ وَدُودٌ ٩٠ قَالُواْ يَٰشُعَيۡبُ مَا نَفۡقَهُ كَثِيرًا مِّمَّا تَقُولُ وَإِنَّا لَنَرَىٰكَ فِينَا ضَعِيفًاۖ وَلَوۡلَا رَهۡطُكَ لَرَجَمۡنَٰكَۖ وَمَآ أَنتَ عَلَيۡنَا بِعَزِيزٍ ٩١ قَالَ يَٰقَوۡمِ أَرَهۡطِىٓ أَعَزُّ عَلَيۡكُم مِّنَ ٱللَّهِ وَٱتَّخَذۡتُمُوهُ وَرَآءَكُمۡ ظِهۡرِيًّاۖ إِنَّ رَبِّى بِمَا تَعۡمَلُونَ مُحِيطٌ ٩٢ وَيَٰقَوۡمِ ٱعۡمَلُواْ عَلَىٰ مَكَانَتِكُمۡ إِنِّى عَٰمِلٌۖ سَوۡفَ تَعۡلَمُونَ مَن يَأۡتِيهِ عَذَابٌ يُخۡزِيهِ وَمَنۡ هُوَ كَٰذِبٌۖ وَٱرۡتَقِبُوٓاْ إِنِّى مَعَكُمۡ رَقِيبٌ ٩٣ وَلَمَّا جَآءَ أَمۡرُنَا نَجَّيۡنَا شُعَيۡبًا وَٱلَّذِينَ ءَامَنُواْ مَعَهُۥ بِرَحۡمَةٍ مِّنَّا وَأَخَذَتِ ٱلَّذِينَ ظَلَمُواْ ٱلصَّيۡحَةُ فَأَصۡبَحُواْ فِى دِيَٰرِهِمۡ جَٰثِمِينَ ٩٤ كَأَن لَّمۡ يَغۡنَوۡاْ فِيهَآۗ أَلَا بُعۡدًا لِّمَدۡيَنَ كَمَا بَعِدَتۡ ثَمُودُ ٩٥ ﴾

And to the Madyan (Midian) people (We sent) their brother Shu'aib. He said: "O my people! Worship Allāh, you have no other *ilāh* (god) but Him, and give not short measure or weight. I see you in prosperity and verily, I fear for you the torment of a Day encompassing. And O my people! Give full measure and weight in justice and reduce not the things that are due to the people, and do not commit mischief in the land, causing corruption. That which is left by Allāh for you (after giving the rights of the people) is better for you, if you are believers. And I am not a guardian over you." They said: "O Shu'aib! Does your *Salāt* (prayer) command that we give up what our fathers used to worship, or that we give up doing what we like with our property? Verily, you are the forbearer, right-minded!" (They said this sarcastically). He said: "O my people! Tell me if I have a clear evidence from my Lord and He has given me a good sustenance from Himself (shall I corrupt it by mixing it with the unlawfully earned money). I wish not, in contradiction to you, to do that which I forbid you. I only desire reform to the best of my power. And my guidance cannot come except from Allāh, in Him I trust and to Him I repent. And O my people! Let not my *Shiqāq* cause you to suffer the fate similar to that of the people of Nūh (Noah) or of Hūd or of Sālih (Saleh), and the people of Lūt (Lot) are not far off from you! And ask forgiveness of your Lord and turn to Him in repentance. Verily, my Lord is Most Merciful, Most Loving." They said: "O Shu'aib! We do not understand much of what you say, and we see you weak (it is said that he was a blind man) among us. Were it not for your family, we should certainly have stoned you and you are not powerful against us." He said: "O my people! Is then my family of more weight with you than Allāh? And you have cast Him away behind your backs. Verily, my Lord is surrounding all that you do. And O my people! Act according to your ability and way, and I am acting (on my way). You will come to know who it is on whom descends the torment that will cover him with ignominy, and who is a liar! And watch you! Verily, I too am watching with you." And when Our Commandment came, We saved Shu'aib and those who believed with him by a mercy from Us. And *As-Saihah* (torment — awful cry) seized the wrong doers, and they lay (dead) prostrate in their homes. As if they had never lived there! So away with Madyan (Midian) as away with Thamūd! (All these nations were destroyed).

(Qur'ân 11: 84-95)

﴿وَإِلَىٰ مَدۡيَنَ أَخَاهُمۡ شُعَيۡبٗا فَقَالَ يَٰقَوۡمِ ٱعۡبُدُواْ ٱللَّهَ وَٱرۡجُواْ ٱلۡيَوۡمَ ٱلۡأٓخِرَ وَلَا تَعۡثَوۡاْ فِي ٱلۡأَرۡضِ مُفۡسِدِينَ ٣٦ فَكَذَّبُوهُ فَأَخَذَتۡهُمُ ٱلرَّجۡفَةُ فَأَصۡبَحُواْ فِي دَارِهِمۡ جَٰثِمِينَ ٣٧﴾

And to (the people of) Madyan (Midian), We sent their brother Shu'aib. He said: "O my people! Worship Allāh (Alone) and hope for (the reward of good deeds by worshipping Allāh Alone, on) the last Day (i.e. the Day of Resurrection), and commit no mischief on the earth as *Mufsidūn* (those who commit great crimes, oppressors, tyrants, mischief-makers, corrupters). (*Tafsir At-Tabari*) And they denied him (Shu'aib); so the earthquake seized them, and they lay (dead), prostrate in their dwellings.

(Qur'ân 29: 36, 37)

Allâh ﷻ sent Shu'aib to the people of Madyan ibn Ibrâhim عليه السلام; they lived in the lands of Al-Hijaz, adjacent to Ash-Sham (Syria and surrounding regions), and east of the Gulf of Al-'Aqabah. Near to Madyan is a land full of softwood trees, and at least according to one opinion in the matter, that land is actually the site of the city of Tabûk.

- Qisas Al-Anbiya, by Ibn Kathir: 239
- Qisas Al-Anbiya, by Ath-Tha'labi: 167
- Qisas Al-Anbiya, by At-Tabari: 285
- Qisas Al-Anbiya, by An-Najjâr: 145
- Al-Mo'jam Al-Mufahris Li-Alfâz Al-Qur'ân Al-Karim: 383
- Al-Mo'jam Al-Mufahris Li-Ma'âni Al-Qur'ân Al-Karim: 633

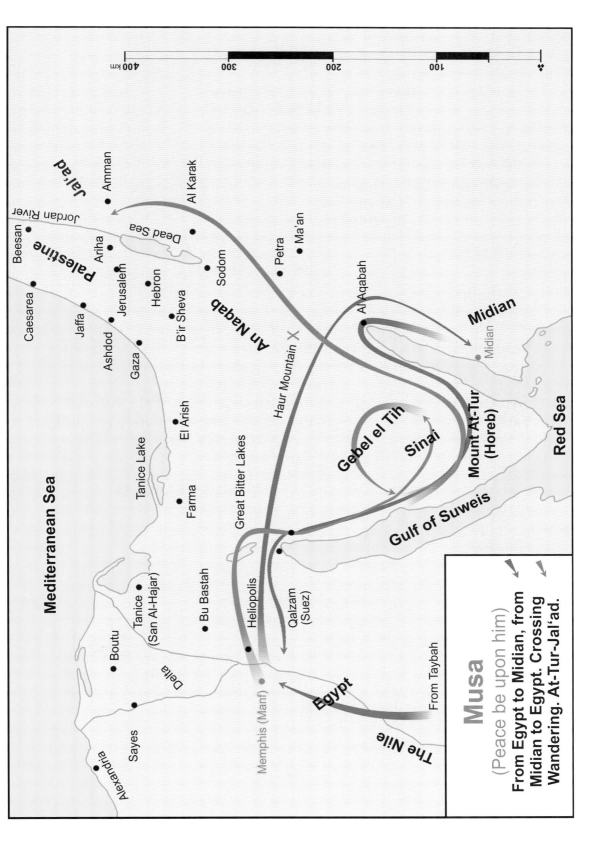

Mediterranean Sea

Alexandria
Sayes
Boutu
Tanice (San Al-Hajar)
Delta
Bu Bastah
Memphis (Manf)
Heliopolis
Qalzam (Suez)

The Nile

Egypt

From Taybah

Farma

Tanice Lake

Great Bitter Lakes

El Arish

An Naqab

Haur Mountain ✕

Gebel el Tih

Sinai

Mount At-Tur (Horeb)

Gulf of Suweis

Red Sea

Al Aqabah

Midian

Midian

Ma'an
Petra
Sodom
B'ir Sheva
Hebron
Jerusalem
Gaza
Ashdod
Jaffa
Caesarea

Palestine

Beesan
Ariha
Dead Sea
Al Karak
Amman
Jordan River

Jal'ad

100
200
300
400 km

Musa

(Peace be upon him)

From Egypt to Midian, from Midian to Egypt. Crossing Wandering. At-Tur-Jal'ad.

Mûsa العليه السلام

Mûsa العليه السلام is mentioned by name 136 times in the Noble Qur'ân:

Chapter Name (Sûrah)	Number of Chapter (Sûrah)	Verse Numbers
Al-Baqarah	2	51, 53, 54, 55, 60, 61, 67, 87, 92, 108, 136, 246, 248
Āl-'Imrân	3	84
An-Nisa'	4	153 (twice), 164
Al-Mâ'idah	5	20, 22, 24
Al-An'âm	6	84, 91, 154
Al-A'râf	7	103, 104, 115, 117, 122, 127, 128, 131, 134, 138, 142 (twice), 143 (twice), 144, 148, 150, 154, 155, 159, 160
Yûnus	10	75, 77, 80, 81, 83, 84, 87, 88
Hûd	11	17, 96, 110
Ibrâhim	14	5, 6, 8
Isra'	17	2, 101 (twice)
Al-Kahf	18	60, 66
Maryam	29	51
Ta-Ha	20	9, 11, 17, 19, 36, 40, 49, 57, 61, 65, 67, 70, 77, 83, 86, 88, 91
Al-Anbiya'	21	48

Chapter Name (Sûrah)	Number of Chapter (Sûrah)	Verse Numbers
Al-Hajj	22	44
Al-Mu'minûn	23	45, 49
Al-Furqân	25	35
Ash-Shu'arâ	26	10, 43, 45, 48, 52, 61, 63, 65
An-Naml	27	7, 9, 10
Al-Qisas	28	3, 7, 10, 15, 18, 19, 20, 29, 30, 31, 36, 37, 38, 43, 44, 48 (twice), 76
Al-'Ankabût	29	39
As-Sajdah	32	23
Al-Ahzâb	33	7, 69
As-Sâffât	37	114, 120
Ghâfir	40	23, 26, 27, 37, 53
Fussilat	41	45
Ash-Shurâ	42	13
Az-Zukhruf	43	46
Al-Ahqâf	46	12, 30
Adh-Dhâriyât	51	38
An-Najm	53	36
As-Saff	61	5
An-Nâzi'ât	79	15
Al-A'la	87	19

﴿وَهَلْ أَتَىٰكَ حَدِيثُ مُوسَىٰ ۝ إِذْ رَءَا نَارًا فَقَالَ لِأَهْلِهِ ٱمْكُثُوٓاْ إِنِّىٓ ءَانَسْتُ نَارًا لَّعَلِّىٓ ءَاتِيكُم مِّنْهَا بِقَبَسٍ أَوْ أَجِدُ عَلَى ٱلنَّارِ هُدًى ۝ فَلَمَّآ أَتَىٰهَا نُودِىَ يَٰمُوسَىٰٓ ۝ إِنِّىٓ أَنَا۠ رَبُّكَ

فَٱخْلَعْ نَعْلَيْكَ إِنَّكَ بِٱلْوَادِ ٱلْمُقَدَّسِ طُوًى ﴿١٢﴾ ۞

And has there come to you the story of Mūsā (Moses)? When he saw a fire, he said to his family: "Wait! Verily, I have seen a fire; perhaps I can bring you some burning brand therefrom, or find some guidance at the fire." And when he came to it (the fire), he was called by name: "O Mūsā (Moses)! Verily, I am your Lord! So take off your shoes; you are in the sacred valley, Tuwa.

(Qur'ân 20: 9-12)

﴿وَمَا تِلْكَ بِيَمِينِكَ يَمُوسَىٰ ﴿١٧﴾ قَالَ هِيَ عَصَايَ أَتَوَكَّؤُا۟ عَلَيْهَا وَأَهُشُّ بِهَا عَلَىٰ غَنَمِى وَلِيَ فِيهَا مَـَٔارِبُ أُخْرَىٰ ﴿١٨﴾ قَالَ أَلْقِهَا يَمُوسَىٰ ﴿١٩﴾ فَأَلْقَىٰهَا فَإِذَا هِيَ حَيَّةٌ تَسْعَىٰ ﴿٢٠﴾ قَالَ خُذْهَا وَلَا تَخَفْ سَنُعِيدُهَا سِيرَتَهَا ٱلْأُولَىٰ ﴿٢١﴾ وَٱضْمُمْ يَدَكَ إِلَىٰ جَنَاحِكَ تَخْرُجْ بَيْضَآءَ مِنْ غَيْرِ سُوٓءٍ ءَايَةً أُخْرَىٰ ﴿٢٢﴾ لِنُرِيَكَ مِنْ ءَايَٰتِنَا ٱلْكُبْرَى ﴿٢٣﴾ ٱذْهَبْ إِلَىٰ فِرْعَوْنَ إِنَّهُۥ طَغَىٰ ﴿٢٤﴾ قَالَ رَبِّ ٱشْرَحْ لِى صَدْرِى ﴿٢٥﴾ وَيَسِّرْ لِىٓ أَمْرِى ﴿٢٦﴾ وَٱحْلُلْ عُقْدَةً مِّن لِّسَانِى ﴿٢٧﴾ يَفْقَهُوا۟ قَوْلِى ﴿٢٨﴾ وَٱجْعَل لِّى وَزِيرًا مِّنْ أَهْلِى ﴿٢٩﴾ هَٰرُونَ أَخِى ﴿٣٠﴾ ٱشْدُدْ بِهِۦٓ أَزْرِى ﴿٣١﴾ وَأَشْرِكْهُ فِىٓ أَمْرِى ﴿٣٢﴾ كَىْ نُسَبِّحَكَ كَثِيرًا ﴿٣٣﴾ وَنَذْكُرَكَ كَثِيرًا ﴿٣٤﴾ إِنَّكَ كُنتَ بِنَا بَصِيرًا ﴿٣٥﴾ قَالَ قَدْ أُوتِيتَ سُؤْلَكَ يَمُوسَىٰ ﴿٣٦﴾ وَلَقَدْ مَنَنَّا عَلَيْكَ مَرَّةً أُخْرَىٰٓ ﴿٣٧﴾ إِذْ أَوْحَيْنَآ إِلَىٰٓ أُمِّكَ مَا يُوحَىٰٓ ﴿٣٨﴾ أَنِ ٱقْذِفِيهِ فِى ٱلتَّابُوتِ فَٱقْذِفِيهِ فِى ٱلْيَمِّ فَلْيُلْقِهِ ٱلْيَمُّ بِٱلسَّاحِلِ يَأْخُذْهُ عَدُوٌّ لِّى وَعَدُوٌّ لَّهُۥ وَأَلْقَيْتُ عَلَيْكَ مَحَبَّةً مِّنِّى وَلِتُصْنَعَ عَلَىٰ عَيْنِىٓ ﴿٣٩﴾ إِذْ تَمْشِىٓ أُخْتُكَ فَتَقُولُ هَلْ أَدُلُّكُمْ عَلَىٰ مَن يَكْفُلُهُۥ فَرَجَعْنَٰكَ إِلَىٰٓ أُمِّكَ كَىْ تَقَرَّ عَيْنُهَا وَلَا تَحْزَنَ وَقَتَلْتَ نَفْسًا فَنَجَّيْنَٰكَ مِنَ ٱلْغَمِّ وَفَتَنَّٰكَ فُتُونًا فَلَبِثْتَ سِنِينَ فِىٓ أَهْلِ مَدْيَنَ ثُمَّ جِئْتَ عَلَىٰ قَدَرٍ يَمُوسَىٰ ﴿٤٠﴾ وَٱصْطَنَعْتُكَ لِنَفْسِى ﴿٤١﴾ ٱذْهَبْ أَنتَ وَأَخُوكَ بِـَٔايَٰتِى وَلَا تَنِيَا فِى ذِكْرِى ﴿٤٢﴾ ٱذْهَبَآ إِلَىٰ فِرْعَوْنَ إِنَّهُۥ طَغَىٰ ﴿٤٣﴾ فَقُولَا لَهُۥ قَوْلًا لَّيِّنًا لَّعَلَّهُۥ يَتَذَكَّرُ أَوْ يَخْشَىٰ ﴿٤٤﴾ قَالَا رَبَّنَآ إِنَّنَا نَخَافُ أَن يَفْرُطَ عَلَيْنَآ أَوْ أَن يَطْغَىٰ ﴿٤٥﴾ قَالَ لَا تَخَافَآ إِنَّنِى مَعَكُمَآ أَسْمَعُ وَأَرَىٰ ﴿٤٦﴾ فَأْتِيَاهُ فَقُولَآ إِنَّا رَسُولَا رَبِّكَ فَأَرْسِلْ مَعَنَا بَنِىٓ إِسْرَٰٓءِيلَ وَلَا تُعَذِّبْهُمْ قَدْ جِئْنَٰكَ بِـَٔايَةٍ مِّن رَّبِّكَ وَٱلسَّلَٰمُ عَلَىٰ مَنِ ٱتَّبَعَ ٱلْهُدَىٰٓ ﴿٤٧﴾ ۞

"And what is that in your right hand, O Mūsā (Moses)?" He

said: "This is my stick, whereon I lean, and wherewith I beat down branches for my sheep, and wherein I find other uses." (Allāh) said: "Cast it down, O Mūsā (Moses)!" He cast it down, and behold! It was a snake, moving quickly. Allāh said:"Grasp it and fear not; We shall return it to its former state, and press your (right) hand to your (left) side: it will come forth white (and shining), without any disease as another sign, that We may show you (some) of Our Greater Signs. Go to Fir'aun (Pharaoh)! Verily, he has transgressed (all bounds in disbelief and disobedience, and has behaved as an arrogant and as a tyrant)." [Mūsā (Moses)] said: "O my Lord! Open for me my chest (grant me self-confidence, contentment, and boldness). And ease my task for me; and loose the knot (the defect) from my tongue, (i.e. remove the incorrectness from my speech) [That occurred as a result of a brand of fire which Mūsā (Moses) put in his mouth when he was an infant.] (*Tafsir At-Tabari*). That they understand my speech. And appoint for me a helper from my family, Hārūn (Aaron), my brother. Increase my strength with him, and let him share my task (of conveying Allāh's Message and Prophethood), that we may glorify You much, and remember You much. Verily, You are Ever a Well-Seer of us." (Allāh) said: "You are granted your request, O Mūsā (Moses)! And indeed We conferred a favor on you another time (before). When We inspired your mother with that which We inspired. (Saying:) 'Put him (the child) into the *Tabūt* (a box or a case or a chest) and put it into the river (Nile); then the river shall cast it up on the bank, and there, an enemy of Mine and an enemy of his shall take him.' And I endued you with love from Me, in order that you may be brought up under My Eye. When your sister went and said: 'Shall I show you one who will nurse him?' So, We restored you to your mother, that she might cool her eyes and she should not grieve. Then you did kill a man, but We saved you from great distress and tried you with a heavy trial. Then you stayed a number of years with the people of Madyan (Midian). Then you came here according to the fixed term which I ordained (for you), O Mūsā (Moses)! And I have chosen you for Myself. Go you and your brother with My *Ayāt* (proofs, evidences, lessons, signs, etc.), and do not, you both, slacken and become weak in My remembrance. Go both of you to Fir'aun (Pharaoh), verily, he has transgressed (all bounds in disbelief and disobedience and behaved as an arrogant and as a tyrant). And speak to him mildly, perhaps he may accept admonition or fear (Allāh)." They said: "Our Lord! Verily, we fear lest he should hasten to punish us or lest he should transgress (all bounds against us)." He (Allāh) said: "Fear not, verily, I am with you both, hearing and seeing. So go you both to him, and say: 'Verily, we are Messengers of your Lord, so let the Children of Israel go with us, and torment them not; indeed, we have come with a sign from your Lord! And peace will be upon him who follows the guidance!'"

(Qur'ân 20: 17-47)

﴿فَلَمَّآ أَنْ أَرَادَ أَن يَبْطِشَ بِٱلَّذِى هُوَ عَدُوٌّ لَّهُمَا قَالَ يَٰمُوسَىٰٓ أَتُرِيدُ أَن تَقْتُلَنِى كَمَا قَتَلْتَ نَفْسًۢا بِٱلْأَمْسِ إِن تُرِيدُ إِلَّآ أَن تَكُونَ جَبَّارًا فِى ٱلْأَرْضِ وَمَا تُرِيدُ أَن تَكُونَ مِنَ ٱلْمُصْلِحِينَ ﴿١٩﴾ وَجَآءَ رَجُلٌ مِّنْ أَقْصَا ٱلْمَدِينَةِ يَسْعَىٰ قَالَ يَٰمُوسَىٰٓ إِنَّ ٱلْمَلَأَ يَأْتَمِرُونَ بِكَ لِيَقْتُلُوكَ فَٱخْرُجْ إِنِّى لَكَ مِنَ ٱلنَّٰصِحِينَ ﴿٢٠﴾ فَخَرَجَ مِنْهَا خَآئِفًا يَتَرَقَّبُ قَالَ رَبِّ نَجِّنِى مِنَ ٱلْقَوْمِ ٱلظَّٰلِمِينَ ﴿٢١﴾ وَلَمَّا تَوَجَّهَ تِلْقَآءَ مَدْيَنَ قَالَ عَسَىٰ رَبِّىٓ أَن يَهْدِيَنِى سَوَآءَ ٱلسَّبِيلِ ﴿٢٢﴾ وَلَمَّا وَرَدَ مَآءَ مَدْيَنَ وَجَدَ عَلَيْهِ أُمَّةً مِّنَ ٱلنَّاسِ يَسْقُونَ وَوَجَدَ مِن دُونِهِمُ ٱمْرَأَتَيْنِ تَذُودَانِ قَالَ مَا خَطْبُكُمَا قَالَتَا لَا نَسْقِى حَتَّىٰ يُصْدِرَ ٱلرِّعَآءُ وَأَبُونَا شَيْخٌ كَبِيرٌ ﴿٢٣﴾ فَسَقَىٰ لَهُمَا ثُمَّ تَوَلَّىٰٓ إِلَى ٱلظِّلِّ فَقَالَ رَبِّ إِنِّى لِمَآ أَنزَلْتَ إِلَىَّ مِنْ خَيْرٍ فَقِيرٌ ﴿٢٤﴾ فَجَآءَتْهُ إِحْدَىٰهُمَا تَمْشِى عَلَى ٱسْتِحْيَآءٍ قَالَتْ إِنَّ أَبِى يَدْعُوكَ لِيَجْزِيَكَ أَجْرَ مَا سَقَيْتَ لَنَا فَلَمَّا جَآءَهُۥ وَقَصَّ عَلَيْهِ ٱلْقَصَصَ قَالَ لَا تَخَفْ نَجَوْتَ مِنَ ٱلْقَوْمِ ٱلظَّٰلِمِينَ ﴿٢٥﴾ قَالَتْ إِحْدَىٰهُمَا يَٰٓأَبَتِ ٱسْتَـْٔجِرْهُ إِنَّ خَيْرَ مَنِ ٱسْتَـْٔجَرْتَ ٱلْقَوِىُّ ٱلْأَمِينُ ﴿٢٦﴾ قَالَ إِنِّىٓ أُرِيدُ أَنْ أُنكِحَكَ إِحْدَى ٱبْنَتَىَّ هَٰتَيْنِ عَلَىٰٓ أَن تَأْجُرَنِى ثَمَٰنِىَ حِجَجٍ فَإِنْ أَتْمَمْتَ عَشْرًا فَمِنْ عِندِكَ وَمَآ أُرِيدُ أَنْ أَشُقَّ عَلَيْكَ سَتَجِدُنِىٓ إِن شَآءَ ٱللَّهُ مِنَ ٱلصَّٰلِحِينَ ﴿٢٧﴾ قَالَ ذَٰلِكَ بَيْنِى وَبَيْنَكَ أَيَّمَا ٱلْأَجَلَيْنِ قَضَيْتُ فَلَا عُدْوَٰنَ عَلَىَّ وَٱللَّهُ عَلَىٰ مَا نَقُولُ وَكِيلٌ ﴿٢٨﴾ ۞ فَلَمَّا قَضَىٰ مُوسَى

100

الْأَجَلَ وَسَارَ بِأَهْلِهِ ءَانَسَ مِن جَانِبِ الطُّورِ نَارًاقَالَ لِأَهْلِهِ امْكُثُوٓا۟ إِنِّىٓ ءَانَسْتُ نَارًا لَّعَلِّىٓ ءَاتِيكُم مِّنْهَا بِخَبَرٍ أَوْ جَذْوَةٍ مِّنَ النَّارِ لَعَلَّكُمْ تَصْطَلُونَ ۝ فَلَمَّآ أَتَىٰهَا نُودِىَ مِن شَٰطِئِ الْوَادِ الْأَيْمَنِ فِى الْبُقْعَةِ الْمُبَٰرَكَةِ مِنَ الشَّجَرَةِ أَن يَٰمُوسَىٰٓ إِنِّىٓ أَنَا اللَّهُ رَبُّ الْعَٰلَمِينَ ۞ ۝

Then when he decided to seize the man who was an enemy to both of them, the man said: "O Mūsā (Moses)! Is it your intention to kill me as you killed a man yesterday? Your aim is nothing but to become a tyrant in the land, and not to be one of those who do right." And there came a man running, from the farthest end of the city. He said: "O Mūsā (Moses)! Verily, the chiefs are taking counsel together about you, to kill you, so escape. Truly, I am one of the good advisers to you." So he escaped from there, looking about in a state of fear. He said: "My Lord! Save me from the people who are Zālimūn (polytheists and wrong doers)!" And when he went towards (the land of) Madyan (Midian), he said: "It may be that my Lord guides me to the Right Way." And when he arrived at the water (a well) of Madyan (Midian), he found there a group of men watering (their flocks), and besides them he found two women who were keeping back (their flocks). He said: "What is the matter with you?" They said: "We cannot water (our flocks) until the shepherds take (their flocks). And our father is a very old man." So he watered (their flocks) for them, then he turned back to shade, and said: "My Lord! Truly, I am in need of whatever good that You bestow on me!" Then there came to him one of the two women, walking shyly. She said: "Verily, my father calls you that he may reward you for having watered (our flocks) for us." So when he came to him and narrated the story, he said: "Fear you not. You have escaped from the people who are Zālimūn (polytheists, disbelievers, and wrong doers)." And said one of them (the two women): "O my father! Hire him! Verily, the best of men for you to hire is the strong, the trustworthy." He said: "I intend to wed one of these two daughters of mine to you, on condition that you

101

serve me for eight years; but if you complete ten years, it will be (a favor) from you. But I intend not to place you under a difficulty. If Allāh wills, you will find me one of the righteous." He [Mūsā (Moses)] said: "That (is settled) between me and you: whichever of the two terms I fulfil, there will be no injustice to me, and Allāh is Surety over what we say." Then, when Mūsā (Moses) had fulfilled the term, and was traveling with his family, he saw a fire in the direction of Tūr (Mount). He said to his family: "Wait, I have seen a fire; perhaps I may bring to you from there some information, or a burning firebrand that you may warm yourselves." So when he reached it (the fire), he was called from the right side of the valley, in the blessed place, from the tree: "O Mūsā (Moses)! Verily, I am Allāh, the Lord of the ʿĀlamīn (mankind, jinn and all that exists)!   (Qurʾân 28: 19-30)

﴿وَإِذْ فَرَقْنَا بِكُمُ ٱلْبَحْرَ فَأَنجَيْنَٰكُمْ وَأَغْرَقْنَآ ءَالَ فِرْعَوْنَ وَأَنتُمْ تَنظُرُونَ ۝ وَإِذْ وَٰعَدْنَا مُوسَىٰٓ أَرْبَعِينَ لَيْلَةً ثُمَّ ٱتَّخَذْتُمُ ٱلْعِجْلَ مِنۢ بَعْدِهِۦ وَأَنتُمْ ظَٰلِمُونَ ۝ ﴾

And (remember) when We separated the sea for you and saved you and drowned Firʿaun's (Pharaoh) people while you were looking (at them, when the sea water covered them). And (remember) when We appointed for Mūsā (Moses) forty nights, and (in his absence) you took the calf (for worship), and you were Zālimūn (polytheists and wrong doers).

(Qurʾân 2: 50, 51)

﴿وَإِذْ قَالَ مُوسَىٰ لِقَوْمِهِۦ يَٰقَوْمِ إِنَّكُمْ ظَلَمْتُمْ أَنفُسَكُم بِٱتِّخَاذِكُمُ ٱلْعِجْلَ فَتُوبُوٓا۟ إِلَىٰ بَارِئِكُمْ فَٱقْتُلُوٓا۟ أَنفُسَكُمْ ذَٰلِكُمْ خَيْرٌ لَّكُمْ عِندَ بَارِئِكُمْ فَتَابَ عَلَيْكُمْ إِنَّهُۥ هُوَ ٱلتَّوَّابُ ٱلرَّحِيمُ ۝ وَإِذْ قُلْتُمْ يَٰمُوسَىٰ لَن نُّؤْمِنَ لَكَ حَتَّىٰ نَرَى ٱللَّهَ جَهْرَةً فَأَخَذَتْكُمُ ٱلصَّٰعِقَةُ وَأَنتُمْ تَنظُرُونَ ۝ ثُمَّ بَعَثْنَٰكُم مِّنۢ بَعْدِ مَوْتِكُمْ لَعَلَّكُمْ تَشْكُرُونَ ۝ وَظَلَّلْنَا عَلَيْكُمُ ٱلْغَمَامَ وَأَنزَلْنَا عَلَيْكُمُ ٱلْمَنَّ وَٱلسَّلْوَىٰ كُلُوا۟ مِن طَيِّبَٰتِ مَا رَزَقْنَٰكُمْ وَمَا ظَلَمُونَا وَلَٰكِن كَانُوٓا۟ أَنفُسَهُمْ يَظْلِمُونَ ۝ وَإِذْ قُلْنَا ٱدْخُلُوا۟ هَٰذِهِ ٱلْقَرْيَةَ فَكُلُوا۟ مِنْهَا حَيْثُ شِئْتُمْ رَغَدًا وَٱدْخُلُوا۟ ٱلْبَابَ سُجَّدًا وَقُولُوا۟ حِطَّةٌ نَّغْفِرْ لَكُمْ خَطَٰيَٰكُمْ وَسَنَزِيدُ ٱلْمُحْسِنِينَ ۝ فَبَدَّلَ ٱلَّذِينَ

ظَلَمُواْ قَوْلًا غَيْرَ ٱلَّذِى قِيلَ لَهُمْ فَأَنزَلْنَا عَلَى ٱلَّذِينَ ظَلَمُواْ رِجْزًا مِّنَ ٱلسَّمَآءِ بِمَا كَانُواْ يَفْسُقُونَ ۞ ٥٩ وَإِذِ ٱسْتَسْقَىٰ مُوسَىٰ لِقَوْمِهِۦ فَقُلْنَا ٱضْرِب بِّعَصَاكَ ٱلْحَجَرَ ۖ فَٱنفَجَرَتْ مِنْهُ ٱثْنَتَا عَشْرَةَ عَيْنًا ۖ قَدْ عَلِمَ كُلُّ أُنَاسٍ مَّشْرَبَهُمْ ۖ كُلُواْ وَٱشْرَبُواْ مِن رِّزْقِ ٱللَّهِ وَلَا تَعْثَوْاْ فِى ٱلْأَرْضِ مُفْسِدِينَ ٦٠ وَإِذْ قُلْتُمْ يَٰمُوسَىٰ لَن نَّصْبِرَ عَلَىٰ طَعَامٍ وَٰحِدٍ فَٱدْعُ لَنَا رَبَّكَ يُخْرِجْ لَنَا مِمَّا تُنۢبِتُ ٱلْأَرْضُ مِنۢ بَقْلِهَا وَقِثَّآئِهَا وَفُومِهَا وَعَدَسِهَا وَبَصَلِهَا ۖ قَالَ أَتَسْتَبْدِلُونَ ٱلَّذِى هُوَ أَدْنَىٰ بِٱلَّذِى هُوَ خَيْرٌ ۚ ٱهْبِطُواْ مِصْرًا فَإِنَّ لَكُم مَّا سَأَلْتُمْ ۗ وَضُرِبَتْ عَلَيْهِمُ ٱلذِّلَّةُ وَٱلْمَسْكَنَةُ وَبَآءُو بِغَضَبٍ مِّنَ ٱللَّهِ ۗ ذَٰلِكَ بِأَنَّهُمْ كَانُواْ يَكْفُرُونَ بِـَٔايَٰتِ ٱللَّهِ وَيَقْتُلُونَ ٱلنَّبِيِّـۧنَ بِغَيْرِ ٱلْحَقِّ ۗ ذَٰلِكَ بِمَا عَصَواْ وَّكَانُواْ يَعْتَدُونَ ۞ ٦١

And (remember) when Mūsā (Moses) said to his people: "O my people! Verily, you have wronged yourselves by worshipping the calf. So turn in repentance to your Creator and kill yourselves (the innocent kill the wrong doers among you), that will be better for you with your Creator." Then He accepted your repentance. Truly, He is the One Who accepts repentance, the Most Merciful. And (remember) when you said: "O Mūsā (Moses)! We shall never believe in you until we see Allāh plainly." But you were seized with a thunderbolt (lightning) while you were looking. Then We raised you up after your death, so that you might be grateful. And We shaded you with clouds and sent down on you *Al-Manna* and the quail, (saying): "Eat of the good lawful things We have provided for you," (but they rebelled). And they did not wrong Us but they wronged themselves. And (remember) when We said: "Enter this town (Jerusalem) and eat bountifully therein with pleasure and delight wherever you wish, and enter the gate in prostration (or bowing with humility) and say: 'Forgive us,' and We shall forgive you your sins and shall increase (reward) for the good-doers." But those who did wrong changed the word from that which had been told to them for another, so We sent upon the wrong doers *Rijz* (a punishment) from the heaven because of their rebelling against Allāh's obedience. (*Tafsir At-Tabarī*) And (remember) when Mūsā (Moses) asked

103

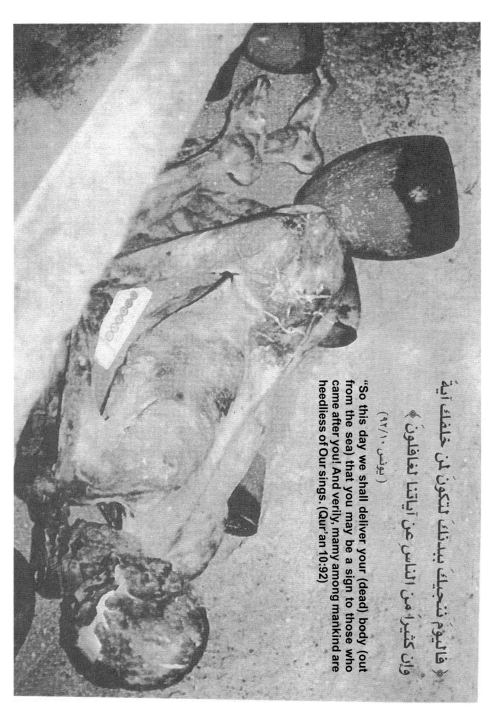

وَنَجَّيْنَاكَ بِبَدَنِكَ لِتَكُونَ لِمَنْ خَلْفَكَ آيَةً ﴿

﴾ وَإِنَّ كَثِيرًا مِنَ النَّاسِ عَنْ آيَاتِنَا لَغَافِلُونَ

(يونس/١٠/٩٢)

"So this day we shall deliver your (dead) body (out
from the sea) that you may be a sign to those who
came after you! And verily, mamy among mankind are
heediless of Our sings. (Qur'an 10:92)

Pharaoh Minfitah in the time of Musa (ﷺ)

for water for his people, We said: "Strike the stone with your stick." Then gushed forth therefrom twelve springs. Each (group of) people knew its own place for water. "Eat and drink of that which Allāh has provided and do not act corruptly, making mischief on the earth." And (remember) when you said, "O Mūsā (Moses)! We cannot endure one kind of food. So invoke your Lord for us to bring forth for us of what the earth grows, its herbs, its cucumbers, its *Fūm* (wheat or garlic), its lentils and its onions." He said, "Would you exchange that which is better for that which is worse? Go you down to any town and you shall find what you want!" And they were covered with humiliation and misery, and they drew on themselves the Wrath of Allāh. That was because they used to disbelieve the *Ayāt* (proofs, evidences, Verses, lessons, signs, revelations etc.) of Allāh and killed the Prophets wrongfully. That was because they disobeyed and used to transgress the bounds (in their disobedience to Allāh, i.e. commit crimes and sins).   (Qur'ân 2: 54-61)

Musa ﷺ left the capital city of the pharaohs in Egypt and, traveling through Sinai, headed towards the lands of Madyan (Midian). On his return journey, he had with him his wife, the daughter of Shu'aib ﷺ. Another significant event occurred during his return journey: Allâh spoke to him at At-Tûr. After that, he returned to Egypt. Musa's life coincided with the rule of the Pharaoh Merneptah (Minfitah), who ruled from the year 1230 before the start of the Christian calendar until the year 1215.

The famous crossing took place north of the Gulf of As-Suweis or in the Great Bitter Lakes which is where Minfitah drowned:

﴿فَٱلْيَوْمَ نُنَجِّيكَ بِبَدَنِكَ لِتَكُونَ لِمَنْ خَلْفَكَ ءَايَةً وَإِنَّ كَثِيرًا مِّنَ ٱلنَّاسِ عَنْ ءَايَٰتِنَا لَغَٰفِلُونَ ۞ (٩٢)﴾

So this day We shall deliver your (dead) body (out from the sea) that you may be a sign to those who come after you! And verily, many among mankind are heedless of Our *Ayāt* (proofs, evidences, Verses, lessons, signs, revelations, etc.).   (Qur'ân 10:92)

The Junction of the Two Seas

Musa Meeting with Al-Khidr

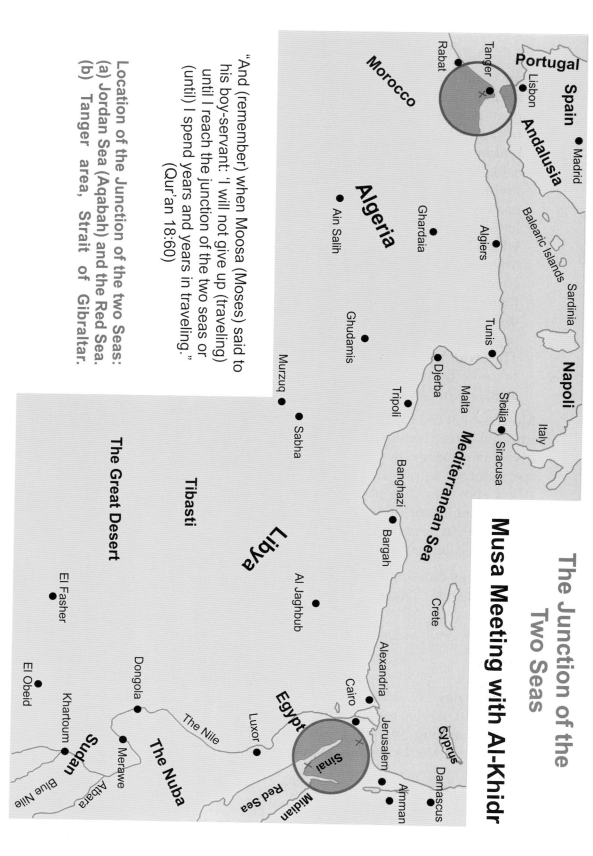

"And (remember) when Moosa (Moses) said to his boy-servant: 'I will not give up (traveling) until I reach the junction of the two seas or (until) I spend years and years in traveling.'"
(Qur'an 18:60)

Location of the Junction of the two Seas:
(a) Jordan Sea (Aqabah) and the Red Sea.
(b) Tanger area, Strait of Gibraltar.

- Mount At-Tûr is in fact Mount Horeb in Sinai.

- The well-known wilderness was in Sinai.

- The crossing of the Jordan River occurred at Ariha.

- In regards to the story of Al-Khidr, the location of the junction of the two seas is made clear in the following map.

After he died, Mûsa ﷺ was buried in Mount Nibu, which is situated east of the Dead Sea.

***

Hârûn ﷺ

And of course, the life of Hârûn ﷺ is closely linked with that of his brother, Musa ﷺ. Hârûn ﷺ is mentioned by name 20 times in the Noble Qur'ân:

Chapter Name (Sûrah)	Number of Chapter (Sûrah)	Verse Numbers
Al-Baqarah	2	248
An-Nisa'	4	163
Al-An'âm	6	84
Al-A'râf	7	122, 142
Yûnus	10	75
Maryam	19	28, 53
Ta-Ha	20	30, 70, 90, 92
Al-Anbiya'	21	48
Al-Mu'minûn	23	45
Al-Furqân	25	35

Chapter Name (Sûrah)	Number of Chapter (Sûrah)	Verse Numbers
Ash-Shu'arâ	26	13, 48
Al-Qisas	28	34
As-Saaffaat	37	114, 120

﴿وَوَاعَدْنَا مُوسَىٰ ثَلَٰثِينَ لَيْلَةً وَأَتْمَمْنَٰهَا بِعَشْرٍ فَتَمَّ مِيقَٰتُ رَبِّهِۦٓ أَرْبَعِينَ لَيْلَةً ۚ وَقَالَ مُوسَىٰ لِأَخِيهِ هَٰرُونَ ٱخْلُفْنِى فِى قَوْمِى وَأَصْلِحْ وَلَا تَتَّبِعْ سَبِيلَ ٱلْمُفْسِدِينَ ۝١٤٢﴾

And We appointed for Mūsā (Moses) thirty nights and added (to the period) ten (more), and he completed the term, appointed by his Lord, of forty nights. And Mūsā (Moses) said to his brother Hārūn (Aaron): "Replace me among my people, act in the right way (by ordering the people to obey Allāh and to worship Him Alone) and follow not the way of the *Mufsidūn* (mischief-makers)." (Qur'ân 7: 142)

﴿قَالَ فَإِنَّا قَدْ فَتَنَّا قَوْمَكَ مِنۢ بَعْدِكَ وَأَضَلَّهُمُ ٱلسَّامِرِىُّ ۝٨٥ فَرَجَعَ مُوسَىٰٓ إِلَىٰ قَوْمِهِۦ غَضْبَٰنَ أَسِفًا ۚ قَالَ يَٰقَوْمِ أَلَمْ يَعِدْكُمْ رَبُّكُمْ وَعْدًا حَسَنًا ۚ أَفَطَالَ عَلَيْكُمُ ٱلْعَهْدُ أَمْ أَرَدتُّمْ أَن يَحِلَّ عَلَيْكُمْ غَضَبٌ مِّن رَّبِّكُمْ فَأَخْلَفْتُم مَّوْعِدِى ۝٨٦ قَالُوا۟ مَآ أَخْلَفْنَا مَوْعِدَكَ بِمَلْكِنَا وَلَٰكِنَّا حُمِّلْنَآ أَوْزَارًا مِّن زِينَةِ ٱلْقَوْمِ فَقَذَفْنَٰهَا فَكَذَٰلِكَ أَلْقَى ٱلسَّامِرِىُّ ۝٨٧ فَأَخْرَجَ لَهُمْ عِجْلًا جَسَدًا لَّهُۥ خُوَارٌ فَقَالُوا۟ هَٰذَآ إِلَٰهُكُمْ وَإِلَٰهُ مُوسَىٰ فَنَسِىَ ۝٨٨ أَفَلَا يَرَوْنَ أَلَّا يَرْجِعُ إِلَيْهِمْ قَوْلًا وَلَا يَمْلِكُ لَهُمْ ضَرًّا وَلَا نَفْعًا ۝٨٩ وَلَقَدْ قَالَ لَهُمْ هَٰرُونُ مِن قَبْلُ يَٰقَوْمِ إِنَّمَا فُتِنتُم بِهِۦ ۖ وَإِنَّ رَبَّكُمُ ٱلرَّحْمَٰنُ فَٱتَّبِعُونِى وَأَطِيعُوٓا۟ أَمْرِى ۝٩٠ قَالُوا۟ لَن نَّبْرَحَ عَلَيْهِ عَٰكِفِينَ حَتَّىٰ يَرْجِعَ إِلَيْنَا مُوسَىٰ ۝٩١ قَالَ يَٰهَٰرُونُ مَا مَنَعَكَ إِذْ رَأَيْتَهُمْ ضَلُّوٓا۟ ۝٩٢ أَلَّا تَتَّبِعَنِ ۖ أَفَعَصَيْتَ أَمْرِى ۝٩٣ قَالَ يَبْنَؤُمَّ لَا تَأْخُذْ بِلِحْيَتِى وَلَا بِرَأْسِىٓ ۖ إِنِّى خَشِيتُ أَن تَقُولَ فَرَّقْتَ بَيْنَ بَنِىٓ إِسْرَٰٓءِيلَ وَلَمْ تَرْقُبْ قَوْلِى ۝٩٤﴾

(Allāh) said: "Verily, We have tried your people in your absence, and As-Sāmirī has led them astray." Then Mūsā

(Moses) returned to his people in a state of anger and sorrow. He said: "O my people! Did not your Lord promise you a fair promise? Did then the promise seem to you long in coming? Or did you desire that wrath should descend from your Lord on you, that you broke your promise to me (i.e. by disbelieving in Allāh and worshipping the calf)?" They said: "We broke not the promise to you, of our own will, but we were made to carry the weight of the ornaments of the [Fir'aun's (Pharaoh)] people, then we cast them (into the fire), and that was what As-Sāmirī did." Then he took out (of the fire) for them (a statue of) a calf which seemed to low. They said: "This is your *ilāh* (god), and the *ilāh* (god) of Mūsā (Moses), but he [Mūsā (Moses)] has forgotten (his god)." Did they not see that it could not return them a word (for answer), and that it had no power either to harm them or to do them good? And Hārūn (Aaron) indeed had said to them before-hand: "O my people! You are being tried in this, and verily, your Lord is (Allāh) the Most Gracious, so follow me and obey my order." They said: "We will not stop worshipping it (i.e. the calf), until Mūsā (Moses) returns to us." [Mūsā (Moses)] said: "O Hārūn (Aaron)! What prevented you when you saw them going astray; that you followed me not (according to my advice to you)? Have you then disobeyed my order?" He [Hārūn (Aaron)] said: "O son of my mother! Seize (me) not by my beard, nor by my head! Verily, I feared lest you should say: 'You have caused a division among the Children of Israel, and you have not respected my word!' " (Qur'ân 20: 85-94)

Of the two Prophet brothers, Hârûn ﷺ was the first to die. He was buried in Mount Haur, one of the mountains of Sinai.

- Târikh Ash-Sharq Al-Adna Al-Qadim: 62, 64
- Qisas Al-Anbiya, by Ibn Kathir: 231
- Qisas Al-Anbiya, by Ath-Tha'labi: 168
- Qisas Al-Anbiya, by At-Tabari: 259
- Qisas Al-Anbiya, by An-Najjâr: 155
- Al-Mo'jam Al-Mufahris Li-Alfâz Al-Qur'ân Al-Karim: 680, 736
- Al-Mo'jam Al-Mufahris Li-Ma'âni Al-Qur'ân Al-Karim: 1159, 1274

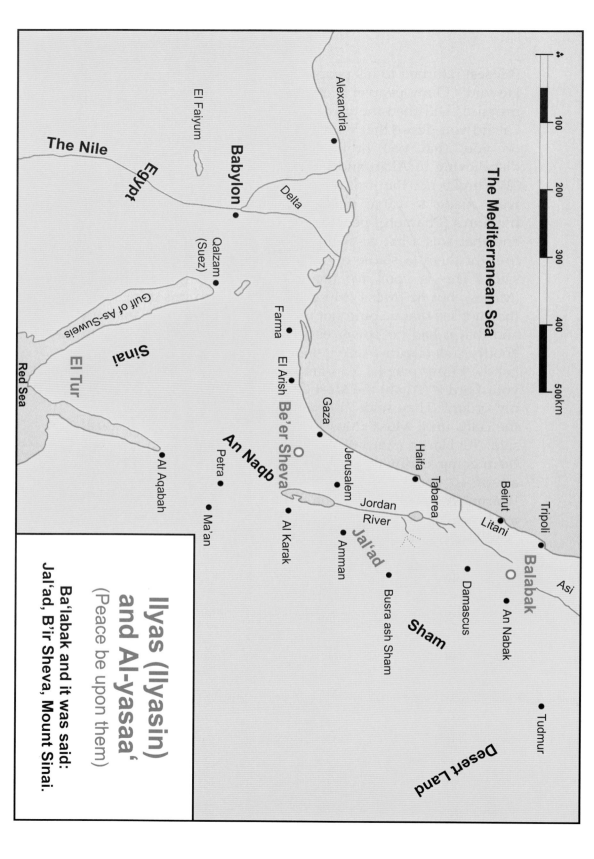

Ilyas (Ilyasin) and Al-yasaa'
(Peace be upon them)

Ba'labak and it was said:
Jal'ad, B'ir Sheva, Mount Sinai.

Ilyâs ﷺ and Al-Yasaa' ﷺ

Ilyâs ﷺ is twice mentioned by name in the Noble Qur'ân:

Chapter Name (Sûrah)	Number of Chapter (Sûrah)	Verse Numbers
Al-An'âm	6	85
As-Sâffât	37	123

﴿وَزَكَرِيَّا وَيَحْيَىٰ وَعِيسَىٰ وَإِلْيَاسَّ كُلٌّ مِّنَ ٱلصَّٰلِحِينَ ٨٥﴾

And Zakariyyā (Zechariah), and Yahyā (John) and 'Īsā (Jesus) and Ilyās (Elias), each one of them was of the righteous.

(Qur'ân 6: 85)

﴿وَإِنَّ إِلْيَاسَ لَمِنَ ٱلْمُرْسَلِينَ ١٢٣﴾

And verily, Ilyās (Elias) was one of the Messengers.

(Qur'ân 37: 123)

﴿وَتَرَكْنَا عَلَيْهِ فِي ٱلْآخِرِينَ ١٢٩ سَلَٰمٌ عَلَىٰ إِلْ يَاسِينَ ١٣٠﴾

And We left for him (a goodly remembrance) among the later generations. "*Salām* (peace) be upon Ilyāsīn (Elias)!"

(Qur'ân 37: 129, 130)

And Al-Yasaa' is also mentioned twice in the Noble Qur'ân:

Chapter Name (Sûrah)	Number of Chapter (Sûrah)	Verse Numbers
Al-An'âm	6	86
Sâd	38	48

﴿ وَإِسْمَٰعِيلَ وَٱلْيَسَعَ وَيُونُسَ وَلُوطاً وَكُلّاً فَضَّلْنَا عَلَى ٱلْعَٰلَمِينَ ٨٦ ﴾

And Ismā'īl (Ishmael) and Al-Yasaa' (Elisha), and Yūnus (Jonah) and Lūt (Lot), and each one of them We preferred to the 'Ālamīn [mankind and jinn (of their times)].

(Qur'ân 6: 86)

﴿ وَٱذْكُرْ إِسْمَٰعِيلَ وَٱلْيَسَعَ وَذَا ٱلْكِفْلِ وَكُلٌّ مِنَ ٱلْأَخْيَارِ ٤٨ ﴾

And remember Ismā'īl (Ishmael), Al-Yasaa' (Elisha), and Dhul-Kifl (Isaiah), all are among the best.

(Qur'ân 38: 48)

Both Ilyâs and Al-Yasaa' lived and died in the land of Ba'labak (Heliopolis: The City of the Sun).

- Al-Qamus Al-Islami: 1/169, 170
- Qisas Al-Anbiya, by Ibn Kathir: 353
- Qisas Al-Anbiya, by Ath-Tha'labi: 261
- Al-Mo'jam Al-Mufahris Li-Alfâz Al-Qur'ân Al-Karim: 75, 773
- Al-Mo'jam Al-Mufahris Li-Ma'âni Al-Qur'ân Al-Karim: 146, 1332

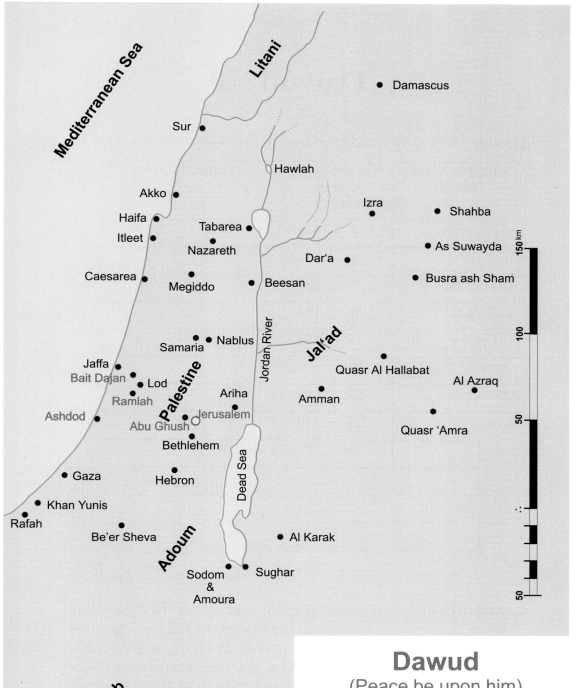

Mediterranean Sea

Litani

● Damascus

Sur ●

Hawlah

Akko ●

Izra ●   ● Shahba

Haifa ●

Tabarea ●

Itleet ●

● As Suwayda

Nazareth

Dar'a ●

● Busra ash Sham

Caesarea ●

Megiddo ●   ● Beesan

Jordan River

Jal'ad

Samaria ● ● Nablus

Jaffa ●

Quasr Al Hallabat

Al Azraq ●

Bait Dajan

● Lod

Palestine

Ramlah

Ariha ●

Amman ●

Ashdod ●

Jerusalem

Abu Ghush ○

Quasr 'Amra

Bethlehem

Dead Sea

● Gaza

Hebron ●

● Khan Yunis

Rafah ●

Adoum

Be'er Sheva

● Al Karak

Sodom & Amoura   Sughar

An Naqb

Petra ●

Ma'an ●

150 km
100
50
50

Dawud
(Peace be upon him)

Ashdod, Bait Dajan, Abu Ghush, Jerusalem, Ramlah

Dawûd عليه السلام

Dawûd عليه السلام is mentioned by name 16 times in the Noble Qur'ân:

Chapter Name (Sûrah)	Number of Chapter (Sûrah)	Verse Numbers
Al-Baqarah	2	251
An-Nisa'	4	163
Al-Mâ'idah	5	78
Al-An'âm	6	84
Al-Isra'	17	55
Al-Anbiya'	21	78, 79
An-Naml	27	15, 16
Saba	34	10, 13
Sâd	38	17, 22, 24, 26, 30

﴿وَدَاوُدَ وَسُلَيْمَنَ إِذْ يَحْكُمَانِ فِي ٱلْحَرْثِ إِذْ نَفَشَتْ فِيهِ غَنَمُ ٱلْقَوْمِ وَكُنَّا لِحُكْمِهِمْ شَهِدِينَ ۞ فَفَهَّمْنَهَا سُلَيْمَنَ وَكُلًّا ءَاتَيْنَا حُكْمًا وَعِلْمًا وَسَخَّرْنَا مَعَ دَاوُدَ ٱلْجِبَالَ يُسَبِّحْنَ وَٱلطَّيْرَ وَكُنَّا فَعِلِينَ ۞ وَعَلَّمْنَهُ صَنْعَةَ لَبُوسٍ لَّكُمْ لِتُحْصِنَكُم مِّنۢ بَأْسِكُمْ فَهَلْ أَنتُمْ شَكِرُونَ ۞﴾

And (remember) Dāwūd (David) and Sulaimān (Solomon), when they gave judgement in the case of the field in which the sheep of certain people had pastured at night; and We were witness to their judgement. And We made Sulaimān (Solomon) to understand (the case); and to each of them We gave *Hukm* (right judgement of the affairs and Prophethood) and knowledge. And We subjected the mountains and the birds to

114

glorify Our Praises along with Dāwūd (David). And it was We Who were the doer (of all these things). And We taught him the making of metal coats of mail (for battles), to protect you in your fighting. Are you then grateful?

(Qur'ân 21: 78-80)

﴿وَلَقَدْ ءَاتَيْنَا دَاوُدَ مِنَّا فَضْلًا يَٰجِبَالُ أَوِّبِى مَعَهُۥ وَٱلطَّيْرَ وَأَلَنَّا لَهُ ٱلْحَدِيدَ ۞ أَنِ ٱعْمَلْ سَٰبِغَٰتٍ وَقَدِّرْ فِى ٱلسَّرْدِ وَٱعْمَلُواْ صَٰلِحًا إِنِّى بِمَا تَعْمَلُونَ بَصِيرٌ ۞﴾

And indeed We bestowed grace on Dāwūd (David) from Us (saying): "O you mountains! Glorify (Allāh) with him! And you birds (also)! And We made the iron soft for him." Saying: "Make you perfect coats of mail, and balance well the rings of chain armour, and work you (men) righteousness. Truly, I am All-Seer of what you do."

(Qur'ân 34: 10, 11)

Daawood عليه السلام fought the dwellers of Palestine at Ashdod, near Gaza. He was victorious, and the realm of his kingdom then expanded until it extended from Ailatul-'Aqabah until the Euphrates River. His grave is located on top of a mountain that lies somewhere between Jerusalem and Ar-Ramlah, after Abu Ghush. He died 963 years before the start of the Christian calendar.

- Qisas Al-Anbiya, by Ibn Kathir: 360
- Qisas Al-Anbiya, by Ath-Tha'labi: 277
- Qisas Al-Anbiya, by At-Tabari: 353
- Qisas Al-Anbiya, by An-Najjâr: 303
- Al-Mo'jam Al-Mufahris Li-Alfâz Al-Qur'ân Al-Karim: 264
- Al-Mo'jam Al-Mufahris Li-Ma'âni Al-Qur'ân Al-Karim: 417

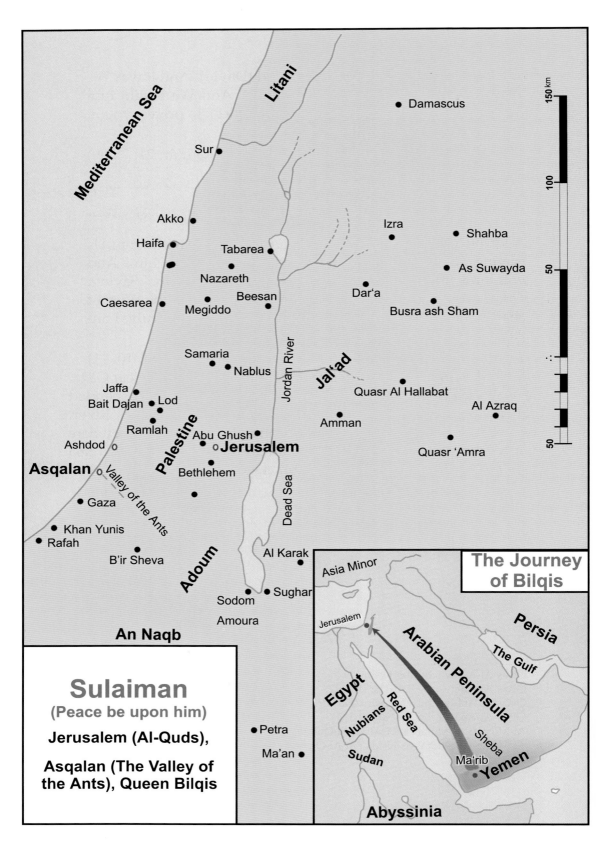

Mediterranean Sea

Litani

• Damascus

• Sur

• Akko

• Izra

• Shahba

• Haifa

• Tabarea

• As Suwayda

• Nazareth

• Caesarea

• Beesan

• Dar'a

• Megiddo

• Busra ash Sham

• Samaria

Jordan River

Jal'ad

• Nablus

• Quasr Al Hallabat

• Al Azraq

• Jaffa

• Lod

Bait Dajan

Palestine

• Amman

• Ramlah

Abu Ghush

Ashdod ○

○ Jerusalem

Asqalan ○

Valley of the Ants

• Bethlehem

• Quasr 'Amra

Dead Sea

• Gaza

• Khan Yunis

• Rafah

• B'ir Sheva

Adoum

• Al Karak

An Naqb

• Sughar

Sodom

Amoura

Sulaiman
(Peace be upon him)

Jerusalem (Al-Quds),

Asqalan (The Valley of the Ants), Queen Bilqis

• Petra

Ma'an •

The Journey of Bilqis

Asia Minor

Jerusalem

Persia

Arabian Peninsula

The Gulf

Egypt

Red Sea

Nubians

Sheba

Sudan

Ma'rib

Yemen

Abyssinia

150 km

100

50

50

Sulaimân عليه السلام

Sulaimaan عليه السلام is mentioned by name 17 times in the Noble Qur'ân:

Chapter Name (Sûrah)	Number of Chapter (Sûrah)	Verse Numbers
Al-Baqarah	2	102 (twice)
An-Nisa'	4	163
Al-An'âm	6	84
Al-Anbiya'	21	78, 79, 81
An-Naml	27	15, 16, 17, 18, 30, 36, 44
Saba	34	12
Sâd	38	30, 34

﴿وَلَقَدْ ءَاتَيْنَا دَاوُدَ وَسُلَيْمَـٰنَ عِلْمًا وَقَالَا ٱلْحَمْدُ لِلَّهِ ٱلَّذِى فَضَّلَنَا عَلَىٰ كَثِيرٍ مِّنْ عِبَادِهِ ٱلْمُؤْمِنِينَ ﴿١٥﴾ وَوَرِثَ سُلَيْمَـٰنُ دَاوُدَ وَقَالَ يَـٰٓأَيُّهَا ٱلنَّاسُ عُلِّمْنَا مَنطِقَ ٱلطَّيْرِ وَأُوتِينَا مِن كُلِّ شَىْءٍ إِنَّ هَـٰذَا لَهُوَ ٱلْفَضْلُ ٱلْمُبِينُ ﴿١٦﴾ وَحُشِرَ لِسُلَيْمَـٰنَ جُنُودُهُۥ مِنَ ٱلْجِنِّ وَٱلْإِنسِ وَٱلطَّيْرِ فَهُمْ يُوزَعُونَ ﴿١٧﴾ حَتَّىٰٓ إِذَآ أَتَوْا۟ عَلَىٰ وَادِ ٱلنَّمْلِ قَالَتْ نَمْلَةٌ يَـٰٓأَيُّهَا ٱلنَّمْلُ ٱدْخُلُوا۟ مَسَـٰكِنَكُمْ لَا يَحْطِمَنَّكُمْ سُلَيْمَـٰنُ وَجُنُودُهُۥ وَهُمْ لَا يَشْعُرُونَ ﴿١٨﴾ فَتَبَسَّمَ ضَاحِكًا مِّن قَوْلِهَا وَقَالَ رَبِّ أَوْزِعْنِىٓ أَنْ أَشْكُرَ نِعْمَتَكَ ٱلَّتِىٓ أَنْعَمْتَ عَلَىَّ وَعَلَىٰ وَٰلِدَىَّ وَأَنْ أَعْمَلَ صَـٰلِحًا تَرْضَىٰهُ وَأَدْخِلْنِى بِرَحْمَتِكَ فِى عِبَادِكَ ٱلصَّـٰلِحِينَ ﴿١٩﴾ وَتَفَقَّدَ ٱلطَّيْرَ فَقَالَ مَا لِىَ لَآ أَرَى ٱلْهُدْهُدَ أَمْ كَانَ مِنَ ٱلْغَآئِبِينَ ﴿٢٠﴾ لَأُعَذِّبَنَّهُۥ عَذَابًا شَدِيدًا أَوْ لَأَا۟ذْبَحَنَّهُۥٓ أَوْ لَيَأْتِيَنِّى بِسُلْطَـٰنٍ مُّبِينٍ ﴿٢١﴾ فَمَكَثَ غَيْرَ بَعِيدٍ فَقَالَ أَحَطتُ بِمَا لَمْ تُحِطْ بِهِۦ وَجِئْتُكَ مِن سَبَإٍۭ بِنَبَإٍ يَقِينٍ ﴿٢٢﴾ إِنِّى وَجَدتُّ ٱمْرَأَةً تَمْلِكُهُمْ وَأُوتِيَتْ مِن كُلِّ شَىْءٍ وَلَهَا عَرْشٌ عَظِيمٌ ﴿٢٣﴾ وَجَدتُّهَا وَقَوْمَهَا يَسْجُدُونَ لِلشَّمْسِ مِن دُونِ ٱللَّهِ وَزَيَّنَ لَهُمُ ٱلشَّيْطَـٰنُ أَعْمَـٰلَهُمْ فَصَدَّهُمْ عَنِ ٱلسَّبِيلِ

And indeed We gave knowledge to Dāwūd (David) and Sulaimān (Solomon), and they both said: "All praise and thanks are Allāh's, Who has preferred us above many of His believing slaves!" And Sulaimān (Solomon) inherited (the knowledge of) Dāwūd (David). He said: "O mankind! We have been taught the language of birds, and on us have been bestowed all things. This, verily, is an evident grace (from Allāh)." And there were gathered before Sulaimān (Solomon) his hosts of jinn and men, and birds, and they all were set in battle order (marching forward). Till, when they came to the valley of the ants, one of the ants said: "O ants! Enter your dwellings, lest Sulaimān (Solomon) and his hosts should crush you, while they perceive not." So he [Sulaimān (Solomon)] smiled, amused at her speech and said: "My Lord! Grant me the power and ability that I may be grateful for Your Favours which You have bestowed on me and on my parents, and that I may do righteous good deeds that will please You, and admit me by Your Mercy among Your righteous slaves." He inspected the birds, and said: "What is the matter that I see not the hoopoe? Or is he among the absentees? I will surely punish him with a severe torment or slaughter him, unless he brings me a clear reason." But the hoopoe stayed not long, he (came up and) said: "I have grasped (the knowledge of a thing) which you have not grasped and I have come to you from Saba' (Sheba) with true news. I found a woman ruling over them, she has been given all things that could be possessed by any ruler of the earth, and she has a great throne. I found her and her people worshipping the sun instead of Allāh, and *Shaitān* (Satan) has made their deeds fair-seeming to them, and has barred them from (Allāh's) way, so they have no guidance."

(Qur'ân 27: 15-24)

﴿قَالَ سَنَنظُرُ أَصَدَقْتَ أَمْ كُنتَ مِنَ ٱلْكَٰذِبِينَ ﴿٢٧﴾ ٱذْهَب بِّكِتَٰبِى هَٰذَا فَأَلْقِهْ إِلَيْهِمْ ثُمَّ

118

تَوَلَّ عَنْهُمْ فَٱنظُرْ مَاذَا يَرْجِعُونَ ۝ قَالَتْ يَـٰٓأَيُّهَا ٱلْمَلَؤُا۟ إِنِّىٓ أُلْقِىَ إِلَىَّ كِتَـٰبٌ كَرِيمٌ ۝ إِنَّهُۥ مِن سُلَيْمَـٰنَ وَإِنَّهُۥ بِسْمِ ٱللَّهِ ٱلرَّحْمَـٰنِ ٱلرَّحِيمِ ۝ أَلَّا تَعْلُوا۟ عَلَىَّ وَأْتُونِى مُسْلِمِينَ ۝ قَالَتْ يَـٰٓأَيُّهَا ٱلْمَلَؤُا۟ أَفْتُونِى فِىٓ أَمْرِى مَا كُنتُ قَاطِعَةً أَمْرًا حَتَّىٰ تَشْهَدُونِ ۝ قَالُوا۟ نَحْنُ أُو۟لُوا۟ قُوَّةٍ وَأُو۟لُوا۟ بَأْسٍ شَدِيدٍ وَٱلْأَمْرُ إِلَيْكِ فَٱنظُرِى مَاذَا تَأْمُرِينَ ۝ قَالَتْ إِنَّ ٱلْمُلُوكَ إِذَا دَخَلُوا۟ قَرْيَةً أَفْسَدُوهَا وَجَعَلُوٓا۟ أَعِزَّةَ أَهْلِهَآ أَذِلَّةً وَكَذَٰلِكَ يَفْعَلُونَ ۝ وَإِنِّى مُرْسِلَةٌ إِلَيْهِم بِهَدِيَّةٍ فَنَاظِرَةٌۢ بِمَ يَرْجِعُ ٱلْمُرْسَلُونَ ۝ فَلَمَّا جَآءَ سُلَيْمَـٰنَ قَالَ أَتُمِدُّونَنِ بِمَالٍ فَمَآ ءَاتَىٰنِۦَ ٱللَّهُ خَيْرٌ مِّمَّآ ءَاتَىٰكُم بَلْ أَنتُم بِهَدِيَّتِكُمْ تَفْرَحُونَ ۝ ٱرْجِعْ إِلَيْهِمْ فَلَنَأْتِيَنَّهُم بِجُنُودٍ لَّا قِبَلَ لَهُم بِهَا وَلَنُخْرِجَنَّهُم مِّنْهَآ أَذِلَّةً وَهُمْ صَـٰغِرُونَ ۝ قَالَ يَـٰٓأَيُّهَا ٱلْمَلَؤُا۟ أَيُّكُمْ يَأْتِينِى بِعَرْشِهَا قَبْلَ أَن يَأْتُونِى مُسْلِمِينَ ۝ قَالَ عِفْرِيتٌ مِّنَ ٱلْجِنِّ أَنَا۠ ءَاتِيكَ بِهِۦ قَبْلَ أَن تَقُومَ مِن مَّقَامِكَ وَإِنِّى عَلَيْهِ لَقَوِىٌّ أَمِينٌ ۝ قَالَ ٱلَّذِى عِندَهُۥ عِلْمٌ مِّنَ ٱلْكِتَـٰبِ أَنَا۠ ءَاتِيكَ بِهِۦ قَبْلَ أَن يَرْتَدَّ إِلَيْكَ طَرْفُكَ فَلَمَّا رَءَاهُ مُسْتَقِرًّا عِندَهُۥ قَالَ هَـٰذَا مِن فَضْلِ رَبِّى لِيَبْلُوَنِىٓ ءَأَشْكُرُ أَمْ أَكْفُرُ وَمَن شَكَرَ فَإِنَّمَا يَشْكُرُ لِنَفْسِهِۦ وَمَن كَفَرَ فَإِنَّ رَبِّى غَنِىٌّ كَرِيمٌ ۝ قَالَ نَكِّرُوا۟ لَهَا عَرْشَهَا نَنظُرْ أَتَهْتَدِىٓ أَمْ تَكُونُ مِنَ ٱلَّذِينَ لَا يَهْتَدُونَ ۝ فَلَمَّا جَآءَتْ قِيلَ أَهَـٰكَذَا عَرْشُكِ قَالَتْ كَأَنَّهُۥ هُوَ وَأُوتِينَا ٱلْعِلْمَ مِن قَبْلِهَا وَكُنَّا مُسْلِمِينَ ۝ وَصَدَّهَا مَا كَانَت تَّعْبُدُ مِن دُونِ ٱللَّهِ إِنَّهَا كَانَتْ مِن قَوْمٍ كَـٰفِرِينَ ۝ قِيلَ لَهَا ٱدْخُلِى ٱلصَّرْحَ فَلَمَّا رَأَتْهُ حَسِبَتْهُ لُجَّةً وَكَشَفَتْ عَن سَاقَيْهَا قَالَ إِنَّهُۥ صَرْحٌ مُّمَرَّدٌ مِّن قَوَارِيرَ قَالَتْ رَبِّ إِنِّى ظَلَمْتُ نَفْسِى وَأَسْلَمْتُ مَعَ سُلَيْمَـٰنَ لِلَّهِ رَبِّ ٱلْعَـٰلَمِينَ ۝

[Sulaimān (Solomon)] said: "We shall see whether you speak the truth or you are (one) of the liars. Go you with this letter of mine and deliver it to them, then draw back from them and see what (answer) they return." She said: "O chiefs! Verily, here is delivered to me a noble letter, Verily, it is from Sulaimān (Solomon), and verily, it (reads): 'In the Name of Allāh, the Most Gracious, the Most Merciful. Be you not exalted against me, but come to me as Muslims (true believers who submit to Allāh with full submission).' " She said: "O chiefs! Advise me in (this) case of mine. I decide no case till you are present with me (and give me your opinions)." They said: "We have great strength, and great ability for war, but it is for you to

119

command; so think over what you will command." She said: "Verily, kings, when they enter a town (country), they despoil it and make the most honorable amongst its people the lowest. And thus they do. But verily, I am going to send him a present, and see with what (answer) the messengers return." So, when (the messengers with the present) came to Sulaimān (Solomon), he said: "Will you help me in wealth? What Allāh has given me is better than that which He has given you! Nay, you rejoice in your gift!" [Then Sulaimān (Solomon) said to the chief of her messengers who brought the present]: "Go back to them. We verily, shall come to them with hosts that they cannot resist, and we shall drive them out from there in disgrace, and they will be abased." He said: "O chiefs! Which of you can bring me her throne before they come to me surrendering themselves in obedience?" An 'Ifrīt (strong one) from the jinn said: "I will bring it to you before you rise from your place (council). And verily, I am indeed strong and trustworthy for such work." One with whom was knowledge of the Scripture said: "I will bring it to you within the twinkling of an eye!" Then when he [Sulaimān (Solomon)] saw it placed before him, he said: "This is by the Grace of my Lord — to test me whether I am grateful or ungrateful! And whoever is grateful, truly, his gratitude is for (the good of) his own self; and whoever is ungrateful, (he is ungrateful only for the loss of his own self). Certainly my Lord is Rich (Free of all needs), Bountiful." He said: "Disguise her throne for her that we may see whether she will be guided (to recognise her throne), or she will be one of those not guided." So when she came, it was said (to her): "Is your throne like this?" She said: "(It is) as though it were the very same." And [Sulaimān (Solomon) said]: "Knowledge was bestowed on us before her, and we were submitted to Allāh (in Islam as Muslims before her)." And that which she used to worship besides Allāh has prevented her (from Islam), for she was of a disbelieving people. It was said to her: "Enter As-Sarh" (a glass surface with water underneath it or a palace): but when she saw it, she thought it was a pool, and she (tucked up her clothes) uncovering her legs. Sulaimān (Solomon) said: "Verily, it is a *Sarh* (a glass surface with water underneath it or a palace)." She said: "My Lord! Verily, I have wronged myself, and I submit [in Islam, together with Sulaimān (Solomon)] to Allāh, the Lord of the *'Ālamīn* (mankind, jinn and all that exists)."

(Qur'ân 27: 27-44)

By the permission of Allâh ﷻ, Sulaimân ﷺ was able to control the winds, thus enabling his trading vessels to travel at super fast speeds in the sea. It is said that he would leave from Jerusalem, take a day nap at Istakhr, and then spend the night at Khurasan; however, this claim is not founded on any reliable narration.

- The valley of the ants is situated in front of 'Asqalân, between Ashdod and Gaza.

- Sulaimân ﷺ is also remembered for the famous story involving him and the queen of Yemen, Sheba (Bilqis).

Sulaimân ﷺ died in Jerusalem, 923 years before the commencement of the Christian calendar, and he was buried there as well.

***

It is interesting to note here that the Al-Kan'âniyyin Arabs lived in the land of Kan'ân, otherwise known as Palestine, at least 2500 years before the commencement of the Christian calendar. It was approximately 1200 years after they settled there that Musa ﷺ and his people migrated to the same land. Then because of the weakness and division of the Al-Kan'âniyyin, Yashu' ibn Nun established a presence there.

Then Talût (Saul) gathered an army in order to fight the inhabitants of Palestine, who were led by Jalût (Goliath). During the army's march towards Palestine, Talût forbade his soldiers from drinking

- Qisas Al-Anbiya, by Ibn Kathir: 371
- Qisas Al-Anbiya, by Ath-Tha'labi: 294
- Qisas Al-Anbiya, by At-Tabari: 362
- Qisas Al-Anbiya, by An-Najjâr: 317
- Al-Mo'jam Al-Mufahris Li-Alfâz Al-Qur'ân Al-Karim: 358
- Al-Mo'jam Al-Mufahris Li-Ma'âni Al-Qur'ân Al-Karim: 583

any water from the Jordan River. They disobeyed his order: Other than of a few among them who abstained and remained patient, they drank from the river. And when they reached their destination, they said, "We have no power today to fight Jalût and his forces." Jalût then demanded that someone from the opposing army should come out to duel with him. Dâwûd ﷺ, who was an ordinary soldier in the army of Talût, came forward and accepted the challenge. He pelted Jalût with a stone, which struck Jalût in the forehead. Dâwûd ﷺ then tûk Jalût's sword from him and severed his head with it. The forces of Jalût were then defeated.

Talût then promised Dâwûd ﷺ to marry him to his daughter, Mikâl; and to make him the chief of his army. But then Talût tried to break his promise, and he began to plot against Dawûd ﷺ. Dawûd ﷺ was saved from his plotting, and that paved the way for Dawûd ﷺ becoming king of the Children of Israel.

- Jalût is mentioned by name three times in *Sûrat Baqarah* (2: 249, 250, 251)

- And Talût is twice mentioned by name in *Sûrat Baqarah* (2: 247, 249)

Dâwûd ﷺ occupied Jerusalem, along with a part of Canaan (Kan'ân) territory, 1000 years before the commencement of the Christian calendar. But another part of the Kan'ân territory remained in the hands of the Kan'âniyyûn. In the year 931 (before the commencement of the Christian calendar), the Hebrews separated into two entities:

First, Sâmirah, who lived in the north, and whose capital was Sabsatiyyah. The Āshûriyyun, under the leadership of Surjun the Second, destroyed them in the year 722 (before the commencement of the Christian calendar).

Second, Yahudha, who lived in the south, and whose capital was Jerusalem. The Kaldâniyyun, under the leadership of Nebuchadnezzar (Bukhtanassar), destroyed them in the year 586 (before the commencement of the Christian calendar). And some they took as slaves. What is important, though, is that both groups were wiped out from the area.

Throughout all of these happenings, the native dwellers of those lands never left, a fact that is even supported by texts in the Torah. These native dwellers had a strong influence on the culture, language, and customs of the Jews. Therefore, the presence of the Jews in Palestine was brief and incidental in the long history of that Arab land.

- Tarikh Ash-Sharq Al-Adna Al-Qadim: pg. 390 and what comes after it
- Al-Qamus Al-Islami: 1, 557 and 4/433
- Qisas Al-Anbiya, by Ath-Tha'labi: 272
- Qisas Al-Anbiya, by An-Najjâr: 305
- Mufassal Al-'Arab Wal-Yahud Fit-Târikh: pg. 565 and what comes after it

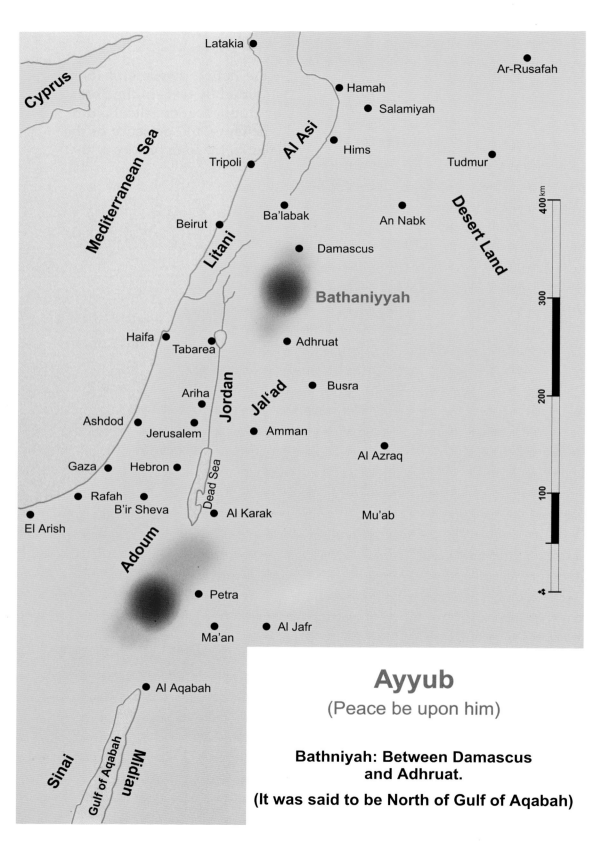

Cyprus

Latakia

Ar-Rusafah

Mediterranean Sea

Hamah

Salamiyah

Al Asi

Hims

Tudmur

Tripoli

Ba'labak

An Nabk

Desert Land

Beirut

Damascus

Litani

Bathaniyyah

Haifa

Adhruat

Tabarea

Jordan

Jal'ad

Busra

Ariha

Ashdod

Amman

Jerusalem

Gaza

Hebron

Al Azraq

Dead Sea

Rafah

B'ir Sheva

El Arish

Al Karak

Mu'ab

Adoum

Petra

Ma'an

Al Jafr

Ayyub

(Peace be upon him)

Al Aqabah

Sinai

Gulf of Aqabah

Midian

**Bathniyah: Between Damascus
and Adhruat.**

(It was said to be North of Gulf of Aqabah)

400 km

300

200

100

Ayyûb السلام عليه

Ayyûb عليه السلام is mentioned by name a total of 4 times in the Noble Qur'ân:

Chapter Name (Sûrah)	Number of Chapter (Sûrah)	Verse Numbers
Al-Baqarah	2	163
Al-An'âm	6	84
Al-Anbiya'	21	83
Sâd	37	41

﴿وَأَيُّوبَ إِذْ نَادَىٰ رَبَّهُ أَنِّي مَسَّنِيَ ٱلضُّرُّ وَأَنتَ أَرْحَمُ ٱلرَّٰحِمِينَ ٨٣ فَٱسْتَجَبْنَا لَهُ فَكَشَفْنَا مَا بِهِۦ مِن ضُرٍّ وَءَاتَيْنَٰهُ أَهْلَهُۥ وَمِثْلَهُم مَّعَهُمْ رَحْمَةً مِّنْ عِندِنَا وَذِكْرَىٰ لِلْعَٰبِدِينَ ٨٤﴾

And (remember) Ayyūb (Job), when he cried to his Lord: "Verily, distress has seized me, and You are the Most Merciful of all those who show mercy." So We answered his call, and We removed the distress that was on him, and We restored his family to him (that he had lost) and the like thereof along with them as a mercy from Ourselves and a Reminder for all those who worship Us.

(Qur'ân 21: 83, 84)

﴿وَٱذْكُرْ عَبْدَنَآ أَيُّوبَ إِذْ نَادَىٰ رَبَّهُۥٓ أَنِّي مَسَّنِيَ ٱلشَّيْطَٰنُ بِنُصْبٍ وَعَذَابٍ ٤١ ٱرْكُضْ بِرِجْلِكَ هَٰذَا مُغْتَسَلٌۢ بَارِدٌ وَشَرَابٌ ٤٢ وَوَهَبْنَا لَهُۥٓ أَهْلَهُۥ وَمِثْلَهُم مَّعَهُمْ رَحْمَةً مِّنَّا وَذِكْرَىٰ لِأُوْلِي ٱلْأَلْبَٰبِ ٤٣ وَخُذْ بِيَدِكَ ضِغْثًا فَٱضْرِب بِّهِۦ وَلَا تَحْنَثْ إِنَّا وَجَدْنَٰهُ صَابِرًا نِّعْمَ ٱلْعَبْدُ إِنَّهُۥٓ أَوَّابٌ ٤٤﴾

And remember Our slave Ayyūb (Job), when he invoked his

Lord (saying): "Verily, *Shaitān* (Satan) has touched me with distress (by ruining my health) and torment (by ruining my wealth)!" (Allāh said to him): "Strike the ground with your foot. This is (a spring of) water to wash in, cool and a (refreshing) drink." And We gave him (back) his family, and along with them the like thereof, as a Mercy from Us, and a Reminder for those who understand. "And take in your hand a bundle of thin grass and strike therewith (your wife), and break not your oath." Truly, We found him patient. How excellent a slave! Verily, he was ever oft-returning in repentance (to Us)!

(Qur'ân 38: 41-44)

Ayyûb ﷺ either lived in the land of 'Aus, beside Mount Sa'ir, or in the lands of Adoum, which are situated southwest of the Dead Sea and north of the Gulf of Al-'Aqabah. However, At-Tabari and Yâqût Al-Hamawi maintained that he either lived in Al-Bathaniyyah, between Damascus and Adhru'at, or on the outskirts of Damascus itself.

- Al-Qamus Al-Islami: 1/230
- Qisas Al-Anbiya, by At-Tabari: 214
- Qisas Al-Anbiya, by An-Najjâr: 249
- Al-Mo'jam Al-Mufahris Li-Alfâz Al-Qur'ân Al-Karim: 108
- Al-Mo'jam Al-Mufahris Li-Ma'âni Al-Qur'ân Al-Karim: 181

Damascus

Dhul-Kifl السَّلامُ عَلَيْه

Dhul-Kifl السَّلامُ عَلَيْه is twice mentioned by name in the Noble Qur'ân:

Chapter Name (Sûrah)	Number of Chapter (Sûrah)	Verse Numbers
Al-Anbiya'	21	85
Sâd	38	48

﴿وَإِسْمَاعِيلَ وَإِدْرِيسَ وَذَا ٱلْكِفْلِ كُلٌّ مِّنَ ٱلصَّابِرِينَ ۝ وَأَدْخَلْنَاهُمْ فِى رَحْمَتِنَآ إِنَّهُم مِّنَ ٱلصَّالِحِينَ ۝﴾

And (remember) Isma'il (Ishmael), Idrīs and Dhul-Kifl (Isaiah): all were from among *As-Sābirūn* (the patient). And We admitted them to Our Mercy. Verily, they were of the righteous.

(Qur'ân 21: 85, 86)

﴿وَٱذْكُرْ إِسْمَاعِيلَ وَٱلْيَسَعَ وَذَا ٱلْكِفْلِ وَكُلٌّ مِّنَ ٱلْأَخْيَارِ ۝﴾

And remember Isma'īl (Ishmael), Alyasâ' (Elisha), and Dhul-Kifl (Isaiah), all are among the best.

(Qur'ân 38: 48)

The name Dhul-Kifl is often juxtaposed with the names of the Prophets. For this and other reasons, most scholars maintain that Dhul-Kifl السَّلامُ عَلَيْه was in fact a Prophet. There are others, however, who maintain that he was not a Prophet, but was simply a righteous man, who was a just and wise judge. At-Tabari remained undecided, saying that he was not sure whether he was or wasn't a Prophet. Some people even claim that Dhul-Kifl السَّلامُ عَلَيْه was the son of Ayyûb السَّلامُ عَلَيْه. It is interesting to note that on Mount Qâsiyun, which overlooks Damascus from the north, is a place that has been named Dhul-Kifl.

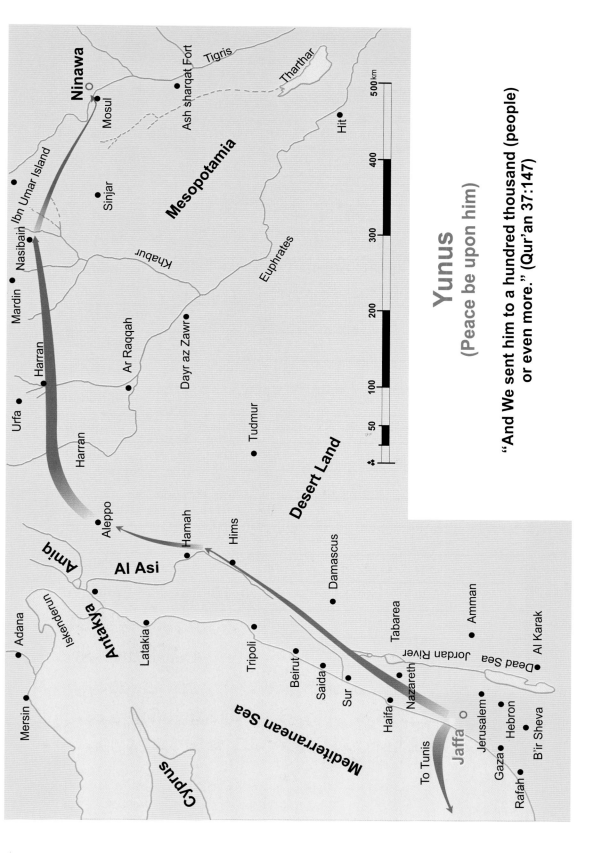

Ninawa

Tigris

Ash sharqat Fort

Tharthar

Mosul

Mesopotamia

Ibn Umar Island

Sinjar

Hit

Nasibain

Mardin

Khabur

Harran

Euphrates

Urfa

Harran

Ar Raqqah

Dayr az Zawr

Harran

Tudmur

Desert Land

50   100   200   300   400   500 km

Aleppo

Amiq

Al Asi

Hamah

Hims

Antakya

Iskenderun

Damascus

Adana

Latakia

Tripoli

Beirut

Saida

Tabarea

Amman

Mersin

Mediterranean Sea

Sur

Jordan River

Nazareth

Dead Sea

Al Karak

Haifa

Jerusalem

Cyprus

To Tunis

Jaffa

Gaza

Hebron

B'ir Sheva

Rafah

Yunus
(Peace be upon him)

"And We sent him to a hundred thousand (people) or even more." (Qur'an 37:147)

Yûnus عَلَيْهِ السَّلَام

Yûnus عَلَيْهِ السَّلَام is mentioned by name 4 times in the Noble Qur'ân:

Chapter Name (Sûrah)	Number of Chapter (Sûrah)	Verse Numbers
An-Nisa'	4	163
Al-An'âm	6	86
Yûnus	10	98
As-Sâffât	37	139

وَذَا ٱلنُّونِ إِذ ذَّهَبَ مُغَاضِبًا فَظَنَّ أَن لَّن نَّقْدِرَ عَلَيْهِ فَنَادَىٰ فِى ٱلظُّلُمَٰتِ أَن لَّآ إِلَٰهَ إِلَّآ أَنتَ سُبْحَٰنَكَ إِنِّى كُنتُ مِنَ ٱلظَّٰلِمِينَ ۝ فَٱسْتَجَبْنَا لَهُ وَنَجَّيْنَٰهُ مِنَ ٱلْغَمِّ وَكَذَٰلِكَ نُـۨجِى ٱلْمُؤْمِنِينَ ۝

And (remember) Dhun-Nūn [Yūnus (Jonah)], when he went off in anger, and imagined that We shall not punish him (i.e. the calamities which had befallen him)! But he cried through the darkness (saying): "Lā ilāhā illā Anta [none has the right to be worshipped but You (O Allāh)], Glorified (and Exalted) are You [above all that (evil) they associate with You]! Truly, I have been of the wrong doers." So, We answered his call, and delivered him from the distress. And thus We do deliver the believers (who believe in the Oneness of Allāh, abstain from evil and work righteousness).

(Qur'ân 21: 87, 88)

وَإِنَّ يُونُسَ لَمِنَ ٱلْمُرْسَلِينَ ۝ إِذْ أَبَقَ إِلَى ٱلْفُلْكِ ٱلْمَشْحُونِ ۝ فَسَاهَمَ فَكَانَ مِنَ ٱلْمُدْحَضِينَ ۝ فَٱلْتَقَمَهُ ٱلْحُوتُ وَهُوَ مُلِيمٌ ۝ فَلَوْلَآ أَنَّهُۥ كَانَ مِنَ ٱلْمُسَبِّحِينَ ۝ لَلَبِثَ فِى بَطْنِهِۦ إِلَىٰ يَوْمِ يُبْعَثُونَ ۝ فَنَبَذْنَٰهُ بِٱلْعَرَآءِ وَهُوَ سَقِيمٌ ۝ وَأَنۢبَتْنَا عَلَيْهِ شَجَرَةً مِّن

يَقْطِينٍ ﴿١٤٦﴾ وَأَرْسَلْنَٰهُ إِلَىٰ مِائَةِ أَلْفٍ أَوْ يَزِيدُونَ ﴿١٤٧﴾ فَآمَنُوا فَمَتَّعْنَٰهُمْ إِلَىٰ حِينٍ ﴿١٤٨﴾ ✾

And verily, Yūnus (Jonah) was one of the Messengers. When
he ran to the laden ship: Then he (agreed to) cast lots, and he
was among the losers. Then a (big) fish swallowed him as he
had done an act worthy of blame. Had he not been of them
who glorify Allāh, He would have indeed remained inside its
belly (the fish) till the Day of Resurrection. But We cast him
forth on the naked shore while he was sick, And We caused a
plant of gourd to grow over him. And We sent him to a
hundred thousand (people) or even more. And they believed;
so We gave them enjoyment for a while.

(Qur'ân 37: 139-148)

Wanting to flee to Tirshish (where Tunisia is located today), Younus
عليه السلام stayed at Yâfa (Jaffa). After his episode in the sea – when the
whale swallowed him, when he asked forgiveness from Allâh, and
when he was then expelled from the whale – he went to Ninawa,
near Mosul.

﴿وَأَرْسَلْنَٰهُ إِلَىٰ مِائَةِ أَلْفٍ أَوْ يَزِيدُونَ ﴿١٤٧﴾ فَآمَنُوا فَمَتَّعْنَٰهُمْ إِلَىٰ حِينٍ ﴿١٤٨﴾ ✾

And We sent him to a hundred thousand (people) or even
more. And they believed; so We gave them enjoyment for a
while.

(Qur'ân 37: 147, 148)

- Qisas Al-Anbiya, by Ibn Kathir: 225
- Qisas Al-Anbiya, by Ath-Tha'labi: 410
- Qisas Al-Anbiya, by At-Tabari: 221
- Qisas Al-Anbiya, by An-Najjâr: 362
- Al-Mo'jam Al-Mufahris Li-Alfâz Al-Qur'ân Al-Karim: 775
- Al-Mo'jam Al-Mufahris Li-Ma'âni Al-Qur'ân Al-Karim: 1360

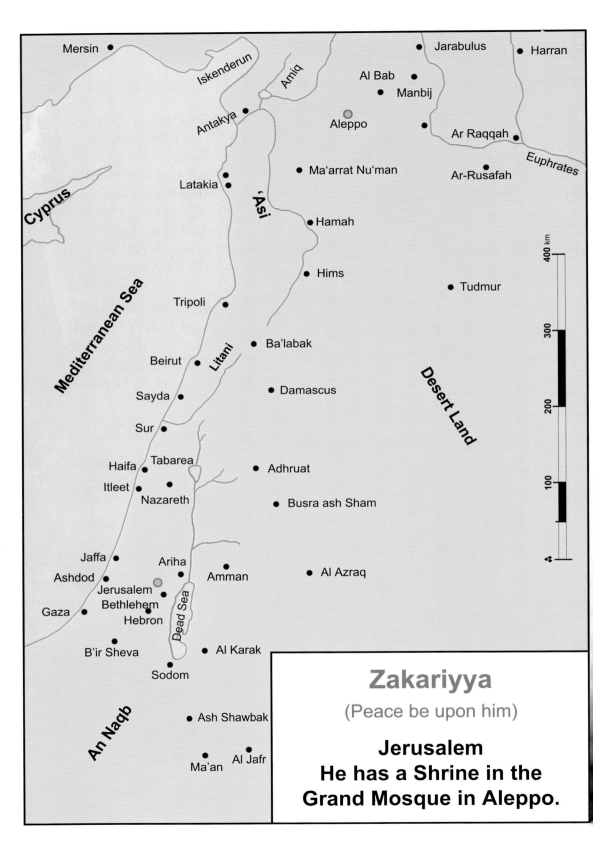

Mersin

Iskenderun

Amiq

Jarabulus

Harran

Al Bab

Manbij

Antakya

Aleppo

Ar Raqqah

Euphrates

Ma'arrat Nu'man

Ar-Rusafah

Latakia

'Asi

Cyprus

Hamah

Hims

Tudmur

Tripoli

Ba'labak

Mediterranean Sea

Litani

Beirut

Damascus

Desert Land

Sayda

Sur

Haifa

Tabarea

Adhruat

Itleet

Nazareth

Busra ash Sham

Jaffa

Ariha

Ashdod

Amman

Al Azraq

Jerusalem

Bethlehem

Dead Sea

Gaza

Hebron

B'ir Sheva

Al Karak

Sodom

An Naqb

Ash Shawbak

Ma'an

Al Jafr

400 km

300

200

100

Zakariyya

(Peace be upon him)

**Jerusalem
He has a Shrine in the
Grand Mosque in Aleppo.**

Zakariyyâ عَلَيْهِ السَّلَام

Zakariyyâ عَلَيْهِ السَّلَام is mentioned by name 7 times in the Noble Qur'ân:

Chapter Name (Sûrah)	Number of Chapter (Sûrah)	Verse Numbers
Āl-'Imrân	3	37 (twice), 38
Al-An'âm	6	85
Maryam	19	2, 7
Al-Anbiya'	21	89

﴿فَتَقَبَّلَهَا رَبُّهَا بِقَبُولٍ حَسَنٍ وَأَنبَتَهَا نَبَاتًا حَسَنًا وَكَفَّلَهَا زَكَرِيَّا كُلَّمَا دَخَلَ عَلَيْهَا زَكَرِيَّا ٱلْمِحْرَابَ وَجَدَ عِندَهَا رِزْقًا قَالَ يَٰمَرْيَمُ أَنَّىٰ لَكِ هَٰذَا قَالَتْ هُوَ مِنْ عِندِ ٱللَّهِ إِنَّ ٱللَّهَ يَرْزُقُ مَن يَشَاءُ بِغَيْرِ حِسَابٍ ﴿٣٧﴾ هُنَالِكَ دَعَا زَكَرِيَّا رَبَّهُۥ قَالَ رَبِّ هَبْ لِى مِن لَّدُنكَ ذُرِّيَّةً طَيِّبَةً إِنَّكَ سَمِيعُ ٱلدُّعَاءِ ﴿٣٨﴾ فَنَادَتْهُ ٱلْمَلَٰئِكَةُ وَهُوَ قَائِمٌ يُصَلِّى فِى ٱلْمِحْرَابِ أَنَّ ٱللَّهَ يُبَشِّرُكَ بِيَحْيَىٰ مُصَدِّقًا بِكَلِمَةٍ مِّنَ ٱللَّهِ وَسَيِّدًا وَحَصُورًا وَنَبِيًّا مِّنَ ٱلصَّٰلِحِينَ ﴿٣٩﴾ قَالَ رَبِّ أَنَّىٰ يَكُونُ لِى غُلَٰمٌ وَقَدْ بَلَغَنِىَ ٱلْكِبَرُ وَٱمْرَأَتِى عَاقِرٌ قَالَ كَذَٰلِكَ ٱللَّهُ يَفْعَلُ مَا يَشَاءُ ﴿٤٠﴾ قَالَ رَبِّ ٱجْعَل لِّىٓ ءَايَةً قَالَ ءَايَتُكَ أَلَّا تُكَلِّمَ ٱلنَّاسَ ثَلَٰثَةَ أَيَّامٍ إِلَّا رَمْزًا وَٱذْكُر رَّبَّكَ كَثِيرًا وَسَبِّحْ بِٱلْعَشِىِّ وَٱلْإِبْكَٰرِ ﴿٤١﴾﴾

So, her Lord (Allāh) accepted her with goodly acceptance. He made her grow in a good manner and put her under the care of Zakariyyā (Zechariah). Every time he entered *Al-Mihrāb* to (visit) her, he found her supplied with sustenance. He said: "O Maryam (Mary)! From where have you got this?" She said, "This is from Allāh." Verily, Allāh provides sustenance to whom He wills, without limit. At that time Zakariyyā (Zechariah) invoked his Lord, saying: "O my Lord! Grant me from You, a good offspring. You are indeed the All-Hearer of invocation." Then the angels called him, while he was standing in prayer in *Al-Mihrāb* (a praying place or a private room), (saying): "Allāh gives you glad tidings of Yahyā (John), confirming (believing in) the Word from Allāh [i.e. the creation of 'Īsā (Jesus) ﷺ, the Word from Allāh ("Be!" — and he was!)], noble, keeping away from sexual relations with women, a Prophet, from among the righteous." He said: "O my Lord! How can I have a son when I am very old, and my wife is barren?" (Allāh) said: "Thus Allāh does what He wills." He said: "O my Lord! Make a sign for me." (Allāh) said: "Your sign is that you shall not speak to mankind for three days except with signals. And remember your Lord much (by praising Him again and again), and glorify (Him) in the afternoon and in the morning."

(Qur'ân 3: 37-41)

Zakariyyâ ﷺ was a carpenter. It is said that he died a natural death, but it is also said that he died in the incident in which his son, Yahya ﷺ, was killed in Jerusalem. There is a large monument for him in Haleb's (Aleppo) central gathering place.

- Qisas Al-Anbiya, by Ibn Kathir: 404
- Qisas Al-Anbiya, by Ath-Tha'labi: 373
- Qisas Al-Anbiya, by At-Tabari: 441
- Qisas Al-Anbiya, by An-Najjâr: 368
- Al-Mo'jam Al-Mufahris Li-Alfâz Al-Qur'ân Al-Karim: 331
- Al-Mo'jam Al-Mufahris Li-Ma'âni Al-Qur'ân Al-Karim: 532

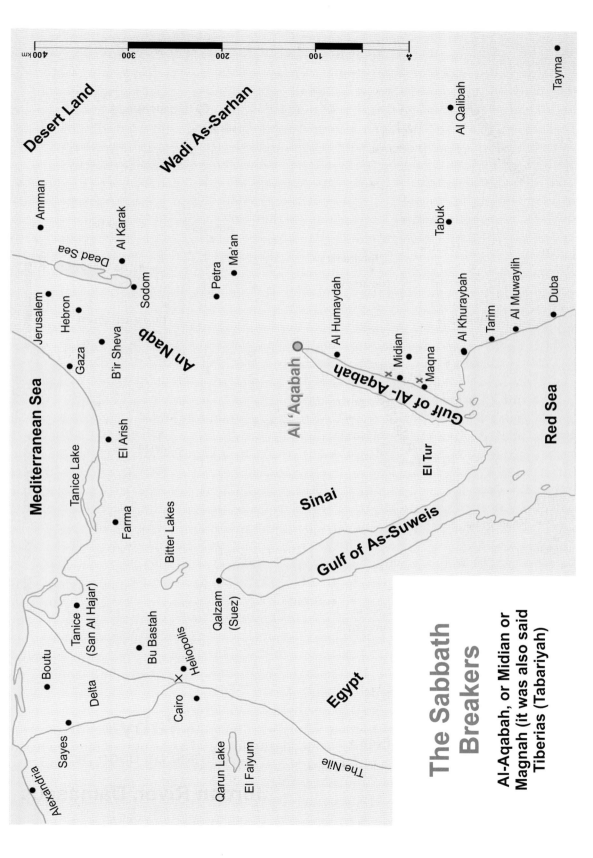

The Sabbath Breakers

Al-'Aqabah, or Midian or Magnah (it was also said Tiberias (Tabariyah)

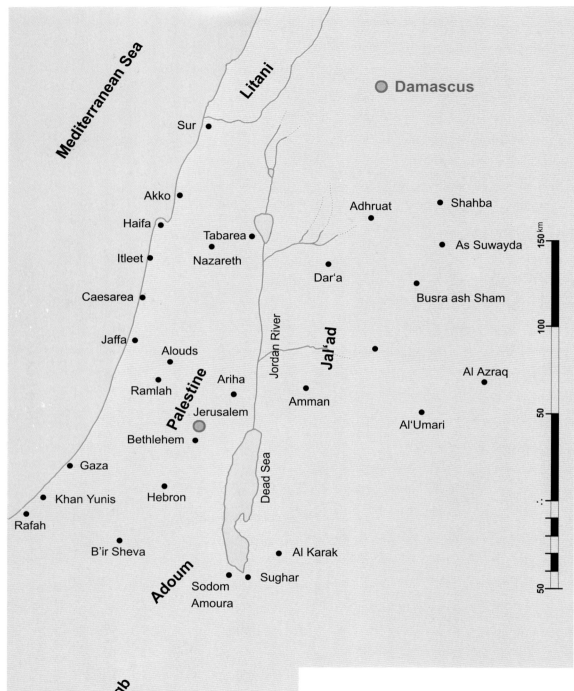

Mediterranean Sea

Litani

○ Damascus

Sur

Akko

Haifa

Tabarea

Itleet

Nazareth

Adhruat

Shahba

As Suwayda

Dar'a

Caesarea

Busra ash Sham

Jaffa

Alouds

Jordan River

Jal'ad

Ramlah

Ariha

Palestine

Jerusalem

Amman

Al Azraq

Bethlehem

Al'Umari

Gaza

Dead Sea

Khan Yunis

Hebron

Rafah

B'ir Sheva

Al Karak

Adoum

Sodom

Sughar

Amoura

An Naqb

Petra

Ma'an

150 km

100

50

50

Yahya

(Peace be upon him)

Jordan River, Damascus

Yahyâ عَلَيْهِ السَّلَام

Yahyâ عَلَيْهِ السَّلَام is mentioned by name 5 times in the Noble Qur'ân:

Chapter Name (Sûrah)	Number of Chapter (Sûrah)	Verse Numbers
Āl-'Imrân	3	39
Al-An'âm	6	85
Maryam	19	7, 12
Al-Anbiya'	21	90

﴿يَـٰزَكَرِيَّآ إِنَّا نُبَشِّرُكَ بِغُلَـٰمٍ ٱسْمُهُ يَحْيَىٰ لَمْ نَجْعَل لَّهُۥ مِن قَبْلُ سَمِيًّا ۝ قَالَ رَبِّ أَنَّىٰ يَكُونُ لِى غُلَـٰمٌ وَكَانَتِ ٱمْرَأَتِى عَاقِرًا وَقَدْ بَلَغْتُ مِنَ ٱلْكِبَرِ عِتِيًّا ۝ قَالَ كَذَٰلِكَ قَالَ رَبُّكَ هُوَ عَلَىَّ هَيِّنٌ وَقَدْ خَلَقْتُكَ مِن قَبْلُ وَلَمْ تَكُ شَيْـًٔا ۝ قَالَ رَبِّ ٱجْعَل لِّىٓ ءَايَةً قَالَ ءَايَتُكَ أَلَّا تُكَلِّمَ ٱلنَّاسَ ثَلَـٰثَ لَيَالٍ سَوِيًّا ۝ فَخَرَجَ عَلَىٰ قَوْمِهِۦ مِنَ ٱلْمِحْرَابِ فَأَوْحَىٰٓ إِلَيْهِمْ أَن سَبِّحُوا۟ بُكْرَةً وَعَشِيًّا ۝ يَـٰيَحْيَىٰ خُذِ ٱلْكِتَـٰبَ بِقُوَّةٍ وَءَاتَيْنَـٰهُ ٱلْحُكْمَ صَبِيًّا ۝ وَحَنَانًا مِّن لَّدُنَّا وَزَكَوٰةً وَكَانَ تَقِيًّا ۝ وَبَرًّۢا بِوَٰلِدَيْهِ وَلَمْ يَكُن جَبَّارًا عَصِيًّا ۝ وَسَلَـٰمٌ عَلَيْهِ يَوْمَ وُلِدَ وَيَوْمَ يَمُوتُ وَيَوْمَ يُبْعَثُ حَيًّا ۝﴾

(Allāh said:) "O Zakariyyā (Zechariah)! Verily, We give you the glad tidings of a son, whose name will be Yahyā (John). We have given that name to none before (him)." He said: "My Lord! How can I have a son, when my wife is barren, and I have reached the extreme old age." He said: "So (it will be). Your Lord says: It is easy for Me. Certainly I have created you before, when you had been nothing!" [Zakariyyā (Zechariah)] said: "My Lord! Appoint for me a sign." He said: "Your sign is that you shall not speak to mankind for three nights, though having no bodily defect." Then he came out to his people from

Yahya's Monument (Umawi Masjid, Damascus)

Al-Miḥrāb (a praying place or a private room) and he told them by signs to glorify Allāh's Praises in the morning and in the afternoon. (It was said to his son): "O Yahyā (John)! Hold fast the Scripture [the Taurāt (Torah)]." And We gave him wisdom while yet a child. And (made him) sympathetic to men as a mercy (or a grant) from Us, and pure from sins [i.e. Yahyā (John)] and he was righteous, And dutiful towards his parents, and he was neither arrogant nor disobedient (to Allāh or to his parents). And *Salām* (peace) be on him the day he was born, and the day he dies, and the day he will be raised up to life (again)!

(Qur'ân 19: 7-15)

Yahyâ ﷺ baptized Messiah ﷺ at River Jordan, and so he is also called John the Beptist and Ma'madân.

Yahyâ ﷺ was killed upon a rock (Sakhrah) in Jerusalem, and his head was then taken to Damascus. The reason for his killing has to do with a king who wanted to marry one of his relatives. Yahyâ ﷺ refused his proposal, and bitter feelings then continued to fester in the man's heart. Later on, when the man ended up marrying the same woman, he sent someone to kill Yahyâ ﷺ. It is maintained by some that Yahyâ ﷺ was killed not in Jerusalem, but instead in Damascus. And until this day, there remains a monument for him in the Umawi Masjid.

- Qisas Al-Anbiya, by Ibn Kathir: 404
- Qisas Al-Anbiya, by Ath-Tha'labi: 377
- Qisas Al-Anbiya, by At-Tabari: 317
- Qisas Al-Anbiya, by An-Najjâr: 329
- Al-Mo'jam Al-Mufahris Li-Alfâz Al-Qur'ân Al-Karim: 225
- Al-Mo'jam Al-Mufahris Li-Ma'âni Al-Qur'ân Al-Karim: 1328

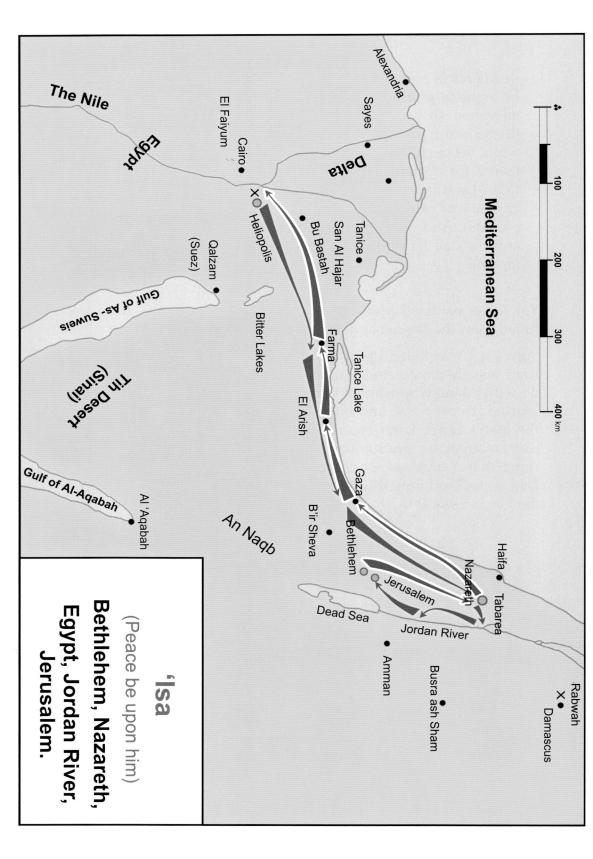

'Isa
(Peace be upon him)
Bethlehem, Nazareth,
Egypt, Jordan River,
Jerusalem.

'Īsâ السَّلَامُ عَلَيْهِ

'Īsâ السَّلَامُ عَلَيْهِ is mentioned very often in the Noble Qur'ân; as the charts below illustrate, he is mentioned by name ('Īsâ السَّلَامُ عَلَيْهِ) 25 times, by the title Al-Masih 11 times, and by the name Ibn Maryam (the son of Mary) 23 times.

1) Verses in which 'Īsâ السَّلَامُ عَلَيْهِ is mentioned by name:

Chapter Name (Sûrah)	Number of Chapter (Sûrah)	Verse Numbers
Al-Baqarah	2	87, 136, 253
Āl-'Imrân	3	45, 52, 55, 59, 84
An-Nisa'	4	157, 163, 171
Al-Mâ'idah	5	46, 78, 110, 112, 114, 116
Al-An'âm	6	85
Maryam	19	34
Al-Ahzâb	33	7
Ash-Shûra	42	13
Az-Zukhruf	43	63
Al-Hadid	57	27
As-Saff	61	6, 14

2) Verses in which he ﷺ is mentioned by the title, Al-Masih:

Chapter Name (Sûrah)	Number of Chapter (Sûrah)	Verse Numbers
Āl-'Imrân	3	45
An-Nisa'	4	157, 171, 172
Al-Mâ'idah	5	17 (twice), 72 (twice), 75
At-Taubah	9	30, 31

3) Verses in which he ﷺ is mentioned by the name Ibn Maryam:

Chapter Name (Sûrah)	Number of Chapter (Sûrah)	Verse Numbers
Al-Baqarah	2	87, 253
Āl-'Imrân	3	45
An-Nisa'	4	157, 171
Al-Mâ'idah	5	17 (twice), 46, 72, 75, 78, 110, 112, 114, 116
At-Taubah	9	31
Maryam	19	34
Al-Mu'minûn	23	50
Al-Ahzâb	33	7
Az-Zukhruf	43	57
Al-Hadid	57	27
As-Saff	61	6, 14

﴿إِنَّ مَثَلَ عِيسَىٰ عِندَ ٱللَّهِ كَمَثَلِ ءَادَمَ خَلَقَهُۥ مِن تُرَابٍ ثُمَّ قَالَ لَهُۥ كُن فَيَكُونُ ۝﴾

Verily, the likeness of 'Īsā (Jesus) before Allāh is the likeness of Adam. He created him from dust, then (He) said to him: "Be!"

— and he was.

(Qur'ân 3: 59)

﴿يَٰٓأَهْلَ ٱلْكِتَٰبِ لَا تَغْلُوا۟ فِى دِينِكُمْ وَلَا تَقُولُوا۟ عَلَى ٱللَّهِ إِلَّا ٱلْحَقَّ إِنَّمَا ٱلْمَسِيحُ عِيسَى ٱبْنُ مَرْيَمَ رَسُولُ ٱللَّهِ وَكَلِمَتُهُۥٓ أَلْقَىٰهَآ إِلَىٰ مَرْيَمَ وَرُوحٌ مِّنْهُ فَـَٔامِنُوا۟ بِٱللَّهِ وَرُسُلِهِۦ وَلَا تَقُولُوا۟ ثَلَٰثَةٌ ٱنتَهُوا۟ خَيْرًا لَّكُمْ إِنَّمَا ٱللَّهُ إِلَٰهٌ وَٰحِدٌ سُبْحَٰنَهُۥٓ أَن يَكُونَ لَهُۥ وَلَدٌ لَّهُۥ مَا فِى ٱلسَّمَٰوَٰتِ وَمَا فِى ٱلْأَرْضِ وَكَفَىٰ بِٱللَّهِ وَكِيلًا ﴿١٧١﴾﴾

O people of the Scripture (Christians)! Do not exceed the limits in your religion, nor say of Allāh aught but the truth. The Messiah ʿĪsā (Jesus), son of Maryam (Mary), was (no more than) a Messenger of Allāh and His Word, ("Be!" — and he was) which He bestowed on Maryam (Mary) and a spirit (*Rūh*) created by Him; so believe in Allāh and His Messengers. Say not: "Three (trinity)!" Cease! (it is) better for you. For Allāh is (the only) One *Ilāh* (God), Glorified is He (Far Exalted is He) above having a son. To Him belongs all that is in the heavens and all that is in the earth. And Allāh is All-Sufficient as a Disposer of affairs.

(Qur'ân 4: 171)

﴿وَرَسُولًا إِلَىٰ بَنِىٓ إِسْرَٰٓءِيلَ أَنِّى قَدْ جِئْتُكُم بِـَٔايَةٍ مِّن رَّبِّكُمْ أَنِّىٓ أَخْلُقُ لَكُم مِّنَ ٱلطِّينِ كَهَيْـَٔةِ ٱلطَّيْرِ فَأَنفُخُ فِيهِ فَيَكُونُ طَيْرًا بِإِذْنِ ٱللَّهِ وَأُبْرِئُ ٱلْأَكْمَهَ وَٱلْأَبْرَصَ وَأُحْىِ ٱلْمَوْتَىٰ بِإِذْنِ ٱللَّهِ وَأُنَبِّئُكُم بِمَا تَأْكُلُونَ وَمَا تَدَّخِرُونَ فِى بُيُوتِكُمْ إِنَّ فِى ذَٰلِكَ لَـَٔايَةً لَّكُمْ إِن كُنتُم مُّؤْمِنِينَ ﴿٤٩﴾﴾

And will make him [ʿĪsā (Jesus)] a Messenger to the Children of Israel (saying): "I have come to you with a sign from your Lord, that I design for you out of clay, a figure like that of a bird, and breathe into it, and it becomes a bird by Allāh's Leave; and I heal him who was born blind, and the leper, and I bring the dead to life by Allāh's Leave. And I inform you of what you eat, and what you store in your houses. Surely, in that is a sign for you, if you are believers. (Qur'ân 3: 49)

﴿فَأَشَارَتْ إِلَيْهِ قَالُوا كَيْفَ نُكَلِّمُ مَن كَانَ فِي ٱلْمَهْدِ صَبِيًّا ﴿٢٩﴾ قَالَ إِنِّي عَبْدُ ٱللَّهِ ءَاتَنِيَ ٱلْكِتَبَ وَجَعَلَنِي نَبِيًّا ﴿٣٠﴾ وَجَعَلَنِي مُبَارَكًا أَيْنَ مَا كُنتُ وَأَوْصَنِي بِٱلصَّلَوٰةِ وَٱلزَّكَوٰةِ مَا دُمْتُ حَيًّا ﴿٣١﴾ وَبَرًّا بِوَلِدَتِي وَلَمْ يَجْعَلْنِي جَبَّارًا شَقِيًّا ﴿٣٢﴾ وَٱلسَّلَمُ عَلَىَّ يَوْمَ وُلِدتُّ وَيَوْمَ أَمُوتُ وَيَوْمَ أُبْعَثُ حَيًّا ﴿٣٣﴾﴾

Then she pointed to him. They said: "How can we talk to one who is a child in the cradle?" He ['Īsā (Jesus)] said: "Verily, I am a slave of Allāh, He has given me the Scripture and made me a Prophet; and He has made me blessed wheresoever I be, and has enjoined on me *Salāt* (prayer) and *Zakāt* (obligatory charity), as long as I live. And dutiful to my mother, and made me not arrogant, unblest. And *Salām* (peace) be upon me the day I was born, and the day I die, and the day I shall be raised alive!"

(Qur'ân 19: 29-33)

﴿وَقَوْلِهِمْ إِنَّا قَتَلْنَا ٱلْمَسِيحَ عِيسَى ٱبْنَ مَرْيَمَ رَسُولَ ٱللَّهِ وَمَا قَتَلُوهُ وَمَا صَلَبُوهُ وَلَكِن شُبِّهَ لَهُمْ وَإِنَّ ٱلَّذِينَ ٱخْتَلَفُوا فِيهِ لَفِي شَكٍّ مِّنْهُ مَا لَهُم بِهِ مِنْ عِلْمٍ إِلَّا ٱتِّبَاعَ ٱلظَّنِّ وَمَا قَتَلُوهُ يَقِينًا ﴿١٥٧﴾ بَل رَّفَعَهُ ٱللَّهُ إِلَيْهِ وَكَانَ ٱللَّهُ عَزِيزًا حَكِيمًا ﴿١٥٨﴾ وَإِن مِّنْ أَهْلِ ٱلْكِتَبِ إِلَّا لَيُؤْمِنَنَّ بِهِ قَبْلَ مَوْتِهِ وَيَوْمَ ٱلْقِيَمَةِ يَكُونُ عَلَيْهِمْ شَهِيدًا ﴿١٥٩﴾﴾

And because of their saying (in boast), "We killed Messiah 'Īsā (Jesus), son of Maryam (Mary), the Messenger of Allāh," — but they killed him not, nor crucified him, but it appeared so to them [the resemblance of 'Īsā (Jesus) was put over another man (and they killed that man)], and those who differ therein are full of doubts. They have no (certain) knowledge, they follow nothing but conjecture. For surely, they killed him not [i.e. 'Īsā (Jesus), son of Maryam (Mary) ﷺ]: But Allāh raised him ['Īsā (Jesus)] up (with his body and soul) to Himself (and he ﷺ is in the heavens). And Allāh is Ever All-Powerful, All-Wise. And there is none of the people of the Scripture (Jews and Christians) but must believe in him ['Īsā (Jesus), son of Maryam (Mary), as only a Messenger of Allāh and a human

Bethlehem

An-Nasirah

being] before his ['Īsā (Jesus) ﷺ or a Jew's or a Christian's] death (at the time of the appearance of the angel of death). And on the Day of Resurrection, he ['Īsā (Jesus)] will be a witness against them.

(Qur'ân 4: 157-159)

﴿وَإِذْ قَالَ اللَّهُ يَٰعِيسَى ابْنَ مَرْيَمَ ءَأَنتَ قُلْتَ لِلنَّاسِ اتَّخِذُونِى وَأُمِّىَ إِلَٰهَيْنِ مِن دُونِ اللَّهِ قَالَ سُبْحَٰنَكَ مَا يَكُونُ لِى أَنْ أَقُولَ مَا لَيْسَ لِى بِحَقٍّ إِن كُنتُ قُلْتُهُ فَقَدْ عَلِمْتَهُ تَعْلَمُ مَا فِى نَفْسِى وَلَآ أَعْلَمُ مَا فِى نَفْسِكَ إِنَّكَ أَنتَ عَلَّٰمُ الْغُيُوبِ ۝ مَا قُلْتُ لَهُمْ إِلَّا مَا أَمَرْتَنِى بِهِۦ أَنِ اعْبُدُوا اللَّهَ رَبِّى وَرَبَّكُمْ وَكُنتُ عَلَيْهِمْ شَهِيدًا مَّا دُمْتُ فِيهِمْ فَلَمَّا تَوَفَّيْتَنِى كُنتَ أَنتَ الرَّقِيبَ عَلَيْهِمْ وَأَنتَ عَلَىٰ كُلِّ شَىْءٍ شَهِيدٌ ۝ إِن تُعَذِّبْهُمْ فَإِنَّهُمْ عِبَادُكَ وَإِن تَغْفِرْ لَهُمْ فَإِنَّكَ أَنتَ الْعَزِيزُ الْحَكِيمُ ۝﴾

And (remember) when Allāh will say (on the Day of Resurrection): "O 'Īsā (Jesus), son of Maryam (Mary)! Did you say to men: 'Worship me and my mother as two gods besides Allāh?'" He will say: "Glorified are You! It was not for me to say what I had no right (to say). Had I said such a thing, You would surely have known it. You know what is in my inner self though I do not know what is in Yours; truly, You, only You, are the All-Knower of all that is hidden (and unseen). Never did I say to them aught except what You (Allāh) did command me to say: 'Worship Allāh, my Lord and your Lord.' And I was a witness over them while I dwelt amongst them, but when You took me up, You were the Watcher over them; and You are a Witness to all things. (This is a great admonition and warning to the Christians of the whole world). If You punish them, they are Your slaves, and if You forgive them, verily, You, only You are the All-Mighty, the All-Wise."

(Qur'ân 5: 116-118)

﴿مَّا الْمَسِيحُ ابْنُ مَرْيَمَ إِلَّا رَسُولٌ قَدْ خَلَتْ مِن قَبْلِهِ الرُّسُلُ وَأُمُّهُ صِدِّيقَةٌ كَانَا يَأْكُلَانِ الطَّعَامَ انظُرْ كَيْفَ نُبَيِّنُ لَهُمُ الْآيَٰتِ ثُمَّ انظُرْ أَنَّىٰ يُؤْفَكُونَ ۝﴾

The Messiah ['Īsā (Jesus)], son of Maryam (Mary), was no more than a Messenger; many were the Messengers that passed away before him. His mother [Maryam (Mary)] was a *Siddīqah* [i.e. she believed in the Words of Allāh and His Books (see Verse 66:12)]. They both used to eat food (as any other human being, while Allāh does not eat). Look how We make the *Ayāt* (proofs, evidences, Verses, lessons, signs, revelations, etc.) clear to them; yet look how they are deluded away (from the truth).

(Qur'ân 5: 75)

'Īsâ ﷺ was born in Bethlehem in Palestine. There was the famous date tree in the area as well as the small river mentioned regarding his birth. His roots trace back to An-Nâsirah, in northern Palestine. In fact, it is in An-Nâsirah (Nazareth) that 'Īsâ ﷺ lived with his chaste and pious mother. Some sources mention that he went on a journey with his mother and Yusuf, the carpenter, to Ain Shams (Helispolis) Egypt. They stayed beside Al-Matriyyah, the Virgin Tree. The family then returned to An-Nâsirah. The Bible then mentions nothing whatsoever about his life from the time he was 12 years old until he reached the age of 30, when it is mentioned that he met Yahya ﷺ and was baptized in the Jordan River. Some Western thinkers claim that, during the period in which nothing is mentioned about him, he traveled to India, where he came across the teachings of the Buddha.

In 1975, UNESCO distributed texts from the Bible that were uncovered in Naj' Humaadee, in the highlands of Egypt; they were actually discovered in the year 1945. Among those texts is the following passage, which is mentioned here word for word:

"It was another person who drank the bitterness and vinegar, and not I. And it was another (Simon Peter) who carried the cross on his shoulders; and it was yet another who placed a crown of thorns upon his head. Meanwhile, I was above, laughing at their ignorance."

Now the Qur'ân reveals:

﴿وَقَوْلِهِمْ إِنَّا قَتَلْنَا ٱلْمَسِيحَ عِيسَى ٱبْنَ مَرْيَمَ رَسُولَ ٱللَّهِ وَمَا قَتَلُوهُ وَمَا صَلَبُوهُ وَلَكِن شُبِّهَ لَهُمْ وَإِنَّ ٱلَّذِينَ ٱخْتَلَفُوا۟ فِيهِ لَفِى شَكٍّ مِّنْهُ مَا لَهُم بِهِۦ مِنْ عِلْمٍ إِلَّا ٱتِّبَاعَ ٱلظَّنِّ وَمَا قَتَلُوهُ يَقِينَۢا

﷽ (١٥٨) بَل رَّفَعَهُ ٱللَّهُ إِلَيْهِ ۚ وَكَانَ ٱللَّهُ عَزِيزًا حَكِيمًا (١٥٧)

And because of their saying (in boast), "We killed Messiah 'Īsā (Jesus), son of Maryam (Mary), the Messenger of Allāh," — but they killed him not, nor crucified him, but it appeared so to them [the resemblance of 'Īsā (Jesus) was put over another man (and they killed that man)], and those who differ therein are full of doubts. They have no (certain) knowledge, they follow nothing but conjecture. For surely, they killed him not [i.e. 'Īsā (Jesus), son of Maryam (Mary) ﷺ]: But Allāh raised him ['Īsā (Jesus)] up (with his body and soul) to Himself (and he ﷺ is in the heavens). And Allāh is Ever All-Powerful, All-Wise.

(Qur'ân 4: 157, 158)

- Al-'Aqâid Al-Wathaniyyah Fid-Diyânah An-Nasrâniyyah: 77
- Qisas Al-Anbiya, by Ibn Kathir: 416
- Qisas Al-Anbiya, by Ath-Tha'labi: 383
- Qisas Al-Anbiya, by At-Tabari: 449
- Qisas Al-Anbiya, by An-Najjâr: 371
- Majallatul-Majallah: Issue # 712, October, 1993
- Al-Mo'jam Al-Mufahris Li-Alfâz Al-Qur'ân Al-Karim: 494, 665, 666
- Al-Mo'jam Al-Mufahris Li-Ma'âni Al-Qur'ân Al-Karim: 856
- Yanâbi' Al-Masihiyyah: 160

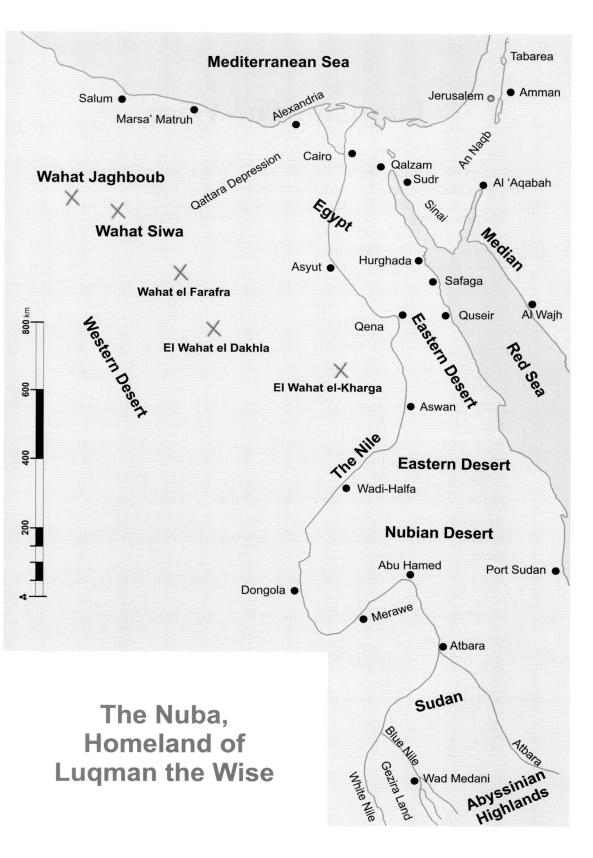

Luqmân, The Wise

Luqmân ﷺ is twice mentioned by name in the Noble Qur'ân, both times in the Sûrah (Chapter) that is named after him:

Chapter Name (Sûrah)	Number of Chapter (Sûrah)	Verse Numbers
Luqmân	31	12, 13

﷽ وَلَقَدْ ءَاتَيْنَا لُقْمَٰنَ ٱلْحِكْمَةَ أَنِ ٱشْكُرْ لِلَّهِ وَمَن يَشْكُرْ فَإِنَّمَا يَشْكُرُ لِنَفْسِهِۦ وَمَن كَفَرَ فَإِنَّ ٱللَّهَ غَنِيٌّ حَمِيدٌ ﴿١٢﴾ وَإِذْ قَالَ لُقْمَٰنُ لِٱبْنِهِۦ وَهُوَ يَعِظُهُۥ يَٰبُنَىَّ لَا تُشْرِكْ بِٱللَّهِ إِنَّ ٱلشِّرْكَ لَظُلْمٌ عَظِيمٌ ﴿١٣﴾ ﷽

And indeed We bestowed upon Luqmān *Al-Hikmah* (wisdom and religious understanding saying:) "Give thanks to Allāh." And whoever gives thanks, he gives thanks for (the good of) his own self. And whoever is unthankful, then verily, Allāh is All-Rich (Free of all needs), Worthy of all praise. And (remember) when Luqmān said to his son when he was advising him: "O my son! Join not in worship others with Allāh. Verily, joining others in worship with Allāh is a great *Zūlm* (wrong) indeed.

(Qur'ân 31: 12, 13)

﷽ وَوَصَّيْنَا ٱلْإِنسَٰنَ بِوَٰلِدَيْهِ حَمَلَتْهُ أُمُّهُۥ وَهْنًا عَلَىٰ وَهْنٍ وَفِصَٰلُهُۥ فِى عَامَيْنِ أَنِ ٱشْكُرْ لِى وَلِوَٰلِدَيْكَ إِلَىَّ ٱلْمَصِيرُ ﴿١٤﴾ وَإِن جَٰهَدَاكَ عَلَىٰٓ أَن تُشْرِكَ بِى مَا لَيْسَ لَكَ بِهِۦ عِلْمٌ فَلَا تُطِعْهُمَا وَصَاحِبْهُمَا فِى ٱلدُّنْيَا مَعْرُوفًا وَٱتَّبِعْ سَبِيلَ مَنْ أَنَابَ إِلَىَّ ثُمَّ إِلَىَّ مَرْجِعُكُمْ فَأُنَبِّئُكُم بِمَا كُنتُمْ تَعْمَلُونَ ﴿١٥﴾ يَٰبُنَىَّ إِنَّهَآ إِن تَكُ مِثْقَالَ حَبَّةٍ مِّنْ خَرْدَلٍ فَتَكُن فِى صَخْرَةٍ أَوْ فِى ٱلسَّمَٰوَٰتِ أَوْ فِى ٱلْأَرْضِ يَأْتِ بِهَا ٱللَّهُ إِنَّ ٱللَّهَ لَطِيفٌ خَبِيرٌ ﴿١٦﴾ يَٰبُنَىَّ أَقِمِ ٱلصَّلَوٰةَ وَأْمُرْ بِٱلْمَعْرُوفِ وَٱنْهَ عَنِ ٱلْمُنكَرِ وَٱصْبِرْ عَلَىٰ مَآ أَصَابَكَ إِنَّ ذَٰلِكَ مِنْ عَزْمِ

$$\text{ٱلْأُمُورِ} \ ⑰ \ \text{وَلَا تُصَعِّرْ خَدَّكَ لِلنَّاسِ وَلَا تَمْشِ فِي ٱلْأَرْضِ مَرَحًا إِنَّ ٱللَّهَ لَا يُحِبُّ كُلَّ مُخْتَالٍ}$$

$$\text{فَخُورٍ} \ ⑱ \ \text{وَٱقْصِدْ فِي مَشْيِكَ وَٱغْضُضْ مِن صَوْتِكَ إِنَّ أَنكَرَ ٱلْأَصْوَاتِ لَصَوْتُ ٱلْحَمِيرِ}$$

$$⑲ ❧$$

And We have enjoined on man (to be dutiful and good) to his parents. His mother bore him in weakness and hardship upon weakness and hardship, and his weaning is in two years — give thanks to Me and to your parents. To Me is the final destination. But if they (both) strive with you to make you join in worship with Me others that of which you have no knowledge, then obey them not; but behave with them in the world kindly, and follow the path of him who turns to Me in repentance and in obedience. Then to Me will be your return, and I shall tell you what you used to do. "O my son! If it be (anything) equal to the weight of a grain of mustard seed, and though it be in a rock, or in the heavens or in the earth, Allāh will bring it forth. Verily, Allāh is Subtle (in bringing out that grain), Well-Acquainted (with its place). O my son! *Aqim-is-Salāt* (perform prayers), enjoin (on people) *Al-Ma'rūf* (Islamic Monotheism and all that is good), and forbid (people) from *Al-Munkar* (i.e. disbelief in the Oneness of Allāh, polytheism of all kinds and all that is evil and bad), and bear with patience whatever befalls you. Verily, these are some of the important commandments (ordered by Allāh with no exemption). And turn not your face away from men with pride, nor walk in insolence through the earth. Verily, Allāh likes not any arrogant boaster. And be moderate (or show no insolence) in your walking, and lower your voice. Verily, the harshest of all voices is the braying of the asses."

(Qur'ân 31: 14-19)

Luqmân ﷺ is either Ayyûb's nephew (the son of Ayyûb's sister), or Ayyûb's cousin (Ayyûb's mother's, sister's son). It is said that he lived until the time of Prophet Dâwûd ﷺ. When Dâwûd ﷺ proclaimed his prophethood, Luqmân ﷺ stopped issuing legal rulings. When he was asked about the reason, he said, "Shall I not deem sufficient what has been made sufficient for me (i.e., it now became Prophet Dâwûd's duty to issue legal verdicts)?" Luqmân الﻌﻠﻴﻪ is originally from the lands of Nuba, which extend from northern Sudan to southern Egypt.

The following is related from Ibn 'Abbâs ﷺ: He (i.e., Luqmân) was neither a Prophet nor a king. Rather, he was a shepherd who was freed by his owner. That owner once ordered him to slaughter a sheep and to remove from it its two best parts. Luqmân then removed the tongue and the heart. His owner gave him a similar order a few days later, but this time to remove the two foulest parts. Luqmân again removed the tongue and the heart. When his owner asked him about that, he said, "If they remain pure and good, they are the best two body parts; and if they become spoiled and evil, they are the two most foul body parts." Among the many wise sayings that are ascribed to Luqmân الﻌﻠﻴﻪ is the following: "Silence is wisdom, and few are its practitioners."

- Mausu'ah Al-Qarn Al-'Ishrin: 8/380

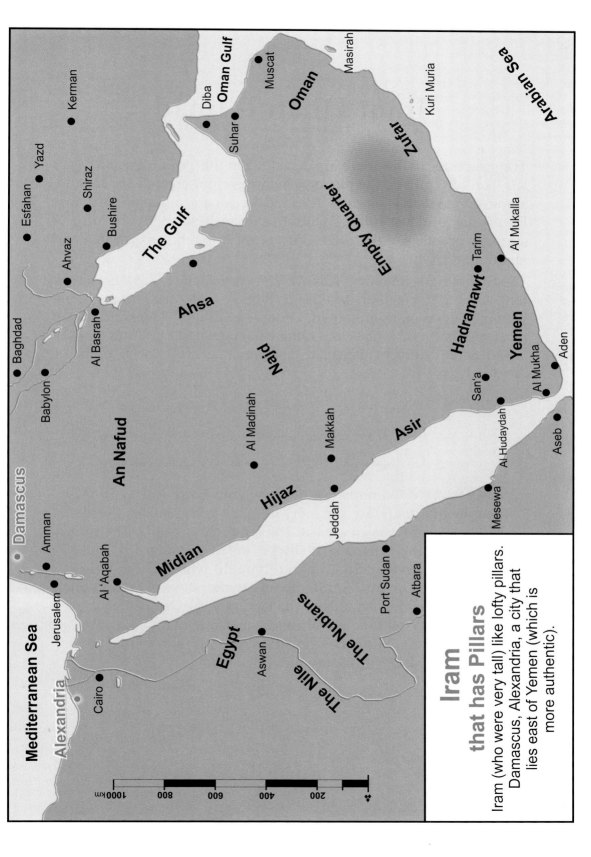

Iram
that has Pillars

Iram (who were very tall) like lofty pillars. Damascus, Alexandria, a city that lies east of Yemen (which is more authentic).

Mediterranean Sea

Alexandria
Cairo
Jerusalem
Amman
Damascus
Al 'Aqabah

Midian
Egypt
Aswan
The Nile
The Nubians
Atbara
Port Sudan
Mesewa
Aseb

Hijaz
Jeddah
Makkah
Al Madinah
Asir
Al Hudaydah
San'a
Al Mukha
Aden
Yemen
Hadramawt
Tarim
Al Mukalla

An Nafud
Najd
Ahsa
Empty Quarter
Zufar
Oman

Baghdad
Babylon
Al Basrah
The Gulf
Ahvaz
Bushire
Shiraz
Esfahan
Yazd
Kerman

Diba
Oman Gulf
Muscat
Suhar
Oman
Masirah
Kuri Muria
Arabian Seas

1000 Km
800
600
400
200
0

Iram Dhâtul-'Imâd

The structures of this place are described in the Qur'ân as being very tall like lofty pillars, the like of which were not created in the land. Some say that this place is Alexandria; others maintain that it is Damascus; and yet others, whose opinion is strongest by dint of stronger proofs, say that it is a city near 'Adan, between San'â and Hadramawt.

The following is an entry from *Mo'jam Al-Buldân* (1/155): Some say that it is a land that has been blotted out, and so its exact whereabouts remain unknown. Others say that it is Alexandria, yet most say that it is Damascus... Others have related that Iram Dhâtul-'Imâd is in Yemen, between Hadramawt and San'a built by Shaddâd bin 'Ād.

﴿أَلَمْ تَرَ كَيْفَ فَعَلَ رَبُّكَ بِعَادٍ ۝ إِرَمَ ذَاتِ ٱلْعِمَادِ ۝ ٱلَّتِي لَمْ يُخْلَقْ مِثْلُهَا فِى ٱلْبِلَٰدِ ۝ وَثَمُودَ ٱلَّذِينَ جَابُوا۟ ٱلصَّخْرَ بِٱلْوَادِ ۝ وَفِرْعَوْنَ ذِى ٱلْأَوْتَادِ ۝ ٱلَّذِينَ طَغَوْا۟ فِى ٱلْبِلَٰدِ ۝ فَأَكْثَرُوا۟ فِيهَا ٱلْفَسَادَ ۝ فَصَبَّ عَلَيْهِمْ رَبُّكَ سَوْطَ عَذَابٍ ۝ إِنَّ رَبَّكَ لَبِٱلْمِرْصَادِ ۝﴾

Saw you (O Muhammad ﷺ) not how your Lord dealt with 'Ād (people) of Iram (who were very tall) like (lofty) pillars, the like of which were not created in the land? And (with) Thamūd (people), who hewed out rocks in the valley (to make dwellings)? And (with) Fir'aun (Pharaoh) who had the stakes (to torture men by binding them to the stakes)? Who did transgress beyond bounds in the lands (in the disobedience of Allāh). And made therein much mischief. So, your Lord poured on them different kinds of severe torment. Verily, your Lord is Ever Watchful (over them).

(Qur'ân 89: 6-14)

154

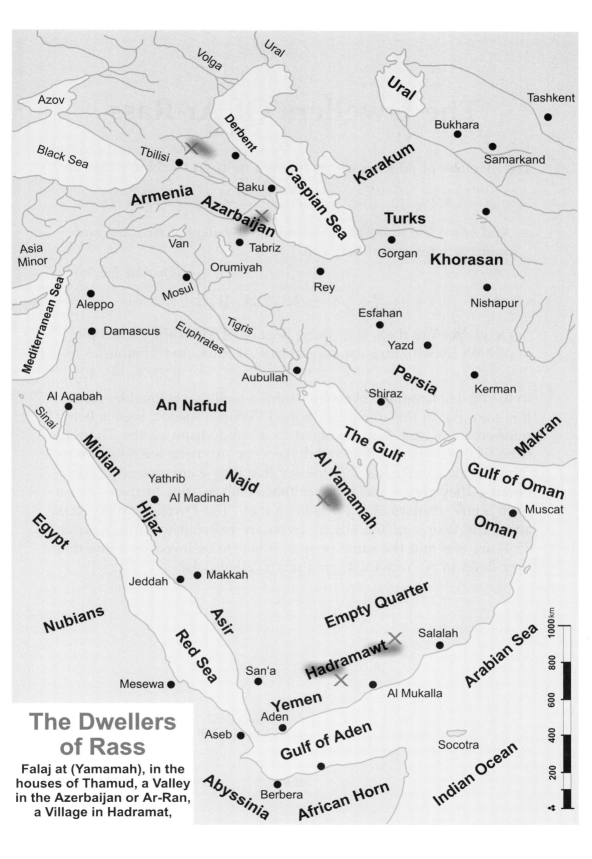

Azov

Black Sea

Ural

Volga

Ural

Tashkent

Bukhara

Samarkand

Derbent

Tbilisi

Caspian Sea

Karakum

Baku

Armenia

Azarbaijan

Turks

Khorasan

Van

Tabriz

Gorgan

Orumiyah

Asia
Minor

Mediterranean Sea

Mosul

Rey

Nishapur

Aleppo

Esfahan

Damascus

Euphrates

Tigris

Yazd

Kerman

Aubullah

Persia

Al Aqabah

An Nafud

Shiraz

Sinai

The Gulf

Makran

Midian

Al Yamamah

Gulf of Oman

Yathrib

Najd

Muscat

Al Madinah

Hijaz

Oman

Egypt

Jeddah

Makkah

Empty Quarter

Salalah

Nubians

Asir

Hadramawt

Arabian Sea

Red Sea

San'a

Mesewa

Yemen

Al Mukalla

Aden

Aseb

Gulf of Aden

Socotra

**The Dwellers
of Rass**

Berbera

Abyssinia

African Horn

Indian Ocean

**Falaj at (Yamamah), in the
houses of Thamud, a Valley
in the Azerbaijan or Ar-Ran,
a Village in Hadramat,**

1000 km

800

600

400

200

The Dwellers Of Ar-Rass

The dwellers of Al-Rass are mentioned twice in the Noble Qur'ân:

﴿وَعَادًا وَثَمُودَا۟ وَأَصْحَٰبَ ٱلرَّسِّ وَقُرُونًۢا بَيْنَ ذَٰلِكَ كَثِيرًا ۝﴾

And (also) 'Ād and Thamūd, and the dwellers of Ar-Rass, and many generations in between.

(Qur'ân 25: 38)

﴿كَذَّبَتْ قَبْلَهُمْ قَوْمُ نُوحٍ وَأَصْحَٰبُ ٱلرَّسِّ وَثَمُودُ ۝﴾

Denied before them (i.e., these pagans of Makkah) the people of Nūh (Noah), and the dwellers of Ar-Rass, and Thamūd.

(Qur'ân 50: 12)

In the Arabic language, Ar-Rass means a well that is lined by stones. It is said that in the above-mentioned Verses a specific well is being referred to, a well that belonged to a subdivision of the Thamûd tribe. The members of that subdivision or sub-tribe were known as 'The Dwellers of Ar-Rass.' Some say that they were given that name because they threw the Prophet that Allâh ﷻ sent to them into a well. Some scholars of *Tafsir* believe that "The Dwellers of Ar-Rass and "The People of the Ditch" (who are referred to in the Qur'ân 85:4) are one and the same people. It is also believed by some that they lived in Al-Yamâmah, in a town called Falaj.

- Al-Qaamus Al-Islami: 1/120
- Al-Mo'jam Al-Mufahris Li-Alfâz Al-Qur'ân Al-Karim: 312
- Al-Mo'jam Al-Mufahris Li-Ma'âni Al-Qur'ân Al-Karim: 500
- Mausu'ah Al-Qarn Al-'Ishrin: 4/215

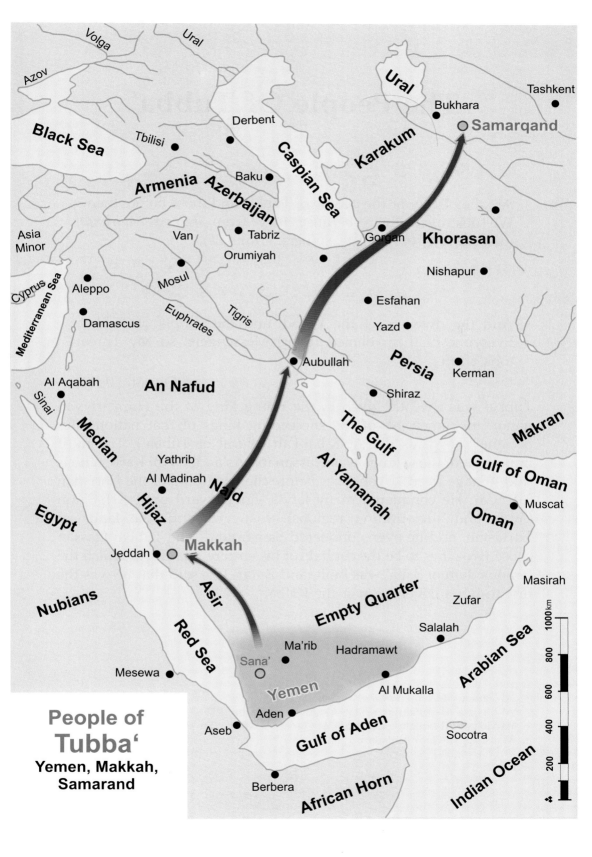

Volga
Ural
Azov
Black Sea
Tbilisi
Derbent
Ural
Bukhara
Tashkent
Samarqand
Armenia
Azerbaijan
Baku
Caspian Sea
Karakum
Khorasan
Asia Minor
Van
Tabriz
Orumiyah
Gorgan
Nishapur
Cyprus
Mediterranean Sea
Aleppo
Mosul
Euphrates
Tigris
Esfahan
Damascus
Yazd
Persia
Kerman
Al Aqabah
Aubullah
Shiraz
Sinai
An Nafud
Makran
The Gulf
Gulf of Oman
Median
Yathrib
Al Madinah
Najd
Al Yamamah
Oman
Muscat
Egypt
Hijaz
Makkah
Masirah
Nubians
Jeddah
Asir
Empty Quarter
Zufar
Salalah
Red Sea
Ma'rib
Hadramawt
Arabian Sea
Sana'
Mesewa
Yemen
Al Mukalla
Aseb
Aden
Gulf of Aden
Socotra
Berbera
African Horn
Indian Ocean

1000 km
800
600
400
200

People of Tubba'
Yemen, Makkah, Samarand

The People Of Tubba'

﴿أَهُمْ خَيْرٌ أَمْ قَوْمُ تُبَّعٍ وَالَّذِينَ مِن قَبْلِهِمْ أَهْلَكْنَاهُمْ إِنَّهُمْ كَانُوا مُجْرِمِينَ ۝﴾ (٣٧)

Are they better or the people of Tubba' and those before them? We destroyed them because they were indeed *Mujrimūn* (disbelievers, polytheists, sinners, criminals).

(Qur'ân 44: 37)

﴿وَأَصْحَابُ الْأَيْكَةِ وَقَوْمُ تُبَّعٍ كُلٌّ كَذَّبَ الرُّسُلَ فَحَقَّ وَعِيدِ ۝﴾ (١٤)

And the dwellers of the Wood, and the people of Tubba'. Everyone of them denied (their) Messengers, so My Threat took effect.

(Qur'ân 50: 14)

Tubba' was the title given to the ruling king of the Himyariyyah nation in Yemen; all of the succeeding kings of that nation later became known as the At-Tabâbi'ah (plural of Tubba'). The most important of those kings was Hassân ibn As'ad ibn Abi Karb, who is said to have lived 12 centuries before the beginning of the Christian calendar. He conquered many lands – northward until Ash-Sham (Syria and surrounding regions), eastward until the lands of Turkistan, and he even conquered Samarqand. The Tubba' Hassân chose two cities to be the capitals of his empire: Ma'rib, in which the famous dam of Sabâ' was built, and Zufâr. It is said that he was the first to put a covering over the Ka'bah.

- Al-Qâmus Al-Islami: 1/437
- Al-Mo'jam Al-Mufahris Li-Alfâz Al-Qur'ân Al-Karim: 152
- Al-Mo'jam Al-Mufahris Li-Ma'âni Al-Qur'ân Al-Karim: 221
- Mausu'ah Al-Qarn Al-'Ishrin: 2/523

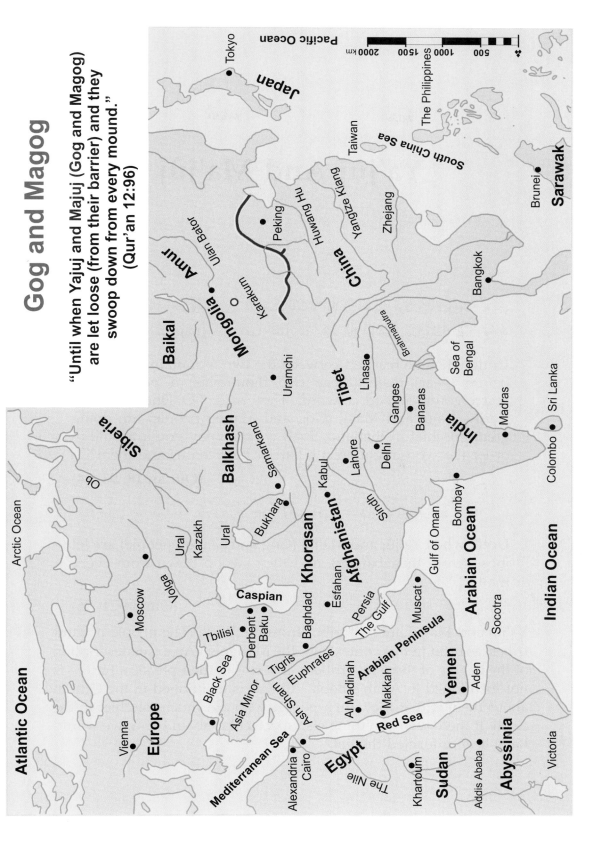

Gog and Magog

"Until when Yajuj and Majuj (Gog and Magog) are let loose (from their barrier) and they swoop down from every mound."
(Qur'an 12:96)

Ya'jûj And Ma'jûj

﴾حَتَّىٰ إِذَا بَلَغَ بَيْنَ ٱلسَّدَّيْنِ وَجَدَ مِن دُونِهِمَا قَوْمًا لَّا يَكَادُونَ يَفْقَهُونَ قَوْلًا ۝ قَالُوا يَٰذَا ٱلْقَرْنَيْنِ إِنَّ يَأْجُوجَ وَمَأْجُوجَ مُفْسِدُونَ فِي ٱلْأَرْضِ فَهَلْ نَجْعَلُ لَكَ خَرْجًا عَلَىٰ أَن تَجْعَلَ بَيْنَنَا وَبَيْنَهُمْ سَدًّا ۝﴿

Until, when he reached between the two mountains, he found before (near) them (those two mountains) a people who scarcely understood a word. They said: "O Dhul-Qarnain! Verily, Yajûj and Majûj (Gog and Magog people) are doing great mischief in the land. Shall we then pay you a tribute in order that you might erect a barrier between us and them?"

(Qur'ân 18: 93, 94)

﴾حَتَّىٰ إِذَا فُتِحَتْ يَأْجُوجُ وَمَأْجُوجُ وَهُم مِّن كُلِّ حَدَبٍ يَنسِلُونَ ۝﴿

Until, when Ya'jûj and Ma'jûj (Gog and Magog people) are let loose (from their barrier), and they swoop down from every mound.

(Qur'ân 21: 96)

Ya'jûj and Ma'jûj are two tribes from the Turk. (The people of Turk tribes, as used in this context, are the Mongols.) An exact description of the people of these two tribes – in terms of their physical traits – is not mentioned in Allâh's Book. All that is mentioned in the Qur'ân about them is that they are a people who did much mischief in the earth. If there were anything else spectacular about them, we would have been informed thereof.

They were a strong and violent people, who would attack and pillage the lands of neighboring peoples. Thus does the meaning of the following verse become clear: "Verily, Ya'jûj and Ma'jûj are doing great mischief in the land." (Qur'ân 18: 94)

In terms of doing mischief, they would plunder towns, kill some of the inhabitants, and take others as slaves. Therefore, we can discount all of the far-fetched things that are said about Ya'jûj and Ma'jûj and that are not mentioned in the Book of Allâh or the authentic *Sunnah* of His Messenger ﷺ.

- Dâiratul Ma'ârif Al-Qarn Al-'Ishrin: 1/ 68
- Al-Mo'jam Al-Mufahris Li-Alfâz Al-Qur'ân Al-Karim: 770
- Al-Mo'jam Al-Mufahris Li-Ma'âni Al-Qur'ân Al-Karim: 1326

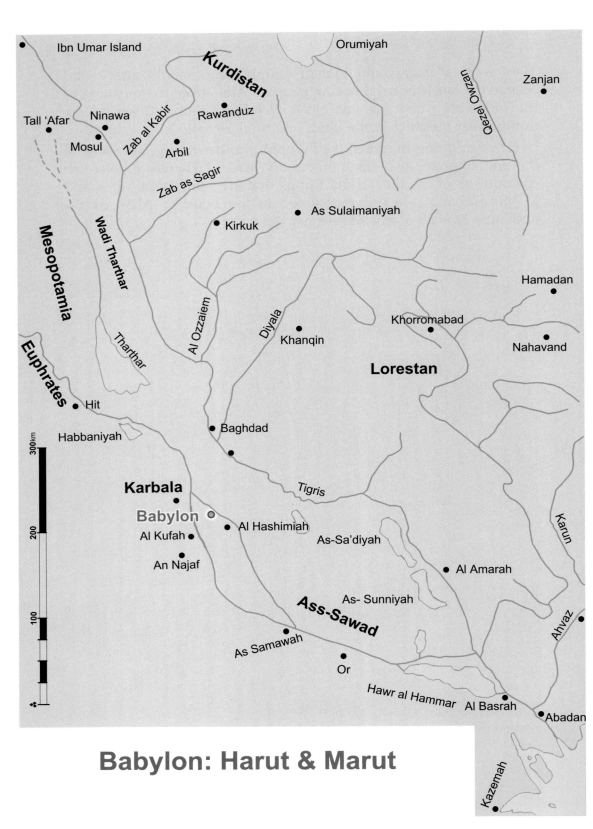

Ibn Umar Island

Orumiyah

Kurdistan

Zanjan

Tall 'Afar

Ninawa

Rawanduz

Mosul

Arbil

Zab al Kabir

Zab as Sagir

As Sulaimaniyah

Kirkuk

Mesopotamia

Hamadan

Wadi Tharthar

Diyala

Al Ozzaiem

Khorromabad

Nahavand

Tharthar

Khanqin

Lorestan

Euphrates

Hit

Habbaniyah

Baghdad

Tigris

Karun

Karbala

Babylon

Al Hashimiah

As-Sa'diyah

Al Kufah

An Najaf

Al Amarah

As- Sunniyah

Ahvaz

300km

200

100

Ass-Sawad

As Samawah

Or

Hawr al Hammar

Al Basrah

Abadan

Kazemah

Babylon: Harut & Marut

Hârût and Mârût In Babylon

$$\{ \text{وَلَكِنَّ الشَّيَاطِينَ كَفَرُوا يُعَلِّمُونَ النَّاسَ السِّحْرَ وَمَا أُنزِلَ عَلَى الْمَلَكَيْنِ بِبَابِلَ} \\ \text{هَارُوتَ وَمَارُوتَ} \}$$

....but the *Shayātīn* (devils) disbelieved, teaching men magic and such things that came down at Babylon to the two angels, Hârût and Mârût...

(Qur'ân 2: 102)

When magic became a widespread practice among the Jews, Allâh ﷻ sent two angels Hârût and Mârût – to the kingdom of Babylon, which was situated between two rivers: The Tigris and the Euphrates. Allâh ﷻ sent these angels as a trial and test for the people:

> But neither of these two (angels) taught anyone (such things) till they had said, "We are only for trial, so disbelieve not (by learning this magic from us)." (Qur'ân 2: 102)

And so the two angels would not teach anyone magic until they first advised them, telling them, in so many words: 'What we are describing to you is a test and trial from Allâh, so do not use it for evil, and do not disbelieve because of it. Whoever learns it to prevent himself from harming others, is saved. And whoever learns it to harm others, goes astray and becomes destroyed.'

At the time, magic was practiced on a widespread scale. Perhaps one of the reasons why the angels came to teach magic was so that people could gain an appreciation of the difference between magic and bona fide miracles; and so that they could identify lying magicians who falsely claimed to be Prophets.

- At-Tafsir Al-Munir: 1/244
- Safwatut-Tafâsir: 1/83
- Al-Mo'jam Al-Mufahris Li-Alfâz Al-Qur'ân Al-Karim: 736
- Al-Mo'jam Al-Mufahris Li-Ma'âni Al-Qur'ân Al-Karim: 1274

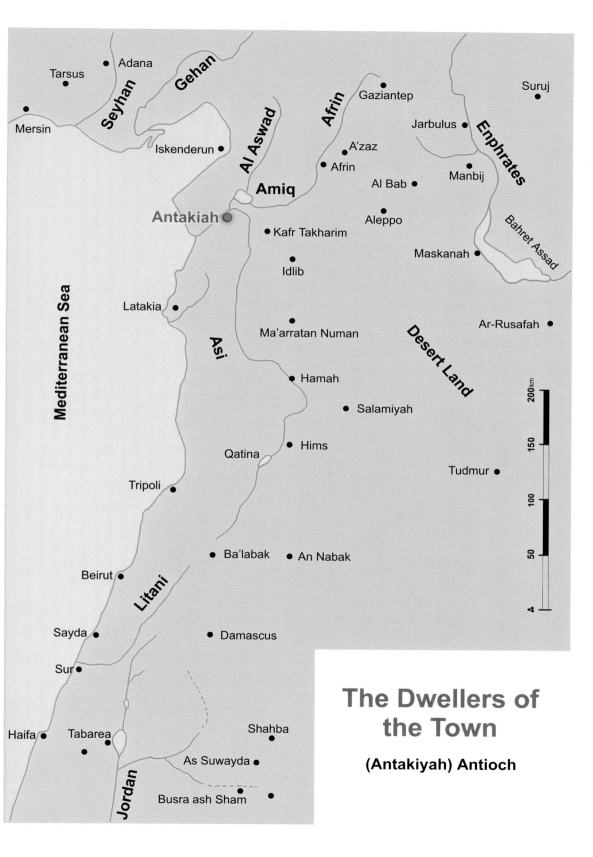

Tarsus
Adana
Seyhan
Gehan
Mersin
Iskenderun
Al Aswad
Afrin
Gaziantep
Suruj
Jarbulus
Enphrates
A'zaz
Afrin
Al Bab
Manbij
Amiq
Antakiah
Aleppo
Bahret Assad
Kafr Takharim
Maskanah
Idlib
Latakia
Ma'arratan Numan
Ar-Rusafah
Mediterranean Sea
Asi
Desert Land
Hamah
Salamiyah
Qatina
Hims
Tudmur
Tripoli
200km
150
100
Ba'labak
An Nabak
Beirut
50
Litani
Sayda
Damascus
Sur
Haifa
Tabarea
Shahba

The Dwellers of the Town

(Antakiyah) Antioch

As Suwayda
Jordan
Busra ash Sham

The Dwellers Of The Town

﴿وَٱضۡرِبۡ لَهُم مَّثَلًا أَصۡحَٰبَ ٱلۡقَرۡيَةِ إِذۡ جَآءَهَا ٱلۡمُرۡسَلُونَ ۝ إِذۡ أَرۡسَلۡنَآ إِلَيۡهِمُ ٱثۡنَيۡنِ فَكَذَّبُوهُمَا فَعَزَّزۡنَا بِثَالِثٍ فَقَالُوٓاْ إِنَّآ إِلَيۡكُم مُّرۡسَلُونَ ۝ ﴾

And put forward to them a similitude; the (story of the) Dwellers of the Town, [it is said that the town was Antioch (Antākiyah)], when there came Messengers to them. When We sent to them two Messengers, they denied them both; so We reinforced them with a third, and they said: "Verily, we have been sent to you as Messengers." (Qur'ân 36: 13, 14)

"The Dwellers of the Town" are the people of Antioch, a point that is agreed upon by all of the *Mufassirin* (Scholars of *Tafsir*). Antioch was situated just before the mouth of the 'Aasi river in As-Suwaidiyyah, which is beside the Mediterranean Sea. The town was built by Selauqas the First in the year 307 (before the commencement of the Christian calendar). He made it the capital of his kingdom after Alexander III of Macedon. In the Abbasid period, it was the main city of the province Awâsim. The area is known for its pristine beauty, its wholesome air, its sweet water, and its many blessings.

Al-Qurtubi said: The town is Antioch, to which Al-Masih sent three messengers: Sâdiq, Masduq, and Sham'un.

﴿قَالُواْ مَآ أَنتُمۡ إِلَّا بَشَرٞ مِّثۡلُنَا وَمَآ أَنزَلَ ٱلرَّحۡمَٰنُ مِن شَيۡءٍ إِنۡ أَنتُمۡ إِلَّا تَكۡذِبُونَ ۝ قَالُواْ رَبُّنَا يَعۡلَمُ إِنَّآ إِلَيۡكُمۡ لَمُرۡسَلُونَ ۝ وَمَا عَلَيۡنَآ إِلَّا ٱلۡبَلَٰغُ ٱلۡمُبِينُ ۝ قَالُوٓاْ إِنَّا تَطَيَّرۡنَا بِكُمۡ لَئِن لَّمۡ تَنتَهُواْ لَنَرۡجُمَنَّكُمۡ وَلَيَمَسَّنَّكُم مِّنَّا عَذَابٌ أَلِيمٞ ۝ قَالُواْ طَٰٓئِرُكُم مَّعَكُمۡ أَئِن ذُكِّرۡتُم بَلۡ أَنتُمۡ قَوۡمٞ مُّسۡرِفُونَ ۝ وَجَآءَ مِنۡ أَقۡصَا ٱلۡمَدِينَةِ رَجُلٞ يَسۡعَىٰ قَالَ يَٰقَوۡمِ ٱتَّبِعُواْ ٱلۡمُرۡسَلِينَ ۝ ٱتَّبِعُواْ مَن لَّا يَسۡـَٔلُكُمۡ أَجۡرٗا وَهُم مُّهۡتَدُونَ ۝ وَمَا لِيَ لَآ أَعۡبُدُ ٱلَّذِي فَطَرَنِي وَإِلَيۡهِ تُرۡجَعُونَ ۝ ءَأَتَّخِذُ مِن دُونِهِۦٓ ءَالِهَةً إِن يُرِدۡنِ ٱلرَّحۡمَٰنُ بِضُرّٖ لَّا تُغۡنِ عَنِّي شَفَٰعَتُهُمۡ شَيۡـٔٗا وَلَا يُنقِذُونِ ۝ إِنِّيٓ إِذٗا لَّفِي ضَلَٰلٖ مُّبِينٍ ۝ إِنِّيٓ ءَامَنتُ بِرَبِّكُمۡ فَٱسۡمَعُونِ ﴾

(٢٥) قِيلَ ٱدْخُلِ ٱلْجَنَّةَ قَالَ يَٰلَيْتَ قَوْمِى يَعْلَمُونَ (٢٦) بِمَا غَفَرَ لِى رَبِّى وَجَعَلَنِى مِنَ ٱلْمُكْرَمِينَ ﴾

They (people of the town) said: "You are only human beings like ourselves, and the Most Gracious (Allāh) has revealed nothing. You are only telling lies." The Messengers said: "Our Lord knows that we have been sent as Messengers to you, and our duty is only to convey plainly (the Message)." They (people) said: "For us, we see an evil omen from you; if you cease not, we will surely stone you, and a painful torment will touch you from us." They (Messengers) said: "Your evil omens be with you! (Do you call it 'evil omen') because you are admonished? Nay, but you are a people *Musrifūn* (transgressing all bounds by committing all kinds of great sins, and by disobeying Allāh)." And there came a man running from the farthest part of the town. He said: "O my people! Obey the Messengers. "Obey those who ask no wages of you (for themselves), and who are rightly guided. And why should I not worship Him (Allāh Alone) Who has created me and to Whom you shall be returned. Shall I take besides Him *ālihah* (gods)? If the Most Gracious (Allāh) intends me any harm, their intercession will be of no use for me whatsoever, nor can they save me. Then verily, I should be in plain error. Verily, I have believed in your Lord, so listen to me!" It was said (to him when the disbelievers killed him): "Enter Paradise." He said: "Would that my people knew "That my Lord (Allāh) has forgiven me, and made me of the honored ones!"

(Qur'ân 36: 15-27)

This man was Habib An-Najjâr who came to help them, and he announced his faith before them. The people attacked him, stamping him with their feet until he died. And then Allâh ﷻ destroyed the town.

- Safwatut-Tafâsir: 3/9
- Al-Qâmus Al-Islâmi 1/202 - Mo'jam Al-Buldân: 1/266
- Al-Mo'jam Al-Mufahris Li-Alfâz Al-Qur'ân Al-Karim: 459

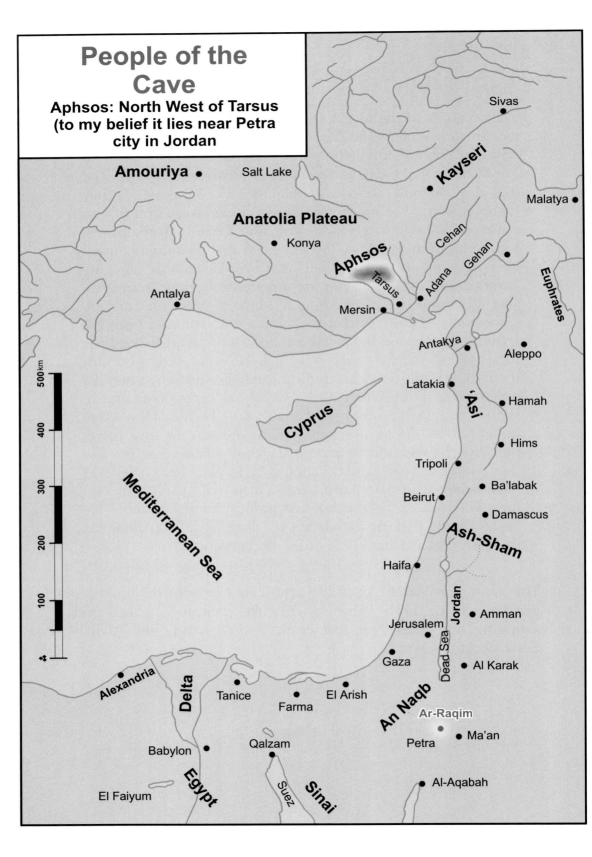

People of the Cave

Aphsos: North West of Tarsus (to my belief it lies near Petra city in Jordan

Sivas

Amouriya

Salt Lake

Kayseri

Malatya

Anatolia Plateau

Konya

Cehan

Aphsos

Gehan

Euphrates

Tarsus

Adana

Mersin

Antalya

Antakya

Aleppo

Latakia

'Asi

Hamah

Cyprus

Hims

Tripoli

Ba'labak

Beirut

Damascus

Mediterranean Sea

Ash-Sham

Haifa

Jordan

Amman

Jerusalem

Dead Sea

Gaza

Al Karak

Alexandria

Delta

Tanice

El Arish

An Naqb

Farma

Ar-Raqim

Ma'an

Babylon

Qalzam

Petra

Egypt

Suez

Sinai

Al-Aqabah

El Faiyum

500 km
400
300
200
100

The People Of The Cave

﴿ أَمْ حَسِبْتَ أَنَّ أَصْحَٰبَ ٱلْكَهْفِ وَٱلرَّقِيمِ كَانُوا۟ مِنْ ءَايَٰتِنَا عَجَبًا ۝ إِذْ أَوَى ٱلْفِتْيَةُ إِلَى ٱلْكَهْفِ فَقَالُوا۟ رَبَّنَآ ءَاتِنَا مِن لَّدُنكَ رَحْمَةً وَهَيِّئْ لَنَا مِنْ أَمْرِنَا رَشَدًا ۝ فَضَرَبْنَا عَلَىٰٓ ءَاذَانِهِمْ فِى ٱلْكَهْفِ سِنِينَ عَدَدًا ۝ ثُمَّ بَعَثْنَٰهُمْ لِنَعْلَمَ أَىُّ ٱلْحِزْبَيْنِ أَحْصَىٰ لِمَا لَبِثُوٓا۟ أَمَدًا ۝ نَّحْنُ نَقُصُّ عَلَيْكَ نَبَأَهُم بِٱلْحَقِّ إِنَّهُمْ فِتْيَةٌ ءَامَنُوا۟ بِرَبِّهِمْ وَزِدْنَٰهُمْ هُدًى ۝ وَرَبَطْنَا عَلَىٰ قُلُوبِهِمْ إِذْ قَامُوا۟ فَقَالُوا۟ رَبُّنَا رَبُّ ٱلسَّمَٰوَٰتِ وَٱلْأَرْضِ لَن نَّدْعُوَا۟ مِن دُونِهِۦٓ إِلَٰهًا لَّقَدْ قُلْنَآ إِذًا شَطَطًا ۝ هَٰٓؤُلَآءِ قَوْمُنَا ٱتَّخَذُوا۟ مِن دُونِهِۦٓ ءَالِهَةً لَّوْلَا يَأْتُونَ عَلَيْهِم بِسُلْطَٰنٍۭ بَيِّنٍ فَمَنْ أَظْلَمُ مِمَّنِ ٱفْتَرَىٰ عَلَى ٱللَّهِ كَذِبًا ۝ وَإِذِ ٱعْتَزَلْتُمُوهُمْ وَمَا يَعْبُدُونَ إِلَّا ٱللَّهَ فَأْوُۥٓا۟ إِلَى ٱلْكَهْفِ يَنشُرْ لَكُمْ رَبُّكُم مِّن رَّحْمَتِهِۦ وَيُهَيِّئْ لَكُم مِّنْ أَمْرِكُم مِّرْفَقًا ۝ ۞ وَتَرَى ٱلشَّمْسَ إِذَا طَلَعَت تَّزَٰوَرُ عَن كَهْفِهِمْ ذَاتَ ٱلْيَمِينِ وَإِذَا غَرَبَت تَّقْرِضُهُمْ ذَاتَ ٱلشِّمَالِ وَهُمْ فِى فَجْوَةٍ مِّنْهُ ذَٰلِكَ مِنْ ءَايَٰتِ ٱللَّهِ مَن يَهْدِ ٱللَّهُ فَهُوَ ٱلْمُهْتَدِ وَمَن يُضْلِلْ فَلَن تَجِدَ لَهُۥ وَلِيًّا مُّرْشِدًا ۝ وَتَحْسَبُهُمْ أَيْقَاظًا وَهُمْ رُقُودٌ وَنُقَلِّبُهُمْ ذَاتَ ٱلْيَمِينِ وَذَاتَ ٱلشِّمَالِ وَكَلْبُهُم بَٰسِطٌ ذِرَاعَيْهِ بِٱلْوَصِيدِ لَوِ ٱطَّلَعْتَ عَلَيْهِمْ لَوَلَّيْتَ مِنْهُمْ فِرَارًا وَلَمُلِئْتَ مِنْهُمْ رُعْبًا ۝ وَكَذَٰلِكَ بَعَثْنَٰهُمْ لِيَتَسَآءَلُوا۟ بَيْنَهُمْ قَالَ قَآئِلٌ مِّنْهُمْ كَمْ لَبِثْتُمْ قَالُوا۟ لَبِثْنَا يَوْمًا أَوْ بَعْضَ يَوْمٍ قَالُوا۟ رَبُّكُمْ أَعْلَمُ بِمَا لَبِثْتُمْ فَٱبْعَثُوٓا۟ أَحَدَكُم بِوَرِقِكُمْ هَٰذِهِۦٓ إِلَى ٱلْمَدِينَةِ فَلْيَنظُرْ أَيُّهَآ أَزْكَىٰ طَعَامًا فَلْيَأْتِكُم بِرِزْقٍ مِّنْهُ وَلْيَتَلَطَّفْ وَلَا يُشْعِرَنَّ بِكُمْ أَحَدًا ۝ إِنَّهُمْ إِن يَظْهَرُوا۟ عَلَيْكُمْ يَرْجُمُوكُمْ أَوْ يُعِيدُوكُمْ فِى مِلَّتِهِمْ وَلَن تُفْلِحُوٓا۟ إِذًا أَبَدًا ۝ وَكَذَٰلِكَ أَعْثَرْنَا عَلَيْهِمْ لِيَعْلَمُوٓا۟ أَنَّ وَعْدَ ٱللَّهِ حَقٌّ وَأَنَّ ٱلسَّاعَةَ لَا رَيْبَ فِيهَآ إِذْ يَتَنَٰزَعُونَ بَيْنَهُمْ أَمْرَهُمْ فَقَالُوا۟ ٱبْنُوا۟ عَلَيْهِم بُنْيَٰنًا رَّبُّهُمْ أَعْلَمُ بِهِمْ قَالَ ٱلَّذِينَ غَلَبُوا۟ عَلَىٰٓ أَمْرِهِمْ لَنَتَّخِذَنَّ عَلَيْهِم مَّسْجِدًا ۝ سَيَقُولُونَ ثَلَٰثَةٌ رَّابِعُهُمْ كَلْبُهُمْ وَيَقُولُونَ خَمْسَةٌ سَادِسُهُمْ كَلْبُهُمْ رَجْمًۢا بِٱلْغَيْبِ وَيَقُولُونَ سَبْعَةٌ وَثَامِنُهُمْ كَلْبُهُمْ قُل رَّبِّىٓ أَعْلَمُ بِعِدَّتِهِم مَّا يَعْلَمُهُمْ إِلَّا قَلِيلٌ فَلَا تُمَارِ

فِيهِمْ إِلَّا مِرَآءً ظَـٰهِرًا وَلَا تَسْتَفْتِ فِيهِم مِّنْهُمْ أَحَدًا ﴿٢٢﴾

Do you think that the people of the Cave and the Inscription (the news or the names of the people of the Cave) were a wonder among Our Signs? (Remember) when the young men fled for refuge (from their disbelieving folk) to the Cave. They said: "Our Lord! Bestow on us mercy from Yourself, and facilitate for us our affair in the right way!" Therefore, We covered up their (sense of) hearing (causing them to go in deep sleep) in the Cave for a number of years. Then We raised them up (from their sleep), that We might test which of the two parties was best at calculating the time period that they had tarried. We narrate to you (O Muhammad ﷺ) their story with truth: Truly, they were young men who believed in their Lord (Allāh), and We increased them in guidance. And We made their hearts firm and strong (with the light of faith in Allāh and bestowed upon them patience to bear the separation of their kith and kin and dwellings) when they stood up and said: "Our Lord is the Lord of the heavens and the earth, never shall we call upon any *ilāh* (god) other than Him; if we did, we should indeed have uttered an enormity in disbelief. These our people have taken for worship *ālihah* (gods) other than Him (Allāh). Why do they not bring for them a clear authority? And who does more wrong than he who invents a lie against Allāh." (The young men said to one another:) "And when you withdraw from them, and that which they worship, except Allāh, then seek refuge in the Cave; your Lord will open a way for you from His Mercy and will make easy for you your affair (i.e. will give you what you will need of provision, dwelling)." And you might have seen the sun, when it rose, declining to the right from their Cave, and when it set, turning away from them to the left, while they lay in the midst of the Cave. That is (one) of the *Ayāt* (proofs, evidences, signs) of Allāh. He whom Allāh guides, he is the rightly-guided; but he whom He sends astray, for him you will find no *Walī* (guiding friend) to lead him (to the Right Path). And you would have thought them awake, whereas they were asleep. And We turned them on their right and on their left sides, and their dog stretching forth his two forelegs at the entrance [of the Cave or in the space near to the entrance of the Cave (as a guard at the gate)]. Had you looked at them, you would certainly have turned back from them in flight, and would certainly have been filled with awe of them. Likewise, We awakened them (from their long deep sleep) that they might question one another. A speaker from among them said: "How long have you stayed (here)?" They said: "We have stayed (perhaps) a day or part of a day." They said: "Your Lord (Alone) knows best how long you have stayed (here). So send one of you with this silver coin of yours to the town, and let him find out which is the good lawful food, and bring some of that to you. And let him be careful and let no man know of you. For, if they come to know of you, they will stone you (to death or abuse and harm you) or turn you back to their religion; and in that case you will never be successful." And thus We made their case known (to the people), that they might know that the Promise of Allāh is true, and that there can be no doubt about the Hour. (Remember) when they (the people of the city) disputed among themselves about their case, they said: "Construct a building over them; their Lord knows best about them;" (then) those who won their point said (most probably the disbelievers): "We verily, shall build a place of worship over them." (Some) say they were three, the dog being the fourth among them; and (others) say they were five, the dog being the sixth, guessing at the unseen; (yet others) say they were seven, and the dog being the eighth. Say (O Muhammad ﷺ): "My Lord knows best their number; none knows them but a few." So, debate not (about their number) except with the clear proof (which We have revealed to you). And consult not any of them (people of the Scripture — Jews and Christians) about (the affair of) the people of the Cave.

(Qur'ân 18: 9-22)

"The People of the Cave" are given that name because of the story of how they fled from evil and took refuge in a spacious mountain cave. *Ar-Raqim* (the Inscription) in the above-mentioned Verses refs, according to the most broadly accepted view, to a tablet on which was written the names of the People of the Cave.

During that time, a polytheist king by the name of Diqyanus was ruler of Rome; and Tarasus was the name of a city that was a part of his realm. It was a rule with him to kill every single believer. When a group of youths saw the evil that was happening around them, they became very sad and fled from the king and his tyranny. Along with a shepherd and his dog, they took refuge in a cave, near Tarasus. Allâh then caused them to fall into a state of deep slumber. Without them realizing it, they continued to sleep for 300 sun years, which is equivalent to 309 moon years.

When Allâh ﷻ then caused them to wake up, they thought that they had been there for only a day or part of a day. They sent one among them to go out and buy food for them. When he went out and saw that everything had changed, he thought that he had lost his way. When he came across people, they were amazed at the kind of money he had with him. Everyone then discovered what had really happened. Allâh ﷻ then caused the People of the Cave to die in their cave. The people (most probably the disbelievers) then said:

"We verily shall build a place of worship over them." (Qur'ân 18: 21)

- At-Tafsir Al-Munir: 15/207
- Dâ'iratul- Ma'ârif Al-Qarn Al-'Ishrin: 8/220
- Safwatut-Tafâsir: 2/183

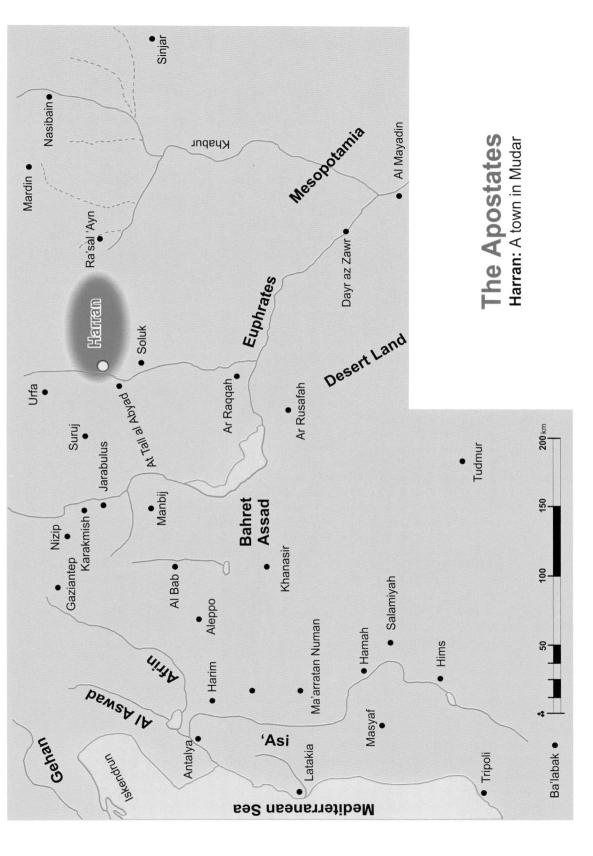

The Apostates
Harran: A town in Mudar

The Sabians (The Apostates)

The Sabians are mentioned three times in the Noble Qur'ân:

Chapter Name (Sûrah)	Number of Chapter (Sûrah)	Verse Numbers
Al-Baqarah	2	62
Al-Mâ'idah	5	69
Al-Hajj	22	17

﴿إِنَّ ٱلَّذِينَ ءَامَنُواْ وَٱلَّذِينَ هَادُواْ وَٱلنَّصَٰرَىٰ وَٱلصَّٰبِئِينَ مَنْ ءَامَنَ بِٱللَّهِ وَٱلْيَوْمِ ٱلْأَخِرِ وَعَمِلَ صَٰلِحًا فَلَهُمْ أَجْرُهُمْ عِندَ رَبِّهِمْ وَلَا خَوْفٌ عَلَيْهِمْ وَلَا هُمْ يَحْزَنُونَ ۝﴾

Verily, those who believe and those who are Jews and Christians, and Sabians, whoever believes in Allâh and the Last Day and does righteous good deeds shall have their reward with their Lord, on them shall be no fear, nor shall they grieve.

(Qur'ân 2: 62)

﴿إِنَّ ٱلَّذِينَ ءَامَنُواْ وَٱلَّذِينَ هَادُواْ وَٱلصَّٰبِئُونَ وَٱلنَّصَٰرَىٰ مَنْ ءَامَنَ بِٱللَّهِ وَٱلْيَوْمِ ٱلْأَخِرِ وَعَمِلَ صَٰلِحًا فَلَا خَوْفٌ عَلَيْهِمْ وَلَا هُمْ يَحْزَنُونَ ۝﴾

Surely, those who believe (in the Oneness of Allâh, in His Messenger Muhammad ﷺ and all that was revealed to him from Allâh), and those who are the Jews and the Sabians and the Christians, — whosoever believed in Allâh and the Last Day, and worked righteousness, on them shall be no fear, nor shall they grieve.

(Qur'ân 5: 69)

﴿إِنَّ ٱلَّذِينَ ءَامَنُواْ وَٱلَّذِينَ هَادُواْ وَٱلصَّٰبِئِينَ وَٱلنَّصَٰرَىٰ وَٱلْمَجُوسَ وَٱلَّذِينَ أَشْرَكُوٓاْ إِنَّ

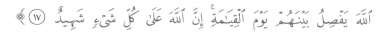

Verily, those who believe (in Allāh and in His Messenger Muhammad ﷺ), and those who are Jews, and the Sabians, and the Christians, and the Majūs (Magians) and those who worship others besides Allāh; truly, Allāh will judge between them on the Day of Resurrection. Verily, Allāh is over all things a Witness.

(Qur'ân 22: 17)

The Sabians that Allâh mentioned in the Noble Qur'ân were pure monotheists who lived before the first Jews and Christians. They worshiped Allâh alone, and they believed that Allâh ﷻ created the universe. They also believed in the resurrection of our bodies. Later on, their beliefs became strongly linked to the planets and stars, until they became accused of polytheism. Sabians are a religious group that did exist and continue to exist in northern Iraq; their central place was Harrân, and it then moved to Baghdad and elsewhere since the time of the first 'Abbasid rule. Some of them even accepted Islam. Much of their time has been dedicated to the study of natural phenomenon. And they are known for having translated many Greek and Asyrrian works into Arabic. Today, they are few in number and live in northern Iraq. As a protective measure, their beliefs are clouded in secrecy, for they fear that, as time goes on, their religion will end up changing.

- Dâ'iratul- Ma'arif Al-Qarn Al-'Ishrin: 5/ 426
- Al-Qâmus Al-Islami: 4/223
- Mo'jam Al-Buldân: 2/235
- Al-Mo'jam Al-Mufahris Li-Alfâz Al-Qur'ân Al-Karim: 399
- Al-Mo'jam Al-Mufahris Li-Ma'âni Al-Qur'ân Al-Karim: 657

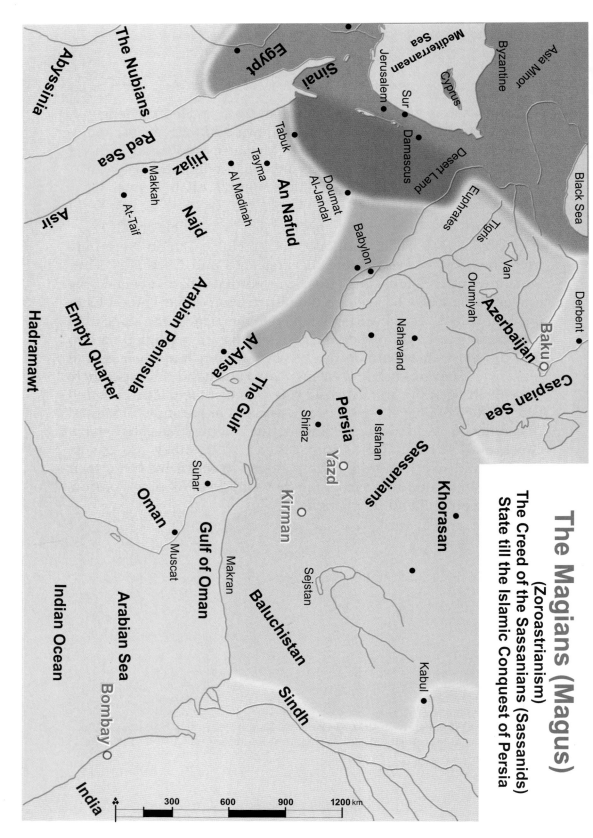

The Magians (Magus)

(Zoroastrianism)

The Creed of the Sassanians (Sassanids)
State till the Islamic Conquest of Persia

Mediterranean Sea

Byzantine

Asia Minor

Cyprus

Jerusalem

Sur

Damascus

Desert Land

Black Sea

Egypt

Sinai

Tabuk

Tayma

Al Madinah

Doumat
Al-Jandal

Babylon

Euphrates

Tigris

Van

Orumiyah

Derbent

Baku

Caspian Sea

Azerbaijan

Makkah

At-Taif

An Nafud

Najid

Hijaz

Asir

Red Sea

The Nubians

Abyssinia

Nahavand

Isfahan

Empty Quarter

Arabian Peninsula

Al-Ahsa

The Gulf

Persia

Shiraz

Yazd

Sassanians

Khorasan

Hadramawt

Suhar

Oman

Muscat

Gulf of Oman

Kirman

Kabul

Baluchistan

Sejstan

Makran

Arabian Sea

Bombay

Sindh

Indian Ocean

India

300   600   900   1200 km

A Fire Temple near Baku (Azerbaijan)

The Magians (Magus)

﴿إِنَّ ٱلَّذِينَ ءَامَنُوا۟ وَٱلَّذِينَ هَادُوا۟ وَٱلصَّٰبِـِٔينَ وَٱلنَّصَٰرَىٰ وَٱلْمَجُوسَ وَٱلَّذِينَ أَشْرَكُوٓا۟ إِنَّ ٱللَّهَ يَفْصِلُ بَيْنَهُمْ يَوْمَ ٱلْقِيَٰمَةِ إِنَّ ٱللَّهَ عَلَىٰ كُلِّ شَىْءٍ شَهِيدٌ﴾

Verily, those who believe (in Allāh and in His Messenger Muhammad ﷺ), and those who are Jews, and the Sabians, and the Christians, and the Majūs (Magians) and those who worship others besides Allāh; truly, Allāh will judge between them on the Day of Resurrection. Verily, Allāh is over all things a Witness.

(Qur'ân 22: 17)

Born in the city of Maydiyyah in Ar-Ra'yi, 600 years before the advent of the Christian calendar, Zoroaster (Zarathushtra) established the final doctrines of the Magians. Some sources claim that he was the Prophet. Originally from Azerbaijan, he authored a book that he called Avesta (Az-Zindafastâ); in it he prophesied the coming of Muhammad ﷺ, as is mentioned by Fideyârti in his book, *Muhammad in the Holy Books of the World.*

At the dawn of Islam, the Persian religion Zoroastrianism was the dominant religion among the people of Fâris. And approximately 900 years before the advent of Islam, it was the official religion of the Sassanian nation. The principal beliefs of the Magians revolve around a constant struggle between the god of goodness or light, Ahura Mazda and the god of evil or darkness, Ahriman. Deeming fire to be holy, they would ignite it in honor of Ahura Mazda. Some of their ancient fire temples are still intact today. The most important and famous of them is the one that is in Baku, the capital of Azerbaijan. There is also a similar temple on the peak of a hill beside Isfahan. And the people of Faris left behind a temple of fire in Yemen; its structure is still preserved today. There are still remnants of the religion Zoroastrianism in Bombay, India, as well as in Yazd and Kirman, which are both situated in the central part of Iran.

- Târikh AL-'Aalam: 4/366
- Al-Hadarah Al-'Arabiyyah Al-Islamiyyah: 68
- Dâ'iratul- Ma'arif Al-Qarn Al-'Ishrin: 4/550
- Al-Qamus Al-Islami: 3/44
- Qissatul-Hadârah: 2/424
- Al-Mo'jam Al-Mufahris Li-Alfâz Al-Qur'ân Al-Karim: 661
- Al-Mo'jam Al-Mufahris Li-Ma'âni Al-Qur'ân Al-Karim: 1071

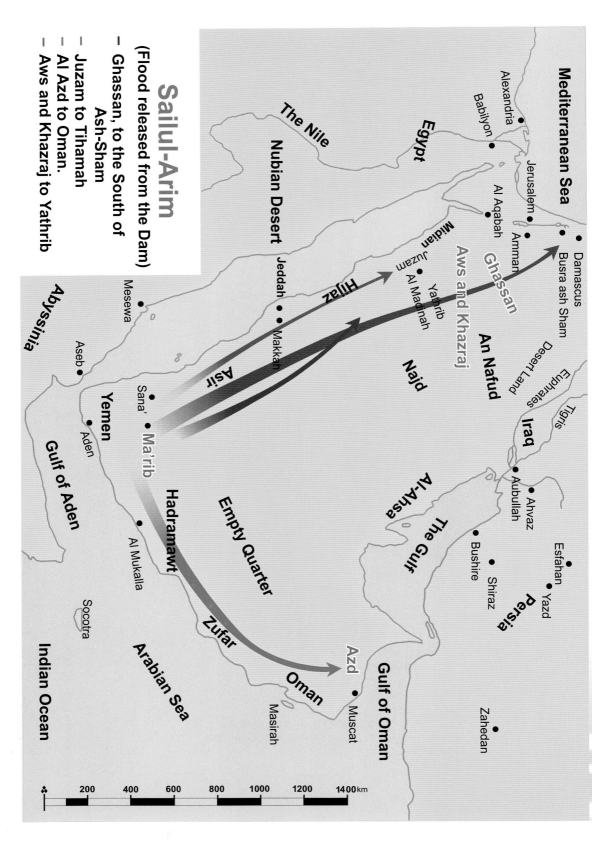

Sailul-Arim

(Flood released from the Dam)

- Ghassan, to the South of Ash-Sham
- Juzam to Tihamah
- Al Azd to Oman.
- Aws and Khazraj to Yathrib

Mediterranean Sea

Alexandria
Babilyon
Jerusalem
Amman
Damascus
Busra ash Sham

Egypt

The Nile

Nubian Desert

Al Aqabah

Jeddah
Makkah

Hijaz

Midian
Juzam
Al Madinah
Yathrib

Ghassan

Aws and Khazraj

An Nafud

Najd

Desert Land

Euphrates
Tigris

Iraq

Aubullah
Ahvaz

Esfahan
Yazd

Asir

Mesewa
Aseb

Yemen

Sana'
Ma'rib
Aden

Abyssinia

Gulf of Aden

Al-Ahsa

The Gulf

Bushire
Shiraz

Persia

Zahedan

Hadramawt

Al Mukalla

Socotra

Empty Quarter

Zufar

Azd

Oman

Muscat

Gulf of Oman

Masirah

Arabian Sea

Indian Ocean

200 400 600 800 1000 1200 1400km

Sailul-'Arim

﴿لَقَدْ كَانَ لِسَبَإٍ فِى مَسْكَنِهِمْ ءَايَةٌ جَنَّتَانِ عَن يَمِينٍ وَشِمَالٍ كُلُوا۟ مِن رِّزْقِ رَبِّكُمْ وَٱشْكُرُوا۟ لَهُۥ بَلْدَةٌ طَيِّبَةٌ وَرَبٌّ غَفُورٌ ۝ فَأَعْرَضُوا۟ فَأَرْسَلْنَا عَلَيْهِمْ سَيْلَ ٱلْعَرِمِ وَبَدَّلْنَـٰهُم بِجَنَّتَيْهِمْ جَنَّتَيْنِ ذَوَاتَىْ أُكُلٍ خَمْطٍ وَأَثْلٍ وَشَىْءٍ مِّن سِدْرٍ قَلِيلٍ ۝ ذَٰلِكَ جَزَيْنَـٰهُم بِمَا كَفَرُوا۟ وَهَلْ نُجَـٰزِىٓ إِلَّا ٱلْكَفُورَ ۝ ﴾

Indeed there was for Saba (Sheba) a sign in their dwelling place — two gardens on the right hand and on the left; (and it was said to them:) "Eat of the provision of your Lord, and be grateful to Him." A fair land and an Oft-Forgiving Lord! But they turned away (from the obedience of Allāh), so We sent against them *Sailul-'Arim* (flood released from the dam), and We converted their two gardens into gardens producing bitter bad fruit, and tamarisks, and some few lote trees. Like this We requited them because they were ungrateful disbelievers. And never do We requite in such a way except those who are ungrateful (disbelievers).

(Qur'ân 34: 15-17)

Having a deep and ancient history, Saba is a nation that was established in Yemen (from the years 950-115 before the beginning of the Christian calendar). The capital city was Ma'rib. Later on, it was The Al-Himyariyyun – who themselves were from the Sabaiyyin – who ruled that nation. And it was the nation of Al-Himyariyyah that involved itself in a struggle first with Al-Habashah and then with the people of Faris, until it was finally wiped out.

The city of Saba is also known by the name Ma'rib, which linguistically means 'plentiful water.' The waters of floods would gather in an adjacent valley, which is where the famous dam was built. It is from there that the inhabitants of Saba would draw water

181

to drink and to irrigate their gardens.

The famous flood that is referred to in the above-mentioned Verse (Sailul-'Arim) is what occurred after the collapse of the dam of Ma'rib. This all took place approximately 400 years before the advent of Islam. And it is said that Al-'Arim is the name of the valley over which the dam was built.

- Dâ'iratul- Ma'arif Al-Qarn Al-'Ishrin: 6/390
- Al-Qâmus Al-Islami: 3/221, 610
- Al-Mo'jam Al-Mufahris Li-Alfâz Al-Qur'ân Al-Karim: 374
- Al-Mo'jam Al-Mufahris Li-Ma'âni Al-Qur'ân Al-Karim: 612

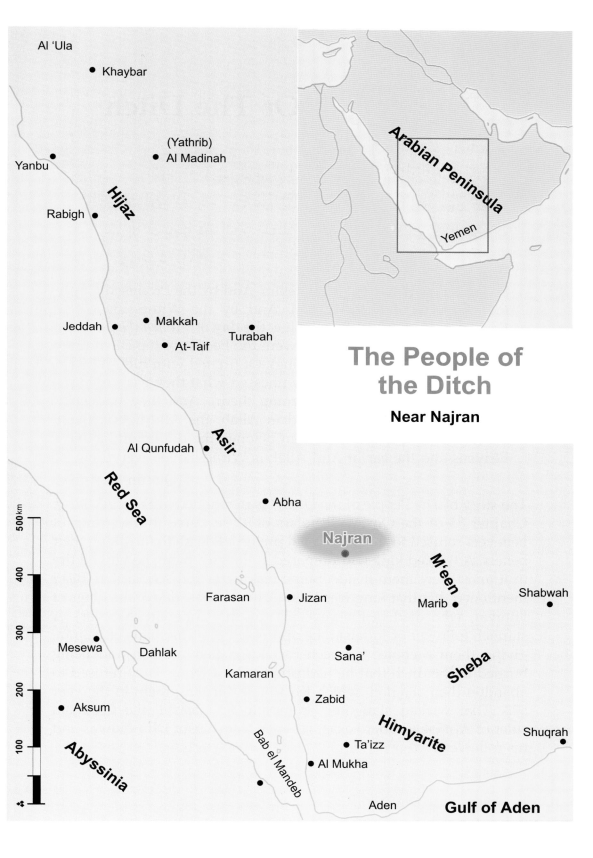

Al ʻUla

Khaybar

Arabian Peninsula

Yemen

(Yathrib)
Al Madinah

Yanbu

Hijaz

Rabigh

The People of
the Ditch

Near Najran

Jeddah

Makkah

At-Taif

Turabah

Al Qunfudah

Asir

Red Sea

Abha

Najran

M'een

Farasan

Jizan

Marib

Shabwah

500 km

400

Mesewa

Dahlak

Sana'

Sheba

300

Kamaran

200

Zabid

Aksum

Himyarite

Shuqrah

100

Abyssinia

Bab el Mandeb

Ta'izz

Al Mukha

Aden

Gulf of Aden

The People Of The Ditch

وَٱلسَّمَآءِ ذَاتِ ٱلْبُرُوجِ ﴿١﴾ وَٱلْيَوْمِ ٱلْمَوْعُودِ ﴿٢﴾ وَشَاهِدٍ وَمَشْهُودٍ ﴿٣﴾ قُتِلَ أَصْحَـٰبُ ٱلْأُخْدُودِ ﴿٤﴾ ٱلنَّارِ ذَاتِ ٱلْوَقُودِ ﴿٥﴾ إِذْ هُمْ عَلَيْهَا قُعُودٌ ﴿٦﴾ وَهُمْ عَلَىٰ مَا يَفْعَلُونَ بِٱلْمُؤْمِنِينَ شُهُودٌ ﴿٧﴾ وَمَا نَقَمُوا۟ مِنْهُمْ إِلَّآ أَن يُؤْمِنُوا۟ بِٱللَّهِ ٱلْعَزِيزِ ٱلْحَمِيدِ ﴿٨﴾ ٱلَّذِى لَهُۥ مُلْكُ ٱلسَّمَـٰوَٰتِ وَٱلْأَرْضِ وَٱللَّهُ عَلَىٰ كُلِّ شَىْءٍ شَهِيدٌ ﴿٩﴾

By the heaven holding the big stars. And by the Promised Day (i.e. the Day of Resurrection). And by the Witnessing (i.e. Friday), and by the Witnessed [i.e. the day of 'Arafah (Hajj), the ninth of Dhul-Hijjah]; Cursed were the People of the Ditch (in the story of the Boy and the King). Of fire fed with fuel, When they sat by it (fire), And they witnessed what they were doing against the believers (i.e., burning them). And they had no fault except that they believed in Allāh, the All-Mighty, the Worthy of all praise! To Whom belongs the dominion of the heavens and the earth! And Allāh is Witness over everything.

(Qur'ân 85: 1-9)

The story of The People of the Ditch'' is mentioned in *Sûrat Al-Burûj*, Chapter 85 of the Qur'ân. Scholars of *Tafsir* agree that a group of believers refused to apostatize and preferred death to forsaking their beliefs. A wicked king had prepared a ditch for them; he ignited fire in it and threw them inside. Some historians and scholars of *Tafsir* mentioned that that king was Yusuf Dhu-Nuwâs, one of the kings of Himyar, who died in the year 524 (by the Christian calendar). A staunch follower of Judaism, he oppressed the Christians of Najrân, giving them a choice between forsaking their religion and being burned in the ditch that he had prepared for them. They refused to abandon their religion, which led to him burning them in the year 523. That wicked slaughter prompted An-Najâshi, the Christian ruler of Al-Habashah, to exact revenge from Yusuf Dhu-Nuwas and his followers.

After the king ignited fire in the ditch, he ordered his soldiers to bring every male and female believer and to show them the fire. Anyone that did not abandon his religion was to be thrown into the fire, which is what ended up happening. When the turn came for a woman who had her young son with her to fall into the ditch, she hesitated. Her son then said, "O Mother, be patient, for indeed you are upon the truth." (The story of the woman and her child is related in *Sahih Muslim*)

- At-Tafsir Al-Munir: 30/155
- Safwatut-Tafâsir: 3/540
- Al-Qâmus Al-Islami: 1/120
- Al-Mo'jam Al-Mufahris Li-Alfâz Al-Qur'ân Al-Karim: 227
- Al-Mo'jam Al-Mufahris Li-Ma'âni Al-Qur'ân Al-Karim: 80
- Al-Mausu'ah Al-Yamaniyyah: 2/1035,

The People of the Garden

Dawran: From the fortresses of Yemen owned by Bani Al-Harsh (south of Sana')

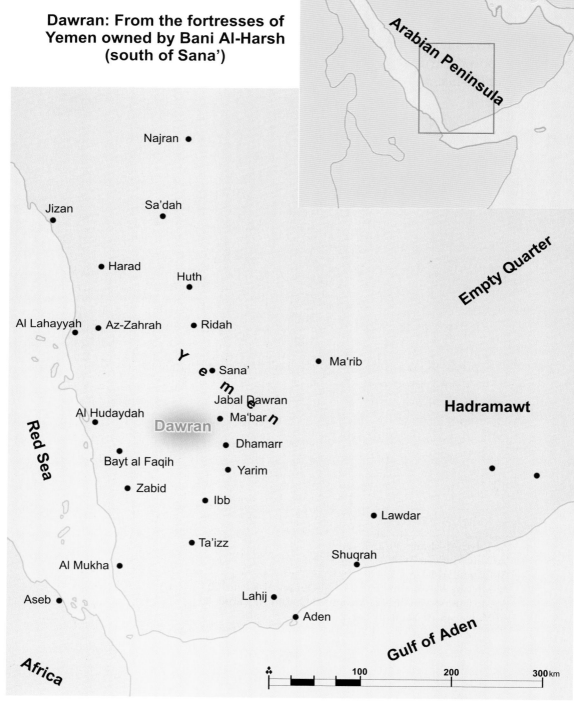

The People Of The Garden

﴿إِنَّا بَلَوْنَٰهُمْ كَمَا بَلَوْنَآ أَصْحَٰبَ ٱلْجَنَّةِ إِذْ أَقْسَمُوا۟ لَيَصْرِمُنَّهَا مُصْبِحِينَ ۝ وَلَا يَسْتَثْنُونَ ۝ فَطَافَ عَلَيْهَا طَآئِفٌ مِّن رَّبِّكَ وَهُمْ نَآئِمُونَ ۝ فَأَصْبَحَتْ كَٱلصَّرِيمِ ۝ فَتَنَادَوْا۟ مُصْبِحِينَ ۝ أَنِ ٱغْدُوا۟ عَلَىٰ حَرْثِكُمْ إِن كُنتُمْ صَٰرِمِينَ ۝ فَٱنطَلَقُوا۟ وَهُمْ يَتَخَٰفَتُونَ ۝ أَن لَّا يَدْخُلَنَّهَا ٱلْيَوْمَ عَلَيْكُم مِّسْكِينٌ ۝ وَغَدَوْا۟ عَلَىٰ حَرْدٍ قَٰدِرِينَ ۝ فَلَمَّا رَأَوْهَا قَالُوٓا۟ إِنَّا لَضَآلُّونَ ۝ بَلْ نَحْنُ مَحْرُومُونَ ۝ قَالَ أَوْسَطُهُمْ أَلَمْ أَقُل لَّكُمْ لَوْلَا تُسَبِّحُونَ ۝ قَالُوا۟ سُبْحَٰنَ رَبِّنَآ إِنَّا كُنَّا ظَٰلِمِينَ ۝ فَأَقْبَلَ بَعْضُهُمْ عَلَىٰ بَعْضٍ يَتَلَٰوَمُونَ ۝ قَالُوا۟ يَٰوَيْلَنَآ إِنَّا كُنَّا طَٰغِينَ ۝ عَسَىٰ رَبُّنَآ أَن يُبْدِلَنَا خَيْرًا مِّنْهَآ إِنَّآ إِلَىٰ رَبِّنَا رَٰغِبُونَ ۝ كَذَٰلِكَ ٱلْعَذَابُ وَلَعَذَابُ ٱلْءَاخِرَةِ أَكْبَرُ لَوْ كَانُوا۟ يَعْلَمُونَ ۝﴾

Verily, We have tried them as We tried the People of the Garden, when they swore to pluck the fruits of the (garden) in the morning, Without saying: *In shā' Allāh* (If Allāh wills). Then there passed by on it (the garden) a visitation (fire) from your Lord (at night and burnt it) while they were asleep. So the (garden) became black by the morning, like a pitch dark night (in complete ruins). Then they called out one to another as soon as the morning broke. Saying: "Go to your tilth in the morning, if you would pluck the fruits." So they departed, conversing in secret low tones (saying): "No *Miskīn* (needy man) shall enter upon you into it today." And they went in the morning with strong intention, thinking that they have power (to prevent the poor taking anything of the fruits therefrom). But when they saw the (garden), they said: "Verily, we have gone astray." (Then they said): "Nay! Indeed we are deprived of (the fruits)!" The best among them said: "Did I not tell you, why say you not: *In shā' Allāh* (If Allāh wills)." They said: "Glory to Our Lord! Verily, we have been *Zālimūn* (wrong doers)." Then they turned one against another, blaming. They said: "Woe to us! Verily, we were *Tāghūn* (transgressors and disobedient). We hope that our Lord will give us in exchange a better (garden) than this. Truly, we turn to our Lord (wishing for good that He may forgive our sins and reward us in the Hereafter)." Such is the punishment (in this life), but truly, the punishment of the Hereafter is greater if they but knew.

(Qur'ân 68: 17-33)

The people of the Garden were in Dawran. Dawran, which belonged to Bani Harsh, was one of the fortified cities of Yemen. And Dawraan is also the name of a mountain that actually overlooks the city.

- At-Tafsir Al-Munir: 29/59
- Safwatut-Tafâsir: 3/427
- Mo'jam Al-Buldân: 3/464

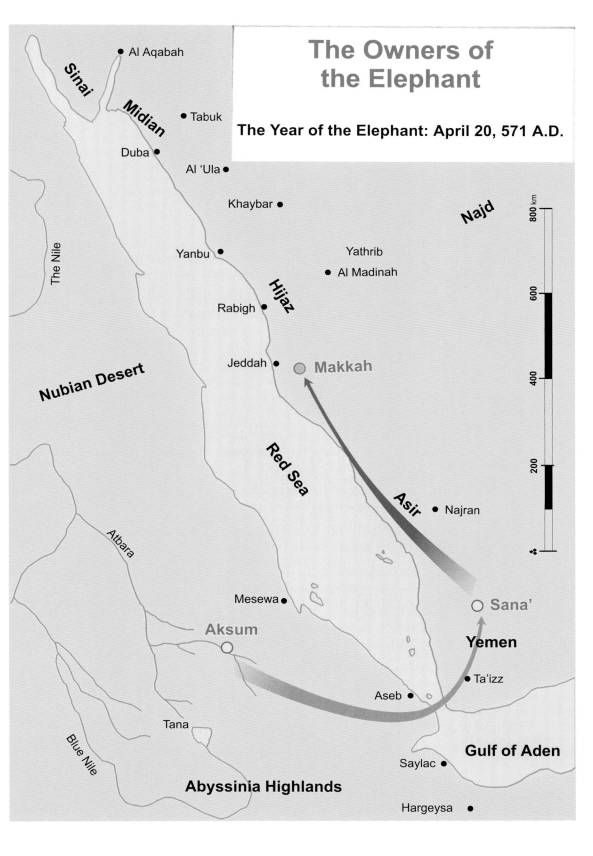

The Owners of
the Elephant

The Year of the Elephant: April 20, 571 A.D.

Al Aqabah

Sinai

Midian

Tabuk

Duba

Al 'Ula

Khaybar

The Nile

Yanbu

Najd

Yathrib

Al Madinah

Hijaz

Rabigh

Nubian Desert

Jeddah

Makkah

Red Sea

Asir

Najran

Atbara

Mesewa

Sana'

Aksum

Yemen

Ta'izz

Tana

Aseb

Blue Nile

Gulf of Aden

Saylac

Abyssinia Highlands

Hargeysa

800 km

600

400

200

The Owners Of The Elephant

﴿أَلَمْ تَرَ كَيْفَ فَعَلَ رَبُّكَ بِأَصْحَٰبِ ٱلْفِيلِ ۝ أَلَمْ يَجْعَلْ كَيْدَهُمْ فِي تَضْلِيلٍ ۝ وَأَرْسَلَ عَلَيْهِمْ طَيْرًا أَبَابِيلَ ۝ تَرْمِيهِم بِحِجَارَةٍ مِّن سِجِّيلٍ ۝ فَجَعَلَهُمْ كَعَصْفٍ مَّأْكُولٍۭ ۝﴾

Have you (O Muhammad ﷺ) not seen how your Lord dealt with the Owners of the Elephant? [The Elephant Army which came from Yemen under the command of Abrahah Al-Ashram intending to destroy the Ka'bah at Makkah]. Did He not make their plot go astray? And He sent against them birds, in flocks, Striking them with stones of *Sijjīl* (baked clay). And He made them like (an empty field of) stalks (of which the corn) has been eaten up (by cattle).

(Qur'ân 105: 1-5)

"The Owners Of The Elephant" refers to the army of Abrahah ibn Al-Ashram Al-Habashi, who became ruler of Yemen after the demise of Yusuf Dhu-Nuwas. In the year 571 (of the Christian calendar), the same year in which the Messenger of Allâh ﷺ was born, Abrahah led his army towards the inviolable city of Makkah with the intention of destroying the Ka'bah. He wanted the Arabs to stop performing pilgrimage to Makkah, and to instead perform pilgrimage to the Al-Qullais church, which he had built in San'a.

As the army marched forward, a huge elephant remained at the front of it. One narration mentions that when Abrahah was preparing to enter Makkah, the elephant knelt down, refusing to go forward. As much as they tried to get the elephant to move, it wouldn't budge. When they turned it away from Makkah and made it face Ash-Sham, it began to race forward. Then they turned it towards Yemen, and it did the same. But whenever they tried to turn it towards Makkah, it wouldn't move.

On his way to Makkah, Abrahah usurped the wealth of many Arabs. Among the wealth he stole, were camels that belonged to

'Abdul-Muttalib ibn Hashim, the grandfather of the Messenger of Allâh ﷺ. 'Abdul-Muttalib presented himself before Abrahah and demanded that he return his wealth back to him. Abrahah was somewhat taken aback by his words, and so he said, "You speak to me about 200 camels that I took from you, yet you care nothing for the House (the Ka'bah), which represents your religion and the religion of your fathers! I have come to destroy it, yet you say nothing to me about that!" 'Abdul-Muttalib said, "Indeed, I am the lord of these camels, and indeed, the House has a Lord Who will prevent you from (harming) it."

Then Allâh ﷺ sent many flocks of birds, birds with stones of *Sijjîl* (stony, hard clay). They pelted the soldiers of Abrahah with them, and the army then became like an empty field of stalks of which the corn has been eaten up by cattle.

There was a traitor Abu Righal who guided the enemy to Makkah. His grave is at Mughammus on the way to Tâ'if. It is said that even today the Arabs pelt stones at his grave.

- At-Tafsir Al-Munir: 30/404
- Safwatut-Tafâsir: 3/604
- Al-Qâmûs Al-Islami: 1/121

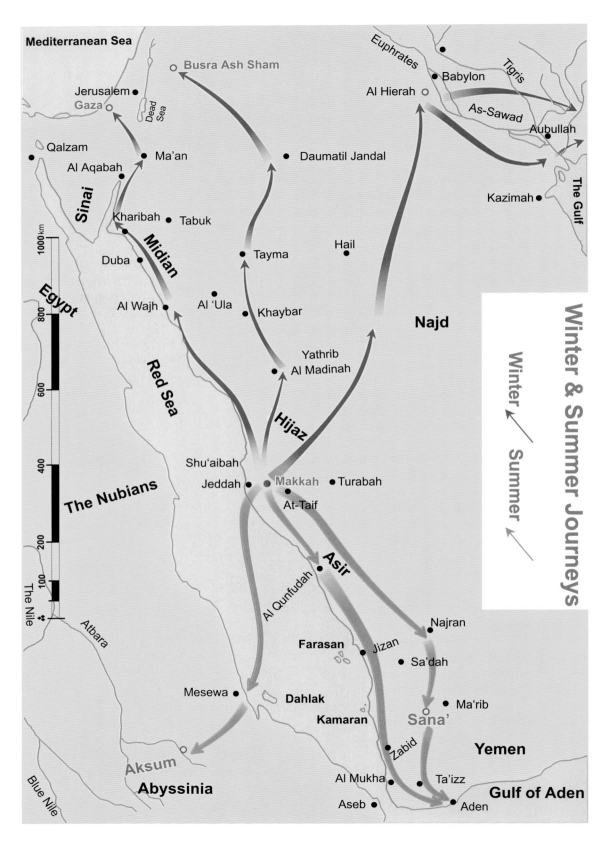

Mediterranean Sea

Euphrates

Tigris

Busra Ash Sham

Babylon

Al Hierah

As-Sawad

Jerusalem

Gaza

Dead Sea

Daumatil Jandal

Aubullah

Qalzam

Ma'an

Kazimah

The Gulf

Al Aqabah

Sinai

Kharibah

Tabuk

Midian

Hail

Duba

Tayma

Al Wajh

Al 'Ula

Khaybar

Najd

Egypt

Red Sea

Yathrib
Al Madinah

The Nubians

Hijaz

Shu'aibah

Makkah

Turabah

Jeddah

At-Taif

Asir

Al Qunfudah

Najran

Farasan

Jizan

Sa'dah

Mesewa

Dahlak

Ma'rib

Kamaran

Sana'

Aksum

Zabid

Yemen

Abyssinia

Al Mukha

Ta'izz

Aseb

Aden

Gulf of Aden

Atbara

The Nile

Blue Nile

1000 km
800
600
400
200
100

Winter & Summer Journeys

Winter

Summer

Gaza Hashim

Old Sana'

The Winter And Summer Journeys

﴿ لِإِيلَٰفِ قُرَيۡشٍ ۝ إِۦلَٰفِهِمۡ رِحۡلَةَ ٱلشِّتَآءِ وَٱلصَّيۡفِ ۝ فَلۡيَعۡبُدُواْ رَبَّ هَٰذَا ٱلۡبَيۡتِ ۝ ٱلَّذِىٓ أَطۡعَمَهُم مِّن جُوعٍ وَءَامَنَهُم مِّنۡ خَوۡفِۢ ۝ ﴾

(It is a great grace from Allāh) for the protection of the Quraish, (and with all those Allāh's grace and protections, We cause) the (Quraish) caravans to set forth safe in winter (to the south) and in summer (to the north without any fear). So let them worship (Allāh) the Lord of this House (the Ka'bah in Makkah), (He) Who has fed them against hunger, and has made them safe from fear.

(Qur'ân Quraish 106: 1 - 4)

Every year, the leaders of the Quraish would make preparations for two journeys, one in the winter and one in the summer. In the winter, they would travel to Yemen and Al-Habashah. And in the summer, they would travel to Ash-Sham and Iraq. It was the four sons of 'Abd Manâf who would lead the caravans. Hashim headed the caravan that would go to Ash-Sham and particularly to the area of Gaza; his journeys to Gaza became so famous that the town soon became known as Gaza of Hashim. Al-Muttalib headed the caravan that would go to Yemen. 'Abd Shams headed the caravan that would go to Al-Habashah. And Naufal headed the caravan that would go to Iraq. These trading caravans of the Quraish would travel in complete safety; no one dared to harm them on their way, for they were the neighbors of the House of Allâh, the dwellers of His inviolable city.

- At-Tafsir Al-Munir: 30/412
- Safwatut-Tafâsir: 3/606
- Al-Qâmûs Al-Islami (2/507)

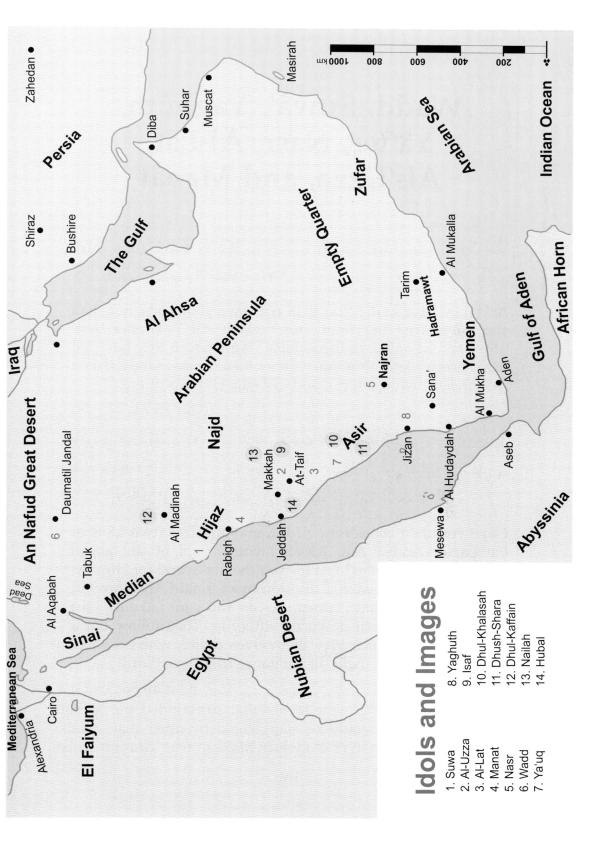

Idols and Images

1. Suwa
2. Al-Uzza
3. Al-Lat
4. Manat
5. Nasr
6. Wadd
7. Ya'uq
8. Yaghuth
9. Isaf
10. Dhul-Khalasah
11. Dhush-Shara
12. Dhul-Kaffain
13. Nailah
14. Hubal

Wadd, Suwâ', Yaghûth, Ya'ûq, Nasr, Al-Lât, Al-'Uzza, and Manât

﴿وَقَالُواْ لَا تَذَرُنَّ ءَالِهَتَكُمْ وَلَا تَذَرُنَّ وَدًّا وَلَا سُوَاعًا وَلَا يَغُوثَ وَيَعُوقَ وَنَسْرًا ۝ وَقَدْ أَضَلُّواْ كَثِيرًا وَلَا تَزِدِ ٱلظَّـٰلِمِينَ إِلَّا ضَلَـٰلًا ۝﴾

And they have said: "You shall not leave your gods, nor shall you leave *Wadd*, nor *Suwā'*, nor *Yaghūth*, nor *Ya'ūq*, nor *Nasr'* (these are the names of their idols).'' And indeed they have led many astray. And (O Allāh): "Grant no increase to the *Zālimūn* (polytheists, wrong doers, and disbelievers) except error.''

(Qur'ân 71: 23 - 24)

﴿أَفَرَءَيْتُمُ ٱللَّـٰتَ وَٱلْعُزَّىٰ ۝ وَمَنَوٰةَ ٱلثَّالِثَةَ ٱلْأُخْرَىٰ ۝ أَلَكُمُ ٱلذَّكَرُ وَلَهُ ٱلْأُنثَىٰ ۝ تِلْكَ إِذًا قِسْمَةٌ ضِيزَىٰ ۝ إِنْ هِىَ إِلَّا أَسْمَاءٌ سَمَّيْتُمُوهَا أَنتُمْ وَءَابَاؤُكُم مَّا أَنزَلَ ٱللَّهُ بِهَا مِن سُلْطَـٰنٍ إِن يَتَّبِعُونَ إِلَّا ٱلظَّنَّ وَمَا تَهْوَى ٱلْأَنفُسُ وَلَقَدْ جَاءَهُم مِّن رَّبِّهِمُ ٱلْهُدَىٰ ۝﴾

Have you then considered *Al-Lāt*, and *Al-'Uzzā* (two idols of the pagan Arabs) And *Manāt* (another idol of the pagan Arabs), the other third? Is it for you the males and for Him the females? That indeed is a division most unfair! They are but names which you have named — you and your fathers — for which Allāh has sent down no authority. They follow but a guess and that which they themselves desire, whereas there has surely come to them the guidance from their Lord!

(Qur'ân 53: 19-23)

An-Nusub and *Al-Ansâb* were stones that surrounded the Ka'bah. Upon them animals would be slaughtered by other than Allâh's name. The first person to erect idols in Makkah was 'Amr bin Luhai

196

Al-Azdi, who brought them from the lands of Ash-Sham (Syria and surrounding regions). These are the most important idols that people worshipped before the advent of Islam:

- Isâf and Nâ'ilah, which were located beside the door of the Ka'bah.

- Al-Uqaisar: the idol of Quda'ah, Lakhm, and 'Āmilah; it was located in the highlands of Ash-Sham.

- Al-Jalsad: an idol in Hadramawt; the tribe of Kindah worshipped it.

- Dhul-Khalasah: it was located in Tubâlah, between Makkah and Yemen. The tribes of Kath'am, Bujailah, Azd As-Surât, and those Arabs who were near them from the sub-tribes of Hawâzin, would glorify [and worship] Dhul-Khalasah.

- Dhush-Shara: an idol that belonged to Bani Al-Hârith ibn Mubasshir Al-Azdi.

- Dhul-Kaffain: the idol of the Daus tribe.

- Suwa': the idol of Hudhail in Madrakah, in the land of Yanbu', near Al-Madinah Al-Munawwarah.

- Ad-Daizanân (two idols): these two idols belonged to Judhaimah Al-Abrash in Hirah. It is said that Al-Mundhir Al-Akbar placed them at the gate of Al-Hirah. As a test of their loyalty and obedience, people who entered the gate of the city were required to perform prostration before the idols.

- 'Ā'im: the idol of Azd As-Surât.

- Al-'Uzza: this idol was placed in Makkah, on the right side of a way that led to Iraq. Al-'Uzza was the most venerated and important of Quraish's idols.

- Al-Lât: the idol of At-Tâ'if. In its place now stands the minaret of a Masjid in At-Tâ'if.

- Manât: Of all the idols that belonged to Arabs, Manât is the oldest. It was placed on the shores of the sea, in the direction of Al-Mushallal at Qudaid, which is somewhere between Makkah and Al-Madinah.

- Nasr: it was located in Yemen. The Himyar tribe worshiped it in the land of Balkha'.

- Hubal: this idol was placed inside of the Ka'bah.

- Wadd: the tribe of Kalb worshiped it in Daumatil-Jandal.

- Ya'uq: the tribe of Hamdaan worshiped it in the town of Khaiwân, near San'a.

- Yaghûth: Madhij, Jurash, and others worshiped this idol.

- Al-Asnâm (A number of pages throughout the book)
- Al-'Alâm: 5/84
- Al-Qâmus Al-Islami (A number of places throughout various volumes of the book)

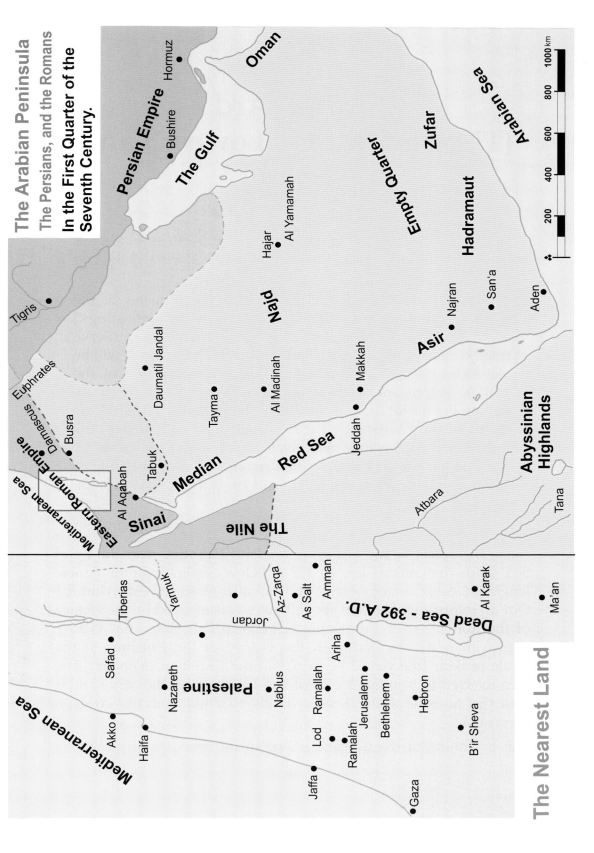

The Arabian Peninsula
The Persians, and the Romans
In the First Quarter of the Seventh Century.

The Nearest Land

Adnal-Ard
(The Nearest Or Lowest Land)

الٓمٓ ۝ غُلِبَتِ ٱلرُّومُ ۝ فِىٓ أَدْنَى ٱلْأَرْضِ وَهُم مِّنۢ بَعْدِ غَلَبِهِمْ سَيَغْلِبُونَ ۝ فِى بِضْعِ سِنِينَ لِلَّهِ ٱلْأَمْرُ مِن قَبْلُ وَمِنۢ بَعْدُ وَيَوْمَئِذٍ يَفْرَحُ ٱلْمُؤْمِنُونَ ۝ بِنَصْرِ ٱللَّهِ يَنصُرُ مَن يَشَآءُ وَهُوَ ٱلْعَزِيزُ ٱلرَّحِيمُ ۝

Alif-Lām-Mīm. [These letters are one of the miracles of the Qur'ān, and none but Allāh (Alone) knows their meanings.] The Romans have been defeated. In the nearest land (Syria, Iraq, Jordan, and Palestine), and they, after their defeat, will be victorious. Within three to nine years. The decision of the matter, before and after (these events) is only with Allāh, (before the defeat of the Romans by the Persians, and after the defeat of the Persians by the Romans). And on that day, the believers (i.e. Muslims) will rejoice (at the victory given by Allāh to the Romans against the Persians) — With the Help of Allāh. He helps whom He wills, and He is the All-Mighty, the Most Merciful.

(Qur'ân 30: 1-5)

Adnal-Ard refers to the low-lying lands of Palestine near the Dead Sea, lands that sink as low as 392 m below sea level. In the Arabic language, *Adna* means nearest and can also mean lowest. What the Qur'ân informs us of in the above Verses was realized by the victory of the Romans over the people of Faris in Palestine. That victory approximately coincided with the victory of the Muslims in the battle of Badr (the year 2 H, or 624 in the Christian calendar). The area referred to is in fact the most low-lying part of the earth, and it was the nearest of the Roman lands to Faris and the Arabian Peninsula.

The beginning of the Chapter is one of the miracles of the Noble

Qur'ân. It mentions events that were to take place after the Chapter was revealed, events that did actually come to pass shortly afterwards. Hence those Verses are from the clear signs that attest to the truthfulness of the Prophet ﷺ and to the Qur'ân being from Allâh ﷻ.

- At-Tafsir Al-Munir: 21/42
- Safwatut-Tafâsir: 2/470
- Lisân Al-'Arab (a dictionary), for the words, 'Dana' and 'Safula.'

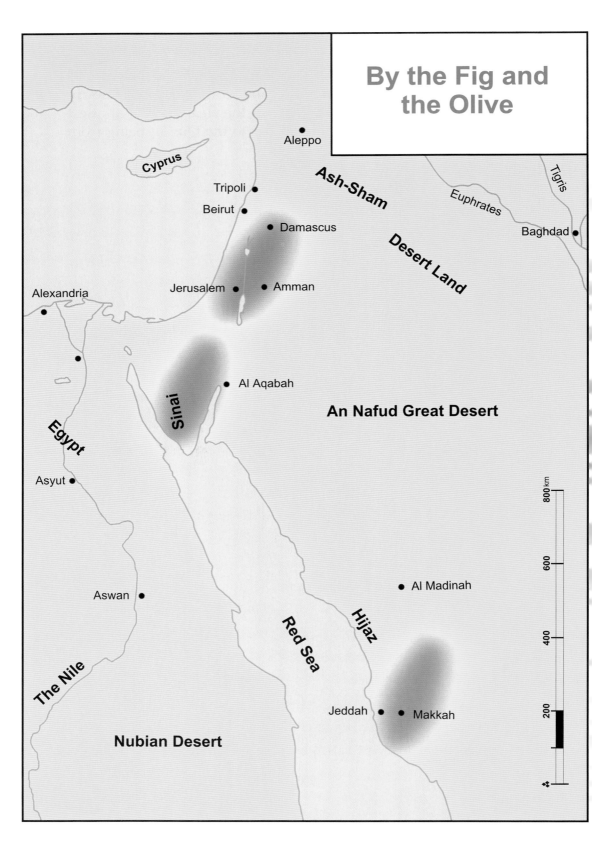

By the Fig and the Olive

Aleppo

Cyprus

Ash-Sham

Tigris

Tripoli

Euphrates

Beirut

Damascus

Baghdad

Desert Land

Alexandria

Jerusalem

Amman

Sinai

Al Aqabah

An Nafud Great Desert

Egypt

Asyut

Aswan

Al Madinah

Hijaz

Red Sea

The Nile

Jeddah

Makkah

Nubian Desert

800 km

600

400

200

The Fig And The Olive, Mount Sinai, And The City Of Security (Makkah)

﴿وَالتِّينِ وَالزَّيْتُونِ ۝ وَطُورِ سِينِينَ ۝ وَهَٰذَا ٱلْبَلَدِ ٱلْأَمِينِ ۝ لَقَدْ خَلَقْنَا ٱلْإِنسَٰنَ فِى أَحْسَنِ تَقْوِيمٍ ۝ ثُمَّ رَدَدْنَٰهُ أَسْفَلَ سَٰفِلِينَ ۝ إِلَّا ٱلَّذِينَ ءَامَنُوا۟ وَعَمِلُوا۟ ٱلصَّٰلِحَٰتِ فَلَهُمْ أَجْرٌ غَيْرُ مَمْنُونٍ ۝ فَمَا يُكَذِّبُكَ بَعْدُ بِٱلدِّينِ ۝ أَلَيْسَ ٱللَّهُ بِأَحْكَمِ ٱلْحَٰكِمِينَ ۝﴾

By the fig, and the olive. By Mount Sinai. By this city of security (Makkah). Verily, We created man in the best stature (mould). Then We reduced him to the lowest of the low. Except those who believe (in Islamic Monotheism) and do righteous deeds. Then they shall have a reward without end (Paradise). Then what (or who) causes you (O disbelievers) to deny the Recompense (i.e. the Day of Resurrection)? Is not Allâh the Best of judges?'

(Qur'ân 95: 1-8)

Here, Allâh ﷻ swears by holy and honored places, places that He ﷻ chose for revelation to come down to His Prophets and Messengers. The first of those places is Ash-Sham (Syria and surrounding regions) in general, and Jerusalem in particular, for figs and olives grow in those lands. It is as if Allâh ﷻ is swearing by the message that was revealed to 'Īsâ ﷺ.

Mount Sinai is in the area of Sinai. It is as if Allâh ﷻ is swearing by the message that was revealed to Musa ﷺ on Mount Sinai; '*Sinin*' in the above-mentioned verse literally means, 'blessed.' And 'this city of security' refers to Makkah Al-Mukarramah, which is where Prophet Muhammad ﷺ received Revelation.

Therefore, it is as if the Verses are oaths taken by the divine messages that were revealed to 'Īsâ ﷺ, Musa ﷺ, and Muhammad

ﷺ. This points to a spirit of brotherhood between the Prophets ﷺ, for though the laws they came with differed, their religion was one and the same – the religion of Islam.

"Truly, the religion with Allâh is Islam." (Qur'ân 3: 19)

- At-Tafsir Al-Munir: 30/301
- Safwatut-Tafâsir: 3/ 577

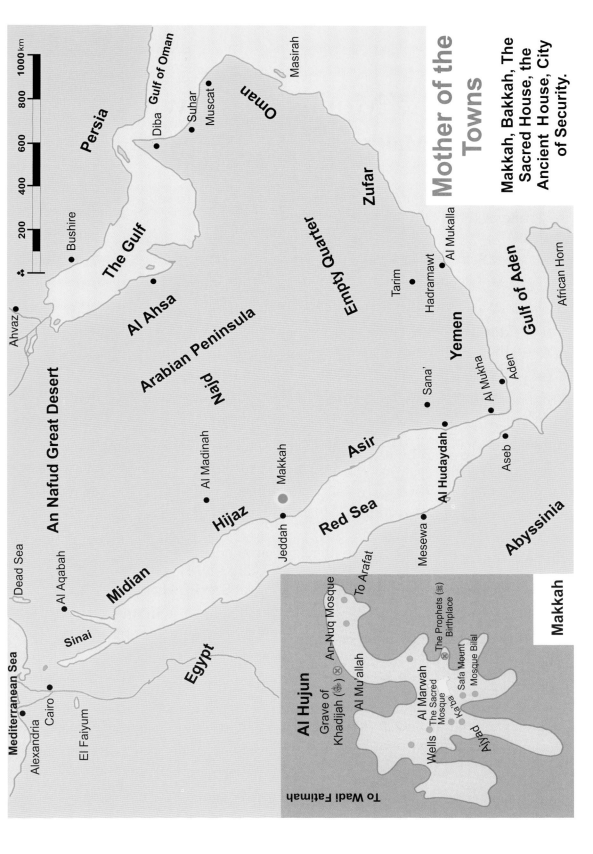

Mother of the Towns

Makkah, Bakkah, The Sacred House, the Ancient House, City of Security.

Makkah

Al Hujun

Grave of Khadijah (⚜) ⊗ An-Nuq Mosque

Al Mu'allah

To Arafat

The Prophets (⚜) Birthplace ⊗

Al Marwah

The Sacred Mosque

Wells

Ka'ba

Safa Mount

Mosque Bilal

Aiyad

To Wadi Fatimah

The Mother of Towns
(Makkah Al-Mukarramah)

In the Noble Qur'ân, different names are used to refer to Makkah, one of them being "The Mother of Towns".

﴿وَهَٰذَا كِتَٰبٌ أَنزَلْنَٰهُ مُبَارَكٌ مُّصَدِّقُ ٱلَّذِي بَيْنَ يَدَيْهِ وَلِتُنذِرَ أُمَّ ٱلْقُرَىٰ وَمَنْ حَوْلَهَا وَٱلَّذِينَ يُؤْمِنُونَ بِٱلْءَاخِرَةِ يُؤْمِنُونَ بِهِۦ وَهُمْ عَلَىٰ صَلَاتِهِمْ يُحَافِظُونَ ٩٢﴾

And this (the Qur'ān) is a blessed Book which We have sent down, confirming (the Revelations) which came before it, so that you may warn the Mother of Towns (i.e., Makkah) and all those around it. Those who believe in the Hereafter believe in it (the Qur'ān), and they are constant in guarding their *Salāt* (prayers).

(Qur'ân 6: 92)

It is referred to by its name, Makkah, in the following verse:

﴿وَهُوَ ٱلَّذِي كَفَّ أَيْدِيَهُمْ عَنكُمْ وَأَيْدِيَكُمْ عَنْهُم بِبَطْنِ مَكَّةَ مِنۢ بَعْدِ أَنْ أَظْفَرَكُمْ عَلَيْهِمْ وَكَانَ ٱللَّهُ بِمَا تَعْمَلُونَ بَصِيرًا ٢٤﴾

And He it is Who has withheld their hands from you and your hands from them in the midst of Makkah, after He had made you victors over them. And Allāh is Ever All-Seer of what you do.

(Qur'ân 48: 24)

It is referred to by another name, Bakkah, in the following verse:

﴿إِنَّ أَوَّلَ بَيْتٍ وُضِعَ لِلنَّاسِ لَلَّذِي بِبَكَّةَ مُبَارَكًا وَهُدًى لِّلْعَٰلَمِينَ ٩٦﴾

Verily, the first House (of worship) appointed for mankind was that at *Bakkah* (Makkah), full of blessing, and a guidance for *Al-'Ālamīn* (mankind and jinn).   (Qur'ân 3: 96)

206

In the following verse, it is called "The Sacred House," because of the presence of the Ka'bah in its precincts:

﴿يَٰٓأَيُّهَا ٱلَّذِينَ ءَامَنُوا۟ لَا تُحِلُّوا۟ شَعَٰٓئِرَ ٱللَّهِ وَلَا ٱلشَّهْرَ ٱلْحَرَامَ وَلَا ٱلْهَدْىَ وَلَا ٱلْقَلَٰٓئِدَ وَلَآ ءَآمِّينَ ٱلْبَيْتَ ٱلْحَرَامَ يَبْتَغُونَ فَضْلًا مِّن رَّبِّهِمْ وَرِضْوَٰنًا وَإِذَا حَلَلْتُمْ فَٱصْطَادُوا۟ وَلَا يَجْرِمَنَّكُمْ شَنَـَٔانُ قَوْمٍ أَن صَدُّوكُمْ عَنِ ٱلْمَسْجِدِ ٱلْحَرَامِ أَن تَعْتَدُوا۟ وَتَعَاوَنُوا۟ عَلَى ٱلْبِرِّ وَٱلتَّقْوَىٰ وَلَا تَعَاوَنُوا۟ عَلَى ٱلْإِثْمِ وَٱلْعُدْوَٰنِ وَٱتَّقُوا۟ ٱللَّهَ إِنَّ ٱللَّهَ شَدِيدُ ٱلْعِقَابِ ٢﴾

O you who believe! Violate not the sanctity of the Symbols of Allāh, nor of the Sacred Month, nor of the animals brought for sacrifice, nor the garlanded people or animals, nor the people coming to the Sacred House (Makkah), seeking the bounty and good pleasure of their Lord. But when you finish the *Ihrām* (of *Hajj* or '*Umrah*), you may hunt, and let not the hatred of some people in (once) stopping you from *Al-Masjid Al-Harām* (at Makkah) lead you to transgression (and hostility on your part). Help you one another in *Al-Birr* and *At-Taqwa* (virtue, righteousness and piety); but do not help one another in sin and transgression. And fear Allāh. Verily, Allāh is Severe in punishment.

(Qur'ân 5: 2)

﴿جَعَلَ ٱللَّهُ ٱلْكَعْبَةَ ٱلْبَيْتَ ٱلْحَرَامَ قِيَٰمًا لِّلنَّاسِ وَٱلشَّهْرَ ٱلْحَرَامَ وَٱلْهَدْىَ وَٱلْقَلَٰٓئِدَ ذَٰلِكَ لِتَعْلَمُوٓا۟ أَنَّ ٱللَّهَ يَعْلَمُ مَا فِى ٱلسَّمَٰوَٰتِ وَمَا فِى ٱلْأَرْضِ وَأَنَّ ٱللَّهَ بِكُلِّ شَىْءٍ عَلِيمٌ ٩٧﴾

Allāh has made the Ka'bah, the Sacred House, an asylum of security and benefits (e.g., *Hajj* and '*Umrah*) for mankind, and also (made sacred) the Sacred Month and the animals of offerings and the garlanded (people or animals, marked with the garlands on their necks made from the outer part of the stem of the Makkah trees for their security), that you may know that Allāh has knowledge of all that is in the heavens and all that is in the earth, and that Allāh is All-Knower of each and everything.

(Qur'ân 5: 97)

207

The Ka'bah is given the name, the Ancient House, in the following two Verses:

﴾ ثُمَّ لْيَقْضُوا تَفَثَهُمْ وَلْيُوفُوا نُذُورَهُمْ وَلْيَطَّوَّفُوا بِالْبَيْتِ الْعَتِيقِ ۝ ﴿

Then let them complete their prescribed duties (*Manâsik* of *Hajj*) and perform their vows, and circumambulate the Ancient House (the Ka'bah at Makkah).

(Qur'ân 22: 29)

﴾ لَكُمْ فِيهَا مَنَٰفِعُ إِلَىٰٓ أَجَلٍ مُّسَمًّى ثُمَّ مَحِلُّهَآ إِلَى الْبَيْتِ الْعَتِيقِ ۝ ﴿

In them (cattle offered for sacrifice) are benefits for you for an appointed term, and afterwards they are brought for sacrifice to the Ancient House (the *Haram* — sacred territory of Makkah).

(Qur'ân 22: 33)

And finally, Makkah is called "The City of Security" in the following verse:

﴾ وَهَٰذَا الْبَلَدِ الْأَمِينِ ۝ ﴿

By this city of security (Makkah).

(Qur'ân 95: 3)

Makkah, of course, is the *Qiblah* (place Muslims turn towards when they pray) of the Muslims, and it is the city in which the Prophet ﷺ was born.

Makkah

Makkah, Bakkah, Mother of the Towns, The Sacred House, the Ancient House, City of Security. It is also called An-Nasasah, Umm Ruhm, Ma'd, Al-Hatimah, Ar-Ras Salah, Al-Arsh, Al-Qadis, the Sacred, An-Nasah, Al Bassah, Kutha

(Mojam Al-Buldan 5/181)

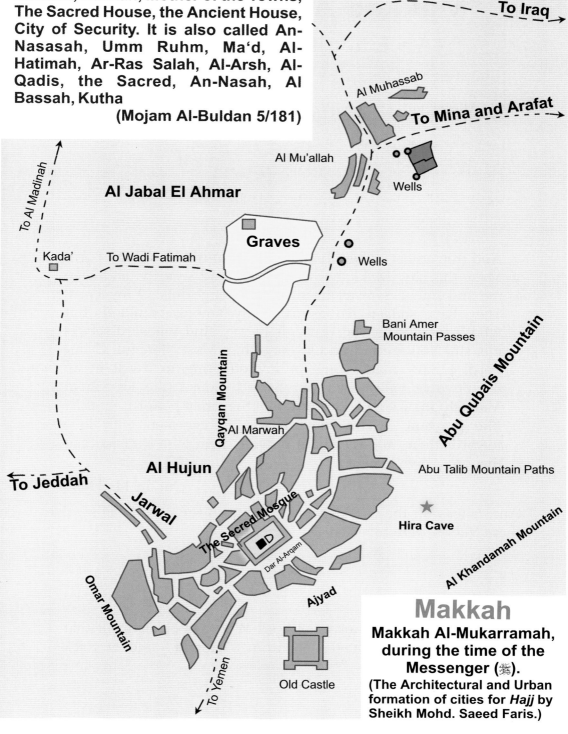

To Iraq

Al Muhassab

To Mina and Arafat

Al Mu'allah

Wells

Al Jabal El Ahmar

To Al Madinah

Kada'

To Wadi Fatimah

Graves

Wells

Bani Amer Mountain Passes

Qayqan Mountain

Al Marwah

Abu Qubais Mountain

Al Hujun

Abu Talib Mountain Paths

To Jeddah

Jarwal

Hira Cave

Al Khandamah Mountain

The Secred Mosque

Dar Al-Arqam

Omar Mountain

Ajyad

To Yemen

Old Castle

Makkah

Makkah Al-Mukarramah, during the time of the Messenger (ﷺ).
(The Architectural and Urban formation of cities for *Hajj* by Sheikh Mohd. Saeed Faris.)

Makkah Al-Mukarramah
(An Uncultiveable Valley)

﴿وَإِذْ قَالَ إِبْرَٰهِيمُ رَبِّ ٱجْعَلْ هَٰذَا ٱلْبَلَدَ ءَامِنًا وَٱجْنُبْنِى وَبَنِىَّ أَن نَّعْبُدَ ٱلْأَصْنَامَ
(٣٥) رَبِّ إِنَّهُنَّ أَضْلَلْنَ كَثِيرًا مِّنَ ٱلنَّاسِ فَمَن تَبِعَنِى فَإِنَّهُۥ مِنِّى وَمَنْ عَصَانِى فَإِنَّكَ غَفُورٌ
رَّحِيمٌ (٣٦) رَّبَّنَآ إِنِّىٓ أَسْكَنتُ مِن ذُرِّيَّتِى بِوَادٍ غَيْرِ ذِى زَرْعٍ عِندَ بَيْتِكَ ٱلْمُحَرَّمِ رَبَّنَا
لِيُقِيمُواْ ٱلصَّلَوٰةَ فَٱجْعَلْ أَفْـِٔدَةً مِّنَ ٱلنَّاسِ تَهْوِىٓ إِلَيْهِمْ وَٱرْزُقْهُم مِّنَ ٱلثَّمَرَٰتِ لَعَلَّهُمْ
يَشْكُرُونَ (٣٧) ﴾

And (remember) when Ibrāhīm (Abraham) said: "O my Lord!
Make this city (Makkah) one of peace and security, and keep
me and my sons away from worshipping idols. O my Lord!
They have indeed led astray many among mankind. But
whoso follows me, he verily, is of me. And whoso disobeys
me, still You are indeed Oft-Forgiving, Most Merciful. O our
Lord! I have made some of my offspring to dwell in an
uncultivable valley by Your Sacred House (the Ka'bah at
Makkah) in order, O our Lord, that they may perform *As-Salāt*
(the prayers). So fill some hearts among men with love
towards them, and (O Allāh) provide them with fruits so that
they may give thanks.

(Qur'ân 14: 35-37)

And it was on the outskirts of Makkah, in the cave of Hira, that
these Verses were revealed:

﴿ٱقْرَأْ بِٱسْمِ رَبِّكَ ٱلَّذِى خَلَقَ (١) خَلَقَ ٱلْإِنسَٰنَ مِنْ عَلَقٍ (٢) ٱقْرَأْ وَرَبُّكَ ٱلْأَكْرَمُ (٣) ٱلَّذِى عَلَّمَ
بِٱلْقَلَمِ (٤) عَلَّمَ ٱلْإِنسَٰنَ مَا لَمْ يَعْلَمْ (٥) ﴾

Read! In the Name of your Lord Who has created (all that
exists). He has created man from a clot (a piece of thick

Al-Masjid Al-Haram

Jabal Nur, in this mountain is the Cave of Hira

coagulated blood). Read! And your Lord is the Most Generous. Who has taught (the writing) by the pen. He has taught man that which he knew not.

(Qur'ân 96: 1-5)

These were the first Verses of the Qur'ân that were revealed, and it was only a matter of some years before Islam spread far in the east and west, as well as in the north and south.

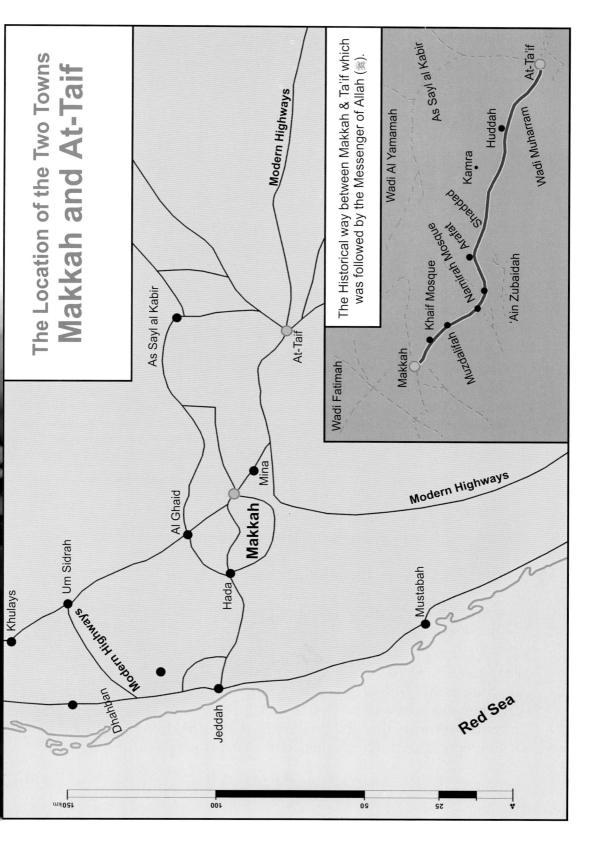

The Location of the Two Towns
Makkah and At-Taif

The Historical way between Makkah & Ta'if which was followed by the Messenger of Allah (ﷺ).

Inset map labels:

Wadi Al Yamamah

As Sayl al Kabir

Huddah

Kamra

Shaddad

Namirah Mosque

Arafat

Khaif Mosque

Muzdalifah

'Ain Zubaidah

Makkah

At-Ta'if

Wadi Muharram

Wadi Fatimah

Main map labels:

Modern Highways

As Sayl al Kabir

At-Taif

Mina

Al Ghaid

Makkah

Hada

Um Sidrah

Khulays

Dhahran

Modern Highways

Jeddah

Mustabah

Red Sea

Modern Highways

150km

100

50

25

The Two Towns

﴿وَقَالُوا لَوْلَا نُزِّلَ هَٰذَا ٱلْقُرْءَانُ عَلَىٰ رَجُلٍ مِّنَ ٱلْقَرْيَتَيْنِ عَظِيمٍ ۝ ٣١﴾

And they say: "Why is not this Qur'ān sent down to some great man of the two towns (Makkah and Tā'if)?"

(Qur'ân 43: 31)

The two towns being referred to in the above Verse are Makkah and Tâ'if. The polytheists said, "The Qur'ân should have been revealed to a great and important man in Makkah or in Tâ'if." The scholars of *Tafsir* clarified that they were referring to Al-Walid ibn Al-Mughirah in Makkah, and to 'Urwah ibn Mas'ud Ath-Thaqafi in Tâ'if.

The Quraish regarded it as being unlikely that the Qur'ân was revealed to Muhammad ﷺ, who had once been poor. They suggested that the Qur'ân should instead be revealed to one of their distinguished leaders, wrongly thinking that one becomes honorable through the possession of wealth and status. They failed to realize that the truly honorable one is he who is honorable in the Judgment of Allâh ﷻ:

﴿ٱللَّهُ أَعْلَمُ حَيْثُ يَجْعَلُ رِسَالَتَهُۥ سَيُصِيبُ ٱلَّذِينَ أَجْرَمُواْ صَغَارٌ عِندَ ٱللَّهِ وَعَذَابٌ شَدِيدٌۢ بِمَا كَانُواْ يَمْكُرُونَ ۝ ١٢٤﴾

Allāh knows best with whom to place His Message. Humiliation and disgrace from Allāh and a severe torment will overtake the criminals (polytheists and sinners) for that which they used to plot.

(Qur'ân 6: 124)

They considered Al-Walid ibn Al-Mughirah ibn 'Abdullah bin 'Amr bin Makhzum (who was born 95 years before *Hijrah* in 530 of the Christian calender and he died in 622 during the first year of *Hijrah*) to be more worthy than the Prophet ﷺ. They used to call him *Al-'Idl*, or 'the equivalent.' They called him that because, with his wealth and status, they considered him to be equivalent to all of the people of Quraish put together. If all of them spent money to prepare the cover of the Ka'bah, he, with no money other than his own, would cover it. The other man, 'Urwah ibn Mas'ud ibn Mu'attib Ath-Thaqafi, was the leader of his people in Tâ'if. He actually accepted Islam, and when he invited his people to do the same, they disobeyed him, and one of them ended up killing him with an arrow in the year 9 H (630 of the Christian calender).

- Al-A'lâm: 4/227 and 8/122
- At-Tafsir Al-Munir: 25/141
- Safwatut-Tafâsir: 3/156
- Hidâyatul-Bayân Fi Tafsir Al-Qur'ân: 4/100

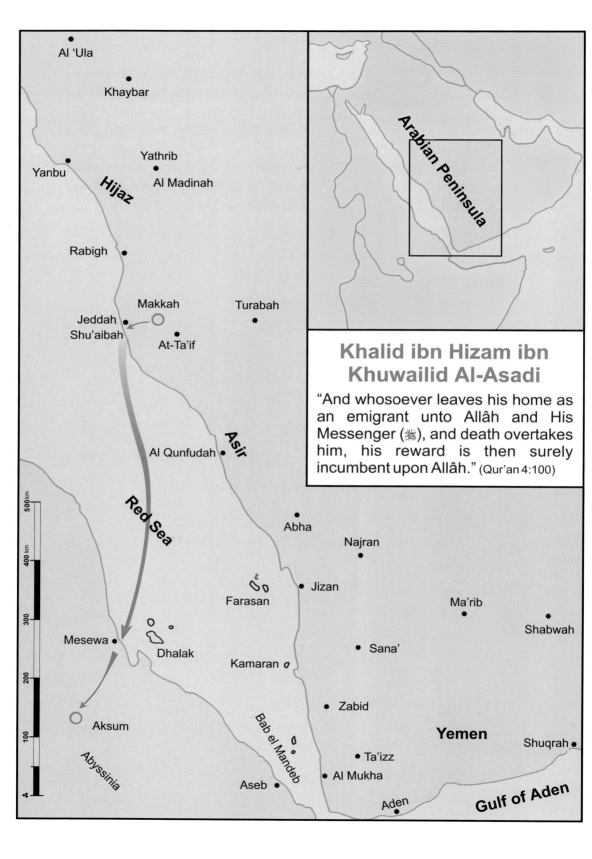

Al 'Ula

Khaybar

Yathrib
Al Madinah

Yanbu

Hijaz

Rabigh

Makkah
Jeddah
Shu'aibah
At-Ta'if

Turabah

Arabian Peninsula

Khalid ibn Hizam ibn Khuwailid Al-Asadi

"And whosoever leaves his home as an emigrant unto Allâh and His Messenger (ﷺ), and death overtakes him, his reward is then surely incumbent upon Allâh." (Qur'an 4:100)

Asir

Al Qunfudah

Red Sea

Abha

Najran

Jizan

Ma'rib

Farasan

Shabwah

Mesewa

Dhalak

Kamaran

Sana'

Aksum

Zabid

Yemen

Shuqrah

Abyssinia

Bab el Mandeb

Ta'izz

Al Mukha

Aseb

Aden

Gulf of Aden

500 km
400 km
300 km
200 km
100 km

And Whosoever Leaves his Home as an Emigrant unto Allâh And His Messenger and then Death Overtakes him

﴿وَمَن يُهَاجِرْ فِى سَبِيلِ ٱللَّهِ يَجِدْ فِى ٱلْأَرْضِ مُرَٰغَمًا كَثِيرًا وَسَعَةً وَمَن يَخْرُجْ مِنۢ بَيْتِهِۦ مُهَاجِرًا إِلَى ٱللَّهِ وَرَسُولِهِۦ ثُمَّ يُدْرِكْهُ ٱلْمَوْتُ فَقَدْ وَقَعَ أَجْرُهُۥ عَلَى ٱللَّهِ وَكَانَ ٱللَّهُ غَفُورًا رَّحِيمًا ١٠٠﴾

He who emigrates (from his home) in the Cause of Allāh, will find on earth many dwelling places and plenty to live by. And whosoever leaves his home as an emigrant to Allāh and His Messenger (ﷺ), and death overtakes him, his reward is then surely incumbent upon Allāh. And Allāh is Ever Oft-Forgiving, Most Merciful.

(Qur'ân 4: 100)

Khâlid ibn Hizâm ibn Khuwailid ibn Asad ibn 'Abdul-'Uzza ibn Qusai ibn Kilâb Al-Qurashi Al-Asdi was the brother of Hakim ibn Hizâm and the cousin of Khadijah bint Khuwailid ﷺ. Khâlid ﷺ was one of the earlier followers of the Prophet ﷺ. He left Makkah in order to be among those who performed the second migration to Al-Habashah, but as a result of a poisonous snakebite, he died before he could enter the land of Al-Habashah. His death is what prompted the revelation of this verse:

> "And whosoever leaves his home as an emigrant unto Allâh and His Messenger, and death overtakes him, his reward is then surely incumbent upon Allâh." (Qur'ân 4: 100)

It has been said, however, that the Verse was revealed for Damrah ibn Jundub. Damrah left his home and instructed his family to take him away from the lands of the polytheists and to the Messenger of

Allâh ﷺ. But he died on the way before he could reach the Messenger of Allâh ﷺ.

And according to a third opinion, the Verse was revealed for Junda' ibn Damrah Al-Laithi, one of the weak and oppressed Muslims of Makkah. He was sick, and so when he heard that Allâh ﷺ gave the Muslims permission to migrate, he said to his family (or close friends), "Take me away from here." Since he was sick, they had to prepare a bed of sorts that they could carry him in. They carried him out of Makkah but he died on the way, at Tan'im.

- Usdul-Ghâbah: 2/92
- Al-Isti'aab: 1/411
- Al-Isaabah: 1/403
- At-Tafsir Al-Munir: 5/227
- Safwatut-Tafâsir: 1/300

The Jinn of Nasibain

(Jinn of the Island)

Caspian Sea

Persia

The Gulf

Al-Ahsa

Karun

Orumiyeh

Ass-Sawad

Or

Tigris

Babylon

Najd

Van

Ninawa

Euphrates

An Nafud Great Desert

Mosul

Al Jazirah

Khabur

Nasibain

Yathrib

Harran

Al Madinah

Desert Land

Aleppo

Hijaz

Damascus

Makkah

Anatolia

Al Aqabah

Jeddah

Median

Red Sea

Cyprus

Jerusalem

Nubians

Sinai

Mediterranean Sea

Eastern Desert

Egypt

El Faiyum

Western Desert

1000 km

800

600

400

200

"Say (O Muhammad ﷺ): It has been revealed to me that a group (from three to ten in number) of jinn listened (to this Qur'ân). They said: 'Verily, we have heard a wonderful Recitation (this Qur'ân). It guides to the Right Path, and we have believed therein, and we shall never join (in worship) anything with our Lord (Allâh)." (Qur'an 72:1,2)

The Jinn Of Nasibain
(From the Jinn of the Island)

﴿قُلْ أُوحِيَ إِلَيَّ أَنَّهُ ٱسْتَمَعَ نَفَرٌ مِّنَ ٱلْجِنِّ فَقَالُوٓاْ إِنَّا سَمِعْنَا قُرْءَانًا عَجَبًا ١ يَهْدِىٓ إِلَى ٱلرُّشْدِ فَـَٔامَنَّا بِهِۦۖ وَلَن نُّشْرِكَ بِرَبِّنَآ أَحَدًا ٢ ﴾

Say (O Muhammad ﷺ): "It has been revealed to me that a group (from three to ten in number) of jinn listened (to this Qur'ān). They said: 'Verily, we have heard a wonderful Recitation (this Qur'ān)! 'It guides to the Right Path, and we have believed therein, and we shall never join (in worship) anything with our Lord (Allāh).

(Qur'ān 72: 1)

﴿وَإِذْ صَرَفْنَآ إِلَيْكَ نَفَرًا مِّنَ ٱلْجِنِّ يَسْتَمِعُونَ ٱلْقُرْءَانَ فَلَمَّا حَضَرُوهُ قَالُوٓاْ أَنصِتُواْ فَلَمَّا قُضِىَ وَلَّوْاْ إِلَىٰ قَوْمِهِم مُّنذِرِينَ ٢٩ قَالُواْ يَٰقَوْمَنَآ إِنَّا سَمِعْنَا كِتَٰبًا أُنزِلَ مِنۢ بَعْدِ مُوسَىٰ مُصَدِّقًا لِّمَا بَيْنَ يَدَيْهِ يَهْدِىٓ إِلَى ٱلْحَقِّ وَإِلَىٰ طَرِيقٍ مُّسْتَقِيمٍ ٣٠ يَٰقَوْمَنَآ أَجِيبُواْ دَاعِىَ ٱللَّهِ وَءَامِنُواْ بِهِۦ يَغْفِرْ لَكُم مِّن ذُنُوبِكُمْ وَيُجِرْكُم مِّنْ عَذَابٍ أَلِيمٍ ٣١ وَمَن لَّا يُجِبْ دَاعِىَ ٱللَّهِ فَلَيْسَ بِمُعْجِزٍ فِى ٱلْأَرْضِ وَلَيْسَ لَهُۥ مِن دُونِهِۦٓ أَوْلِيَآءُۚ أُوْلَٰٓئِكَ فِى ضَلَٰلٍ مُّبِينٍ ٣٢ ﴾

And (remember) when We sent towards you (Muhammad ﷺ) a group (three to ten persons) of the jinn, (quietly) listening to the Qur'ān. When they stood in the presence thereof, they said: "Listen in silence!" And when it was finished, they returned to their people, as warners. They said: "O our people! Verily, we have heard a Book (this Qur'ān) sent down after Mūsā (Moses), confirming what came before it, it guides to the truth and to a Straight Path (i.e. Islam). O our people! Respond (with obedience) to Allāh's Caller (i.e. Allāh's Messenger Muhammad ﷺ), and believe in him (i.e. believe in that which Muhammad ﷺ has brought from Allāh and follow him). He

220

(Allāh) will forgive you of your sins, and will save you from a painful torment (i.e. Hell-fire). And whosoever does not respond to Allāh's Caller, he cannot escape on earth, and there will be no *Auliyā'* (lords, helpers, supporters, protectors) for him besides Allāh (from Allāh's punishment). Those are in manifest error."

(Qur'ân 46: 29-32)

The mention of these jinns involves a severe reprimand to the Quraish in particular, and to the Arabs in general. While the Arabs were slow to accept Islam and have faith, the jinns mentioned above raced to accept *Imân*, which made them better than the disbelieving Arabs. From the moment they heard the Qur'ân, those jinns revered it and believed in it. And they returned to their fellow jinns as warners and callers to Islam. In stark contrast to the jinns were the disbelieving Arabs, who disbelieved even though the Qur'ân was revealed in their language, even though they knew that the speech of the Qur'ân was a miracle, and even though they knew that Muhammad ﷺ was illiterate: he could neither read nor write which was another proof that the Qur'ân had to have come from Allâh ﷻ.

Ibn Mas'ud ؓ was there on the night in which the Messenger of Allâh ﷺ met with the jinns. The jinns that met with the Prophet ﷺ were actually from the Arabian Peninsula, and in *Ad-Durr Al-Manthur* it is mentioned that some say they were seven in number and were from the dwellers of Nasibain.

- At-Tafsir Al-Munir: 29/164
- Ad-Durr Al-Manthur: 6/270
- Safwatut-Tafâsir: 3/457
- At-Tabari: 2/347

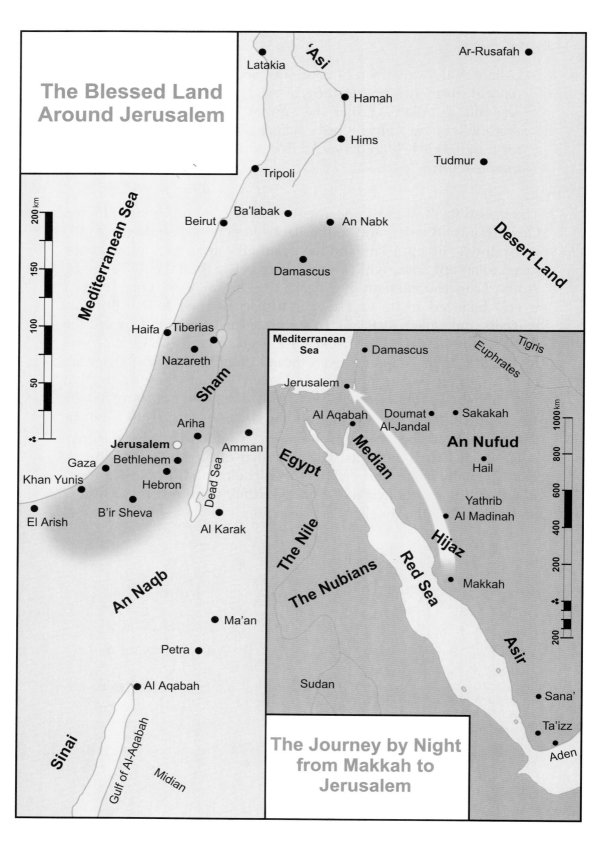

The Blessed Land Around Jerusalem

The Journey by Night from Makkah to Jerusalem

The Neighborhood Whereof We Have Blessed
The Farthest Mosque
(In Jerusalem)

﴿وَأَوْرَثْنَا ٱلْقَوْمَ ٱلَّذِينَ كَانُوا۟ يُسْتَضْعَفُونَ مَشَـٰرِقَ ٱلْأَرْضِ وَمَغَـٰرِبَهَا ٱلَّتِى بَـٰرَكْنَا فِيهَآ وَتَمَّتْ كَلِمَتُ رَبِّكَ ٱلْحُسْنَىٰ عَلَىٰ بَنِىٓ إِسْرَٰٓءِيلَ بِمَا صَبَرُوا۟ وَدَمَّرْنَا مَا كَانَ يَصْنَعُ فِرْعَوْنُ وَقَوْمُهُۥ وَمَا كَانُوا۟ يَعْرِشُونَ ۝١٣٧﴾

And We made the people who were considered weak to inherit the eastern parts of the land and the western parts thereof which We have blessed. And the fair Word of your Lord was fulfilled for the Children of Israel, because of their endurance. And We destroyed completely all the great works and buildings which Fir'aun (Pharaoh) and his people erected.

(Qur'ân 7: 137)

﴿سُبْحَـٰنَ ٱلَّذِىٓ أَسْرَىٰ بِعَبْدِهِۦ لَيْلًا مِّنَ ٱلْمَسْجِدِ ٱلْحَرَامِ إِلَى ٱلْمَسْجِدِ ٱلْأَقْصَا ٱلَّذِى بَـٰرَكْنَا حَوْلَهُۥ لِنُرِيَهُۥ مِنْ ءَايَـٰتِنَآ إِنَّهُۥ هُوَ ٱلسَّمِيعُ ٱلْبَصِيرُ ۝١﴾

Glorified (and Exalted) is He (Allāh) [above all that (evil) they associate with Him] (*Tafsir Qurtubī*) Who took His slave (Muhammad ﷺ) for a journey by night from *Al-Masjid Al-Harām* (at Makkah) to *Al-Masjid Al-Aqsā* (in Jerusalem), the neighbourhood whereof We have blessed, in order that We might show him (Muhammad ﷺ) of Our *Ayāt* (proofs, evidences, lessons, signs, etc.). Verily, He is the All-Hearer, the All-Seer.

(Qur'ân 17: 1)

Al-Masjid Al-Aqsa

﴾قُلْنَا يَـٰنَارُ كُونِى بَرْدًا وَسَلَـٰمًا عَلَىٰٓ إِبْرَٰهِيمَ ٦٩ وَأَرَادُوا۟ بِهِۦ كَيْدًا فَجَعَلْنَـٰهُمُ ٱلْأَخْسَرِينَ ٧٠ وَنَجَّيْنَـٰهُ وَلُوطًا إِلَى ٱلْأَرْضِ ٱلَّتِى بَـٰرَكْنَا فِيهَا لِلْعَـٰلَمِينَ ٧١ ﴿

We (Allāh) said: "O fire! Be you coolness and safety for Ibrāhīm (Abraham)!" And they wanted to harm him, but We made them the worst losers. And We rescued him and Lūt (Lot) to the land which We have blessed for the *'Ālamīn* (mankind and jinn)."

(Qur'ân 21: 69-71)

﴾وَلِسُلَيْمَـٰنَ ٱلرِّيحَ عَاصِفَةً تَجْرِى بِأَمْرِهِۦٓ إِلَى ٱلْأَرْضِ ٱلَّتِى بَـٰرَكْنَا فِيهَا وَكُنَّا بِكُلِّ شَىْءٍ عَـٰلِمِينَ ٨١ ﴿

And to Sulaimān (Solomon) (We subjected) the wind strongly raging, running by his command towards the land which We had blessed. And of everything We are All-Knower.

(Qur'ân 21: 81)

Allâh ﷻ favored Jerusalem and neighboring lands with many blessings, both of the physical and spiritual kind. In regards to "The neighborhood whereof We have blessed," 'neighborhood' refers to the lands of Ash-Sham (Syria and surrounding regions). These lands were the dwelling places of the Prophets and the landing places of the pure angels.

To be sure, the Prophet ﷺ could have ascended to the heavens directly from Makkah on the night of *Al-Isrâ'* and *Mi'râj*, but the Prophet's ascension to the heavens was a heavenly event that could not be confirmed for the Quraish by any kind of material proof. What I mean is, who from the Quraish, for example, had already seen *Sidratul-Muntaha* and could test the Prophet ﷺ by asking him to describe it for him? Of course, the answer is no one. But the earthbound journey of the Prophet ﷺ from Makkah to Jerusalem could be confirmed and seen as the miracle that it was. For when the Prophet ﷺ returned to Makkah, he gave a precise and detailed description of Jerusalem to those disbelieving members of the Quraish who had already visited it; and of course, the Prophet ﷺ

The Dome of the Rock

had never visited it prior to the previous evening. Then the Quraish inquired about a caravan that was returning to them. Since the Prophet ﷺ had seen it on the way back to Makkah, he told them precisely the situation of the caravan and the number of camels that were in it. He even told them when it was going to arrive. And he accurately described one of the camels in the caravan. When the caravan eventually arrived, people realized that everything that the Prophet ﷺ had said turned out to be true.

- At-Tafsir Al-Munir: 15/11
- Safwatut-Tafâsir: 2/151

Hijrah (Migration)

"And (remember) when the disbelievers plotted against you (O Muhammad ﷺ) to imprison you, or to kill you, or to get you out (from your home, i.e., Makkah); they were plotting and Allâh too was plotting; and Allâh is the Best of those who plot." (Qur'an 8:30)

"If you help him (Muhammad ﷺ) not (it does not matter), for Allâh did indeed help him when the disbelievers drove him out, the second of the two; when they (Muhammad ﷺ and Abu Bakr ﷺ) were in the cave, he (ﷺ) said to his companion (Abu Bakr ﷺ): 'Be not sad (or afraid), surely, Allâh is with us.' Then Allâh sent down His *Sakeenah* (calmness, tranquillity, peace) upon him, and strengthened him with forces (angels) which you saw not." (Qur'an 8:40)

Hijrah Route

Regular Caravan Route

Dhat Al-Jaish

Atiq

Al Madinah

Quba'

Dhul-Hulaifah

Batn R'im

Hamra Al-Asad

Al-Araj

Thu-Salam
Juda-Jid

Batn Thee Kishr
Marjah Mahaj
Muwlijah Hujjaj

Thanniyat Al-Murrah

Badr

Al-Juhfah

Rabigh

Qulliyah

Umm Ma'bad
Tent

Qudaid

Mushallal

Khulays

Amj

Red Sea

Kadid

Ghadir Al-Ashtat

Thanniyat Al-Ghezal

Usfan

Saraf

Jeddah

Al Hudaybiah

Makkah

Mount Thawr

At-Ta'if

The *Hijrah*

(The Migration from Makkah to Al-Madinah)

﴿وَإِذْ يَمْكُرُ بِكَ ٱلَّذِينَ كَفَرُوا لِيُثْبِتُوكَ أَوْ يَقْتُلُوكَ أَوْ يُخْرِجُوكَ وَيَمْكُرُونَ وَيَمْكُرُ ٱللَّهُ وَٱللَّهُ خَيْرُ ٱلْمَٰكِرِينَ ۝﴾

And (remember) when the disbelievers plotted against you (O Muhammad ﷺ) to imprison you, or to kill you, or to get you out (from your home, i.e., Makkah); they were plotting and Allāh too was plotting; and Allāh is the Best of those who plot.

(Qur'ân 8: 30)

﴿إِلَّا تَنصُرُوهُ فَقَدْ نَصَرَهُ ٱللَّهُ إِذْ أَخْرَجَهُ ٱلَّذِينَ كَفَرُوا ثَانِيَ ٱثْنَيْنِ إِذْ هُمَا فِى ٱلْغَارِ إِذْ يَقُولُ لِصَٰحِبِهِ لَا تَحْزَنْ إِنَّ ٱللَّهَ مَعَنَا فَأَنزَلَ ٱللَّهُ سَكِينَتَهُ عَلَيْهِ وَأَيَّدَهُ بِجُنُودٍ لَّمْ تَرَوْهَا وَجَعَلَ كَلِمَةَ ٱلَّذِينَ كَفَرُوا ٱلسُّفْلَىٰ وَكَلِمَةُ ٱللَّهِ هِىَ ٱلْعُلْيَا وَٱللَّهُ عَزِيزٌ حَكِيمٌ ۝﴾

If you help him (Muhammad ﷺ) not (it does not matter), for Allāh did indeed help him when the disbelievers drove him out, the second of the two; when they (Muhammad ﷺ and Abu Bakr ﷺ) were in the cave, he (ﷺ) said to his companion (Abu Bakr ﷺ): "Be not sad (or afraid), surely, Allāh is with us." Then Allāh sent down His *Sakīnah* (calmness, tranquillity, peace) upon him, and strengthened him with forces (angels) which you saw not, and made the word of those who disbelieved the lowermost, while the Word of Allāh that became the uppermost; and Allāh is All-Mighty, All-Wise.

(Qur'ân 9: 40)

After the *Bai'atul-'Aqabah Al-Ula* and *Bai'atul 'Aqabah Ath-Thâniyah* in which the inhabitants of Al-Madinah pledged to obey and defend the Prophet ﷺ the Quraish began to feel that they were losing

Mount Thawr having the Cave Thawr

control of the situation. Its leaders then gathered in Dâr An-Nadwah to try to find a solution to their problems. During their meeting, many solutions were proposed: one was to imprison the Prophet ﷺ until he died and another was to banish him from Makkah, by tying him to a camel and then steering that camel into the desert. The proposed solution that they agreed upon was much more sinister than the rest; they decided that a strong, young man from each sub-tribe should be chosen and that they should all strike the Prophet ﷺ with a single blow. The benefit of doing this was to spread the culpability of the heinous crime to all of the sub-tribes, so that no single sub-tribe had to fear retribution.

But their plan was of course thwarted. Taking many precautions that are outlined in the books of *Seerah*, the Prophet ﷺ left Makkah with Abu Bakr ﷺ. They hired a guide so as to avoid taking the normal roads, a step that was necessary since the Quraish offered a huge reward to anyone who brought the Prophet ﷺ back, dead or alive.

Here are some of the more important outcomes of the *Hijrah* (migration):

1) Having gathered together in one land, the Muslims were able to defend Islam and openly proclaim its teachings.

2) The Muslims had an actual country that was based on solid foundations, and that enabled them to take the necessary steps to keep that country stable and strong.

3) The Muslims were able to invite people to Islam not only in Makkah or Al-Madinah, but also in most of the inhabited world.

4) In Makkah, when the Muslims were weak, there were no hypocrites. But when the Muslims established themselves in Al-Madinah, it was in the interest of some of Islam's enemies to feign to be Muslims, in order to attack Islam from within. Hence the appearance of the hypocrites, who were led by 'Abdullah ibn Ubai ibn Salûl.

5) Before the Prophet's migration to Al-Madinah, the trading caravans of the Quraish traveled in safety during their summer

and winter journeys. But after the Muslims established themselves in Al-Madinah, and because the Quraish had seized all of the wealth of the Muslims in Makkah, the trading caravans of the Quraish were threatened by the presence of Muslims in Al-Madinah, since those caravans had to pass Al-Madinah on their way to Ash-Sham (Syria and surrounding regions).

- Ibn Sa'd: 1/227
- Ibn Hisham: 2/89
- Al-Bidâyah wan-Nihayah: 3/170
- At-Tabari: 2/370
- Al-Kamil Fit-Tarikh: 2/53
- 'Uyun Al-Athar: 2/81
- Muruj Adh-Dhahab: 2/85
- Al-Wafâ Bi-Ahwâl Al-Mustafah: 1/235

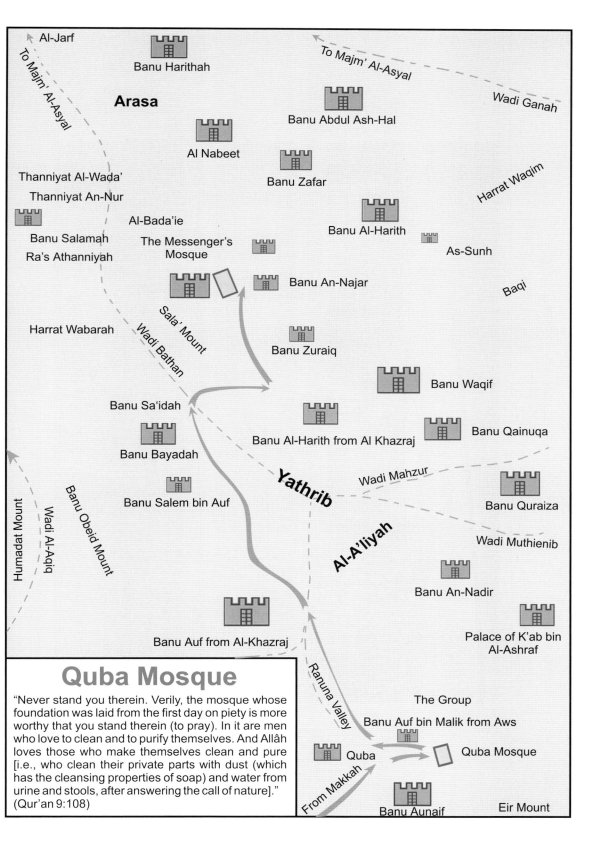

Al-Jarf

To Majm' Al-Asyal

Banu Harithah

Arasa

To Majm' Al-Asyal

Wadi Ganah

Banu Abdul Ash-Hal

Al Nabeet

Thanniyat Al-Wada'
Thanniyat An-Nur

Banu Zafar

Harrat Waqim

Banu Al-Harith

Al-Bada'ie

As-Sunh

Banu Salamah
Ra's Athanniyah

The Messenger's
Mosque

Baqi

Banu An-Najar

Harrat Wabarah

Sala' Mount

Wadi Bathan

Banu Zuraiq

Banu Waqif

Banu Sa'idah

Banu Al-Harith from Al Khazraj

Banu Qainuqa

Banu Bayadah

Banu Salem bin Auf

Yathrib

Wadi Mahzur

Banu Quraiza

Humadat Mount

Wadi Al-Aqiq

Banu Obeid Mount

Al-A'liyah

Wadi Muthienib

Banu An-Nadir

Banu Auf from Al-Khazraj

Ranuna Valley

Palace of K'ab bin
Al-Ashraf

The Group

Quba Mosque

"Never stand you therein. Verily, the mosque whose foundation was laid from the first day on piety is more worthy that you stand therein (to pray). In it are men who love to clean and to purify themselves. And Allâh loves those who make themselves clean and pure [i.e., who clean their private parts with dust (which has the cleansing properties of soap) and water from urine and stools, after answering the call of nature]." (Qur'an 9:108)

Banu Auf bin Malik from Aws

Quba

Quba Mosque

From Makkah

Banu Aunaif

Eir Mount

Masjid Quba

Masjid Quba'

(The Masjid Whose Foundation Was Laid On Piety)

﴿لَا تَقُمْ فِيهِ أَبَدًا لَمَسْجِدٌ أُسِّسَ عَلَى ٱلتَّقْوَىٰ مِنْ أَوَّلِ يَوْمٍ أَحَقُّ أَن تَقُومَ فِيهِ رِجَالٌ يُحِبُّونَ أَن يَتَطَهَّرُوا وَٱللَّهُ يُحِبُّ ٱلْمُطَّهِّرِينَ ۝١٠٨﴾

Never stand you therein. Verily, the mosque whose foundation was laid from the first day on piety is more worthy that you stand therein (to pray). In it are men who love to clean and to purify themselves. And Allāh loves those who make themselves clean and pure [i.e., who clean their private parts with dust (which has the cleansing properties of soap) and water from urine and stools, after answering the call of nature].

(Qur'ân 9: 108)

Quba', which is adjacent to Al-Madinah Al-Munawwarah, is best known for Masjid Quba', 'the Masjid whose foundation was laid from the first day on piety' and the first Masjid to be built since the advent of Islam. When the Prophet ﷺ migrated to Al-Madinah, he first stopped at Quba', arriving there on a Monday and staying there for four days. On the Friday of that week, the Prophet ﷺ went to Al-Madinah Al-Munawwarah.

Then in the year 9 H, just before the Battle of Tabûk, a group of 12 hypocrites built Masjid Dirar (mosque of hypocrites), the purpose of which was to promote harm and disbelief, and to disunite the believers. They asked the Prophet ﷺ to pray in their Masjid, and he ﷺ answered, "Indeed, I am upon a journey (for the Battle of Tabûk) and am much occupied; had we approached [there], we would have come to you and prayed in it." But after he ﷺ went to Tabûk, the following Verses were revealed:

﴿وَٱلَّذِينَ ٱتَّخَذُوا مَسْجِدًا ضِرَارًا وَكُفْرًا وَتَفْرِيقًا بَيْنَ ٱلْمُؤْمِنِينَ وَإِرْصَادًا لِّمَنْ

The Prophet's Mosque, Al-Madinah Al-Munawwarah

حَارَبَ ٱللَّهَ وَرَسُولَهُ مِن قَبْلُ وَلَيَحْلِفُنَّ إِنْ أَرَدْنَآ إِلَّا ٱلْحُسْنَىٰ وَٱللَّهُ يَشْهَدُ إِنَّهُمْ لَكَذِبُونَ ١٠٧ لَا تَقُمْ فِيهِ أَبَدًا لَمَسْجِدٌ أُسِّسَ عَلَى ٱلتَّقْوَىٰ مِنْ أَوَّلِ يَوْمٍ أَحَقُّ أَن تَقُومَ فِيهِ رِجَالٌ يُحِبُّونَ أَن يَتَطَهَّرُواْ وَٱللَّهُ يُحِبُّ ٱلْمُطَّهِّرِينَ ١٠٨ أَفَمَنْ أَسَّسَ بُنْيَـٰنَهُ عَلَىٰ تَقْوَىٰ مِنَ ٱللَّهِ وَرِضْوَانٍ خَيْرٌ أَم مَّنْ أَسَّسَ بُنْيَـٰنَهُ عَلَىٰ شَفَا جُرُفٍ هَارٍ فَٱنْهَارَ بِهِۦ فِي نَارِ جَهَنَّمَ وَٱللَّهُ لَا يَهْدِى ٱلْقَوْمَ ٱلظَّـٰلِمِينَ ١٠٩ لَا يَزَالُ بُنْيَـٰنُهُمُ ٱلَّذِى بَنَوْاْ رِيبَةً فِي قُلُوبِهِمْ إِلَّآ أَن تَقَطَّعَ قُلُوبُهُمْ وَٱللَّهُ عَلِيمٌ حَكِيمٌ ١١٠

And as for those who put up a mosque by way of harm and disbelief and to disunite the believers and as an outpost for those who warred against Allāh and His Messenger (Muhammad ﷺ) aforetime, they will indeed swear that their intention is nothing but good. Allāh bears witness that they are certainly liars. Never stand you therein. Verily, the mosque whose foundation was laid from the first day on piety is more worthy that you stand therein (to pray). In it are men who love to clean and to purify themselves. And Allāh loves those who make themselves clean and pure [i.e. who clean their private parts with dust (which has the cleansing properties of soap) and water from urine and stools, after answering the call of nature]. Is it then he who laid the foundation of his building on piety to Allāh and His Good Pleasure better, or he who laid the foundation of his building on the brink of an undetermined precipice ready to crumble down, so that it crumbled to pieces with him into the fire of Hell. And Allāh guides not the people who are the *Zālimūn* (cruel, violent, proud, polytheist and wrong doer). The building which they built will never cease to be a cause of hypocrisy and doubt in their hearts unless their hearts are cut to pieces (i.e. till they die). And Allāh is All-Knowing, All-Wise. (Qur'ân 9: 107-110)

- At-Tafsir Al-Munir: 11/38
- Ad-Durr Al-Manthur: 3/276
- Safwatut-Tafâsir: 1/518

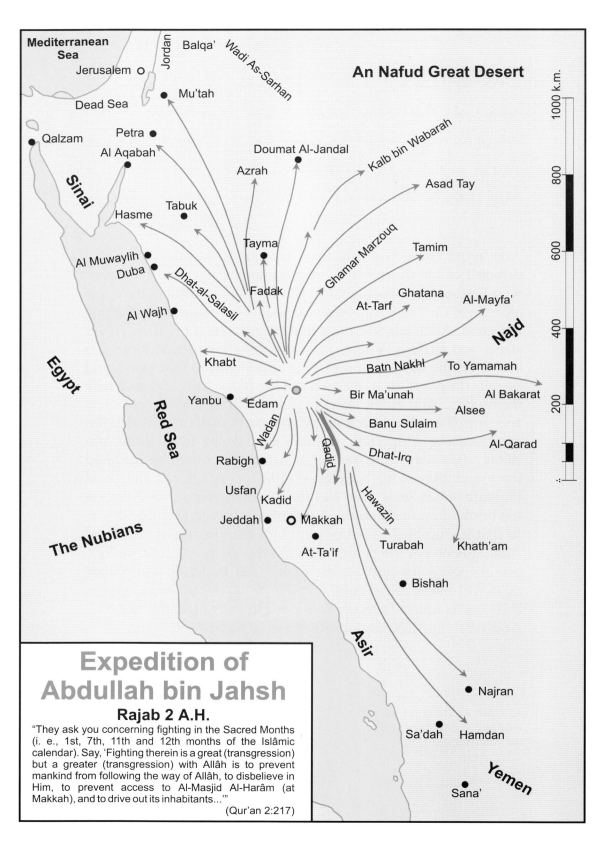

Mediterranean Sea

Jerusalem

Jordan

Balqa'

Wadi As-Sarhan

An Nafud Great Desert

Mu'tah

Dead Sea

Qalzam

Petra

Al Aqabah

Doumat Al-Jandal

Kalb bin Wabarah

Azrah

Asad Tay

Sinai

Tabuk

Hasme

Tayma

Ghamar Marzouq

Tamim

Al Muwaylih

Duba

Dhat-al-Salasil

Fadak

Ghatana

Al-Mayfa'

At-Tarf

Al Wajh

Egypt

Khabt

Najd

Batn Nakhl

To Yamamah

Red Sea

Yanbu

Edam

Bir Ma'unah

Al Bakarat

Alsee

Wadan

Banu Sulaim

Al-Qarad

Qadid

Dhat-Irq

Rabigh

Usfan

Hawazin

Kadid

Jeddah

Makkah

The Nubians

At-Ta'if

Turabah

Khath'am

Bishah

Asir

Najran

Expedition of
Abdullah bin Jahsh
Rajab 2 A.H.

"They ask you concerning fighting in the Sacred Months (i. e., 1st, 7th, 11th and 12th months of the Islâmic calendar). Say, 'Fighting therein is a great (transgression) but a greater (transgression) with Allâh is to prevent mankind from following the way of Allâh, to disbelieve in Him, to prevent access to Al-Masjid Al-Harâm (at Makkah), and to drive out its inhabitants...'"

(Qur'an 2:217)

Sa'dah

Hamdan

Yemen

Sana'

1000 k.m.

800

600

400

200

The Unit Of 'Abdullah ibn Jahsh ﵁ that Was Sent To Batn Nakhlah

﴿يَسۡـَٔلُونَكَ عَنِ ٱلشَّهۡرِ ٱلۡحَرَامِ قِتَالٍ فِيهِۖ قُلۡ قِتَالٌ فِيهِ كَبِيرٌۖ وَصَدٌّ عَن سَبِيلِ ٱللَّهِ وَكُفۡرُۢ بِهِۦ وَٱلۡمَسۡجِدِ ٱلۡحَرَامِ وَإِخۡرَاجُ أَهۡلِهِۦ مِنۡهُ أَكۡبَرُ عِندَ ٱللَّهِۚ وَٱلۡفِتۡنَةُ أَكۡبَرُ مِنَ ٱلۡقَتۡلِۗ وَلَا يَزَالُونَ يُقَٰتِلُونَكُمۡ حَتَّىٰ يَرُدُّوكُمۡ عَن دِينِكُمۡ إِنِ ٱسۡتَطَٰعُواْۚ وَمَن يَرۡتَدِدۡ مِنكُمۡ عَن دِينِهِۦ فَيَمُتۡ وَهُوَ كَافِرٌ فَأُوْلَٰٓئِكَ حَبِطَتۡ أَعۡمَٰلُهُمۡ فِي ٱلدُّنۡيَا وَٱلۡأٓخِرَةِۖ وَأُوْلَٰٓئِكَ أَصۡحَٰبُ ٱلنَّارِۖ هُمۡ فِيهَا خَٰلِدُونَ ٢١٧﴾

They ask you concerning fighting in the Sacred Months (i.e. 1st, 7th, 11th and 12th months of the Islamic calendar). Say, "Fighting therein is a great (transgression) but a greater (transgression) with Allāh is to prevent mankind from following the way of Allāh, to disbelieve in Him, to prevent access to *Al-Masjid Al-Harām* (at Makkah), and to drive out its inhabitants, and *Al-Fitnah* is worse than killing." And they will never cease fighting you until they turn you back from your religion (Islamic Monotheism) if they can. And whosoever of you turns back from his religion and dies as a disbeliever, then his deeds will be lost in this life and in the Hereafter, and they will be the dwellers of the Fire. They will abide therein forever. (Qur'ân 2: 217)

In Jumâda Al-Ākhirah, of the year 2 H, the Messenger of Allâh ﷺ sent a unit headed by 'Abdullah ibn Jahsh ﵁ to lie in wait for a small trading caravan that belonged to the Quraish. The Quraish had seized all of the wealth that the Muslims left behind in Makkah, and the Muslims were going to now try and cripple their trade routes. The members of that caravan were 'Amr bin Al-Hadrami and three others. The Muslim unit intercepted the caravan, and in the ensuing struggle, 'Amr was killed and two others were taken prisoner. 'Abdullah ibn Jahsh ﷺ and his companions then returned with the caravan, which consisted of many goods. The struggle that happened earlier took place on the first day of Rajab, one of the sacred months; the Muslims in the unit had mistakenly thought that it was one of the last days of Jumâda Al-Ākhirah. When the unit returned, the Prophet ﷺ said, "By Allâh, I had not ordered you to fight in (one of) the Sacred Month(s)." And the leaders of the Quraish said, "Muhammad has made lawful the Sacred Month, the month in which the fearful one feels safe, (the month in which) people go out to earn their living." Then Allâh ﷻ revealed these Verses:

﴿يَسْـَٔلُونَكَ عَنِ ٱلشَّهْرِ ٱلْحَرَامِ قِتَالٍ فِيهِ قُلْ قِتَالٌ فِيهِ كَبِيرٌ وَصَدٌّ عَن سَبِيلِ ٱللَّهِ وَكُفْرٌ بِهِ وَٱلْمَسْجِدِ ٱلْحَرَامِ وَإِخْرَاجُ أَهْلِهِ مِنْهُ أَكْبَرُ عِندَ ٱللَّهِ وَٱلْفِتْنَةُ أَكْبَرُ مِنَ ٱلْقَتْلِ وَلَا يَزَالُونَ يُقَٰتِلُونَكُمْ حَتَّىٰ يَرُدُّوكُمْ عَن دِينِكُمْ إِنِ ٱسْتَطَٰعُوا وَمَن يَرْتَدِدْ مِنكُمْ عَن دِينِهِ فَيَمُتْ وَهُوَ كَافِرٌ فَأُوْلَٰٓئِكَ حَبِطَتْ أَعْمَٰلُهُمْ فِي ٱلدُّنْيَا وَٱلْءَاخِرَةِ وَأُوْلَٰٓئِكَ أَصْحَٰبُ ٱلنَّارِ هُمْ فِيهَا خَٰلِدُونَ ۝ إِنَّ ٱلَّذِينَ ءَامَنُوا وَٱلَّذِينَ هَاجَرُوا وَجَٰهَدُوا فِي سَبِيلِ ٱللَّهِ أُوْلَٰٓئِكَ يَرْجُونَ رَحْمَتَ ٱللَّهِ وَٱللَّهُ غَفُورٌ رَّحِيمٌ ۝﴾

They ask you concerning fighting in the Sacred Months (i.e., 1st, 7th, 11th and 12th months of the Islamic calendar). Say, "Fighting therein is a great (transgression) but a greater (transgression) with Allāh is to prevent mankind from following the way of Allāh, to disbelieve in Him, to prevent access to *Al-Masjid Al-Harām* (at Makkah), and to drive out its inhabitants, and *Al-Fitnah* is worse than killing." And they will never cease fighting you until they turn you back from your religion (Islamic Monotheism) if they can. And whoso-ever of you turns back from his religion and dies as a disbeliever, then his deeds will be lost in this life and in the Hereafter, and they will be the dwellers of the Fire. They will abide therein forever. Verily, those who have believed, and those who have emigrated (for Allāh's religion) and have striven hard in the way of Allāh, all these hope for Allāh's Mercy. And Allāh is Oft-Forgiving, Most-Merciful.

(Qur'ân 2: 217, 218)

Units that the Prophet ﷺ sent on missions, as listed in *Tabagat ibn Sa'd*:

No.	Name Of Mission Or Mission Leader	Date Of Mission	Place	Muslim Participants	Participants From The Polytheists
1	Hamzah ibn 'Abdul-Muttalib ﷺ	Ramadan, 1 H.	The shores of the Red Sea	30 Muhâjirûn	30 men
2	'Ubaidah ibn Al-Hârith ibn 'Abdul-Muttalib ﷺ	Shawâl, 1 H.	Batn-Râbigh	60 Muhâjirûn	200 men
3	Sa'ad ibn Abi Waqqâs ﷺ	Dhil-Qa'dah, 1 H.	Al-Khurâz, near the Khum Crik	20 Muhâjirûn	A caravan of the Quraish
4	'Abdullah ibn Jahsh Al-Asdi ﷺ	Rajab, 2 H.	Batn Nakhlah	4 Muhâjirûn	A caravan of the Quraish
5	'Umair ibn 'Adi ibn Khurshah Al-Khatmi ﷺ	Ramadan, 2 H.	Al-Madinah Al-Munaw-warah	'Umair ﷺ by himself	'Asmâ bint Mirwân
6	Sâlim ibn 'Umair Al-'Umari ﷺ	Shawâl, 2 H.	–	Sâlim ﷺ by himself	Abu 'Ifk Al-Yahûdi
7	Muhammad ibn Maslamah ﷺ	Rabi' Al-Awwal, 3 H.	The outskirts of Al-Madinah	5 Muslims	Ka'ab Al-Ash-raf
8	Zaid ibn Hârithah ﷺ	Jumâda Al-Aakhirah, 3 H.	Al-Qaradah, in Najd	100 Riders	A caravan of Safwân
9	Abu Salamah Al-Makhzûmi ﷺ	Al-Muharram, 3 H.	Qatan	150 Men	A group of people from Banu Asad
10	'Abdullah ibn Unais ﷺ	Al-Muharram, 3 H.	'Uranah	'Abdullah ﷺ by himself	Sufyân Al-Hudhali
11	Al-Mundhir ibn 'Amr As-Sâ'idi ﷺ	Safar, 3 H.	The Ma'ûnah Well	70 men	Banu Sualaim
12	Marthad ibn Abi Marthad Al-Gha-nawi ﷺ	Safar, 3 H.	Ar-Raji'	10 men	Qârah and 'Adal
13	Muhammad ibn Maslamah ﷺ	10th of Muharram, 3 H.	Al-Quratâ	30 riders	Banu Bakr

No.	Name Of Mission Or Mission Leader	Date Of Mission	Place	Muslim Participants	Participants From The Polytheists
14	'Ukkâshah ibn Mihsan Al-Asadi ❧	Rabi' Al-Awwal, 6 h.	Al-Ghamr (water source that belonged to Bani Asad)	40 men	–
15	Muhammad ibn Maslamah ❧	Rabi' Al-Ākhir, 6 h.	Banu Tha'la-bah	10 men	Banu Tha'la-bah
16	Abu 'Ubaidah ibn Al-Jarrâh ❧	Rabi' Al-Ākhir, 6 h.	Dhul-Qissah	40 men	Banu Mahârib
17	Zaid ibn Hârithah ❧	Rabi' Al-Ākhir, 6 h.	Al-Jamûm	A number of Companions ❧	Banu Sulaim
18	Zaid ibn Hârithah ❧	Jumâdah Al-Ula, 6 h.	Al-'Ais	170 horsemen	Sâhil Al-Bahr
19	Zaid ibn Hârithah ❧	Jumâda Al-Ākhirah, 6 h.	At-Taraf	15 men	Banu Tha'la-bah
20	Zaid ibn Hârithah ❧	Jumâda Al-Aakhirah, 6 h.	Hasmah	500 men	Banu Judhâm
21	Zaid ibn Hârithah ❧	Rajab, 6 h.	The Al-Qura Valley	A number of Companions ❧	Jews from the Al-Qura Val-ley
22	'Abdur-Rahmân ibn 'Auf ❧	Sha'bân, 6 h.	Damatul-Jan-dal	A number of Companions ❧	Banu Kalb
23	'Ali ibn Abi Tâlib ❧	Sha'bân, 6 h.	Fadak	100 men	Banu Sa'ad
24	Zaid ibn Hârithah ❧	Ramadan, 6 h.	The Al-Qurrah Valley	A number of Companions ❧	Fazarah
25	'Abdullah ibn 'Atik ❧	Ramadan, 6 h.	Khaibar	5 men	Abu Râfai' An-Nadri
26	'Abdullah ibn Rawâhah ❧	Shawâl, 6 h.	Khaibar	30 men	Asir ibn Zar-am
27	Kurz ibn Jâbir Al-Fihri ❧	Shawâl, 6 h.	'Urainah	20 horsemen	'Urainah
28	'Amr bin Umayyah Ad-Damri ❧	6 h.	–	2 men	Abu Sufyân
29	'Umar ibn Al-Khattâb ❧	Sha'bân, 7 h.	Turabah	30 men	Hawazin
30	Abu Bakr As-Siddiq ❧	Sha'bân, 7 h.	Najd	–	Banu Kilâb

No.	Name Of Mission Or Mission Leader	Date Of Mission	Place	Muslim Participants	Participants From The Polytheists
31	Bashir ibn Sa'd Al-Ansâri ﷺ	Sha'bân, 7 h.	Fadak	30 men	Banu Murrah
32	Ghâlib ibn 'Abdullah Al-Laithi ﷺ	Ramadan, 7 h.	Batn Nakhl	130 men	Banu 'Awâl
33	Bashir ibn Sa'd ﷺ	Shawâl, 7 h.	Yemen and Ja-bâr	300 men	Ghatafân
34	Ibn Abi Al-'Aujâ As-Sulami ﷺ	Dhil-Hijjah, 7 h.	Bani Salim	50 men	Banu Sulaim
35	Ghâlib ibn 'Abdullah Al-Laithi ﷺ	Safar, 8 h.	Kadid	200 men	Banu Al-Mallooh
36	Ghâlib ibn 'Abdullah Al-Laithi ﷺ	Safar 8 h.	Fada	200 men	Banu Murrah
37	Shujâ' ibn Wahb Al-Asadi ﷺ	Rabi' Al-Awwal, 8 h.	As-Sai	24 men	Hawazin
38	Ka'ab ibn 'Umair Al-Ghaffâri ﷺ	Rabi' Al-Awwal, 8 h.	Dhât Atlâh	15 men	Polytheists in the highlands of Ash-Sham
39	Zaid ﷺ, Ja'far ﷺ, 'Abdullah ﷺ	Jumâda Al-Ula, 8 h.	Al-Balqâ	3000 men	100 000 men
40	'Amr bin Al-'Aas ﷺ	Jumâda Al-Aakhirah, 8 h.	Dhat As-Salâsil	300 men	Qudâ'ah
41	Abu 'Ubaidah ibn Al-Jarrâh ﷺ	Rajab, 8 h.	Al-Qabaliyyah	300 men	Juhainah
42	Abu Qatâdah Al-Ansâri ﷺ	Sha'bân, 8 h.	Khadirah	15 men	Ghatafan
43	Abu Qatâdah Al-Ansâri ﷺ	Ramadan, 8 h.	Batn Idam	8 men	
44	Khâlid ibn Al-Walid ﷺ	Ramadan, 8 h.	Nakhl	30 horsemen	Hadm Al-'Uzzah
45	'Amr ibn Al-'Aas ﷺ	Ramadan, 8 h.	Hadam Sanan Suwâ'	A number of Companions ﷺ	Banu Hudhail
46	Sa'ad ibn Zaid Al-Ashhali ﷺ	Ramadan, 8 h.	Al-Mushallal	20 horsemen	–
47	Khâlid ibn Al-Walid ﷺ	Shawâl, 8 h.	Southern Makkah	350 men	Banu Judhaimah
48	At-Tufail ibn 'Amr Ad-Dausi ﷺ	Shawâl, 8 h.	–	–	–
49	'Uyainah ibn Hisn Al-Fazâri ﷺ	Al-Muharram, 9 h.	Banu Tamim	50 horsemen	Banu Tamim

No.	Name Of Mission Or Mission Leader	Date Of Mission	Place	Muslim Participants	Participants From The Polytheists
50	Qutbah ibn 'Aamir ﷺ	Safar, 9 h.	Tubalah	20 men	Banu Khath'am
51	Ad-Dahhak Al-Kulabi ﷺ	Rabi' Al-Awwal, 9 h.	Zujj Lawah	A number of Companions ﷺ	Banu Kilâb
52	'Alqamah bin Mujazziz Al-Mudliji ﷺ	Rabi' Al-Aakhir, 9 h.	Jeddah	300 men	A group from Habashah
53	'Ali ibn Abi Tâlib ﷺ	Rabi' Al-Ākhir, 9 h.	Ard Hatim At-Tai	150 men	Tai
54	'Ukkashah ibn Mihsan Al-Asadi ﷺ	Rabi' Al-Ākhir, 9 h.	The Land of 'Adhrah and Balli	A number of Companions ﷺ	Al-Janab
55	Khalid ibn Al-Walid ﷺ	Rabi' Al-Awwal, 10 h.	Najran	A number of Companions ﷺ	Banu 'Abdul-Madan
56	'Ali ibn Abi Tâlib ﷺ	Ramadan, 10 h.	Yemen	300 horsemen	Banu Madhhaj

- Tabaqât Ibn Sa'd: Vol. 2, pg. 5 and subsequent pages

The Greater Battle of Badr

(The Day of Criterion, the day when the two forces met.)

17 Ramadan 2 A.H.
13 March 624 A.D.

"Verily, Allâh loves those who fight in His Cause in rows (ranks) as if they were a solid structure." (Qur'an 61:4)

"And Allâh has already made you victorious at Badr, when you were a weak little force. So fear Allâh much that you may be grateful."
(Qur'an 3:123)

The Near Side

Date Palm Orchards

To Al Madinah

Location of the Muslim Command

Line System

Swordsmen
Archers
Spearmen

x Miqdad bin 'Amr Horse
x Hamzah

Well of Badr

Az-Zubair bin 'Awwam Horse

Ali x

'Ubaidah x

The Duel

Al Walid x

Shaibah x

'Utbah x

Muslims in Pursuit of Polytheists

Muslims in Pursuit of Polytheists

The Farthest Side

The way to Makkah

Shattering Polytheists Attacks

Polytheists Army (950)

Polytheists Fighting According to the Method of Attack and Retreat

The Site of Badr

Al Madinah

Hijaz

Badr

Al-Juhfah

Rabigh

Red Sea

50
100
150 km

The Greater Battle Of Badr

وَلَقَدْ نَصَرَكُمُ ٱللَّهُ بِبَدْرٍ وَأَنتُمْ أَذِلَّةٌ ۖ فَٱتَّقُوا ٱللَّهَ لَعَلَّكُمْ تَشْكُرُونَ ۝١٢٣ إِذْ تَقُولُ لِلْمُؤْمِنِينَ أَلَن يَكْفِيَكُمْ أَن يُمِدَّكُمْ رَبُّكُم بِثَلَٰثَةِ ءَالَٰفٍ مِّنَ ٱلْمَلَٰٓئِكَةِ مُنزَلِينَ ۝١٢٤ بَلَىٰٓ إِن تَصْبِرُوا۟ وَتَتَّقُوا۟ وَيَأْتُوكُم مِّن فَوْرِهِمْ هَٰذَا يُمْدِدْكُمْ رَبُّكُم بِخَمْسَةِ ءَالَٰفٍ مِّنَ ٱلْمَلَٰٓئِكَةِ مُسَوِّمِينَ ۝١٢٥ وَمَا جَعَلَهُ ٱللَّهُ إِلَّا بُشْرَىٰ لَكُمْ وَلِتَطْمَئِنَّ قُلُوبُكُم بِهِۦ ۗ وَمَا ٱلنَّصْرُ إِلَّا مِنْ عِندِ ٱللَّهِ ٱلْعَزِيزِ ٱلْحَكِيمِ ۝١٢٦

And Allāh has already made you victorious at Badr, when you were a weak little force. So fear Allāh much that you may be grateful. (Remember) when you (Muhammad ﷺ) said to the believers, "Is it not enough for you that your Lord (Allāh) should help you with three thousand angels sent down? Yes, if you hold on to patience and piety, and the enemy comes rushing at you; your Lord will help you with five thousand angels having marks (of distinction)." Allāh made it not but as a message of good news for you and as an assurance to your hearts. And there is no victory except from Allāh, the All-Mighty, the All-Wise.

(Qur'ân 3: 123-126)

After the Quraish seized the wealth that the Muslims left behind when they migrated to Al-Madinah, the Muslims began to think about cutting off their trade routes. The Muslims then left Al-Madinah to intercept a caravan that was headed by Abu Sufyân, in what was to be a legitimate economic embargo. Meanwhile, the Quraish had left Makkah to intercept the Muslims, and this resulted in the Greater Battle of Badr, which took place on the 17th of Ramadan, in the year 2 H. Allâh ﷻ said:

And Allâh has already made you victorious at Badr, when you were a weak little force. So fear Allâh much (abstain from all kinds of sins and evil dids which He has forbidden and love

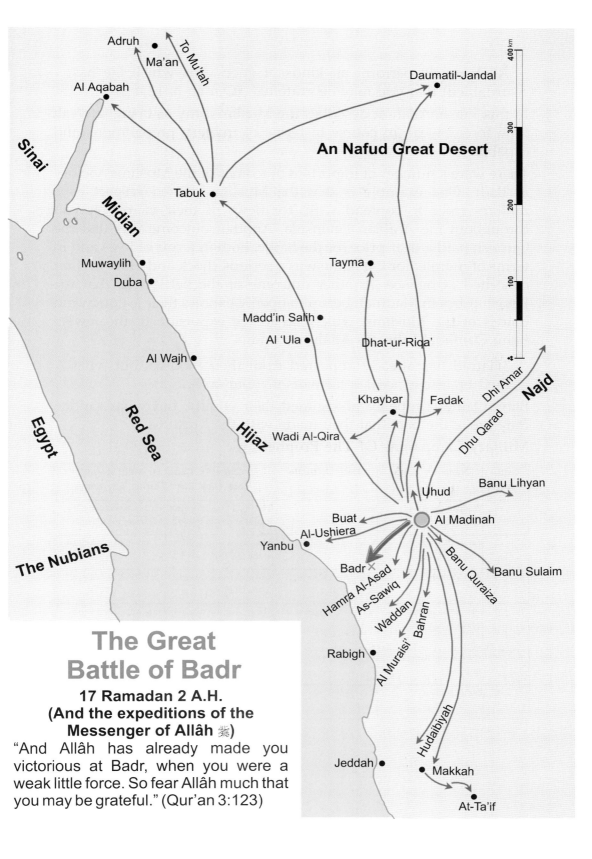

Adruh

Ma'an

To Mu'tah

Al Aqabah

Daumatil-Jandal

Sinai

An Nafud Great Desert

Midian

Tabuk

Muwaylih

Duba

Tayma

Madd'in Salih

Al 'Ula

Dhat-ur-Riqa'

Al Wajh

Khaybar

Fadak

Dhi Amar

Najd

Wadi Al-Qira

Dhu Qarad

Red Sea

Hijaz

Egypt

Uhud

Banu Lihyan

Buat

Al-Ushiera

Al Madinah

Yanbu

The Nubians

Badr ✕

Banu Quraiza

Banu Sulaim

Hamra Al-Asad

As-Sawiq

Waddan

Bahran

Al Muraisi'

Rabigh

Jeddah

Hudaibiyah

Makkah

At-Ta'if

The Great
Battle of Badr

17 Ramadan 2 A.H.
**(And the expeditions of the
Messenger of Allâh ﷺ)**

"And Allâh has already made you victorious at Badr, when you were a weak little force. So fear Allâh much that you may be grateful." (Qur'an 3:123)

Allâh much, perform all kinds of good dids which He has ordained) that you may be grateful." (Qur'ân 3: 123)

In this Verse, Allâh ﷻ describes the Muslim army as being 'a weak little force,' weak of course in terms of military preparations and capability.

There were a number of important outcomes of the Muslims' victory at Badr. One example is that the Muslims gained respect as a military force to contend with, for news of their victory spread throughout the Arabian Peninsula. Another outcome was that the Quraish paid a dear price for the battle, both in terms of lives and in terms of morale for the battle was a serious shock and blow to their conceited arrogance. Another outcome of the battle was that the Jewish tribes in Madinah began to openly express their jealousy and hatred of the Muslims, which led to the expulsion of the Jewish Banu Qainuqa' tribe. As Allâh has said:

"Hatred has already appeared from their mouths, but what their breasts conceal is far worse." (Qur'ân 3: 118)

Banu Qainuqa' openly proclaimed their enmity, but what's more, they broke the pact that they made with the Muslims.

Military Campaigns Of The Prophet ﷺ:

Battle Number	Name Of Battle	Date Of Battle	Cause Of Battle Or Main Events That Took Place During The Battle
1	Waddan (Al-Abwa)	Safar, 2 H.	The first of the Prophet's military expeditions. Its goal was hinder trading concerns of the Quraish
2	Bawât (Radwâ)	Rabi' Al-Awwal, 2 H.	The goal was to overtake a caravan that belonged to the Quraish
3	Al-'Ushairah	Jumâda Al-Ākhirah, 2 H.	The goal was to overtake a caravan that belonged to the Quraish
4	First Battle of Badr (Safawân)	Jumâda Al-Ākhirah, 2 H.	The goal of this mission was to apprehend Kurz ibn Jâbir Al-Fihri, who raided one of Madinah's pastures
5	The Greater Battle of Badr	Ramadan, 2 H.	The initial goal of this expedition was to overtake a caravan that belonged to the Quraish
6	Banu Qainuqa'	Shawal, 2 H.	This battle occurred as a result of the Jews breaking their pact with the Muslims

Spring of Badr and Masjid Al-Arish

Battle Number	Name Of Battle	Date Of Battle	Cause Of Battle Or Main Events That Took Place During The Battle
7	Banu Sulaim	Shawâl, 2 h.	The Messenger of Allâh ﷺ traveled until Qarqarah Al-Kadar, in order to break up the gathering of Banu Sulaim and Ghatafan
8	As-Sawiq	Dhil-Hijjah, 2 h.	The goal of this mission was to thwart Abu Sufyan's plans, for he had come to Al-Madinah, in order to exact revenge for the Battle of Badr
9	Dhi Amar	Rabi' Al-Awwal, 3 h.	The goal of this mission was to break up the gathering of Banu Tha'labah and Maharib before they could launch an assault upon Al-Madinah
10	Buhrân	Jumâda Al-Ulah, 3 h.	The goal of this mission was to break up the gathering of Banu Sulaim
11	Uhud	Shawâl, 3 h.	The goal of this battle was to defeat the army of the Quraish that had come to fight the Muslims in Al-Madinah
12	Hamra Al-Asad	Shawâl, 3 h.	The goal of this mission was to impede Abu Sufyân, who was planning to launch an assault on Al-Madinah
13	Banu An-Nudair	Rabi' Al-Awwal, 4 h.	Because the tribe of Banu An-Nadir was plotting to kill the Messenger of Allâh ﷺ through treacherous means, the Muslims went to them and expelled them from Al-Madinah
14	Dhat Ar-Riqa'	Al-Muharram, 4 h.	The goal of this mission was to break up the gathering of Anmar and Tha'labah
15	Last [Battle of] Badr	Sha'bân, 4 h.	The goal of this mission was to overtake Abu Sufyân
16	Dumatil-Jundal	Rabi' Al-Awwal, 5 h.	The goal of this mission was to disband a group of highway robbers, who were planning a surprise attack on Al-Madinah
17	Al-Muraisi'	Sha'bân, 5 h.	The goal here was to break up the gathered forces of Banu Al-Mustaliq (from the Khuza'ah)
18	Al-Khandaq	Shawâl, 5 h.	The goal of this battle was to impede the confederates, who were headed by the Quraish
19	Banu Quraizah	Dhil-Qa'dah, 5 h.	The cause of this expedition was the treachery of the Banu Quraidhah tribe, who broke their covenant with the Muslims during the Siege of the Confederates
20	Banu Laihyan	Rabi' Al-Awwal, 6 h.	The purpose of this expedition was to punish Banu Laihyan from the Hudhail for killing some Companions ﷺ (Ar-Raji')

Battle Number	Name Of Battle	Date Of Battle	Cause Of Battle Or Main Events That Took Place During The Battle
21	Dhi Qarad (Al-Ghabah)	Rabi' Al-Awwal, 6 h.	The purpose of this mission was to repel 'Uyainah ibn Hisn Al-Fazari, who had raided a part of Al-Madinah
22	Al-Hudaibiyyah	Dhil-Qa'dah, 6 h.	The Muslims had set out to perform the minor pilgrimage ('*Umrah*) to Allâh's Inviolable House in Makkah, but the Quraish blocked their way
23	Khaibar	Muharram, 7 h.	The purpose here was to break up the Confederates who had gathered to launch an attack on Al-Madinah
24	Mu'tah	Jumada Al-Ulah, 8 h.	Although the Prophet ﷺ didn't participate in this particular battle, the events of the battle were made known to him while he was in Al-Madinah. While standing on the pulpit of his Masjid, the Prophet ﷺ gave a live description of those events to his Companions ﷺ.
25	The Conquering of Makkah	Ramadan, 8 h.	The Muslims marched towards Makkah and took it easily. They did so only after the Quraish broke the conditions of the pact they agrid upon in the Treaty of Al-Hudaibiyyah
26	Hunain and Ta'if	Shawal, 8 h.	The purpose of these battles was to break up the gathered forces of Thaqif
27	Tabuk (Al-'Usrah)	Rajab, 9 h.	The purpose of this expedition was to mit with the gathered forces of Rome, forces that had gathered in order to launch an attack against Al-Madinah

The Messenger of Allâh ﷺ never initiated war, since he strived hard to avoid the spilling of blood; he was, after all, the Prophet of Mercy. Even when he ﷺ went out to fight, it was because the other party had showed enmity, had broken an agreement with the Muslims, or was preparing for an attack. So when a battle was inevitable, the Prophet ﷺ was at the forefront, determined and strong. He ﷺ was excellent both in his mercy towards people and in his preparations and planning for war.

Of the many caravans that passed Al-Madinah or near to it, the Prophet ﷺ would only intercept those caravans that belonged to the Quraish, for it was the leaders of the Quraish who started the economic war with the embargo in the Valley of Abu Talib; and it was they who seized the wealth of the Muslims that migrated to Al-Madinah.

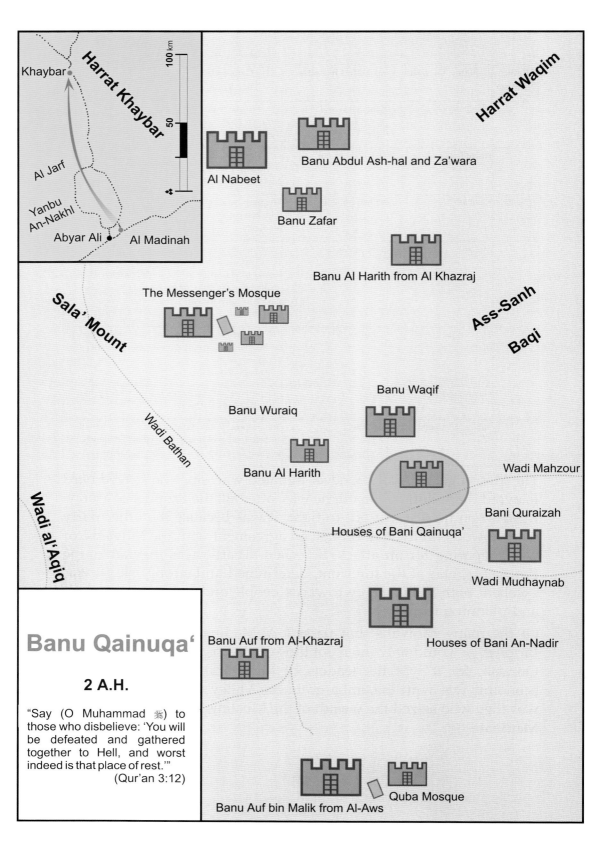

Khaybar

Harrat Khaybar

100 km

50

Al Jarf

Yanbu
An-Nakhl

Abyar Ali   Al Madinah

Harrat Waqim

Al Nabeet

Banu Abdul Ash-hal and Za'wara

Banu Zafar

Banu Al Harith from Al Khazraj

The Messenger's Mosque

Sala' Mount

Ass-Sanh

Baqi

Banu Waqif

Banu Wuraiq

Wadi Bathan

Banu Al Harith

Wadi Mahzour

Houses of Bani Qainuqa'

Bani Quraizah

Wadi al'Aqiq

Wadi Mudhaynab

Houses of Bani An-Nadir

Banu Auf from Al-Khazraj

Banu Qainuqaʻ

2 A.H.

"Say (O Muhammad ﷺ) to those who disbelieve: 'You will be defeated and gathered together to Hell, and worst indeed is that place of rest.'"
(Qur'an 3:12)

Banu Auf bin Malik from Al-Aws

Quba Mosque

Banu Qainuqa'

﴿قُل لِّلَّذِينَ كَفَرُواْ سَتُغْلَبُونَ وَتُحْشَرُونَ إِلَىٰ جَهَنَّمَ ۚ وَبِئْسَ ٱلْمِهَادُ ۝۱۲﴾

Say (O Muhammad ﷺ) to those who disbelieve: "You will be defeated and gathered together to Hell, and worst indeed is that place of rest."

(Qur'ân 3: 12)

﴿يَـٰٓأَيُّهَا ٱلَّذِينَ ءَامَنُواْ لَا تَتَّخِذُواْ بِطَانَةً مِّن دُونِكُمْ لَا يَأْلُونَكُمْ خَبَالًا وَدُّواْ مَا عَنِتُّمْ قَدْ بَدَتِ ٱلْبَغْضَآءُ مِنْ أَفْوَٰهِهِمْ وَمَا تُخْفِى صُدُورُهُمْ أَكْبَرُ ۚ قَدْ بَيَّنَّا لَكُمُ ٱلْءَايَـٰتِ ۖ إِن كُنتُمْ تَعْقِلُونَ ۝۱۱۸﴾

O you who believe! Take not as (your) *Bitānah* (advisors, consultants, protectors, helpers, friends) those outside your religion (pagans, Jews, Christians, and hypocrites) since they will not fail to do their best to corrupt you. They desire to harm you severely. Hatred has already appeared from their mouths, but what their breasts conceal is far worse. Indid We have made plain to you the *Ayāt* (proofs, Verses, evidences) if you understand.

(Qur'ân 3: 118)

When the Messenger of Allâh ﷺ arrived in Al-Madinah, he ﷺ made a peace pact with the Jewish tribes of Al-Madinah. There were two important conditions in that pact:

1) The Jews would not help anyone that attacked the Muslims.

2) If any enemy launched a surprise attack on Al-Madinah, the Jews would help the Muslims.

But after many polytheists from the Quraish were killed in the Battle of Badr, the Jewish tribes of Al-Madinah openly proclaimed their hatred of the Muslims. They boasted that, "Muhammad has not faced anyone that knows how to fight. If we were to meet him in battle, he would face fighting which (in its intensity and fierceness) no one else can come near to"

After openly proclaiming their hatred, they began to ridicule the Muslims. Things went too far one day when a Muslim woman went to the marketplace of Banu Qainuqa', intending to sell some jewelry that she had with her. She sat down beside a jeweler from the Jewish Banu Qainuqa' tribe. That jeweler went behind her and tied the edge of her garment to her back, so that when she later stood, her private areas became exposed. While the jeweler and those with him began to laugh, she let out a scream. A Muslim man who was nearby jumped on the jeweler and killed him; then a group of Jews ganged up on the Muslim and killed him.

It was in this manner that Banu Qainuqa' became the first of Madinah's Jewish tribes to break the pact that they all made with the Messenger of Allâh ﷺ. After news of what happened in the marketplace of Banu Qainuqa' reached the Messenger of Allâh ﷺ, he set out with his Companions ﷺ and together they surrounded the tribe's fortresses, waiting for them to come out. The siege lasted for 15 nights, after which Banu Qainuqa' surrendered. Through the intercession of 'Abdullah ibn Ubai ibn Salûl, they were not physically punished, but were instead expelled from Al-Madinah Al-Munawwarah.

- Ibn Hisham: 2/118
- Al-Bidayah wan-Nihayah: 4/3
- At-Tabari: 2/481

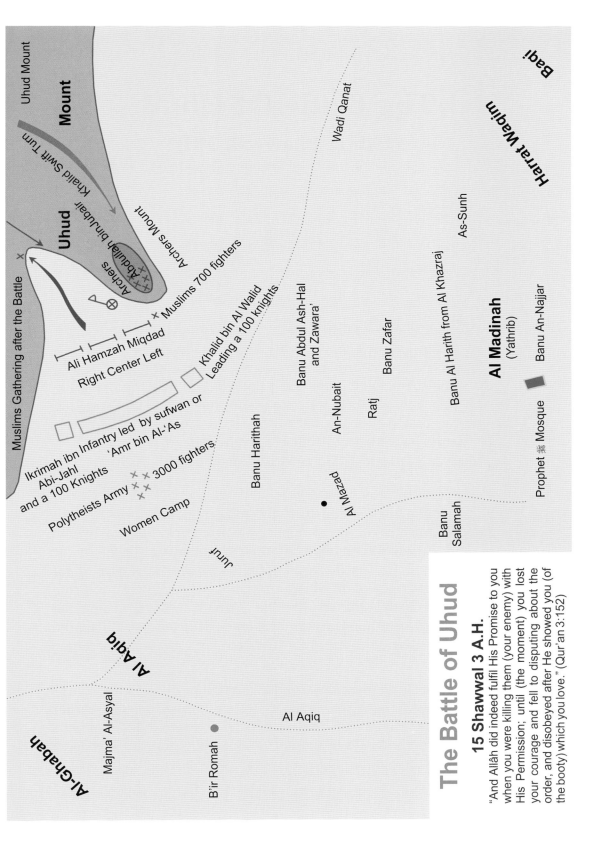

The Battle of Uhud

15 Shawwal 3 A.H.

"And Allâh did indeed fulfil His Promise to you when you were killing them (your enemy) with His Permission; until (the moment) you lost your courage and fell to disputing about the order, and disobeyed after He showed you (of the booty) which you love." (Qur'an 3:152)

The Battle Of Uhud

(15th of Shawwâl, 3 H)

﴿وَلَقَدْ صَدَقَكُمُ ٱللَّهُ وَعْدَهُۥٓ إِذْ تَحُسُّونَهُم بِإِذْنِهِۦ حَتَّىٰٓ إِذَا فَشِلْتُمْ وَتَنَٰزَعْتُمْ فِى ٱلْأَمْرِ وَعَصَيْتُم مِّنۢ بَعْدِ مَآ أَرَىٰكُم مَّا تُحِبُّونَ مِنكُم مَّن يُرِيدُ ٱلدُّنْيَا وَمِنكُم مَّن يُرِيدُ ٱلْءَاخِرَةَ ثُمَّ صَرَفَكُمْ عَنْهُمْ لِيَبْتَلِيَكُمْ وَلَقَدْ عَفَا عَنكُمْ وَٱللَّهُ ذُو فَضْلٍ عَلَى ٱلْمُؤْمِنِينَ ﴿١٥٢﴾ ﴾

And Allāh did indeed fulfil His Promise to you when you were killing them (your enemy) with His Permission; until (the moment) you lost your courage and fell to disputing about the order, and disobeyed after He showed you (of the booty) which you love. Among you are some that desire this world and some that desire the Hereafter. Then He made you flee from them (your enemy), that He might test you. But surely, He forgave you, and Allāh is Most Gracious to the believers.

(Qur'ân 3: 152)

From the profits they made in their trade with peoples of other lands, the Quraish saved up to finance a war against the Muslims in Al-Madinah, a war of revenge for their humiliating defeat in the Battle of Badr (2 H). As the army of the Quraish approached for battle, the Messenger of Allâh ﷺ prepared a practically foolproof plan. He placed 50 archers on the 'Ainain Mountain (or the Mountain of the Archers), under the leadership of 'Abdullah ibn Jubair ﷺ. The mission of the archers was to kip Quraish's horsemen at bay.

But it is often a single moment or false move that dictates the course of a battle. The Quraish was actually losing the battle in its earlier stages. But then most of the archers disobeyed the Prophet's command. He ﷺ had said to them, "Do not leave (your places) even

256

if you see us being killed, do not help us or defend us. For indeed, we will remain victorious as long as you stay or remain firm in your places." When the archers came down to share in the spoils, horsemen from the Quraish were able to come from behind, and the Muslims now had to fight on two fronts. The Quraish now achieved momentum and were able to achieve victory in the battle, yet they were not able to do a number of things: they couldn't completely destroy the Muslims that day; they couldn't put a stop to the Prophet's *Da'wah*, and so Islam continued to spread; and they couldn't open a way for their trade caravans that traveled to Ash-Sham.

At the end of the *Sûrat Âl 'Imrân* are many Verses that describe the events that took place on the Day of Uhud:

۞ إِن تَمْسَسْكُمْ حَسَنَةٌ تَسُؤْهُمْ وَإِن تُصِبْكُمْ سَيِّئَةٌ يَفْرَحُوا بِهَا وَإِن تَصْبِرُوا وَتَتَّقُوا لَا يَضُرُّكُمْ كَيْدُهُمْ شَيْئًا إِنَّ ٱللَّهَ بِمَا يَعْمَلُونَ مُحِيطٌ ﴿١٢٠﴾ وَإِذْ غَدَوْتَ مِنْ أَهْلِكَ تُبَوِّئُ ٱلْمُؤْمِنِينَ مَقَاعِدَ لِلْقِتَالِ وَٱللَّهُ سَمِيعٌ عَلِيمٌ ﴿١٢١﴾ إِذْ هَمَّت طَّآئِفَتَانِ مِنكُمْ أَن تَفْشَلَا وَٱللَّهُ وَلِيُّهُمَا وَعَلَى ٱللَّهِ فَلْيَتَوَكَّلِ ٱلْمُؤْمِنُونَ ﴿١٢٢﴾ وَلَقَدْ نَصَرَكُمُ ٱللَّهُ بِبَدْرٍ وَأَنتُمْ أَذِلَّةٌ فَٱتَّقُوا ٱللَّهَ لَعَلَّكُمْ تَشْكُرُونَ ﴿١٢٣﴾ إِذْ تَقُولُ لِلْمُؤْمِنِينَ أَلَن يَكْفِيَكُمْ أَن يُمِدَّكُمْ رَبُّكُم بِثَلَاثَةِ ءَالَافٍ مِّنَ ٱلْمَلَائِكَةِ مُنزَلِينَ ﴿١٢٤﴾ بَلَى إِن تَصْبِرُوا وَتَتَّقُوا وَيَأْتُوكُم مِّن فَوْرِهِمْ هَذَا يُمْدِدْكُمْ رَبُّكُم بِخَمْسَةِ ءَالَافٍ مِّنَ ٱلْمَلَائِكَةِ مُسَوِّمِينَ ﴿١٢٥﴾ وَمَا جَعَلَهُ ٱللَّهُ إِلَّا بُشْرَى لَكُمْ وَلِتَطْمَئِنَّ قُلُوبُكُم بِهِ وَمَا ٱلنَّصْرُ إِلَّا مِنْ عِندِ ٱللَّهِ ٱلْعَزِيزِ ٱلْحَكِيمِ ﴿١٢٦﴾ لِيَقْطَعَ طَرَفًا مِّنَ ٱلَّذِينَ كَفَرُوا أَوْ يَكْبِتَهُمْ فَيَنقَلِبُوا خَائِبِينَ ﴿١٢٧﴾ لَيْسَ لَكَ مِنَ ٱلْأَمْرِ شَيْءٌ أَوْ يَتُوبَ عَلَيْهِمْ أَوْ يُعَذِّبَهُمْ فَإِنَّهُمْ ظَالِمُونَ ﴿١٢٨﴾ وَلِلَّهِ مَا فِي ٱلسَّمَوَاتِ وَمَا فِي ٱلْأَرْضِ يَغْفِرُ لِمَن يَشَاءُ وَيُعَذِّبُ مَن يَشَاءُ وَٱللَّهُ غَفُورٌ رَّحِيمٌ ﴿١٢٩﴾ يَأَيُّهَا ٱلَّذِينَ ءَامَنُوا لَا تَأْكُلُوا ٱلرِّبَوٰا أَضْعَافًا مُّضَاعَفَةً وَٱتَّقُوا ٱللَّهَ لَعَلَّكُمْ تُفْلِحُونَ ﴿١٣٠﴾ وَٱتَّقُوا ٱلنَّارَ ٱلَّتِي أُعِدَّتْ لِلْكَافِرِينَ ﴿١٣١﴾ وَأَطِيعُوا ٱللَّهَ وَٱلرَّسُولَ لَعَلَّكُمْ تُرْحَمُونَ ﴿١٣٢﴾ وَسَارِعُوا إِلَى مَغْفِرَةٍ مِّن رَّبِّكُمْ وَجَنَّةٍ عَرْضُهَا ٱلسَّمَوَاتُ وَٱلْأَرْضُ أُعِدَّتْ لِلْمُتَّقِينَ ﴿١٣٣﴾ ٱلَّذِينَ يُنفِقُونَ فِي ٱلسَّرَّاءِ وَٱلضَّرَّاءِ وَٱلْكَاظِمِينَ ٱلْغَيْظَ وَٱلْعَافِينَ عَنِ ٱلنَّاسِ وَٱللَّهُ يُحِبُّ ٱلْمُحْسِنِينَ ﴿١٣٤﴾ وَٱلَّذِينَ إِذَا فَعَلُوا فَاحِشَةً أَوْ ظَلَمُوا

أَنفُسَهُمْ ذَكَرُواْ ٱللَّهَ فَٱسْتَغْفَرُواْ لِذُنُوبِهِمْ وَمَن يَغْفِرُ ٱلذُّنُوبَ إِلَّا ٱللَّهُ وَلَمْ يُصِرُّواْ عَلَىٰ مَا فَعَلُواْ وَهُمْ يَعْلَمُونَ ۝١٣٥ أُوْلَٰٓئِكَ جَزَآؤُهُم مَّغْفِرَةٌ مِّن رَّبِّهِمْ وَجَنَّٰتٌ تَجْرِى مِن تَحْتِهَا ٱلْأَنْهَٰرُ خَٰلِدِينَ فِيهَا وَنِعْمَ أَجْرُ ٱلْعَٰمِلِينَ ۝١٣٦ قَدْ خَلَتْ مِن قَبْلِكُمْ سُنَنٌ فَسِيرُواْ فِى ٱلْأَرْضِ فَٱنظُرُواْ كَيْفَ كَانَ عَٰقِبَةُ ٱلْمُكَذِّبِينَ ۝١٣٧ هَٰذَا بَيَانٌ لِّلنَّاسِ وَهُدًى وَمَوْعِظَةٌ لِّلْمُتَّقِينَ ۝١٣٨ وَلَا تَهِنُواْ وَلَا تَحْزَنُواْ وَأَنتُمُ ٱلْأَعْلَوْنَ إِن كُنتُم مُّؤْمِنِينَ ۝١٣٩ إِن يَمْسَسْكُمْ قَرْحٌ فَقَدْ مَسَّ ٱلْقَوْمَ قَرْحٌ مِّثْلُهُۥ وَتِلْكَ ٱلْأَيَّامُ نُدَاوِلُهَا بَيْنَ ٱلنَّاسِ وَلِيَعْلَمَ ٱللَّهُ ٱلَّذِينَ ءَامَنُواْ وَيَتَّخِذَ مِنكُمْ شُهَدَآءَ وَٱللَّهُ لَا يُحِبُّ ٱلظَّٰلِمِينَ ۝١٤٠ وَلِيُمَحِّصَ ٱللَّهُ ٱلَّذِينَ ءَامَنُواْ وَيَمْحَقَ ٱلْكَٰفِرِينَ ۝١٤١ أَمْ حَسِبْتُمْ أَن تَدْخُلُواْ ٱلْجَنَّةَ وَلَمَّا يَعْلَمِ ٱللَّهُ ٱلَّذِينَ جَٰهَدُواْ مِنكُمْ وَيَعْلَمَ ٱلصَّٰبِرِينَ ۝١٤٢ وَلَقَدْ كُنتُمْ تَمَنَّوْنَ ٱلْمَوْتَ مِن قَبْلِ أَن تَلْقَوْهُ فَقَدْ رَأَيْتُمُوهُ وَأَنتُمْ تَنظُرُونَ ۝١٤٣ وَمَا مُحَمَّدٌ إِلَّا رَسُولٌ قَدْ خَلَتْ مِن قَبْلِهِ ٱلرُّسُلُ أَفَإِيْن مَّاتَ أَوْ قُتِلَ ٱنقَلَبْتُمْ عَلَىٰٓ أَعْقَٰبِكُمْ وَمَن يَنقَلِبْ عَلَىٰ عَقِبَيْهِ فَلَن يَضُرَّ ٱللَّهَ شَيْـًٔا وَسَيَجْزِى ٱللَّهُ ٱلشَّٰكِرِينَ ۝١٤٤ وَمَا كَانَ لِنَفْسٍ أَن تَمُوتَ إِلَّا بِإِذْنِ ٱللَّهِ كِتَٰبًا مُّؤَجَّلًا وَمَن يُرِدْ ثَوَابَ ٱلدُّنْيَا نُؤْتِهِۦ مِنْهَا وَمَن يُرِدْ ثَوَابَ ٱلْأَخِرَةِ نُؤْتِهِۦ مِنْهَا وَسَنَجْزِى ٱلشَّٰكِرِينَ ۝١٤٥ وَكَأَيِّن مِّن نَّبِىٍّ قَٰتَلَ مَعَهُۥ رِبِّيُّونَ كَثِيرٌ فَمَا وَهَنُواْ لِمَآ أَصَابَهُمْ فِى سَبِيلِ ٱللَّهِ وَمَا ضَعُفُواْ وَمَا ٱسْتَكَانُواْ وَٱللَّهُ يُحِبُّ ٱلصَّٰبِرِينَ ۝١٤٦ وَمَا كَانَ قَوْلَهُمْ إِلَّآ أَن قَالُواْ رَبَّنَا ٱغْفِرْ لَنَا ذُنُوبَنَا وَإِسْرَافَنَا فِىٓ أَمْرِنَا وَثَبِّتْ أَقْدَامَنَا وَٱنصُرْنَا عَلَى ٱلْقَوْمِ ٱلْكَٰفِرِينَ ۝١٤٧ فَـَٔاتَىٰهُمُ ٱللَّهُ ثَوَابَ ٱلدُّنْيَا وَحُسْنَ ثَوَابِ ٱلْأَخِرَةِ وَٱللَّهُ يُحِبُّ ٱلْمُحْسِنِينَ ۝١٤٨ يَٰٓأَيُّهَا ٱلَّذِينَ ءَامَنُواْ إِن تُطِيعُواْ ٱلَّذِينَ كَفَرُواْ يَرُدُّوكُمْ عَلَىٰٓ أَعْقَٰبِكُمْ فَتَنقَلِبُواْ خَٰسِرِينَ ۝١٤٩ بَلِ ٱللَّهُ مَوْلَىٰكُمْ وَهُوَ خَيْرُ ٱلنَّٰصِرِينَ ۝١٥٠ سَنُلْقِى فِى قُلُوبِ ٱلَّذِينَ كَفَرُواْ ٱلرُّعْبَ بِمَآ أَشْرَكُواْ بِٱللَّهِ مَا لَمْ يُنَزِّلْ بِهِۦ سُلْطَٰنًا وَمَأْوَىٰهُمُ ٱلنَّارُ وَبِئْسَ مَثْوَى ٱلظَّٰلِمِينَ ۝١٥١ وَلَقَدْ صَدَقَكُمُ ٱللَّهُ وَعْدَهُۥٓ إِذْ تَحُسُّونَهُم بِإِذْنِهِۦ حَتَّىٰٓ إِذَا فَشِلْتُمْ وَتَنَٰزَعْتُمْ فِى ٱلْأَمْرِ وَعَصَيْتُم مِّنۢ بَعْدِ مَآ أَرَىٰكُم مَّا تُحِبُّونَ مِنكُم مَّن يُرِيدُ ٱلدُّنْيَا وَمِنكُم مَّن يُرِيدُ ٱلْأَخِرَةَ ثُمَّ صَرَفَكُمْ عَنْهُمْ لِيَبْتَلِيَكُمْ وَلَقَدْ عَفَا عَنكُمْ وَٱللَّهُ ذُو فَضْلٍ عَلَى ٱلْمُؤْمِنِينَ ۝١٥٢ إِذْ تُصْعِدُونَ وَلَا تَلْوُۥنَ عَلَىٰٓ أَحَدٍ

وَٱلرَّسُولُ يَدْعُوكُمْ فِىٓ أُخْرَىٰكُمْ فَأَثَٰبَكُمْ غَمَّۢا بِغَمٍّ لِّكَيْلَا تَحْزَنُوا۟ عَلَىٰ مَا فَاتَكُمْ وَلَا مَآ أَصَٰبَكُمْ ۗ وَٱللَّهُ خَبِيرٌۢ بِمَا تَعْمَلُونَ ۝١٥٣ ثُمَّ أَنزَلَ عَلَيْكُم مِّنۢ بَعْدِ ٱلْغَمِّ أَمَنَةً نُّعَاسًا يَغْشَىٰ طَآئِفَةً مِّنكُمْ ۖ وَطَآئِفَةٌ قَدْ أَهَمَّتْهُمْ أَنفُسُهُمْ يَظُنُّونَ بِٱللَّهِ غَيْرَ ٱلْحَقِّ ظَنَّ ٱلْجَٰهِلِيَّةِ ۖ يَقُولُونَ هَل لَّنَا مِنَ ٱلْأَمْرِ مِن شَىْءٍ ۗ قُلْ إِنَّ ٱلْأَمْرَ كُلَّهُۥ لِلَّهِ ۗ يُخْفُونَ فِىٓ أَنفُسِهِم مَّا لَا يُبْدُونَ لَكَ ۖ يَقُولُونَ لَوْ كَانَ لَنَا مِنَ ٱلْأَمْرِ شَىْءٌ مَّا قُتِلْنَا هَٰهُنَا ۗ قُل لَّوْ كُنتُمْ فِى بُيُوتِكُمْ لَبَرَزَ ٱلَّذِينَ كُتِبَ عَلَيْهِمُ ٱلْقَتْلُ إِلَىٰ مَضَاجِعِهِمْ ۖ وَلِيَبْتَلِىَ ٱللَّهُ مَا فِى صُدُورِكُمْ وَلِيُمَحِّصَ مَا فِى قُلُوبِكُمْ ۗ وَٱللَّهُ عَلِيمٌۢ بِذَاتِ ٱلصُّدُورِ ۝١٥٤ إِنَّ ٱلَّذِينَ تَوَلَّوْا۟ مِنكُمْ يَوْمَ ٱلْتَقَى ٱلْجَمْعَانِ إِنَّمَا ٱسْتَزَلَّهُمُ ٱلشَّيْطَٰنُ بِبَعْضِ مَا كَسَبُوا۟ ۖ وَلَقَدْ عَفَا ٱللَّهُ عَنْهُمْ ۗ إِنَّ ٱللَّهَ غَفُورٌ حَلِيمٌ ۝١٥٥ يَٰٓأَيُّهَا ٱلَّذِينَ ءَامَنُوا۟ لَا تَكُونُوا۟ كَٱلَّذِينَ كَفَرُوا۟ وَقَالُوا۟ لِإِخْوَٰنِهِمْ إِذَا ضَرَبُوا۟ فِى ٱلْأَرْضِ أَوْ كَانُوا۟ غُزًّى لَّوْ كَانُوا۟ عِندَنَا مَا مَاتُوا۟ وَمَا قُتِلُوا۟ لِيَجْعَلَ ٱللَّهُ ذَٰلِكَ حَسْرَةً فِى قُلُوبِهِمْ ۗ وَٱللَّهُ يُحْىِۦ وَيُمِيتُ ۗ وَٱللَّهُ بِمَا تَعْمَلُونَ بَصِيرٌ ۝١٥٦ وَلَئِن قُتِلْتُمْ فِى سَبِيلِ ٱللَّهِ أَوْ مُتُّمْ لَمَغْفِرَةٌ مِّنَ ٱللَّهِ وَرَحْمَةٌ خَيْرٌ مِّمَّا يَجْمَعُونَ ۝١٥٧ وَلَئِن مُّتُّمْ أَوْ قُتِلْتُمْ لَإِلَى ٱللَّهِ تُحْشَرُونَ ۝١٥٨ فَبِمَا رَحْمَةٍ مِّنَ ٱللَّهِ لِنتَ لَهُمْ ۖ وَلَوْ كُنتَ فَظًّا غَلِيظَ ٱلْقَلْبِ لَٱنفَضُّوا۟ مِنْ حَوْلِكَ ۖ فَٱعْفُ عَنْهُمْ وَٱسْتَغْفِرْ لَهُمْ وَشَاوِرْهُمْ فِى ٱلْأَمْرِ ۖ فَإِذَا عَزَمْتَ فَتَوَكَّلْ عَلَى ٱللَّهِ ۚ إِنَّ ٱللَّهَ يُحِبُّ ٱلْمُتَوَكِّلِينَ ۝١٥٩ إِن يَنصُرْكُمُ ٱللَّهُ فَلَا غَالِبَ لَكُمْ ۖ وَإِن يَخْذُلْكُمْ فَمَن ذَا ٱلَّذِى يَنصُرُكُم مِّنۢ بَعْدِهِۦ ۗ وَعَلَى ٱللَّهِ فَلْيَتَوَكَّلِ ٱلْمُؤْمِنُونَ ۝١٦٠ وَمَا كَانَ لِنَبِىٍّ أَن يَغُلَّ ۚ وَمَن يَغْلُلْ يَأْتِ بِمَا غَلَّ يَوْمَ ٱلْقِيَٰمَةِ ۚ ثُمَّ تُوَفَّىٰ كُلُّ نَفْسٍ مَّا كَسَبَتْ وَهُمْ لَا يُظْلَمُونَ ۝١٦١ أَفَمَنِ ٱتَّبَعَ رِضْوَٰنَ ٱللَّهِ كَمَنۢ بَآءَ بِسَخَطٍ مِّنَ ٱللَّهِ وَمَأْوَىٰهُ جَهَنَّمُ ۚ وَبِئْسَ ٱلْمَصِيرُ ۝١٦٢ هُمْ دَرَجَٰتٌ عِندَ ٱللَّهِ ۗ وَٱللَّهُ بَصِيرٌۢ بِمَا يَعْمَلُونَ ۝١٦٣ لَقَدْ مَنَّ ٱللَّهُ عَلَى ٱلْمُؤْمِنِينَ إِذْ بَعَثَ فِيهِمْ رَسُولًا مِّنْ أَنفُسِهِمْ يَتْلُوا۟ عَلَيْهِمْ ءَايَٰتِهِۦ وَيُزَكِّيهِمْ وَيُعَلِّمُهُمُ ٱلْكِتَٰبَ وَٱلْحِكْمَةَ وَإِن كَانُوا۟ مِن قَبْلُ لَفِى ضَلَٰلٍ مُّبِينٍ ۝١٦٤ أَوَلَمَّآ أَصَٰبَتْكُم مُّصِيبَةٌ قَدْ أَصَبْتُم مِّثْلَيْهَا قُلْتُمْ أَنَّىٰ هَٰذَا ۖ قُلْ هُوَ مِنْ عِندِ أَنفُسِكُمْ ۗ إِنَّ ٱللَّهَ عَلَىٰ كُلِّ شَىْءٍ قَدِيرٌ ۝١٦٥ وَمَآ أَصَٰبَكُمْ يَوْمَ ٱلْتَقَى ٱلْجَمْعَانِ فَبِإِذْنِ ٱللَّهِ وَلِيَعْلَمَ ٱلْمُؤْمِنِينَ ۝١٦٦ وَلِيَعْلَمَ ٱلَّذِينَ نَافَقُوا۟ ۚ وَقِيلَ لَهُمْ تَعَالَوْا۟ قَٰتِلُوا۟ فِى سَبِيلِ ٱللَّهِ أَوِ ٱدْفَعُوا۟ ۖ قَالُوا۟ لَوْ نَعْلَمُ قِتَالًا لَّٱتَّبَعْنَٰكُمْ ۗ هُمْ لِلْكُفْرِ يَوْمَئِذٍ أَقْرَبُ مِنْهُمْ لِلْإِيمَٰنِ ۚ يَقُولُونَ

بِأَفْوَٰهِهِم مَّا لَيْسَ فِى قُلُوبِهِمْ ۗ وَٱللَّهُ أَعْلَمُ بِمَا يَكْتُمُونَ ﴿١٦٧﴾ ٱلَّذِينَ قَالُوا لِإِخْوَٰنِهِمْ وَقَعَدُوا لَوْ أَطَاعُونَا مَا قُتِلُوا ۗ قُلْ فَٱدْرَءُوا عَنْ أَنفُسِكُمُ ٱلْمَوْتَ إِن كُنتُمْ صَٰدِقِينَ ﴿١٦٨﴾ وَلَا تَحْسَبَنَّ ٱلَّذِينَ قُتِلُوا فِى سَبِيلِ ٱللَّهِ أَمْوَٰتًۢا ۚ بَلْ أَحْيَآءٌ عِندَ رَبِّهِمْ يُرْزَقُونَ ﴿١٦٩﴾ فَرِحِينَ بِمَآ ءَاتَىٰهُمُ ٱللَّهُ مِن فَضْلِهِۦ وَيَسْتَبْشِرُونَ بِٱلَّذِينَ لَمْ يَلْحَقُوا بِهِم مِّنْ خَلْفِهِمْ أَلَّا خَوْفٌ عَلَيْهِمْ وَلَا هُمْ يَحْزَنُونَ ﴿١٧٠﴾ يَسْتَبْشِرُونَ بِنِعْمَةٍ مِّنَ ٱللَّهِ وَفَضْلٍ وَأَنَّ ٱللَّهَ لَا يُضِيعُ أَجْرَ ٱلْمُؤْمِنِينَ ﴿١٧١﴾ ٱلَّذِينَ ٱسْتَجَابُوا لِلَّهِ وَٱلرَّسُولِ مِنۢ بَعْدِ مَآ أَصَابَهُمُ ٱلْقَرْحُ ۚ لِلَّذِينَ أَحْسَنُوا مِنْهُمْ وَٱتَّقَوْا أَجْرٌ عَظِيمٌ ﴿١٧٢﴾ ٱلَّذِينَ قَالَ لَهُمُ ٱلنَّاسُ إِنَّ ٱلنَّاسَ قَدْ جَمَعُوا لَكُمْ فَٱخْشَوْهُمْ فَزَادَهُمْ إِيمَٰنًا وَقَالُوا حَسْبُنَا ٱللَّهُ وَنِعْمَ ٱلْوَكِيلُ ﴿١٧٣﴾ فَٱنقَلَبُوا بِنِعْمَةٍ مِّنَ ٱللَّهِ وَفَضْلٍ لَّمْ يَمْسَسْهُمْ سُوٓءٌ وَٱتَّبَعُوا رِضْوَٰنَ ٱللَّهِ ۗ وَٱللَّهُ ذُو فَضْلٍ عَظِيمٍ ﴿١٧٤﴾ إِنَّمَا ذَٰلِكُمُ ٱلشَّيْطَٰنُ يُخَوِّفُ أَوْلِيَآءَهُۥ فَلَا تَخَافُوهُمْ وَخَافُونِ إِن كُنتُم مُّؤْمِنِينَ ﴿١٧٥﴾ وَلَا يَحْزُنكَ ٱلَّذِينَ يُسَٰرِعُونَ فِى ٱلْكُفْرِ ۚ إِنَّهُمْ لَن يَضُرُّوا ٱللَّهَ شَيْـًٔا ۗ يُرِيدُ ٱللَّهُ أَلَّا يَجْعَلَ لَهُمْ حَظًّا فِى ٱلْءَاخِرَةِ ۖ وَلَهُمْ عَذَابٌ عَظِيمٌ ﴿١٧٦﴾ إِنَّ ٱلَّذِينَ ٱشْتَرَوُا ٱلْكُفْرَ بِٱلْإِيمَٰنِ لَن يَضُرُّوا ٱللَّهَ شَيْـًٔا وَلَهُمْ عَذَابٌ أَلِيمٌ ﴿١٧٧﴾ وَلَا يَحْسَبَنَّ ٱلَّذِينَ كَفَرُوٓا أَنَّمَا نُمْلِى لَهُمْ خَيْرٌ لِّأَنفُسِهِمْ ۚ إِنَّمَا نُمْلِى لَهُمْ لِيَزْدَادُوٓا إِثْمًا ۚ وَلَهُمْ عَذَابٌ مُّهِينٌ ﴿١٧٨﴾ مَّا كَانَ ٱللَّهُ لِيَذَرَ ٱلْمُؤْمِنِينَ عَلَىٰ مَآ أَنتُمْ عَلَيْهِ حَتَّىٰ يَمِيزَ ٱلْخَبِيثَ مِنَ ٱلطَّيِّبِ ۗ وَمَا كَانَ ٱللَّهُ لِيُطْلِعَكُمْ عَلَى ٱلْغَيْبِ وَلَٰكِنَّ ٱللَّهَ يَجْتَبِى مِن رُّسُلِهِۦ مَن يَشَآءُ ۖ فَـَٔامِنُوا بِٱللَّهِ وَرُسُلِهِۦ ۚ وَإِن تُؤْمِنُوا وَتَتَّقُوا فَلَكُمْ أَجْرٌ عَظِيمٌ ﴿١٧٩﴾ وَلَا يَحْسَبَنَّ ٱلَّذِينَ يَبْخَلُونَ بِمَآ ءَاتَىٰهُمُ ٱللَّهُ مِن فَضْلِهِۦ هُوَ خَيْرًا لَّهُم ۖ بَلْ هُوَ شَرٌّ لَّهُمْ ۖ سَيُطَوَّقُونَ مَا بَخِلُوا بِهِۦ يَوْمَ ٱلْقِيَٰمَةِ ۗ وَلِلَّهِ مِيرَٰثُ ٱلسَّمَٰوَٰتِ وَٱلْأَرْضِ ۗ وَٱللَّهُ بِمَا تَعْمَلُونَ خَبِيرٌ ﴿١٨٠﴾ لَّقَدْ سَمِعَ ٱللَّهُ قَوْلَ ٱلَّذِينَ قَالُوٓا إِنَّ ٱللَّهَ فَقِيرٌ وَنَحْنُ أَغْنِيَآءُ ۘ سَنَكْتُبُ مَا قَالُوا وَقَتْلَهُمُ ٱلْأَنۢبِيَآءَ بِغَيْرِ حَقٍّ وَنَقُولُ ذُوقُوا عَذَابَ ٱلْحَرِيقِ ﴿١٨١﴾ ذَٰلِكَ بِمَا قَدَّمَتْ أَيْدِيكُمْ وَأَنَّ ٱللَّهَ لَيْسَ بِظَلَّٰمٍ لِّلْعَبِيدِ ﴿١٨٢﴾ ٱلَّذِينَ قَالُوٓا إِنَّ ٱللَّهَ عَهِدَ إِلَيْنَآ أَلَّا نُؤْمِنَ لِرَسُولٍ حَتَّىٰ يَأْتِيَنَا بِقُرْبَانٍ تَأْكُلُهُ ٱلنَّارُ ۗ قُلْ قَدْ جَآءَكُمْ رُسُلٌ مِّن قَبْلِى بِٱلْبَيِّنَٰتِ وَبِٱلَّذِى قُلْتُمْ فَلِمَ قَتَلْتُمُوهُمْ إِن كُنتُمْ صَٰدِقِينَ ﴿١٨٣﴾ فَإِن كَذَّبُوكَ فَقَدْ كُذِّبَ رُسُلٌ مِّن قَبْلِكَ جَآءُو بِٱلْبَيِّنَٰتِ وَٱلزُّبُرِ وَٱلْكِتَٰبِ ٱلْمُنِيرِ ﴿١٨٤﴾ كُلُّ نَفْسٍ ذَآئِقَةُ ٱلْمَوْتِ ۗ وَإِنَّمَا تُوَفَّوْنَ أُجُورَكُمْ يَوْمَ ٱلْقِيَٰمَةِ ۖ فَمَن زُحْزِحَ عَنِ

النَّارِ وَأُدْخِلَ ٱلْجَنَّةَ فَقَدْ فَازَ وَمَا ٱلْحَيَوٰةُ ٱلدُّنْيَا إِلَّا مَتَٰعُ ٱلْغُرُورِ ۝ لَتُبْلَوُنَّ فِى أَمْوَٰلِكُمْ وَأَنفُسِكُمْ وَلَتَسْمَعُنَّ مِنَ ٱلَّذِينَ أُوتُوا۟ ٱلْكِتَٰبَ مِن قَبْلِكُمْ وَمِنَ ٱلَّذِينَ أَشْرَكُوٓا۟ أَذًى كَثِيرًا وَإِن تَصْبِرُوا۟ وَتَتَّقُوا۟ فَإِنَّ ذَٰلِكَ مِنْ عَزْمِ ٱلْأُمُورِ ۝ وَإِذْ أَخَذَ ٱللَّهُ مِيثَٰقَ ٱلَّذِينَ أُوتُوا۟ ٱلْكِتَٰبَ لَتُبَيِّنُنَّهُۥ لِلنَّاسِ وَلَا تَكْتُمُونَهُۥ فَنَبَذُوهُ وَرَآءَ ظُهُورِهِمْ وَٱشْتَرَوْا۟ بِهِۦ ثَمَنًا قَلِيلًا فَبِئْسَ مَا يَشْتَرُونَ ۝ لَا تَحْسَبَنَّ ٱلَّذِينَ يَفْرَحُونَ بِمَآ أَتَوا۟ وَّيُحِبُّونَ أَن يُحْمَدُوا۟ بِمَا لَمْ يَفْعَلُوا۟ فَلَا تَحْسَبَنَّهُم بِمَفَازَةٍ مِّنَ ٱلْعَذَابِ وَلَهُمْ عَذَابٌ أَلِيمٌ ۝ وَلِلَّهِ مُلْكُ ٱلسَّمَٰوَٰتِ وَٱلْأَرْضِ وَٱللَّهُ عَلَىٰ كُلِّ شَىْءٍ قَدِيرٌ ۝ إِنَّ فِى خَلْقِ ٱلسَّمَٰوَٰتِ وَٱلْأَرْضِ وَٱخْتِلَٰفِ ٱلَّيْلِ وَٱلنَّهَارِ لَءَايَٰتٍ لِّأُو۟لِى ٱلْأَلْبَٰبِ ۝ ٱلَّذِينَ يَذْكُرُونَ ٱللَّهَ قِيَٰمًا وَقُعُودًا وَعَلَىٰ جُنُوبِهِمْ وَيَتَفَكَّرُونَ فِى خَلْقِ ٱلسَّمَٰوَٰتِ وَٱلْأَرْضِ رَبَّنَا مَا خَلَقْتَ هَٰذَا بَٰطِلًا سُبْحَٰنَكَ فَقِنَا عَذَابَ ٱلنَّارِ ۝ رَبَّنَآ إِنَّكَ مَن تُدْخِلِ ٱلنَّارَ فَقَدْ أَخْزَيْتَهُۥ وَمَا لِلظَّٰلِمِينَ مِنْ أَنصَارٍ ۝ رَبَّنَآ إِنَّنَا سَمِعْنَا مُنَادِيًا يُنَادِى لِلْإِيمَٰنِ أَنْ ءَامِنُوا۟ بِرَبِّكُمْ فَـَٔامَنَّا رَبَّنَا فَٱغْفِرْ لَنَا ذُنُوبَنَا وَكَفِّرْ عَنَّا سَيِّـَٔاتِنَا وَتَوَفَّنَا مَعَ ٱلْأَبْرَارِ ۝ رَبَّنَا وَءَاتِنَا مَا وَعَدتَّنَا عَلَىٰ رُسُلِكَ وَلَا تُخْزِنَا يَوْمَ ٱلْقِيَٰمَةِ إِنَّكَ لَا تُخْلِفُ ٱلْمِيعَادَ ۝ فَٱسْتَجَابَ لَهُمْ رَبُّهُمْ أَنِّى لَآ أُضِيعُ عَمَلَ عَٰمِلٍ مِّنكُم مِّن ذَكَرٍ أَوْ أُنثَىٰ بَعْضُكُم مِّنۢ بَعْضٍ فَٱلَّذِينَ هَاجَرُوا۟ وَأُخْرِجُوا۟ مِن دِيَٰرِهِمْ وَأُوذُوا۟ فِى سَبِيلِى وَقَٰتَلُوا۟ وَقُتِلُوا۟ لَأُكَفِّرَنَّ عَنْهُمْ سَيِّـَٔاتِهِمْ وَلَأُدْخِلَنَّهُمْ جَنَّٰتٍ تَجْرِى مِن تَحْتِهَا ٱلْأَنْهَٰرُ ثَوَابًا مِّنْ عِندِ ٱللَّهِ وَٱللَّهُ عِندَهُۥ حُسْنُ ٱلثَّوَابِ ۝ لَا يَغُرَّنَّكَ تَقَلُّبُ ٱلَّذِينَ كَفَرُوا۟ فِى ٱلْبِلَٰدِ ۝ مَتَٰعٌ قَلِيلٌ ثُمَّ مَأْوَىٰهُمْ جَهَنَّمُ وَبِئْسَ ٱلْمِهَادُ ۝ لَٰكِنِ ٱلَّذِينَ ٱتَّقَوْا۟ رَبَّهُمْ لَهُمْ جَنَّٰتٌ تَجْرِى مِن تَحْتِهَا ٱلْأَنْهَٰرُ خَٰلِدِينَ فِيهَا نُزُلًا مِّنْ عِندِ ٱللَّهِ وَمَا عِندَ ٱللَّهِ خَيْرٌ لِّلْأَبْرَارِ ۝ وَإِنَّ مِنْ أَهْلِ ٱلْكِتَٰبِ لَمَن يُؤْمِنُ بِٱللَّهِ وَمَآ أُنزِلَ إِلَيْكُمْ وَمَآ أُنزِلَ إِلَيْهِمْ خَٰشِعِينَ لِلَّهِ لَا يَشْتَرُونَ بِـَٔايَٰتِ ٱللَّهِ ثَمَنًا قَلِيلًا أُو۟لَٰٓئِكَ لَهُمْ أَجْرُهُمْ عِندَ رَبِّهِمْ إِنَّ ٱللَّهَ سَرِيعُ ٱلْحِسَابِ ۝ يَٰٓأَيُّهَا ٱلَّذِينَ ءَامَنُوا۟ ٱصْبِرُوا۟ وَصَابِرُوا۟ وَرَابِطُوا۟ وَٱتَّقُوا۟ ٱللَّهَ لَعَلَّكُمْ تُفْلِحُونَ ۝ ❁

If a good befalls you, it grieves them, but if some evil overtakes you, they rejoice at it. But if you remain patient and become *Al-Muttaqūn* (the pious), not the least harm will their cunning do

261

to you. Surely, Allāh surrounds all that they do. And (remember) when you (Muhammad ﷺ) left your household in the morning to post the believers at their stations for the battle (of Uhud). And Allāh is All-Hearer, All-Knower. When two parties from among you were about to lose heart, but Allāh was their *Walī* (Supporter and Protector). And in Allāh should the believers put their trust. And Allāh has already made you victorious at Badr, when you were a weak little force. So fear Allāh much that you may be grateful. (Remember) when you (Muhammad ﷺ) said to the believers, "Is it not enough for you that your Lord (Allāh) should help you with three thousand angels sent down? Yes, if you hold on to patience and piety, and the enemy comes rushing at you; your Lord will help you with five thousand angels having marks (of distinction)." Allāh made it not but as a message of good news for you and as an assurance to your hearts. And there is no victory except from Allāh, the All-Mighty, the All-Wise. That He might cut off a part of those who disbelieve, or expose them to infamy, so that they retire frustrated. Not for you (O Muhammad ﷺ, but for Allāh) is the decision; whether He turns in mercy to (pardons) them or punishes them; verily, they are the *Zālimūn* (polytheists, wrong doers and the disobedient). And to Allāh belongs all that is in the heavens and all that is in the earth. He forgives whom He wills, and punishes whom He wills. And Allāh is Oft-Forgiving, Most Merciful. O you who believe! Eat not *Ribā* doubled and multiplied, but fear Allāh that you may be successful. And fear the Fire, which is prepared for the disbelievers. And obey Allāh and the Messenger (Muhammad ﷺ) that you may obtain mercy. And march forth in the way (which leads) to forgiveness from your Lord, and for Paradise as wide as the heavens and the earth, prepared for *Al-Muttaqūn* (the pious). Those who spend (in Allāh's Cause) in prosperity and in adversity, who repress anger, and who pardon men; verily, Allāh loves *Al-Muhsinūn* (the good-doers). And those who, when they have committed *Fāhishah* (great sins as illegal sexual intercourse) or wronged themselves with evil, remember Allāh and ask forgiveness for their sins; — and none can forgive sins but Allāh — and do not persist in what (wrong) they have done, while they know. For such, the reward is forgiveness from their Lord, and Gardens with rivers flowing underneath (Paradise), wherein they shall abide forever. How excellent is this reward for the doers (who do righteous dids according to Allāh's Orders). Many similar ways (and mishaps of life) were faced by nations (believers and disbelievers) that have passed away before you (as you have faced in the battle of Uhud), so travel through the earth, and see what was the end of those who disbelieved (in the Oneness of Allāh, and disobeyed Him and His Messengers). This (the Qur'ān) is a plain statement for mankind, a guidance and instruction to those who are *Al-Muttaqūn* (the pious). So, do not become weak (against your enemy), nor be sad, and you will be superior (in victory) if you are indeed (true) believers. If a wound (or killing) has touched you, be assured a similar wound (or killing) has touched the others (disbelievers). And so are the days (good and not so good), that We give to men by turns, that Allāh may test those who believe, and that He may take martyrs from among you. And Allāh likes not the *Zālimūn* (polytheists and wrong doers). And that Allāh may test (or purify) the believers (from sins) and destroy the disbelievers. Or do you think that you will enter Paradise before Allāh tests those of you who fought (in His Cause) and (also) tests those who are *As-Sābirūn* (the patient)? And indeed you used to long for death (*Ash-Shahādah* — martyrdom) before you met it. Now you have seen it openly with your own eyes. And Muhammad (ﷺ) is no more than a Messenger, and indeed (many) Messengers have passed away before him. If he dies or is killed, will you then turn back on your heels (as disbelievers)? And he who turns back on his heels, not the least harm will he do to Allāh; and Allāh will give reward to those who are grateful. And no person can ever die except by Allāh's Leave and at an appointed term. And whoever desires a reward in (this) world, We shall give him of it; and whoever desires a reward in the Hereafter, We shall give him thereof. And We shall reward the grateful. And many a Prophet (i.e. many from amongst the Prophets) fought (in Allāh's Cause) and along with whom (fought) large bands of religious learned men. But they never lost heart for that which did befall them in Allāh's way, nor did they weaken nor degrade themselves. And Allāh loves *As-Sābirūn* (the patient). And they said nothing but: "Our Lord! Forgive us our sins and our transgressions (in keeping our duties to You), establish our feet firmly, and give us victory over the disbelieving folk." So Allāh gave them the reward of this world, and the excellent reward of the Hereafter. And Allāh loves *Al-Muhsinūn* (the good-doers). O you who believe! If you obey those who disbelieve, they will send you back on your heels, and you will turn back (from Faith) as losers. Nay, Allāh is your *Maulā* (Patron, Lord, Helper, Protector), and He is the Best of helpers. We shall cast terror into the hearts of those who disbelieve, because they joined others in worship with Allāh, for which He had sent no authority; their abode will be the Fire and how evil is the abode of the *Zālimūn* (polytheists and wrong doers). And Allāh did indeed fulfil His Promise to you when you were killing them (your enemy) with His Permission; until (the moment) you lost your courage and fell to disputing about the order, and disobeyed after He showed you (of the booty) which you love. Among you are some that desire this world and some that desire the Hereafter. Then He made you flee from them (your enemy), that He might test you. But surely, He forgave you, and Allāh is Most Gracious to the believers. (And remember) when you ran away (dreadfully) without even casting a side glance at anyone, and the Messenger (Muhammad ﷺ) was in the rear calling you back. There did Allāh give you one distress after another by way of requital to teach you not to grieve for that which had escaped you, nor for that which had befallen you. And Allāh is Well-Aware of all that you do. Then after the distress, He sent down security upon you. Slumber overtook a party of you, while another party was thinking about themselves (as how to save their own selves, ignoring the others and the Prophet ﷺ) and thought wrongly of Allāh — the thought of ignorance. They said,

"Have we any part in the affair?" Say (O Muhammad ﷺ): "Indeed the affair belongs wholly to Allāh." They hide within themselves what they dare not reveal to you, saying: "If we had anything to do with the affair, none of us would have been killed here." Say: "Even if you had remained in your homes, those for whom death was decreed would certainly have gone forth to the place of their death," but that Allāh might test what is in your breasts; and to purify that which was in your hearts (sins), and Allāh is All-Knower of what is in (your) breasts. Those of you who turned back on the day the two hosts met (i.e. the battle of Uhud), it was *Shaitān* (Satan) who caused them to backslide (run away from the battlefield) because of some (sins) they had earned. But Allāh, indeed, has forgiven them. Surely, Allāh is Oft-Forgiving, Most Forbearing. O you who believe! Be not like those who disbelieve (hypocrites) and who say about their brethren when they travel through the earth or go out to fight: "If they had stayed with us, they would not have died or been killed," so that Allāh may make it a cause of regret in their hearts. It is Allāh that gives life and causes death. And Allāh is All-Seer of what you do. And if you are killed or die in the way of Allāh, forgiveness and mercy from Allāh are far better than all that they amass (of worldly wealths). And whether you die or are killed, verily, to Allāh you shall be gathered. And by the Mercy of Allāh, you (Muhammad ﷺ) dealt with them gently. And had you been severe and harsh-hearted, they would have broken away from about you; so pass over (their faults), and ask (Allāh's) forgiveness for them; and consult them in the affairs. Then when you have taken a decision, put your trust in Allāh, certainly, Allāh loves those who put their trust (in Him). If Allāh helps you, none can overcome you; and if He forsakes you, who is there after Him that can help you? And in Allāh (Alone) let believers put their trust. It is not for any Prophet to take illegally a part of the booty (*Ghulul*), and whosoever deceives his companions as regards the booty, he shall bring forth on the Day of Resurrection that which he took (illegally). Then every person shall be paid in full what he has earned, and they shall not be dealt with unjustly. Is then one who follows (seeks) the good Pleasure of Allāh (by not taking illegally a part of the booty) like the one who draws on himself the Wrath of Allāh (by taking a part of the booty illegally — *Ghulul*)? — his abode is Hell, and worst indeed is that destination! They are in varying grades with Allāh, and Allāh is All-Seer of what they do. Indeed, Allāh conferred a great favor on the believers when He sent among them a Messenger (Muhammad ﷺ) from among themselves, reciting to them His Verses (the Qur'ān), and purifying them (from sins by their following him), and instructing them (in) the Book (the Qur'ān) and *Al-Hikmah* [the wisdom and the *Sunnah* of the Prophet ﷺ (i.e. his legal ways, statements and acts of worship)], while before that they had been in manifest error. (What is the matter with you?) When a single disaster smites you, although you smote (your enemies) with one twice as great, you say: "From where does this come to us?" Say (to them), "It is from yourselves (because of your evil deeds)." And Allāh has power over all things. And what you suffered (of the disaster) on the day (of the battle of Uhud when) the two armies met, was by the Leave of Allāh, in order that He might test the believers. And that He might test the hypocrites, it was said to them: "Come, fight in the way of Allāh or (at least) defend yourselves." They said: "Had we known that fighting will take place, we would certainly have followed you." They were that day, nearer to disbelief than to Faith, saying with their mouths what was not in their hearts. And Allāh has full knowledge of what they conceal. (They are) the ones who said about their killed brethren while they themselves sat (at home): "If only they had listened to us, they would not have been killed." Say: "Avert death from your own selves, if you speak the truth." Think not of those as dead who are killed in the way of Allāh. Nay, they are alive, with their Lord, and they have provision. They rejoice in what Allāh has bestowed upon them of His bounty and rejoice for the sake of those who have not yet joined them, but are left behind (not yet martyred) that on them no fear shall come, nor shall they grieve. They rejoice in a grace and a bounty from Allāh, and that Allāh will not waste the reward of the believers. Those who answered (the Call of) Allāh and the Messenger (Muhammad ﷺ) after being wounded; for those of them who did good deeds and feared Allāh, there is a great reward. Those (i.e. believers) to whom the people (hypocrites) said, "Verily, the people (pagans) have gathered against you (a great army), therefore, fear them." But it (only) increased them in Faith, and they said: "Allāh (Alone) is Sufficient for us, and He is the Best Disposer of affairs (for us)." So, they returned with grace and bounty from Allāh. No harm touched them; and they followed the good Pleasure of Allāh. And Allāh is the Owner of Great Bounty. It is only *Shaitān* (Satan) that suggests to you the fear of his *Auliyā'* [supporters and friends (polytheists, disbelievers in the Oneness of Allāh and in His Messenger, Muhammad ﷺ)]; so fear them not, but fear Me, if you are (true) believers. And let not those grieve you (O Muhammad ﷺ) who rush with haste to disbelieve; verily, not the least harm will they do to Allāh. It is Allāh's Will to give them no portion in the Hereafter. For them there is a great torment. Verily, those who purchase disbelief at the price of Faith, not the least harm will they do to Allāh. For them, there is a painful torment. And let not the disbelievers think that Our postponing of their punishment is good for them. We postpone the punishment only so that they may increase in sinfulness. And for them is a disgraceful torment. Allāh will not leave the believers in the state in which you are now, until He distinguishes the wicked from the good. Nor will Allāh disclose to you the secrets of the *Ghaib* (Unseen), but Allāh chooses of His Messengers whom He wills. So believe in Allāh and His Messengers. And if you believe and fear Allāh, then for you there is a great reward. And let not those who covetously withhold of that which Allāh has bestowed on them of His bounty (wealth) think that it is good for them (and so they do not pay the obligatory *Zakāt*). Nay, it will be worse for them; the things which they covetously withheld, shall be tied to their necks like a collar on the Day of Resurrection. And to Allāh belongs the heritage of the heavens and the earth; and Allāh is Well-Acquainted with all that you do. Indeed, Allāh has heard the statement of those (Jews) who say: "Truly, Allāh is poor and we are rich!" We shall record what they have said and their killing of the Prophets unjustly, and We shall say: "Taste you the torment of the burning (Fire)." This is because of that (evil) which your hands have sent before you. And certainly, Allāh is never unjust to (His) slaves. Those (Jews) who said: "Verily, Allāh has taken our promise not to believe in any Messenger unless he brings us an offering which the fire (from heaven) shall devour." Say: "Verily, there came to you Messengers before me, with clear signs and even with what you speak of; why then did you kill them, if you are truthful?" Then if they deny you (O Muhammad ﷺ), so were Messengers denied before you, who came with *Al-Baiyyināt* (clear signs, proofs, evidences) and the Scripture and the Book of Enlightenment. Everyone shall taste death. And only on the Day of Resurrection shall you be paid your wages in full. And whoever is removed away from the Fire and admitted to Paradise, he indeed is successful. The life of this world is only the enjoyment of deception (a deceiving thing). You shall certainly be tried and tested in your wealth and properties and in your personal selves, and you shall certainly hear much that will grieve you from those who received the Scripture before you (Jews and Christians) and from those who ascribe partners to Allāh; but if you persevere patiently, and become *Al-Muttaqūn* (the pious) then verily, that will be a determining factor in all affairs (and that is from the great matters which you must hold on with all your efforts). (And remember) when Allāh took a covenant from those who were given the Scripture (Jews and Christians) to make it (the news of the coming of Prophet Muhammad ﷺ and the religious knowledge) known and clear to mankind, and not to hide it, but they threw it away behind their backs, and purchased with it some miserable gain! And indeed worst is that which they bought. Think not that those who rejoice in what they have done (or brought about), and love to be praised for what they have not done, — think not you that they are rescued from the torment, and for them is a painful torment. And to Allāh belongs the dominion of the heavens and the earth, and Allāh has power over all things. Verily, in the creation of the heavens and the earth, and in the alternation of night and day, there are indeed signs for men of understanding. Those who remember Allāh (always, and in prayers) standing, sitting, and lying down on their sides, and think deeply about the creation of the heavens and the earth, (saying): "Our Lord! You have not created (all) this without purpose, glory to You! (Exalted are You above all that they associate with You as partners). Give us salvation from the torment of the Fire. Our Lord! Verily, whom You admit to the Fire, indeed, You have disgraced him; and never will the *Zālimūn* (polytheists and wrong doers) find any helpers. Our Lord! Verily, we have heard the call of one (Muhammad ﷺ) calling to Faith: 'Believe in your Lord,' and we have believed. Our Lord! Forgive us our sins and expiate from us our evil deeds, and make us die (in the state of righteousness) along with *Al-Abrār* (the pious believers of Islamic Monotheism). Our Lord! Grant us what You promised to us through Your Messengers and disgrace us not on the Day of Resurrection, for You never break (Your) Promise." So, their Lord accepted of them (their supplication and answered them), "Never will I allow to be lost the work of any of you, be he male or female. You are (members) one of another, so those who emigrated and were driven out from their homes, and suffered harm in My Cause, and who fought, and were killed (in My Cause), verily, I will expiate from them their evil deeds and admit them into Gardens under which rivers flow (in Paradise); a reward from Allāh, and with Allāh is the best of rewards." Let not the free disposal (and affluence) of the disbelievers throughout the land deceive you. A brief enjoyment; then their ultimate abode is Hell; and worst indeed is that place for rest. But, for those who fear their Lord, are Gardens under which rivers flow (in Paradise); therein are they to dwell for ever, an entertainment from Allāh; and that which is with Allāh is the best for *Al-Abrār* (the pious believers of Islamic

Monotheism). And there are, certainly, among the people of the Scripture (Jews and Christians), those who believe in Allāh and in that which has been revealed to you, and in that which has been revealed to them, humbling themselves before Allāh. They do not sell the Verses of Allāh for a little price, for them is a reward with their Lord. Surely, Allāh is Swift in account. O you who believe! Endure and be more patient (than your enemy), and guard your territory by stationing army units permanently at the places from where the enemy can attack you, and fear Allāh, so that you may be successful.

(Qur'ân 3: 120-200)

- Ibn Hisham: 3/21
- Al-Bidayah wan-Nihayah: 4/17
- At-Tabari: 2/522
- Al-Kamil Fit-Tarikh: 2/110

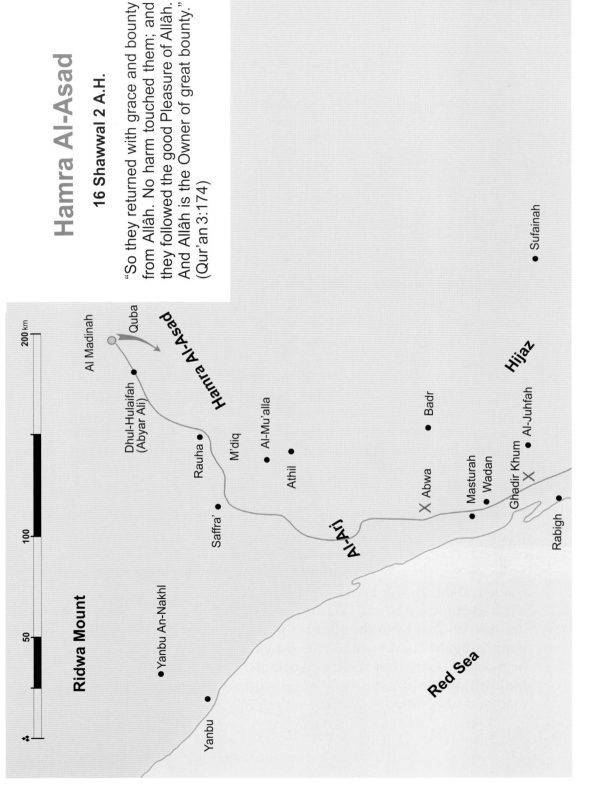

Hamra Al-Asad

16 Shawwal 2 A.H.

"So they returned with grace and bounty from Allâh. No harm touched them; and they followed the good Pleasure of Allâh. And Allâh is the Owner of great bounty." (Qur'an 3:174)

Ridwa Mount

Al Madinah
Quba
Dhul-Hulaifah (Abyar Ali)
Hamra Al-Asad
Rauha
M'diq
Al-Mu'alla
Athil
Saffra'
Al-'Arij
Abwa
Badr
Masturah
Wadan
Ghadir Khum
Al-Juhfah
Hijaz
Rabigh
Sufainah

Yanbu An-Nakhl
Yanbu

Red Sea

200 km   100   50

Hamrâ Al-Asad

(16th of Shawwâl, 3 H)

﴿ ٱلَّذِينَ ٱسْتَجَابُواْ لِلَّهِ وَٱلرَّسُولِ مِنۢ بَعْدِ مَآ أَصَابَهُمُ ٱلْقَرْحُ لِلَّذِينَ أَحْسَنُواْ مِنْهُمْ وَٱتَّقَوْاْ أَجْرٌ عَظِيمٌ ١٧٢ ٱلَّذِينَ قَالَ لَهُمُ ٱلنَّاسُ إِنَّ ٱلنَّاسَ قَدْ جَمَعُواْ لَكُمْ فَٱخْشَوْهُمْ فَزَادَهُمْ إِيمَٰنًا وَقَالُواْ حَسْبُنَا ٱللَّهُ وَنِعْمَ ٱلْوَكِيلُ ١٧٣ فَٱنقَلَبُواْ بِنِعْمَةٍ مِّنَ ٱللَّهِ وَفَضْلٍ لَّمْ يَمْسَسْهُمْ سُوٓءٌ وَٱتَّبَعُواْ رِضْوَٰنَ ٱللَّهِ وَٱللَّهُ ذُو فَضْلٍ عَظِيمٍ ١٧٤ ﴾

Those who answered (the Call of) Allāh and the Messenger (Muhammad ﷺ) after being wounded; for those of them who did good deeds and feared Allāh, there is a great reward. Those (i.e. believers) to whom the people (hypocrites) said, "Verily, the people (pagans) have gathered against you (a great army), therefore, fear them." But it (only) increased them in Faith, and they said: "Allāh (Alone) is Sufficient for us, and He is the Best Disposer of affairs (for us)." So, they returned with grace and bounty from Allāh. No harm touched them; and they followed the good Pleasure of Allāh. And Allāh is the Owner of Great Bounty.

(Qur'ân 3: 172-174)

The day after the Battle of Uhud, the Messenger of Allâh ﷺ gathered whatever forces he could from the Muslims and went out in pursuit of Abu Sufyân and the polytheists. It was important for the Quraish to know that the defeat of the Muslims on the day before did not weaken them in the least. The Prophet ﷺ and his Companions ﷺ reached Hamrâ Al-Asad. During the pursuit, a man named Ma'bad ibn Abi Ma'bad from the Khuzâ'i tribe passed by. Seeing what was happening, Ma'bad went to Abu Sufyân and his people; by the time he reached them, they were at Ar-Rauha, which is situated between Makkah and Al-Madinah. Ma'bad said to Abu Sufyân, "Muhammad and his Companions have set out in your pursuit. I have never

272

seen such a gathered force; they are coming after you with a burning desire.'' Abu Sufyân and his people then quickened their pace as they fled back towards Makkah. That night, at Hamr Al-Asad, the Muslims burned 500 torches or fires, which could be seen far off in the desert. These fires made it seem as if the Muslims numbered in the thousands, which gave the Quraish all the more reason to flee back to Makkah.

﴿ٱلَّذِينَ ٱسْتَجَابُواْ لِلَّهِ وَٱلرَّسُولِ مِنۢ بَعْدِ مَآ أَصَابَهُمُ ٱلْقَرْحُ لِلَّذِينَ أَحْسَنُواْ مِنْهُمْ وَٱتَّقَوْاْ أَجْرٌ عَظِيمٌ ۝ ٱلَّذِينَ قَالَ لَهُمُ ٱلنَّاسُ إِنَّ ٱلنَّاسَ قَدْ جَمَعُواْ لَكُمْ فَٱخْشَوْهُمْ فَزَادَهُمْ إِيمَٰنًا وَقَالُواْ حَسْبُنَا ٱللَّهُ وَنِعْمَ ٱلْوَكِيلُ ۝ ﴾

Those who answered (the Call of) Allāh and the Messenger (Muhammad ﷺ) after being wounded; for those of them who did good deeds and feared Allāh, there is a great reward. Those (i.e., believers) to whom the people (hypocrites) said, "Verily, the people (pagans) have gathered against you (a great army), therefore, fear them." But it (only) increased them in Faith, and they said: "Allāh (Alone) is Sufficient for us, and He is the Best Disposer of affairs (for us)."

(Qur'ân 3: 172, 173)

- Ibn Khaldun: 2/27
- Ibn Hisham: 3/45
- Al-Bidayah wan-Nihayah: 4/47
- 'Uyun Al-Athar: 2/38

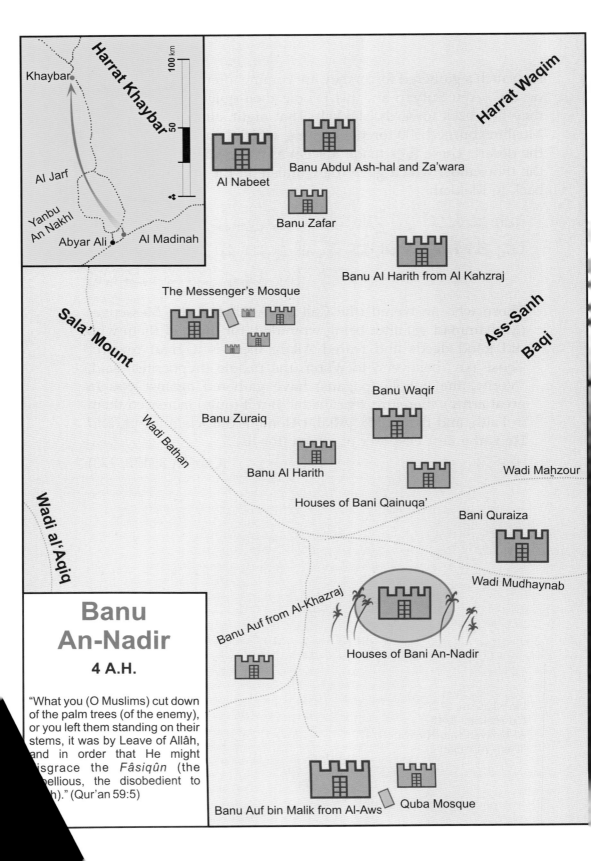

Khaybar

Harrat Khaybar

100 km

50

Al Jarf

Yanbu An Nakhl

Abyar Ali

Al Madinah

Harrat Waqim

Al Nabeet

Banu Abdul Ash-hal and Za'wara

Banu Zafar

Banu Al Harith from Al Kahzraj

The Messenger's Mosque

Sala' Mount

Ass-Sanh

Baqi

Banu Waqif

Wadi Bathan

Banu Zuraiq

Banu Al Harith

Wadi Mahzour

Houses of Bani Qainuqa'

Wadi al'Aqiq

Bani Quraiza

Wadi Mudhaynab

Banu An-Nadir

4 A.H.

Banu Auf from Al-Khazraj

Houses of Bani An-Nadir

"What you (O Muslims) cut down of the palm trees (of the enemy), or you left them standing on their stems, it was by Leave of Allâh, and in order that He might disgrace the *Fâsiqûn* (the rebellious, the disobedient to Allâh)." (Qur'an 59:5)

Banu Auf bin Malik from Al-Aws

Quba Mosque

Banu An-Nadir

(Rabi' Al-Awwal, 4 H)

بِسْمِ اللّٰه أَفَآءَ ٱللَّهُ عَلَىٰ رَسُولِهِۦ مِنْ أَهْلِ ٱلْقُرَىٰ فَلِلَّهِ وَلِلرَّسُولِ وَلِذِى ٱلْقُرْبَىٰ وَٱلْيَتَـٰمَىٰ وَٱلْمَسَـٰكِينِ وَٱبْنِ ٱلسَّبِيلِ كَىْ لَا يَكُونَ دُولَةًۢ بَيْنَ ٱلْأَغْنِيَآءِ مِنكُمْ ۚ وَمَآ ءَاتَىٰكُمُ ٱلرَّسُولُ فَخُذُوهُ وَمَا نَهَىٰكُمْ عَنْهُ فَٱنتَهُوا۟ ۚ وَٱتَّقُوا۟ ٱللَّهَ ۖ إِنَّ ٱللَّهَ شَدِيدُ ٱلْعِقَابِ ۝ لِلْفُقَرَآءِ ٱلْمُهَـٰجِرِينَ ٱلَّذِينَ أُخْرِجُوا۟ مِن دِيَـٰرِهِمْ وَأَمْوَٰلِهِمْ يَبْتَغُونَ فَضْلًا مِّنَ ٱللَّهِ وَرِضْوَٰنًا وَيَنصُرُونَ ٱللَّهَ وَرَسُولَهُۥٓ ۚ أُو۟لَـٰٓئِكَ هُمُ ٱلصَّـٰدِقُونَ ۝

What Allāh gave as booty (*Fai'*) to His Messenger (Muhammad ﷺ) from the people of the townships — it is for Allāh, His Messenger (Muhammad ﷺ), the kindred (of Messenger Muhammad ﷺ), the orphans, *Al-Masākīn* (the needy), and the wayfarer, in order that it may not become a fortune used by the rich among you. And whatsoever the Messenger (Muhammad ﷺ) gives you, take it; and whatsoever he forbids you, abstain (from it). And fear Allāh; verily, Allāh is Severe in punishment. (And there is also a share in this booty) for the poor emigrants, who were expelled from their homes and their property, seeking bounties from Allāh and to please Him, and helping Allāh (i.e. helping His religion — Islamic Monotheism) and His Messenger (Muhammad ﷺ). Such are indeed the truthful (to what they say). (Qur'ân 59: 7, 8)

The Messenger of Allâh ﷺ and a number of his Companions ﷺ went together to the Banu An-Nadir tribe, one of the three Jewish tribes of Al-Madinah. Their purpose was to ask them to help pay blood money for two people that were killed from the Banu 'Aamir tribe. The giving of such help was binding upon Banu An-Nadir: one of the conditions of the peace pact they made with the Muslims was that they would help in the matter of blood money (money that is paid to the family of a victim who is wrongfully killed). When the Prophet ﷺ mentioned the reason for his coming to them, they said, "Yes, O Abal-Qâsim, we will help you but it is time that you come to visit us, so we will first feed you before you go back with what you need."

During the wait, the Prophet ﷺ sat down beside the wall of one of their houses. Seeing how vulnerable the Prophet ﷺ was to an attack, the leaders of Banu An-Nadir said to one another, "Indeed, you will never again find the man to be in a similar situation. Who among us will climb this house and throw a large stone at him, thus freeing us from him?"

The spirit of Islam is both strong and forgiving, but Islam does not allow others to take advantage of its forgiving spirit by hurting Islam or plotting against it. That is why the forgiving spirit of Islam has protection from the strength and justice of Islam's teachings.

The Prophet ﷺ was supported by revelation, and he ﷺ was informed about Banu An-Nadir's plot to kill him. He ﷺ left the precincts of Banu An-Nadir, and he ﷺ then sent Muhammad ibn Maslamah Al-Ansari ؓ to convey to them the message that he knew precisely what it was that they were plotting. Perhaps shocked at being found out, they made no reply. The Messenger of Allâh ﷺ then gave them ten days to clear out of Al-Madinah, warning them that if anyone among still remained after that, he would be killed.

The hypocrites of Al-Madinah told the leaders of Banu An-Nadir that they were on their side. 'Abdullah ibn Ubai ibn Salûl said to them, "Do not leave your houses; instead, protect yourselves in your fortresses. Since the people of Banu An-Nadir refused to leave peacefully, the Prophet ﷺ and his Companions ؓ surrounded them, laying siege to their abodes. A few days passed, and the siege continued. Then, to show that the Muslims were indeed serious about the matter, the Prophet ﷺ ordered for six date trees to be burned. Seeing that there was no way out and that the Muslims were not going to just leave them, the leaders of Banu An-Nadir surrendered. They were allowed to leave and to carry whatever wealth they were able to carry, but not weapons. They ended up leaving with 600 camels and a great deal of wealth, which they

The remains of Jew Forts in Al-Madinah

loaded on top of those camels. After they left Al-Madinah, they set out for Khaibar, where they settled down. The following Verses were revealed about the wealth that Banu An-Nadir left behind in Al-Madinah:

﴿مَّا أَفَاءَ اللَّهُ عَلَىٰ رَسُولِهِ مِنْ أَهْلِ الْقُرَىٰ فَلِلَّهِ وَلِلرَّسُولِ وَلِذِي الْقُرْبَىٰ وَالْيَتَامَىٰ وَالْمَسَاكِينِ وَابْنِ السَّبِيلِ كَيْ لَا يَكُونَ دُولَةً بَيْنَ الْأَغْنِيَاءِ مِنكُمْ وَمَا آتَاكُمُ الرَّسُولُ فَخُذُوهُ وَمَا نَهَاكُمْ عَنْهُ فَانتَهُوا وَاتَّقُوا اللَّهَ إِنَّ اللَّهَ شَدِيدُ الْعِقَابِ ۝ لِلْفُقَرَاءِ الْمُهَاجِرِينَ الَّذِينَ أُخْرِجُوا مِن دِيَارِهِمْ وَأَمْوَالِهِمْ يَبْتَغُونَ فَضْلًا مِّنَ اللَّهِ وَرِضْوَانًا وَيَنصُرُونَ اللَّهَ وَرَسُولَهُ أُولَٰئِكَ هُمُ الصَّادِقُونَ ۝﴾

What Allāh gave as booty (Fai') to His Messenger (Muhammad ﷺ) from the people of the townships — it is for Allāh, His Messenger (Muhammad ﷺ), the kindred (of Messenger Muhammad ﷺ), the orphans, Al-Masākīn (the needy), and the wayfarer, in order that it may not become a fortune used by the rich among you. And whatsoever the Messenger (Muhammad ﷺ) gives you, take it; and whatsoever he forbids you, abstain (from it). And fear Allāh; verily, Allāh is Severe in punishment. (And there is also a share in this booty) for the poor emigrants, who were expelled from their homes and their property, seeking bounties from Allāh and to please Him, and helping Allāh (i.e. helping His religion — Islamic Monotheism) and His Messenger (Muhammad ﷺ). Such are indeed the truthful (to what they say). (Qur'ān 59: 7, 8)

﴿أَلَمْ تَرَ إِلَى الَّذِينَ نَافَقُوا يَقُولُونَ لِإِخْوَانِهِمُ الَّذِينَ كَفَرُوا مِنْ أَهْلِ الْكِتَابِ لَئِنْ أُخْرِجْتُمْ لَنَخْرُجَنَّ مَعَكُمْ وَلَا نُطِيعُ فِيكُمْ أَحَدًا أَبَدًا وَإِن قُوتِلْتُمْ لَنَنصُرَنَّكُمْ وَاللَّهُ يَشْهَدُ إِنَّهُمْ لَكَاذِبُونَ ۝ لَئِنْ أُخْرِجُوا لَا يَخْرُجُونَ مَعَهُمْ وَلَئِن قُوتِلُوا لَا يَنصُرُونَهُمْ وَلَئِن نَّصَرُوهُمْ لَيُوَلُّنَّ الْأَدْبَارَ ثُمَّ لَا يُنصَرُونَ ۝ لَأَنتُمْ أَشَدُّ رَهْبَةً فِي صُدُورِهِم مِّنَ اللَّهِ ذَٰلِكَ بِأَنَّهُمْ قَوْمٌ لَّا يَفْقَهُونَ ۝ لَا يُقَاتِلُونَكُمْ جَمِيعًا إِلَّا فِي قُرًى مُّحَصَّنَةٍ أَوْ مِن وَرَاءِ جُدُرٍ بَأْسُهُم بَيْنَهُمْ شَدِيدٌ تَحْسَبُهُمْ جَمِيعًا وَقُلُوبُهُمْ شَتَّىٰ ذَٰلِكَ بِأَنَّهُمْ قَوْمٌ لَّا يَعْقِلُونَ﴾

بِسْمِ ﴿١٤﴾ كَمَثَلِ ٱلَّذِينَ مِن قَبْلِهِمْ قَرِيبًا ذَاقُوا۟ وَبَالَ أَمْرِهِمْ وَلَهُمْ عَذَابٌ أَلِيمٌ ﴿١٥﴾ كَمَثَلِ ٱلشَّيْطَٰنِ إِذْ قَالَ لِلْإِنسَٰنِ ٱكْفُرْ فَلَمَّا كَفَرَ قَالَ إِنِّى بَرِىٓءٌ مِّنكَ إِنِّىٓ أَخَافُ ٱللَّهَ رَبَّ ٱلْعَٰلَمِينَ ﴿١٦﴾ فَكَانَ عَٰقِبَتَهُمَآ أَنَّهُمَا فِى ٱلنَّارِ خَٰلِدَيْنِ فِيهَا ۚ وَذَٰلِكَ جَزَٰٓؤُا۟ ٱلظَّٰلِمِينَ ﴿١٧﴾ ۞

Have you (O Muhammad ﷺ) not observed the hypocrites who say to their friends among the people of the Scripture who disbelieve: "(By Allāh) if you are expelled, we (too) indeed will go out with you, and we shall never obey any one against you; and if you are attacked (in fight), we shall indeed help you." But Allāh is Witness that they verily are liars. Surely, if they (the Jews) are expelled, never will they (hypocrites) go out with them; and if they are attacked, they will never help them. And (even) if they do help them, they (hypocrites) will turn their backs, and they will not be victorious. Verily, you (believers in the Oneness of Allāh — Islamic Monotheism) are more fearful in their (Jews of Banū An-Nadīr) breasts than Allāh. That is because they are a people who comprehend not (the Majesty and Power of Allāh). They fight not against you even together, except in fortified townships, or from behind walls. Their enmity among themselves is very great. You would think they were united, but their hearts are divided. That is because they are a people who understand not. They are like their immediate predecessors (the Jews of Banū Qainūqā', who suffered); they tasted the evil result of their conduct, and (in the Hereafter, there is) for them a painful torment. (Their allies deceived them) like Shaitān (Satan), when he says to man: "Disbelieve in Allāh." But when (man) disbelieves in Allāh, Shaitān (Satan) says: "I am free of you, I fear Allāh, the Lord of the 'Ālamīn (mankind, jinn and all that exists)!" So, the end of both will be that they will be in the Fire, abiding therein. Such is the recompense of the Zālimūn (i.e., polytheists, wrong doers, disbelievers in Allāh and in His Oneness). (Qur'ân 59: 11-17)

- Ibn Hisham: 3/108
- Al-Bidayah wan-Nihayah: 4/74
- At-Tabari: 2/550
- Al-Kamil Fit-Tarikh: 2/119
- 'Uyun Al-Athar: 2/48

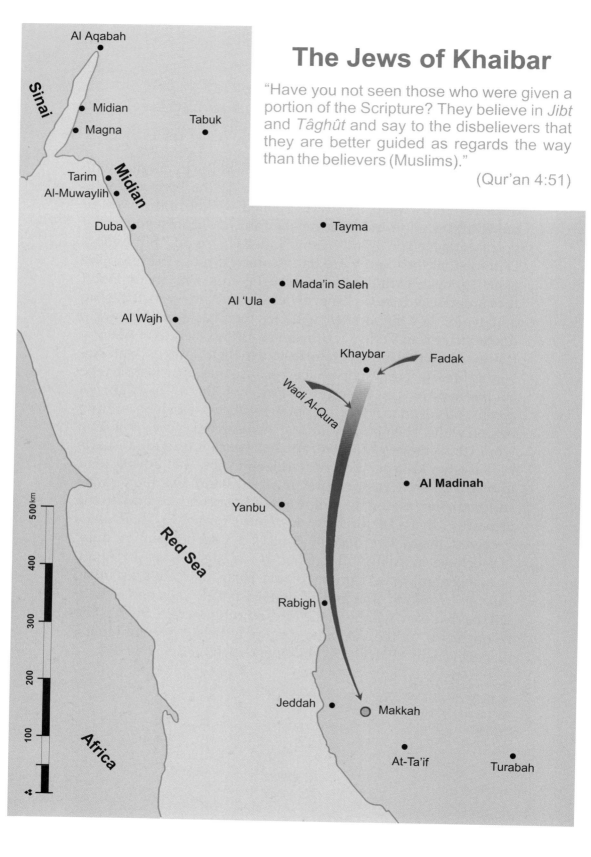

The Jews of Khaibar

"Have you not seen those who were given a portion of the Scripture? They believe in *Jibt* and *Tâghût* and say to the disbelievers that they are better guided as regards the way than the believers (Muslims)."

(Qur'an 4:51)

Sinai

Al Aqabah

Midian

Magna

Tabuk

Midian

Tarim

Al-Muwaylih

Duba

Tayma

Mada'in Saleh

Al 'Ula

Al Wajh

Khaybar

Fadak

Wadi Al-Qura

Al Madinah

Red Sea

Yanbu

500 km

400

300

Rabigh

200

100

Jeddah

Makkah

Africa

At-Ta'if

Turabah

The Jews Of Khaibar

"They believe in *Jibt* and *Tāghut* (false deities)."

﴿أَلَمْ تَرَ إِلَى ٱلَّذِينَ أُوتُواْ نَصِيبًا مِّنَ ٱلْكِتَبِ يُؤْمِنُونَ بِٱلْجِبْتِ وَٱلطَّغُوتِ وَيَقُولُونَ لِلَّذِينَ كَفَرُواْ هَٰٓؤُلَآءِ أَهْدَىٰ مِنَ ٱلَّذِينَ ءَامَنُواْ سَبِيلًا ۝ أُوْلَٰٓئِكَ ٱلَّذِينَ لَعَنَهُمُ ٱللَّهُ وَمَن يَلْعَنِ ٱللَّهُ فَلَن تَجِدَ لَهُ نَصِيرًا ۝﴾

Have you not seen those who were given a portion of the Scripture? They believe in *Al-Jibt* and *At-Tāghūt* and say to the disbelievers that they are better guided as regards the way than the believers (Muslims). They are those whom Allāh has cursed, and he whom Allāh curses, you will not find for him (any) helper.   (Qur'ân 4: 51, 52)

For the reasons discussed in the preceding chapter, Banu An-Nadir were expelled from Al-Madinah. A number of their leaders such as Huyai ibn Akhtab An-Nadri, Salâm ibn Mishkam, Kinânah ibn Abi Al-Huqaiq, and Haudhah ibn Qais Al-Wâ'ili traveled as a delegation to the Quraish, both inviting and encouraging the leaders of the Quraish to continue to wage war on the Messenger of Allâh ﷺ. The delegates from Banu An-Nadir said, "We will indeed fight with you against him, until together, we destroy him."

Abu Sufyân said, "Welcome indeed! The most beloved of people to us are those who help us to fight Muhammad. But we will only trust you and feel safe with you if you perform prostration to our gods." The delegates from Banu An-Nadir then proceeded to perform prostration to Quraish's idols.

The leaders of the Quraish then said, "O group of Jews, you are people of knowledge and people of the first book, inform us about our differences with Muhammad. Is our religion better or is the religion of Muhammad better? Do we follow more correct guidance or does Muhammad (follow more correct guidance)?" The delegates answered, "Rather, your religion is better than his religion, and you are more worthy of the truth than he is. And you are upon a more guided way, for you glorify this House, you give drink to the pilgrims, you sacrifice animals, and you worship that which your fathers used to worship. Therefore, you are certainly more worthy of the truth than he is." Then Allâh ﷻ revealed the following Verses about them:

﴿أَلَمْ تَرَ إِلَى ٱلَّذِينَ أُوتُوا۟ نَصِيبًا مِّنَ ٱلْكِتَٰبِ يُؤْمِنُونَ بِٱلْجِبْتِ وَٱلطَّٰغُوتِ وَيَقُولُونَ لِلَّذِينَ كَفَرُوا۟ هَٰٓؤُلَآءِ أَهْدَىٰ مِنَ ٱلَّذِينَ ءَامَنُوا۟ سَبِيلًا ۝ أُو۟لَٰٓئِكَ ٱلَّذِينَ لَعَنَهُمُ ٱللَّهُ وَمَن يَلْعَنِ ٱللَّهُ فَلَن تَجِدَ لَهُۥ نَصِيرًا ۝﴾

Have you not seen those who were given a portion of the Scripture? They believe in *Al-Jibt* and *At-Tāghūt* and say to the disbelievers that they are better guided as regards the way than the believers (Muslims). They are those whom Allāh has cursed, and he whom Allāh curses, you will not find for him (any) helper. (Qur'ân 4: 51, 52)

Having achieved their aim in Makkah, the leaders of Banu An-Nadir then went to the Ghatafân Tribe, in order to encourage them to wage war against the Messenger of Allâh ﷺ. As an added incentive, they promised Ghatafân half of the date harvest of Khaibar every year if they joined them in their war against the Muslims of Al-Madinah.

The Quraish, Ghatafân, Banu Murrah, Ashja', Sulaim, and Asad– these and other tribes then mustered their forces to attack Al-Madinah. The standoff that ensued became known as the Battle of the Confederates (*Al-Ahzâb*) or Al-Khandaq (The Trenches, since the Muslims made trenches to prevent the enemy from entering Al-Madinah); it took place in Shawwâl, in the year 5 H.

- Ibn Khaldun: 2/29
- Ibn Hisham: 3/137
- Al-Bidayah wan-Nihayah: 4/92
- At-Tabari: 2/564
- 'Uyun Al-Athar: 2/55

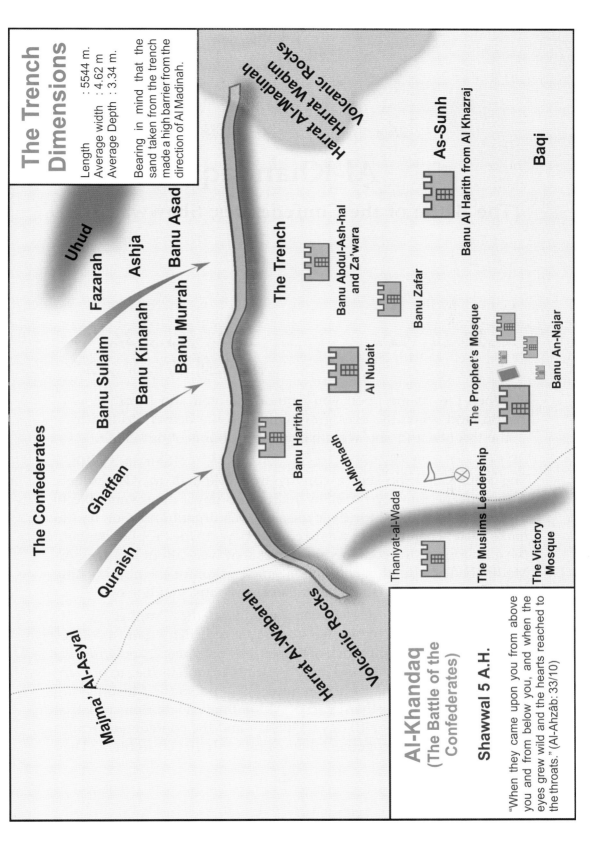

The Trench Dimensions

Length : 5544 m.
Average width : 4.62 m
Average Depth : 3.34 m.

Bearing in mind that the sand taken from the trench made a high barrier from the direction of Al Madinah.

Harrat Al-Madinah
Harrat Waqim
Volcanic Rocks

As-Sunh

Baqi

Banu Al Harith from Al Khazraj

Banu Abdul-Ash-hal and Za'wara

The Trench

Banu Zafar

Al Nubait

The Prophet's Mosque

Banu An-Najar

Banu Harithah

Al-Midhdadah

The Muslims Leadership

Thaniyat-al-Wada

The Victory Mosque

Banu Asad

Banu Murrah

Ashja

Banu Kinanah

Banu Sulaim

Fazarah

Uhud

Ghatfan

The Confederates

Quraish

Majma' Al-Asyal

Harrat Al-Wabarah
Volcanic Rocks

Al-Khandaq
(The Battle of the Confederates)

Shawwal 5 A.H.

"When they came upon you from above you and from below you, and when the eyes grew wild and the hearts reached to the throats." (Al-Ahzâb: 33/10)

Al-Khandaq

(The Battle of the Confederates; Shawwâl, 5 H)

﴿إِذْ جَآءُوكُم مِّن فَوْقِكُمْ وَمِنْ أَسْفَلَ مِنكُمْ وَإِذْ زَاغَتِ ٱلْأَبْصَرُ وَبَلَغَتِ ٱلْقُلُوبُ ٱلْحَنَاجِرَ وَتَظُنُّونَ بِٱللَّهِ ٱلظُّنُونَا۠ ﴿١٠﴾﴾

When they came upon you from above you and from below you, and when the eyes grew wild and the hearts reached to the throats, and you were harbouring doubts about Allāh.

(Qur'ân 33: 10)

The Khuza'ah tribe sent a convoy from Makkah to Al-Madinah. Although the journey normally required 6 days, they were able to make it in four days, for their mission was urgent and they had to make haste. Their mission was to convey news to the Prophet ﷺ about the gathering of the confederate armies that were about to attack Al-Madinah. The situation certainly seemed grim, for the approaching forces had the advantages of numbers, weapons, and horses.

Salmân Al-Fârisi ؓ made a suggestion to the Prophet ﷺ: "O Messenger of Allâh, when we were attacked in the land of Fâris, when we feared the approach of horses (i.e., horsemen), and when we were surrounded, we would build trenches around us (i.e., to prevent the horsemen from being able to attack)." And so the Muslims dug trenches along the northern part of Al-Madinah, a laborious task that they completed in 9 or 10 days. Quraish and the confederate armies then approached; altogether, they came with 10,000 fighters. They

284

A place in Al-Madinah Al-Munawwarah full of volcanic rocks and stones

made camp north of Al-Madinah since it was the only land that was suitable for fighting (especially for the horsemen). The eastern and western approaches to Madinah were unsuitable for fighting, since the surface of the land consisted mainly of volcanic, stony rocks. And southern Madinah was also ill suited for fighting, for the land was filled with date trees as well as Mount 'Aer.

But the Muslim army was still threatened from the south, not by the confederate armies, but by the last of the three Jewish tribes of Al-Madinah, Banu Quraizah a tribe that also had made an agreement to defend the Muslims in battle. They too broke their agreement:

﴿إِذْ جَاءُوكُم مِّن فَوْقِكُمْ وَمِنْ أَسْفَلَ مِنكُمْ وَإِذْ زَاغَتِ ٱلْأَبْصَرُ وَبَلَغَتِ ٱلْقُلُوبُ ٱلْحَنَاجِرَ وَتَظُنُّونَ بِٱللَّهِ ٱلظُّنُونَا۠ ۝ هُنَالِكَ ٱبْتُلِيَ ٱلْمُؤْمِنُونَ وَزُلْزِلُوٓا۟ زِلْزَالًا شَدِيدًا ۝ وَإِذْ يَقُولُ ٱلْمُنَفِقُونَ وَٱلَّذِينَ فِى قُلُوبِهِم مَّرَضٌ مَّا وَعَدَنَا ٱللَّهُ وَرَسُولُهُۥٓ إِلَّا غُرُورًا ۝ وَإِذْ قَالَت طَّآئِفَةٌ مِّنْهُمْ يَٰٓأَهْلَ يَثْرِبَ لَا مُقَامَ لَكُمْ فَٱرْجِعُوا۟ وَيَسْتَـْٔذِنُ فَرِيقٌ مِّنْهُمُ ٱلنَّبِىَّ يَقُولُونَ إِنَّ بُيُوتَنَا عَوْرَةٌ وَمَا هِىَ بِعَوْرَةٍ إِن يُرِيدُونَ إِلَّا فِرَارًا ۝﴾

When they came upon you from above you and from below you, and when the eyes grew wild and the hearts reached to the throats, and you were harbouring doubts about Allāh. There, the believers were tried and shaken with a mighty shaking. And when the hypocrites and those in whose hearts is a disease (of doubts) said: "Allāh and His Messenger (ﷺ) promised us nothing but delusion!" And when a party of them said: "O people of Yathrib (Al-Madinah)! There is no stand (possible) for you (against the enemy attack!) Therefore go back!" And a band of them asked for permission of the Prophet (ﷺ) saying: "Truly, our homes lie open (to the enemy)." And they lay not open. They but wished to flee.

(Qur'ân 33: 10-13)

In the course of the ensuing skirmishes, Sa'd ibn 'Ubâdah ﷺ was injured by an arrow. The Prophet ﷺ had him taken to a special place near his Masjid that had been prepared to receive the wounded. Near to it was the tent of Rafidah Aslamiyyah, she used to look after the wounded persons.

After a siege that lasted for an entire month, Nu'aim bin Mas'ud Al-Ashja'i ﷺ came to the Messenger of Allâh ﷺ. Nu'aim ﷺ had accepted Islam, though the Confederates had no knowledge about him being a Muslim. Seeing that perhaps their ignorance of his Islam might be used to the advantage of the Muslims, Nu'aim ﷺ asked the Messenger of Allâh ﷺ if there was anything he could do to help. The Prophet ﷺ said, "War is stratagem," meaning that stratagem should, when possible, be profitably used to end a war. In a wise an intelligent manner, Nu'aim ﷺ was able to divide the Confederates, who were already tired from waiting in the desert for an entire month. Then Allâh ﷺ sent a strong wind that uprooted their tents, overturned their pots, and extinguished their fires. For these and other reasons, the armies withdrew and retreated to their homelands, having lost all hope of completing their mission.

﴿يَٰٓأَيُّهَا ٱلَّذِينَ ءَامَنُواْ ٱذۡكُرُواْ نِعۡمَةَ ٱللَّهِ عَلَيۡكُمۡ إِذۡ جَآءَتۡكُمۡ جُنُودٞ فَأَرۡسَلۡنَا عَلَيۡهِمۡ رِيحٗا وَجُنُودٗا لَّمۡ تَرَوۡهَاۚ وَكَانَ ٱللَّهُ بِمَا تَعۡمَلُونَ بَصِيرًا ۝﴾

O you who believe! Remember Allāh's Favour to you, when there came against you hosts, and We sent against them a wind and forces that you saw not [i.e., troops of angels during the battle of *Al-Ahzāb* (the Confederates)]. And Allāh is Ever All-Seer of what you do.

(Qur'ân 33: 9)

﴿إِذۡ جَآءُوكُم مِّن فَوۡقِكُمۡ وَمِنۡ أَسۡفَلَ مِنكُمۡ وَإِذۡ زَاغَتِ ٱلۡأَبۡصَٰرُ وَبَلَغَتِ ٱلۡقُلُوبُ ٱلۡحَنَاجِرَ وَتَظُنُّونَ بِٱللَّهِ ٱلظُّنُونَا۠ ۝ هُنَالِكَ ٱبۡتُلِيَ ٱلۡمُؤۡمِنُونَ وَزُلۡزِلُواْ زِلۡزَالٗا شَدِيدٗا ۝ وَإِذۡ يَقُولُ ٱلۡمُنَٰفِقُونَ وَٱلَّذِينَ فِي قُلُوبِهِم مَّرَضٞ مَّا وَعَدَنَا ٱللَّهُ وَرَسُولُهُۥٓ إِلَّا غُرُورٗا ۝ وَإِذۡ قَالَت طَّآئِفَةٞ مِّنۡهُمۡ يَٰٓأَهۡلَ يَثۡرِبَ لَا مُقَامَ لَكُمۡ فَٱرۡجِعُواْۚ وَيَسۡتَـٔۡذِنُ فَرِيقٞ مِّنۡهُمُ ٱلنَّبِيَّ يَقُولُونَ إِنَّ بُيُوتَنَا عَوۡرَةٞ وَمَا هِيَ بِعَوۡرَةٍۖ إِن يُرِيدُونَ إِلَّا فِرَارٗا ۝﴾

When they came upon you from above you and from below you, and when the eyes grew wild and the hearts reached to the throats, and you were harbouring doubts about Allāh. There, the believers were tried and shaken with a mighty shaking. And when the hypocrites and those in whose hearts is a disease (of doubts) said: "Allāh and His Messenger (ﷺ) promised us nothing but delusion!" And when a party of them said: "O people of Yathrib (Al-Madinah)! There is no stand (possible) for you (against the enemy attack!) Therefore go back!" And a band of them ask for permission of the Prophet (ﷺ) saying: "Truly, our homes lie open (to the enemy)." And they lay not open. They but wished to flee.

(Qur'ân 33: 10-13)

- Ibn Khaldun: 2/8
- Ibn Hisham: 3/131
- Al-Bidayah wan-Nihayah: 4/104
- At-Tabari: 2/571
- Al-Kamil Fit-Tarikh: 2/125
- 'Uyun Al-Athar: 2/59

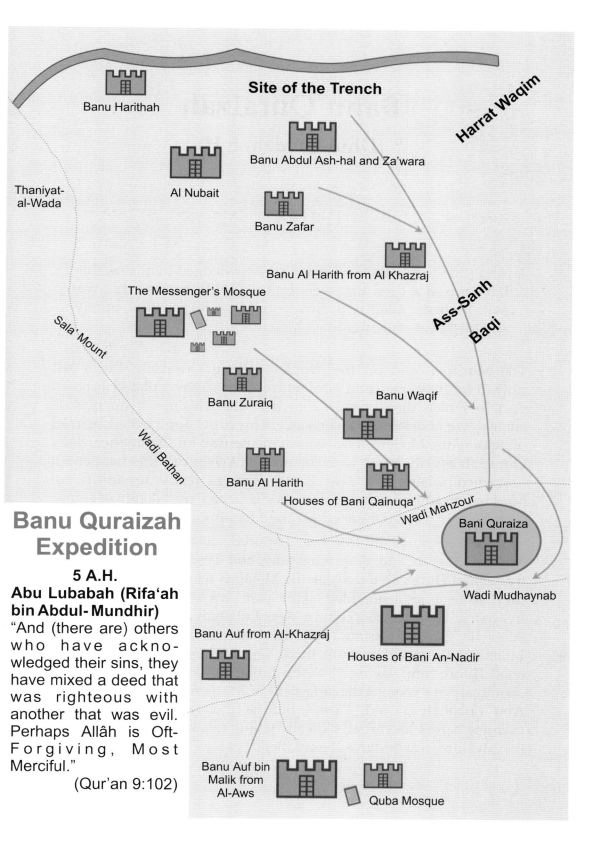

Banu Harithah

Site of the Trench

Harrat Waqim

Banu Abdul Ash-hal and Za'wara

Al Nubait

Thaniyat-al-Wada

Banu Zafar

Banu Al Harith from Al Khazraj

The Messenger's Mosque

Ass-Sanh

Baqi

Sala' Mount

Banu Zuraiq

Banu Waqif

Wadi Bathan

Banu Al Harith

Houses of Bani Qainuqa'

Wadi Mahzour

Bani Quraiza

Banu Quraizah Expedition

5 A.H.
Abu Lubabah (Rifa'ah bin Abdul-Mundhir)
"And (there are) others who have acknowledged their sins, they have mixed a deed that was righteous with another that was evil. Perhaps Allâh is Oft-Forgiving, Most Merciful."

(Qur'an 9:102)

Wadi Mudhaynab

Banu Auf from Al-Khazraj

Houses of Bani An-Nadir

Banu Auf bin Malik from Al-Aws

Quba Mosque

Banu Quraizah

(Dhul-Qa'dah, 5 H)

﴿وَءَاخَرُونَ اعْتَرَفُواْ بِذُنُوبِهِمْ خَلَطُواْ عَمَلًا صَٰلِحًا وَءَاخَرَ سَيِّئًا عَسَى اللَّهُ أَن يَتُوبَ عَلَيْهِمْ إِنَّ
اللَّهَ غَفُورٌ رَّحِيمٌ ۝﴾

And (there are) others who have acknowledged their sins, they
have mixed a deed that was righteous with another that was
evil. Perhaps Allāh will turn to them in forgiveness. Surely,
Allāh is Oft-Forgiving, Most Merciful.

(Qur'ân 9: 102)

The Muslims' raid on the people of Banu Quraizah was a just
reward for their open and insolent treachery. They violated a signed
pact in which they promised to help the Muslims if an outside
enemy ever attacked. But when an enemy army approached, instead
of helping the Muslims or even staying neutral for that matter, Banu
Quraizah openly sided with the enemy. When did this happen? It
happened when they saw 10,000 fighters ready to attack Al-
Madinah from its northern front; they believed mistakenly of course
that the end was guaranteed for the Muslims.

This open betrayal and treachery required a just punishment. So the
Muslims traveled to Banu Quraizah and besieged them. No one
from Banu Quraizah dared ask the Muslims why they had come, for
they were best acquainted with their own recent actions and
treachery. But they did call for Abu Lubâbah ﷺ to come to them.
After he got permission from the Messenger of Allâh ﷺ, Abu
Lubâbah ﷺ entered their fortress. The leaders of Banu Quraizah
cried before him, saying, "O Abu Lubâbah, do you think that we
should agree to accept the judgment of Muhammad regarding us?"
Abu Lubâbah ﷺ said, "Yes," but he then made a gesture by
pointing across his throat, basically telling them that the intention of
the Muslims was to have them killed.

Abu Lubâbah ﷺ later said, "By Allâh, no sooner did my feet leave their places than I knew that I had betrayed Allâh and His Messenger." When he returned to the Masjid of the Messenger of Allâh ﷺ, Abu Lubâbah ﷺ tied himself to one of the corners of the Masjid. He said, "I will not leave this place of mine until Allâh forgives me for what I have done." Abu Lubâbah ﷺ remained tied there for six nights, and according to one narration, for twenty nights. Before each congregational prayer, his wife would come to him and untie his hands, so that he could go and perform ablution; and after that, he would return to his place, where he would tie himself again. This continued until these Verses were revealed:

﴿وَءَاخَرُونَ ٱعْتَرَفُواْ بِذُنُوبِهِمْ خَلَطُواْ عَمَلًا صَٰلِحًا وَءَاخَرَ سَيِّئًا عَسَى ٱللَّهُ أَن يَتُوبَ عَلَيْهِمْ إِنَّ ٱللَّهَ غَفُورٌ رَّحِيمٌ ۝ خُذْ مِنْ أَمْوَٰلِهِمْ صَدَقَةً تُطَهِّرُهُمْ وَتُزَكِّيهِم بِهَا وَصَلِّ عَلَيْهِمْ إِنَّ صَلَوٰتَكَ سَكَنٌ لَّهُمْ وَٱللَّهُ سَمِيعٌ عَلِيمٌ ۝ أَلَمْ يَعْلَمُوٓاْ أَنَّ ٱللَّهَ هُوَ يَقْبَلُ ٱلتَّوْبَةَ عَنْ عِبَادِهِۦ وَيَأْخُذُ ٱلصَّدَقَٰتِ وَأَنَّ ٱللَّهَ هُوَ ٱلتَّوَّابُ ٱلرَّحِيمُ ۝﴾

And (there are) others who have acknowledged their sins, they have mixed a deed that was righteous with another that was evil. Perhaps Allāh will turn to them in forgiveness. Surely, Allāh is Oft-Forgiving, Most Merciful. Take *Sadaqah* (alms) from their wealth in order to purify them and sanctify them with it, and invoke Allāh for them. Verily, your invocations are a source of security for them; and Allāh is All-Hearer, All-Knower. Know they not that Allāh accepts repentance from His slaves and takes the *Sadaqāt* (alms, charities), and that Allāh Alone is the One Who forgives and accepts repentance, Most Merciful?

(Qur'ân 9: 102-104)

The leaders of Banu Quraizah finally agreed to submit to the judgment of Sa'd ibn Mu'âdh ﷺ. In his judgment, Sa'd ﷺ ruled that the men of Banu Quraizah should be killed, that their wealth should be distributed, and that their children and women should be taken as slaves. Regarding the siege of Banu Quraizah, Allâh ﷺ revealed the following Verses:

291

وَرَدَّ اللَّهُ الَّذِينَ كَفَرُوا بِغَيْظِهِمْ لَمْ يَنَالُوا خَيْرًا وَكَفَى اللَّهُ الْمُؤْمِنِينَ الْقِتَالَ وَكَانَ اللَّهُ قَوِيًّا عَزِيزًا ۝ وَأَنزَلَ الَّذِينَ ظَاهَرُوهُم مِّنْ أَهْلِ الْكِتَابِ مِن صَيَاصِيهِمْ وَقَذَفَ فِي قُلُوبِهِمُ الرُّعْبَ فَرِيقًا تَقْتُلُونَ وَتَأْسِرُونَ فَرِيقًا ۝ وَأَوْرَثَكُمْ أَرْضَهُمْ وَدِيَارَهُمْ وَأَمْوَالَهُمْ وَأَرْضًا لَّمْ تَطَئُوهَا وَكَانَ اللَّهُ عَلَى كُلِّ شَيْءٍ قَدِيرًا ۝

And Allāh drove back those who disbelieved in their rage, they gained no advantage (booty). Allāh sufficed for the believers in the fighting (by sending against the disbelievers a severe wind and troops of angels). And Allāh is Ever All-Strong, All-Mighty. And those of the people of the Scripture who backed them (the disbelievers), Allāh brought them down from their forts and cast terror into their hearts, (so that) a group (of them) you killed, and a group (of them) you made captives. And He caused you to inherit their lands, and their houses, and their riches, and a land which you had not trodden (before). And Allāh is Able to do all things.

(Qur'ân 33: 25-27)

- Ibn Hisham: 3/141
- Usdul-Ghabah: 2/375
- Ar-Raud Al-Unuf: 2/268
- At-Tabari: 2/581
- Futuhal-Buldân: 34

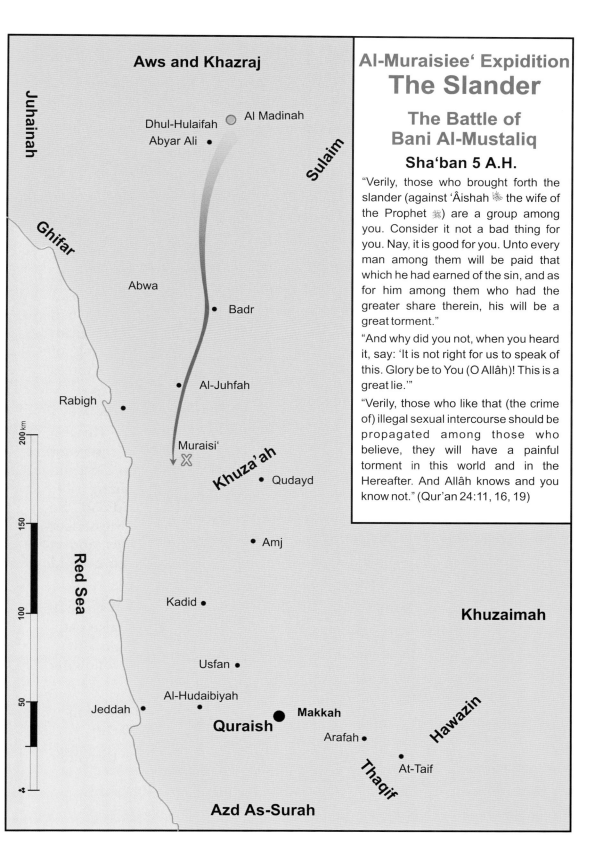

Aws and Khazraj

Juhainah

Al Madinah
Dhul-Hulaifah
Abyar Ali •

Sulaim

Ghifar

Abwa

• Badr

Rabigh

Al-Juhfah

200 km

Muraisi'
X

Khuza'ah

• Qudayd

150

Red Sea

• Amj

100

Kadid •

Khuzaimah

Usfan •

50

Al-Hudaibiyah •

Jeddah •

Quraish

● Makkah

Arafah •

Hawazin

• At-Taif

Thaqif

Azd As-Surah

Al-Muraisiee' Expidition
The Slander
The Battle of Bani Al-Mustaliq
Sha'ban 5 A.H.

"Verily, those who brought forth the slander (against 'Âishah ﷺ the wife of the Prophet ﷺ) are a group among you. Consider it not a bad thing for you. Nay, it is good for you. Unto every man among them will be paid that which he had earned of the sin, and as for him among them who had the greater share therein, his will be a great torment."

"And why did you not, when you heard it, say: 'It is not right for us to speak of this. Glory be to You (O Allâh)! This is a great lie.'"

"Verily, those who like that (the crime of) illegal sexual intercourse should be propagated among those who believe, they will have a painful torment in this world and in the Hereafter. And Allâh knows and you know not." (Qur'an 24:11, 16, 19)

Al-Muraisi'
The Battle Of Bani Al-Mustaliq
(Sha'ban, 5 H)

Al-Hârith ibn Dirâr, chief of Bani Al-Mustaliq (from the Khuzâ'ah), mustered as many fighters as he could from his own people and from nearby Bedouins. He was assembling forces to wage war on the Messenger of Allâh ﷺ. Coming to know what Al-Hârith and his people were up to, the Messenger of Allâh ﷺ didn't wait but instead rode to them with 700 men with him. Leaving on the 2nd of Sha'bân in the year 5 H, their aim was to break up the forces that Al-Hârith had already assembled. The two armies met at the water (spring) of Al-Muraisi', and it didn't take long before Al-Hârith and his forces were defeated.

In the course of the battle, 'Umar ibn Al-Khattâb's servant got into a dispute with Jahjâh ibn Mas'ud, who was an ally of the Khazraj (Khazraj was one of the tribes of Al-Madinah). 'Umar's servant ended up striking Jahjâh; and as a result, 'Abdullah ibn Ubai ibn Salul, the leader of the hypocrites and a member of the Khazraj tribe, was enraged. He said, "By Allâh, if we return to Al-Madinah, the honorable ones among us will expel the lowly ones." The Messenger of Allâh ﷺ was able to bring calm to the brewing tensions, and in order to divert them from mutual fighting, he ﷺ ordered a rapid return to Al-Madinah.

When Zaid ibn Arqam ؓ conveyed Ibn 'Ubai ibn Salul's above words to the Messenger of Allâh ﷺ, Ibn 'Ubai made a false oath, swearing that he never said those words and that Zaid ibn Arqam ؓ was lying. In exculpation of Zaid ؓ, Allâh ﷻ revealed the following Verse:

> That We might make it a remembrance for you, and the keen ear (person) may (hear and) understand it. (Qur'ân 69: 12)

Everyone knew that Zaid ؓ was telling the truth, and he thereafter became known as, "The one with a keen ear."

In regard to the leader of the hypocrites, 'Abdullah ibn Ubai, the following Verses were revealed in *Sûrat Al-Munâfiqun*:

﴿وَإِذَا قِيلَ لَهُمْ تَعَالَوْا يَسْتَغْفِرْ لَكُمْ رَسُولُ ٱللَّهِ لَوَّوْا رُءُوسَهُمْ وَرَأَيْتَهُمْ يَصُدُّونَ وَهُم مُّسْتَكْبِرُونَ ۝ سَوَآءٌ عَلَيْهِمْ أَسْتَغْفَرْتَ لَهُمْ أَمْ لَمْ تَسْتَغْفِرْ لَهُمْ لَن يَغْفِرَ ٱللَّهُ لَهُمْ إِنَّ ٱللَّهَ لَا يَهْدِي ٱلْقَوْمَ ٱلْفَٰسِقِينَ ۝ هُمُ ٱلَّذِينَ يَقُولُونَ لَا تُنفِقُوا عَلَىٰ مَنْ عِندَ رَسُولِ ٱللَّهِ حَتَّىٰ يَنفَضُّوا وَلِلَّهِ خَزَآئِنُ ٱلسَّمَٰوَٰتِ وَٱلْأَرْضِ وَلَٰكِنَّ ٱلْمُنَٰفِقِينَ لَا يَفْقَهُونَ ۝ يَقُولُونَ لَئِن رَّجَعْنَآ إِلَى ٱلْمَدِينَةِ لَيُخْرِجَنَّ ٱلْأَعَزُّ مِنْهَا ٱلْأَذَلَّ وَلِلَّهِ ٱلْعِزَّةُ وَلِرَسُولِهِ وَلِلْمُؤْمِنِينَ وَلَٰكِنَّ ٱلْمُنَٰفِقِينَ لَا يَعْلَمُونَ ۝ ﴾

And when it is said to them: "Come, so that the Messenger of Allāh (ﷺ) may ask forgiveness from Allāh for you," they twist their heads, and you would see them turning away their faces in pride. It is equal to them whether you (Muhammad ﷺ) ask forgiveness or ask not forgiveness for them, Allāh will never forgive them. Verily, Allāh guides not the people who are the *Fāsiqūn* (rebellious, disobedient to Allāh). They are the ones who say: "Spend not on those who are with Allāh's Messenger (ﷺ), until they desert him." And to Allāh belong the treasures of the heavens and the earth, but the hypocrites comprehend not. They (hyprocrites) say: "If we return to Al-Madinah, indeed the more honorable ('Abdūllah bin Ubai bin Salūl, the chief of hyprocrites at Al-Madinah) will expel therefrom the meaner (i.e., Allāh's Messenger ﷺ)." But honor, power and glory belong to Allāh, and to His Messenger (Muhammad ﷺ), and to the believers, but the hypocrites know not.

(Qur'ân 63: 5-8)

Ibn Ubai ibn Salûl was not content with his false oath; in addition to that, he was the one who started the well-known 'Slander Incident,' which began during the very same expedition. His lying and slander led to great trials for the Prophet ﷺ and those who were most beloved to him.

When the Muslim army was returning from the Battle of Banu Al-

Mustaliq, the Muslims made camp for a short while. 'Āishah ﷺ went out of eyesight, in order to look for a necklace that she lost when she had left the camp earlier. Meanwhile, the Muslims left, not noticing that she was missing; and so when she returned to the site of the camp, she saw that she was alone. It was then that Safwân ibn Al-Mu'attal ﷺ passed by; it was his job to remain in the rear of the army, in order to pick up personal belongings that people might have inadvertently dropped on their way back. When he ﷺ saw 'Āishah ﷺ, he recognized her immediately. In a most modest manner, he proffered his camel to her. He then turned in the other direction, so that she could mount it without him seeing her. After that, Safwân ﷺ took the camel by its reins and silently began to steer it in the direction of Al-Madinah. By the time that they reached Al-Madinah, it was midday. When Ibn Ubai ibn Salûl saw them, he said, "The wife of your Prophet has spent the night together with a man until the morning; then he comes, leading her hither. She was not saved from him, and he was not saved from her." Picking up on his cue, the other hypocrites began to spread the slanderous lie, and the entire city of Al-Madinah was shaken by it. After a period of difficulty and trial, Allâh ﷺ revealed Verses that established the innocence of 'Āishah ﷺ, the pure and chaste wife of the Prophet ﷺ:

﴿إِنَّ ٱلَّذِينَ جَآءُو بِٱلْإِفْكِ عُصْبَةٌ مِّنكُمْ لَا تَحْسَبُوهُ شَرًّا لَّكُم بَلْ هُوَ خَيْرٌ لَّكُمْ لِكُلِّ ٱمْرِئٍ مِّنْهُم مَّا ٱكْتَسَبَ مِنَ ٱلْإِثْمِ وَٱلَّذِى تَوَلَّىٰ كِبْرَهُۥ مِنْهُمْ لَهُۥ عَذَابٌ عَظِيمٌ ۝ لَّوْلَآ إِذْ سَمِعْتُمُوهُ ظَنَّ ٱلْمُؤْمِنُونَ وَٱلْمُؤْمِنَـٰتُ بِأَنفُسِهِمْ خَيْرًا وَقَالُوا هَـٰذَآ إِفْكٌ مُّبِينٌ ۝ لَّوْلَا جَآءُو عَلَيْهِ بِأَرْبَعَةِ شُهَدَآءَ فَإِذْ لَمْ يَأْتُوا بِٱلشُّهَدَآءِ فَأُولَـٰٓئِكَ عِندَ ٱللَّهِ هُمُ ٱلْكَـٰذِبُونَ ۝ وَلَوْلَا فَضْلُ ٱللَّهِ عَلَيْكُمْ وَرَحْمَتُهُۥ فِى ٱلدُّنْيَا وَٱلْأَخِرَةِ لَمَسَّكُمْ فِى مَآ أَفَضْتُمْ فِيهِ عَذَابٌ عَظِيمٌ ۝ إِذْ تَلَقَّوْنَهُۥ بِأَلْسِنَتِكُمْ وَتَقُولُونَ بِأَفْوَاهِكُم مَّا لَيْسَ لَكُم بِهِۦ عِلْمٌ وَتَحْسَبُونَهُۥ هَيِّنًا وَهُوَ عِندَ ٱللَّهِ عَظِيمٌ ۝ وَلَوْلَآ إِذْ سَمِعْتُمُوهُ قُلْتُم مَّا يَكُونُ لَنَآ أَن نَّتَكَلَّمَ بِهَـٰذَا سُبْحَـٰنَكَ هَـٰذَا بُهْتَـٰنٌ عَظِيمٌ ۝ يَعِظُكُمُ ٱللَّهُ أَن تَعُودُوا لِمِثْلِهِۦٓ أَبَدًا إِن كُنتُم مُّؤْمِنِينَ ۝ وَيُبَيِّنُ ٱللَّهُ لَكُمُ ٱلْأَيَـٰتِ وَٱللَّهُ عَلِيمٌ حَكِيمٌ ۝ إِنَّ ٱلَّذِينَ يُحِبُّونَ أَن تَشِيعَ ٱلْفَـٰحِشَةُ فِى ٱلَّذِينَ ءَامَنُوا لَهُمْ عَذَابٌ أَلِيمٌ فِى ٱلدُّنْيَا وَٱلْأَخِرَةِ وَٱللَّهُ يَعْلَمُ وَأَنتُمْ لَا تَعْلَمُونَ ۝ وَلَوْلَا فَضْلُ ٱللَّهِ عَلَيْكُمْ وَرَحْمَتُهُۥ وَأَنَّ ٱللَّهَ

رَءُوفٌ رَّحِيمٌ ۞ (٢٠) يَـٰٓأَيُّهَا ٱلَّذِينَ ءَامَنُوا۟ لَا تَتَّبِعُوا۟ خُطُوَٰتِ ٱلشَّيْطَـٰنِ وَمَن يَتَّبِعْ خُطُوَٰتِ ٱلشَّيْطَـٰنِ فَإِنَّهُۥ يَأْمُرُ بِٱلْفَحْشَآءِ وَٱلْمُنكَرِ وَلَوْلَا فَضْلُ ٱللَّهِ عَلَيْكُمْ وَرَحْمَتُهُۥ مَا زَكَىٰ مِنكُم مِّنْ أَحَدٍ أَبَدًا وَلَـٰكِنَّ ٱللَّهَ يُزَكِّى مَن يَشَآءُ وَٱللَّهُ سَمِيعٌ عَلِيمٌ (٢١) وَلَا يَأْتَلِ أُو۟لُوا۟ ٱلْفَضْلِ مِنكُمْ وَٱلسَّعَةِ أَن يُؤْتُوٓا۟ أُو۟لِى ٱلْقُرْبَىٰ وَٱلْمَسَـٰكِينَ وَٱلْمُهَـٰجِرِينَ فِى سَبِيلِ ٱللَّهِ وَلْيَعْفُوا۟ وَلْيَصْفَحُوٓا۟ أَلَا تُحِبُّونَ أَن يَغْفِرَ ٱللَّهُ لَكُمْ وَٱللَّهُ غَفُورٌ رَّحِيمٌ (٢٢) إِنَّ ٱلَّذِينَ يَرْمُونَ ٱلْمُحْصَنَـٰتِ ٱلْغَـٰفِلَـٰتِ ٱلْمُؤْمِنَـٰتِ لُعِنُوا۟ فِى ٱلدُّنْيَا وَٱلْـَٔاخِرَةِ وَلَهُمْ عَذَابٌ عَظِيمٌ (٢٣) ۞

Verily, those who brought forth the slander (against 'Āishah ؓ the wife of the Prophet ﷺ) are a group among you. Consider it not a bad thing for you. Nay, it is good for you. To every man among them will be paid that which he had earned of the sin, and as for him among them who had the greater share therein, his will be a great torment. Why then did not the believers, men and women, when you heard it (the slander), think good of their own people and say: "This (charge) is an obvious lie?" Why did they not produce four witnesses against him? Since they (the slanderers) have not produced witnesses! Then with Allāh, they are the liars. Had it not been for the Grace of Allāh and His Mercy to you in this world and in the Hereafter, a great torment would have touched you for that whereof you had spoken. When you were propagating it with your tongues, and uttering with your mouths that whereof you had no knowledge, you counted it a little thing, while with Allāh it was very great. And why did you not, when you heard it, say: "It is not right for us to speak of this. Glorified are You (O Allāh)! This is a great lie." Allāh forbids you from it and warns you not to repeat the like of it forever, if you are believers. And Allāh makes the *Ayāt* (proofs, evidences, Verses, lessons, signs, revelations, etc.) plain to you, and Allāh is All-Knowing, All-Wise. Verily, those who like that (the crime of) illegal sexual intercourse should be propagated among those who believe, they will have a painful torment in this world and in the Hereafter. And Allāh knows and you know not. And had it not been for the Grace of Allāh and His Mercy on you (Allāh would have hastened the punishment upon you). And that Allāh is full of kindness, Most Merciful. O you who believe! Follow not the footsteps of *Shaitān* (Satan). And whosoever follows the footsteps of *Shaitān* (Satan), then, verily, he commands *Al-Fahshā'* [i.e. to commit indecency (illegal sexual intercourse)], and *Al-Munkar* [disbelief and polytheism (i.e. to do evil and wicked deeds; and to speak or to do what is forbidden in Islam)]. And had it not been for the Grace of Allāh and His Mercy on you, not one of you would ever have been pure from sins. But Allāh purifies (guides to Islam) whom He wills, and Allāh is All-Hearer, All-Knower. And let not those among you who are blessed with graces and wealth swear not to give (any sort of help) to their kinsmen, *Al-Masākīn* (the needy), and those who left their homes for Allāh's Cause. Let them pardon and forgive. Do you not love that Allāh should forgive you? And Allāh is Oft-Forgiving, Most Merciful. Verily, those who accuse believing chaste women, who never even think of anything touching their chastity and are good believers — are cursed in this life and in the Hereafter, and for them will be a great torment —

(Qur'ân 24: 11-23)

- Ibn Khaldun: 2/33
- Ibn Hisham: 3/182
- Al-Bidayah wan-Nihayah: 4/156
- At-Tabari: 2/604
- Al-Kamil Fit-Tarikh: 2/182
- 'Uyun Al-Athar: 2/91

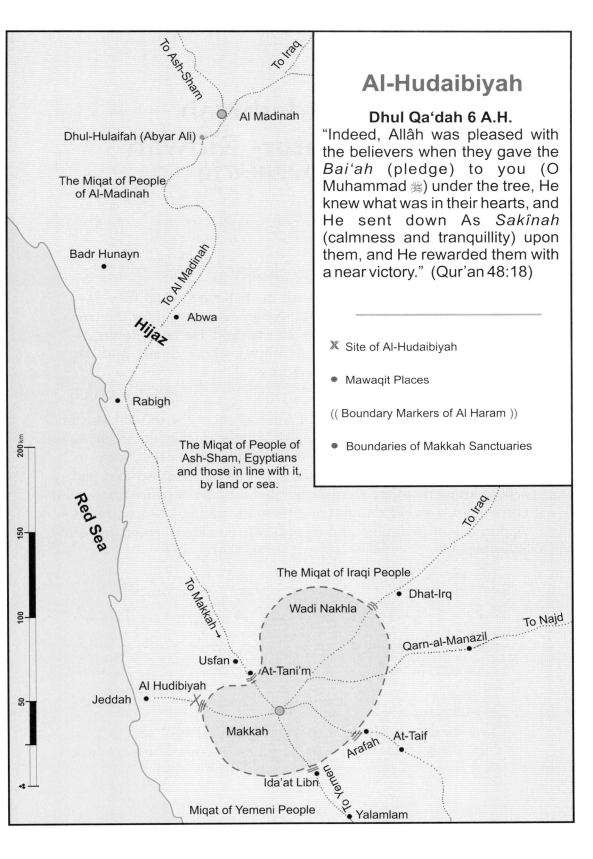

Al-Hudaibiyah

Dhul Qa'dah 6 A.H.

"Indeed, Allâh was pleased with the believers when they gave the *Bai'ah* (pledge) to you (O Muhammad ﷺ) under the tree, He knew what was in their hearts, and He sent down As *Sakînah* (calmness and tranquillity) upon them, and He rewarded them with a near victory." (Qur'an 48:18)

✠ Site of Al-Hudaibiyah

● Mawaqit Places

((Boundary Markers of Al Haram))

● Boundaries of Makkah Sanctuaries

To Ash-Sham

To Iraq

Al Madinah

Dhul-Hulaifah (Abyar Ali)

The Miqat of People of Al-Madinah

To Al Madinah

Badr Hunayn

Hijaz

Abwa

Rabigh

200 km

Red Sea

The Miqat of People of Ash-Sham, Egyptians and those in line with it, by land or sea.

150

To Iraq

The Miqat of Iraqi People

Dhat-Irq

100

Wadi Nakhla

To Najd

Qarn-al-Manazil

To Makkah →

Usfan

At-Tani'm

Al Hudibiyah

50

Jeddah

Makkah

At-Taif

Arafah

To Yemen

Ida'at Libn

Miqat of Yemeni People

Yalamlam

Al-Hudaibiyah
And Bai'atur- Ridwân
(Dhil-Qa'dah, 6 H)

$$﴿لَّقَدْ رَضِيَ ٱللَّهُ عَنِ ٱلْمُؤْمِنِينَ إِذْ يُبَايِعُونَكَ تَحْتَ ٱلشَّجَرَةِ فَعَلِمَ مَا فِي قُلُوبِهِمْ فَأَنزَلَ ٱلسَّكِينَةَ عَلَيْهِمْ وَأَثَٰبَهُمْ فَتْحًا قَرِيبًا ١٨﴾$$

Indeed, Allāh was pleased with the believers when they gave the *Bai'ah* (pledge) to you (O Muhammad ﷺ) under the tree, He knew what was in their hearts, and He sent down *As-Sakīnah* (calmness and tranquillity) upon them, and He rewarded them with a near victory.

(Qur'ân 48: 18)

In the year 6 H, the Messenger of Allâh ﷺ set out with 1400 Muslims with the intention of performing the minor pilgrimage (*'Umrah*) to Makkah. He ﷺ took along with him 70 animals that were to be sacrificed; he ﷺ put distinguishing marks on them, so that people would know that they were designated for later sacrifice and would consequently avoid slaughtering them for immediate consumption. A number of Bedouins and hypocrites remained behind from the pilgrimage.

$$﴿سَيَقُولُ لَكَ ٱلْمُخَلَّفُونَ مِنَ ٱلْأَعْرَابِ شَغَلَتْنَا أَمْوَٰلُنَا وَأَهْلُونَا فَٱسْتَغْفِرْ لَنَا يَقُولُونَ بِأَلْسِنَتِهِم مَّا لَيْسَ فِي قُلُوبِهِمْ قُلْ فَمَن يَمْلِكُ لَكُم مِّنَ ٱللَّهِ شَيْئًا إِنْ أَرَادَ بِكُمْ ضَرًّا أَوْ أَرَادَ بِكُمْ نَفْعًا بَلْ كَانَ ٱللَّهُ بِمَا تَعْمَلُونَ خَبِيرًا ١١ بَلْ ظَنَنتُمْ أَن لَّن يَنقَلِبَ ٱلرَّسُولُ وَٱلْمُؤْمِنُونَ إِلَىٰ أَهْلِيهِمْ أَبَدًا وَزُيِّنَ ذَٰلِكَ فِي قُلُوبِكُمْ وَظَنَنتُمْ ظَنَّ ٱلسَّوْءِ وَكُنتُمْ قَوْمًا بُورًا ١٢ وَمَن لَّمْ يُؤْمِنۢ بِٱللَّهِ وَرَسُولِهِ فَإِنَّا أَعْتَدْنَا لِلْكَٰفِرِينَ سَعِيرًا ١٣﴾$$

Those of the bedouins who lagged behind will say to you: "Our possessions and our families occupied us, so ask

300

forgiveness for us.'' They say with their tongues what is not in their hearts. Say: "Who then has any power at all (to intervene) on your behalf with Allāh, if He intends you hurt or intends you benefit? Nay, but Allāh is Ever Well-Acquainted with what you do. Nay, but you thought that the Messenger (ﷺ) and the believers would never return to their families, and that was made fair-seeming in your hearts, and you did think an evil thought and you became a useless people going for destruction.'' And whosoever does not believe in Allāh and His Messenger (Muhammad ﷺ), then verily, We have prepared for the disbelievers a blazing Fire.

(Qur'ân 48: 11-13)

Not going to fight but instead to perform pilgrimage, the Prophet ﷺ and his Companions ؓ carried no weapons for war, only simple knives or swords that were commonly needed and carried by travelers.

When they came near to Makkah, the Muslims set camp at a place called Al-Hudaibiyah. After emissaries from the Quraish came to negotiate terms with the Prophet ﷺ, 'Uthmân ibn 'Affân ؓ entered Makkah as an emissary of the Muslims. Somehow, it became a widespread though untrue notion that the Quraish had killed 'Uthmân ؓ. Due to the news of the possible treachery, the Muslims gave the famous pledge of Ar-Ridwân under the tree: Either Victory (conquest of Makkah) or Martyrdom.' But when it was established that 'Uthmân ؓ was unharmed and that the Quraish wanted to sign a peace pact, the way became paved for the Treaty of Al-Hudaibiyah.

﴿وَلَوْ قَاتَلَكُمُ ٱلَّذِينَ كَفَرُواْ لَوَلَّوُاْ ٱلْأَدْبَٰرَ ثُمَّ لَا يَجِدُونَ وَلِيًّا وَلَا نَصِيرًا ۝ سُنَّةَ ٱللَّهِ ٱلَّتِي قَدْ خَلَتْ مِن قَبْلُ وَلَن تَجِدَ لِسُنَّةِ ٱللَّهِ تَبْدِيلًا ۝ وَهُوَ ٱلَّذِى كَفَّ أَيْدِيَهُمْ عَنكُمْ وَأَيْدِيَكُمْ عَنْهُم بِبَطْنِ مَكَّةَ مِنۢ بَعْدِ أَنْ أَظْفَرَكُمْ عَلَيْهِمْ وَكَانَ ٱللَّهُ بِمَا تَعْمَلُونَ بَصِيرًا ۝﴾

And if those who disbelieve fight against you, they certainly will turn their backs; then they would have found neither a Walī (protector, guardian) nor a helper. That has been the way of Allāh already with those who passed away before. And you

301

will not find any change in the way of Allāh. And He it is Who has withheld their hands from you and your hands from them in the midst of Makkah, after He had made you victors over them. And Allāh is Ever All-Seer of what you do.

(Qur'ân 48: 22-24)

بِسْمِ اللَّهِ الرَّحْمَٰنِ الرَّحِيمِ ۝ إِنَّ ٱلَّذِينَ يُبَايِعُونَكَ إِنَّمَا يُبَايِعُونَ ٱللَّهَ يَدُ ٱللَّهِ فَوْقَ أَيْدِيهِمْ فَمَن نَّكَثَ فَإِنَّمَا يَنكُثُ عَلَىٰ نَفْسِهِۦ وَمَنْ أَوْفَىٰ بِمَا عَٰهَدَ عَلَيْهُ ٱللَّهَ فَسَيُؤْتِيهِ أَجْرًا عَظِيمًا ۝ سَيَقُولُ لَكَ ٱلْمُخَلَّفُونَ مِنَ ٱلْأَعْرَابِ شَغَلَتْنَآ أَمْوَٰلُنَا وَأَهْلُونَا فَٱسْتَغْفِرْ لَنَا يَقُولُونَ بِأَلْسِنَتِهِم مَّا لَيْسَ فِى قُلُوبِهِمْ قُلْ فَمَن يَمْلِكُ لَكُم مِّنَ ٱللَّهِ شَيْـًٔا إِنْ أَرَادَ بِكُمْ ضَرًّا أَوْ أَرَادَ بِكُمْ نَفْعًا بَلْ كَانَ ٱللَّهُ بِمَا تَعْمَلُونَ خَبِيرًا ۝ بَلْ ظَنَنتُمْ أَن لَّن يَنقَلِبَ ٱلرَّسُولُ وَٱلْمُؤْمِنُونَ إِلَىٰٓ أَهْلِيهِمْ أَبَدًا وَزُيِّنَ ذَٰلِكَ فِى قُلُوبِكُمْ وَظَنَنتُمْ ظَنَّ ٱلسَّوْءِ وَكُنتُمْ قَوْمًۢا بُورًا ۝ وَمَن لَّمْ يُؤْمِنۢ بِٱللَّهِ وَرَسُولِهِۦ فَإِنَّآ أَعْتَدْنَا لِلْكَٰفِرِينَ سَعِيرًا ۝ وَلِلَّهِ مُلْكُ ٱلسَّمَٰوَٰتِ وَٱلْأَرْضِ يَغْفِرُ لِمَن يَشَآءُ وَيُعَذِّبُ مَن يَشَآءُ وَكَانَ ٱللَّهُ غَفُورًا رَّحِيمًا ۝ سَيَقُولُ ٱلْمُخَلَّفُونَ إِذَا ٱنطَلَقْتُمْ إِلَىٰ مَغَانِمَ لِتَأْخُذُوهَا ذَرُونَا نَتَّبِعْكُمْ يُرِيدُونَ أَن يُبَدِّلُوا۟ كَلَٰمَ ٱللَّهِ قُل لَّن تَتَّبِعُونَا كَذَٰلِكُمْ قَالَ ٱللَّهُ مِن قَبْلُ فَسَيَقُولُونَ بَلْ تَحْسُدُونَنَا بَلْ كَانُوا۟ لَا يَفْقَهُونَ إِلَّا قَلِيلًا ۝ قُل لِّلْمُخَلَّفِينَ مِنَ ٱلْأَعْرَابِ سَتُدْعَوْنَ إِلَىٰ قَوْمٍ أُو۟لِى بَأْسٍ شَدِيدٍ تُقَٰتِلُونَهُمْ أَوْ يُسْلِمُونَ فَإِن تُطِيعُوا۟ يُؤْتِكُمُ ٱللَّهُ أَجْرًا حَسَنًا وَإِن تَتَوَلَّوْا۟ كَمَا تَوَلَّيْتُم مِّن قَبْلُ يُعَذِّبْكُمْ عَذَابًا أَلِيمًا ۝ لَّيْسَ عَلَى ٱلْأَعْمَىٰ حَرَجٌ وَلَا عَلَى ٱلْأَعْرَجِ حَرَجٌ وَلَا عَلَى ٱلْمَرِيضِ حَرَجٌ وَمَن يُطِعِ ٱللَّهَ وَرَسُولَهُۥ يُدْخِلْهُ جَنَّٰتٍ تَجْرِى مِن تَحْتِهَا ٱلْأَنْهَٰرُ وَمَن يَتَوَلَّ يُعَذِّبْهُ عَذَابًا أَلِيمًا ۝ لَّقَدْ رَضِىَ ٱللَّهُ عَنِ ٱلْمُؤْمِنِينَ إِذْ يُبَايِعُونَكَ تَحْتَ ٱلشَّجَرَةِ فَعَلِمَ مَا فِى قُلُوبِهِمْ فَأَنزَلَ ٱلسَّكِينَةَ عَلَيْهِمْ وَأَثَٰبَهُمْ فَتْحًا قَرِيبًا ۝

Verily, those who give *Bai'ah* (pledge) to you (O Muhammad ﷺ), they are giving *Bai'ah* (pledge) to Allāh. The Hand of Allāh is over their hands. Then whosoever breaks his pledge, breaks it only to his own harm; and whosoever fulfils what he has covenanted with Allāh, He will bestow on him a great reward. Those of the bedouins who lagged behind will say to you: "Our possessions and our families occupied us, so ask forgiveness for us." They say with their tongues what is not in their hearts. Say: "Who then has any power at all (to intervene) on your behalf with Allāh, if He intends you hurt or intends you benefit? Nay, but Allāh is Ever Well-Acquainted with what you do. "Nay, but you thought that the Messenger (ﷺ) and the believers would never return to their families, and that was made fair-seeming in your hearts, and you did think an evil thought and you became a useless people going for destruction." And whosoever does not believe in Allāh and His Messenger (Muhammad ﷺ), then verily, We have prepared for the disbelievers a blazing Fire. And to Allāh belongs the sovereignty of the heavens and the earth. He forgives whom He wills, and punishes whom He wills. And Allāh is Ever Oft-Forgiving, Most Merciful. Those who lagged behind will say, when you set forth to take the spoils, "Allow us to follow you." They want to change Allāh's Words. Say: "You shall not follow us; thus Allāh has said beforehand." Then they will say: "Nay, you envy us." Nay, but they understand not except a little. Say (O Muhammad ﷺ) to the bedouins who lagged behind: "You shall be called to fight against a people given to great warfare, then you shall fight them, or they shall surrender. Then if you obey, Allāh will give you a fair reward; but if you turn away as you did turn away before, He will punish you with a painful torment." No blame or sin is there upon the blind, nor is there blame or sin upon the lame, nor is there blame or sin upon the sick (that they go not for fighting). And whosoever obeys Allāh and His Messenger (Muhammad ﷺ), He will admit him to Gardens beneath which rivers flow (Paradise); and whosoever turns back, He will punish him with a painful torment. Indeed, Allāh was pleased with the believers when they gave the *Bai'ah* (pledge) to you (O Muhammad ﷺ) under the tree, He knew what was in their hearts, and He sent down *As-Sakīnah* (calmness and tranquillity) upon them, and He rewarded them with a near victory.

(Qur'ân 48: 10-18)

﴿وَهُوَ ٱلَّذِى كَفَّ أَيْدِيَهُمْ عَنكُمْ وَأَيْدِيَكُمْ عَنْهُم بِبَطْنِ مَكَّةَ مِنۢ بَعْدِ أَنْ أَظْفَرَكُمْ عَلَيْهِمْ وَكَانَ ٱللَّهُ بِمَا تَعْمَلُونَ بَصِيرًا ﴿٢٤﴾ هُمُ ٱلَّذِينَ كَفَرُوا۟ وَصَدُّوكُمْ عَنِ ٱلْمَسْجِدِ ٱلْحَرَامِ وَٱلْهَدْىَ مَعْكُوفًا أَن يَبْلُغَ مَحِلَّهُۥ وَلَوْلَا رِجَالٌ مُّؤْمِنُونَ وَنِسَآءٌ مُّؤْمِنَٰتٌ لَّمْ تَعْلَمُوهُمْ أَن تَطَـُٔوهُمْ فَتُصِيبَكُم مِّنْهُم مَّعَرَّةٌ بِغَيْرِ عِلْمٍ لِّيُدْخِلَ ٱللَّهُ فِى رَحْمَتِهِۦ مَن يَشَآءُ لَوْ تَزَيَّلُوا۟ لَعَذَّبْنَا ٱلَّذِينَ كَفَرُوا۟ مِنْهُمْ عَذَابًا أَلِيمًا ﴿٢٥﴾ إِذْ جَعَلَ ٱلَّذِينَ كَفَرُوا۟ فِى قُلُوبِهِمُ ٱلْحَمِيَّةَ حَمِيَّةَ ٱلْجَٰهِلِيَّةِ فَأَنزَلَ ٱللَّهُ سَكِينَتَهُۥ عَلَىٰ رَسُولِهِۦ وَعَلَى ٱلْمُؤْمِنِينَ وَأَلْزَمَهُمْ كَلِمَةَ ٱلتَّقْوَىٰ وَكَانُوٓا۟ أَحَقَّ بِهَا وَأَهْلَهَا وَكَانَ ٱللَّهُ بِكُلِّ شَىْءٍ عَلِيمًا ﴿٢٦﴾ لَّقَدْ صَدَقَ ٱللَّهُ رَسُولَهُ ٱلرُّءْيَا بِٱلْحَقِّ لَتَدْخُلُنَّ ٱلْمَسْجِدَ ٱلْحَرَامَ إِن شَآءَ ٱللَّهُ ءَامِنِينَ مُحَلِّقِينَ رُءُوسَكُمْ وَمُقَصِّرِينَ لَا تَخَافُونَ فَعَلِمَ مَا لَمْ تَعْلَمُوا۟ فَجَعَلَ مِن دُونِ ذَٰلِكَ فَتْحًا قَرِيبًا ﴿٢٧﴾ هُوَ ٱلَّذِىٓ أَرْسَلَ رَسُولَهُۥ بِٱلْهُدَىٰ وَدِينِ ٱلْحَقِّ لِيُظْهِرَهُۥ عَلَى ٱلدِّينِ كُلِّهِۦ وَكَفَىٰ بِٱللَّهِ شَهِيدًا ﴿٢٨﴾ ﴾

And He it is Who has withheld their hands from you and your hands from them in the midst of Makkah, after He had made you victors over them. And Allāh is Ever All-Seer of what you do. They are the ones who disbelieved (in the Oneness of Allāh — Islamic Monotheism) and hindered you from *Al-Masjid Al-Harām* (at Makkah) and detained the sacrificial animals, from reaching their place of sacrifice. Had there not been believing men and believing women whom you did not know, that you may kill them and on whose account a sin would have been committed by you without (your) knowledge, that Allāh might bring into His Mercy whom He wills — if they (the believers and the disbelievers) had been apart, We verily, would have punished those of them who disbelieved with painful torment. When those who disbelieve had put in their hearts pride and haughtiness — the pride and haughtiness of the time of ignorance, — then Allāh sent down His *Sakīnah* (calmness and tranquillity) upon His Messenger (ﷺ) and upon the believers, and made them stick to the word of piety (i.e. none has the right to be worshipped but Allāh); and they were well entitled to it and worthy of it. And Allāh is Ever All-Knower of everything. Indeed Allāh shall fulfil the true vision which He showed to His Messenger (ﷺ) [i.e. the Prophet ﷺ saw a dream that he has entered Makkah along with his Companions, having their (head) hair shaved and cut short] in very truth. Certainly, you shall enter *Al-Masjid Al-Harām*, if Allāh wills, secure, (some) having your heads shaved, and (some) having your head hair cut short, having no fear. He knew what you knew not, and He granted before that a near victory. He it is Who has sent His Messenger (Muhammad ﷺ) with guidance and the religion of truth (Islam), that He may make it (Islam) superior to all religions. And All-Sufficient is Allāh as a Witness.

(Qur'ân 48: 24-28)

- Ibn Khaldun: 2/34
- Ibn Hisham: 3/201
- Al-Bidayah wan-Nihayah: 4/174
- Ar-Raud Al-Unuf: 4/38
- At-Tabari: 2/627
- 'Uyun Al-Athar: 2/117

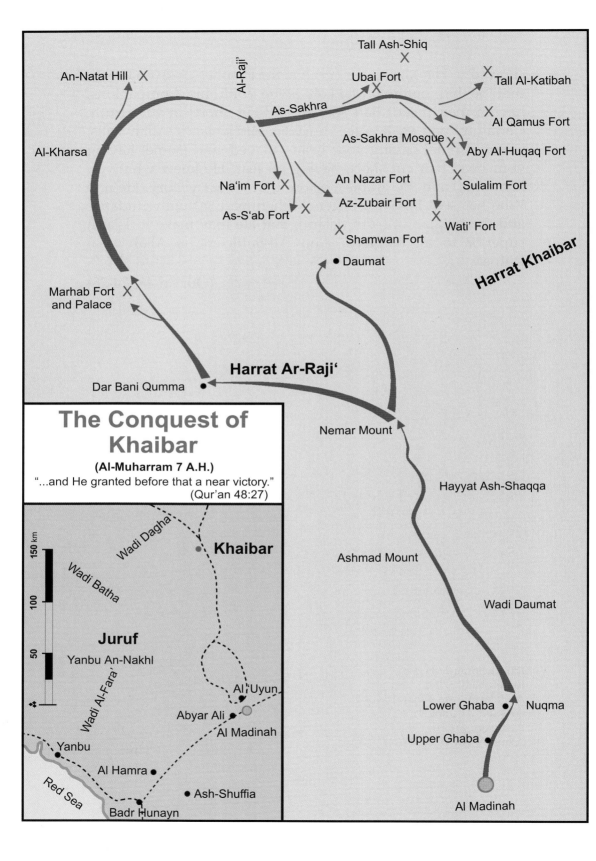

The Conquest of Khaibar
(Al-Muharram 7 A.H.)
"...and He granted before that a near victory."
(Qur'an 48:27)

Khaibar
(Al-Muharram, 7 H)

﴿لَّقَدْ رَضِيَ ٱللَّهُ عَنِ ٱلْمُؤْمِنِينَ إِذْ يُبَايِعُونَكَ تَحْتَ ٱلشَّجَرَةِ فَعَلِمَ مَا فِي قُلُوبِهِمْ فَأَنزَلَ ٱلسَّكِينَةَ عَلَيْهِمْ وَأَثَبَهُمْ فَتْحًا قَرِيبًا ۝ وَمَغَانِمَ كَثِيرَةً يَأْخُذُونَهَا وَكَانَ ٱللَّهُ عَزِيزًا حَكِيمًا ۝﴾

Indeed, Allāh was pleased with the believers when they gave the *Bai'ah* (pledge) to you (O Muhammad ﷺ) under the tree, He knew what was in their hearts, and He sent down *As-Sakīnah* (calmness and tranquillity) upon them, and He rewarded them with a near victory. And abundant spoils that they will capture. And Allāh is Ever All-Mighty, All-Wise.

(Qur'ân 48: 18, 19)

﴿لَّقَدْ صَدَقَ ٱللَّهُ رَسُولَهُ ٱلرُّؤْيَا بِٱلْحَقِّ لَتَدْخُلُنَّ ٱلْمَسْجِدَ ٱلْحَرَامَ إِن شَاءَ ٱللَّهُ ءَامِنِينَ مُحَلِّقِينَ رُءُوسَكُمْ وَمُقَصِّرِينَ لَا تَخَافُونَ فَعَلِمَ مَا لَمْ تَعْلَمُوا فَجَعَلَ مِن دُونِ ذَٰلِكَ فَتْحًا قَرِيبًا ۝﴾

Indeed Allāh shall fulfil the true vision which He showed to His Messenger (ﷺ) [i.e., the Prophet ﷺ saw a dream that he has entered Makkah along with his Companions, having their (head) hair shaved and cut short] in very truth. Certainly, you shall enter *Al-Masjid Al-Harām*, if Allāh wills, secure, (some) having your heads shaved, and (some) having your head hair cut short, having no fear. He knew what you knew not, and He granted before that a near victory.

(Qur'ân 48: 27)

The Jews of Khaibar contacted the people of the Ghatafân tribe, who were known to be mercenaries for hire. As a reward for fighting the Muslims, the Jews of Khaibar offered them a percentage of their yearly harvest, which consisted mainly of fruits and dates. They furthermore established alliances with the tribes of Fadak, Taima'

307

and Wâdi Al-Qura; together, they were to launch a surprise attack on Al-Madinah. Having been informed of their plans, the Muslims who witnessed Al-Hudaibiyah traveled to Khaibar, in order to bring an end to the plotting of its inhabitants and their allies.

Khaibar consisted of many fortresses, the most important of which were the following:

- An-Natât, which was made up of the Nâ'im, As-Sa'b, and Qillah fortresses.

- Ash-Shiq, which was made up of the Ubai and Al-Bary fortresses.

- Al-Katibah, which was made up of the Al-Qamus, Al-Watih, and As-Sulâlim fortresses.

Nâ'im was the first fortress to be overtaken by the Muslims, and Al-Qamus was the greatest and most formidable of Khaibar's fortresses. As for the Al-Watih and As-Sulâlim fortresses, they were surrendered peacefully. According to the pact that was agreed upon, Khaibar remained in the hands of its inhabitants, on the condition that the Muslims were to receive one-half of the harvest of all planting and date trees.

- Ibn Hisham: 3/217
- Al-Bidayah wan-Nihayah: 4/198
- At-Tabari: 3/14
- 'Uyun Al-Athar: 2/138

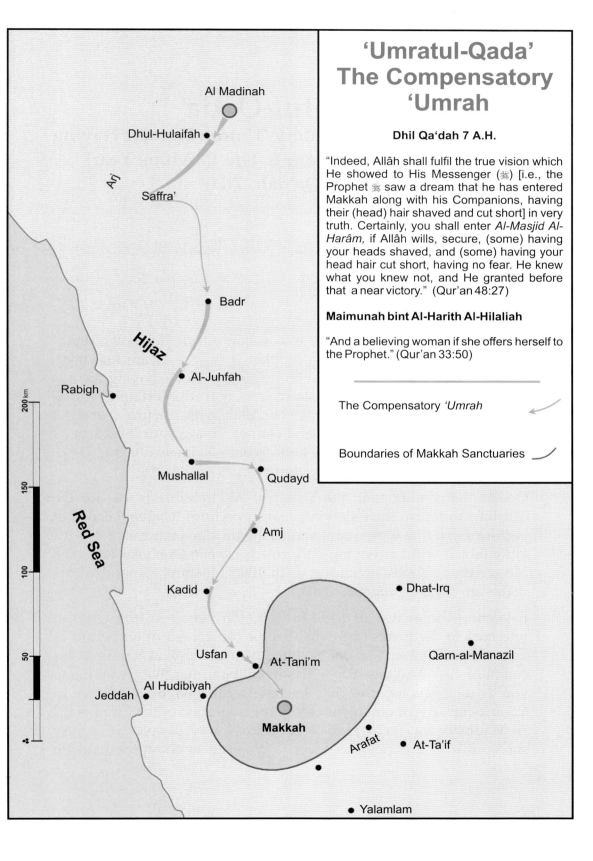

'Umratul-Qada'
The Compensatory
'Umrah

Dhil Qa'dah 7 A.H.

"Indeed, Allâh shall fulfil the true vision which He showed to His Messenger (ﷺ) [i.e., the Prophet ﷺ saw a dream that he has entered Makkah along with his Companions, having their (head) hair shaved and cut short] in very truth. Certainly, you shall enter *Al-Masjid Al-Harâm,* if Allâh wills, secure, (some) having your heads shaved, and (some) having your head hair cut short, having no fear. He knew what you knew not, and He granted before that a near victory." (Qur'an 48:27)

Maimunah bint Al-Harith Al-Hilaliah

"And a believing woman if she offers herself to the Prophet." (Qur'an 33:50)

The Compensatory 'Umrah

Boundaries of Makkah Sanctuaries

Al Madinah

Dhul-Hulaifah

Arj

Saffra'

Badr

Hijaz

Al-Juhfah

Rabigh

200 km

Mushallal

Qudayd

150

Red Sea

Amj

100

Kadid

Dhat-Irq

50

Usfan

At-Tani'm

Qarn-al-Manazil

Al Hudibiyah

Jeddah

Makkah

Arafat

At-Ta'if

Yalamlam

'Umratul-Qada'
(Make-Up or Compensatory 'Umrah For Not Having Been Able To Perform It The Previous Year)
(Dhil-Qa'dah, 7 H)

﴿لَّقَدْ صَدَقَ ٱللَّهُ رَسُولَهُ ٱلرُّءْيَا بِٱلْحَقِّ لَتَدْخُلُنَّ ٱلْمَسْجِدَ ٱلْحَرَامَ إِن شَآءَ ٱللَّهُ ءَامِنِينَ مُحَلِّقِينَ رُءُوسَكُمْ وَمُقَصِّرِينَ لَا تَخَافُونَ فَعَلِمَ مَا لَمْ تَعْلَمُواْ فَجَعَلَ مِن دُونِ ذَٰلِكَ فَتْحًا قَرِيبًا ٢٧﴾

Indeed Allāh shall fulfil the true vision which He showed to His Messenger (ﷺ) [i.e., the Prophet ﷺ saw a dream that he has entered Makkah along with his Companions, having their (head) hair shaved and cut short] in very truth. Certainly, you shall enter *Al-Masjid Al-Harām*, if Allāh wills, secure, (some) having your heads shaved, and (some) having your head hair cut short, having no fear. He knew what you knew not, and He granted before that a near victory.

One of the conditions of the Treaty of Al-Hudaibiyah was for the Muslims to return the following year to perform *'Umrah*, instead of performing it that same year. And so the Muslims returned from Al-Hudaibiyah without having performed *'Umrah*. One year later, the Messenger of Allāh ﷺ set out with 1000 Muslims to perform the make-up *'Umrah* (*'Umratul-Qada'*).

Expecting the arrival of the Muslims, the people of the Quraish retreated to the peaks of mountains for the agreed upon period of three days. They said to one another, "Do not look at him or at his companions." And they began to spread the rumor that, "Coming to you is a delegation that has become weakened by the fever of Yathrib (i.e., Al-Madinah, for before the migration of the Prophet ﷺ, Al-Madinah was known to be a place where people were very susceptible to a dangerous fever)." Wanting to show the Quraish that the Muslims were not weak but strong and energetic, the Prophet ﷺ ordered each Muslim man to lay bare one of his shoulders, and he ﷺ also instructed them to perform a light jog around the Ka'bah for the first three of the seven prescribed circuits. He ﷺ said, "May Allâh have mercy on the one who shows them his strength today."

After difficult wars – Badr, Uhud, and Al-Khandaq – and after the victory at Khaibar, the Muslims entered Makkah with the highest imaginable level of dignity and honor. And in accordance with the Treaty of Al-Hudaibiyah, the Messenger of Allâh ﷺ remained in Makkah for three days only.

The showing that the Muslims gave to the Quraish – who were looking upon them from the peaks of mountains and hills – on that occasion had a strong effect on one of the noble women of Makkah Maimunah bint Al-Hârith Al-Hilâliyyah ﵁; the effect on her was such that she yearned to marry the Prophet ﷺ. She was twenty-six years old at the time, and her husband, Abu Ruhm ibn 'Abdul-'Uzza Al-Qurashi, had recently died. She went to her sister Umm Al-Fadl, the wife of Al-'Abbâs, to tell her about her feelings. Al-'Abbâs conveyed Maimunah's proposal, saying, "She has offered herself to the Prophet." Allâh ﷻ then revealed the following Verse about her:

﴿يَٰٓأَيُّهَا ٱلنَّبِىُّ إِنَّآ أَحۡلَلۡنَا لَكَ أَزۡوَٰجَكَ ٱلَّٰتِىٓ ءَاتَيۡتَ أُجُورَهُنَّ وَمَا مَلَكَتۡ يَمِينُكَ مِمَّآ أَفَآءَ ٱللَّهُ عَلَيۡكَ وَبَنَاتِ عَمِّكَ وَبَنَاتِ عَمَّٰتِكَ وَبَنَاتِ خَالِكَ وَبَنَاتِ خَٰلَٰتِكَ ٱلَّٰتِى هَاجَرۡنَ مَعَكَ وَٱمۡرَأَةً مُّؤۡمِنَةً إِن وَهَبَتۡ نَفۡسَهَا لِلنَّبِىِّ إِنۡ أَرَادَ ٱلنَّبِىُّ أَن يَسۡتَنكِحَهَا خَالِصَةً لَّكَ مِن دُونِ ٱلۡمُؤۡمِنِينَ قَدۡ عَلِمۡنَا مَا فَرَضۡنَا عَلَيۡهِمۡ فِىٓ أَزۡوَٰجِهِمۡ وَمَا مَلَكَتۡ أَيۡمَٰنُهُمۡ لِكَيۡلَا يَكُونَ عَلَيۡكَ حَرَجٌ وَكَانَ ٱللَّهُ غَفُورًا رَّحِيمًا ٥٠﴾

O Prophet (Muhammad ﷺ)! Verily, We have made lawful to you your wives, to whom you have paid their *Mahr* (bridal-money given by the husband to his wife at the time of marriage), and those (slaves) whom your right hand possesses — whom Allāh has given to you, and the daughters of your *'Amm* (paternal uncles) and the daughters of your *'Ammāt* (paternal aunts) and the daughters of your *Khāl* (maternal uncles) and the daughters of your *Khālāt* (maternal aunts) who migrated (from Makkah) with you, and a believing woman if she offers herself to the Prophet (ﷺ), and the Prophet (ﷺ) wishes to marry her — a privilege for you only, not for the (rest of) the believers. Indeed We know what We have enjoined upon them about their wives and those (slaves) whom their right hands possess, in order that there should be no difficulty on you. And Allāh is Ever Oft-Forgiving, Most Merciful.

(Qur'ân 33: 50)

The Prophet ﷺ then married her and took her back with him to Al-Madinah.

- Al-Bidayah wan-Nihayah: 4/220
- At-Tabari: 3/22
- 'Uyun Al-Athar: 2/145

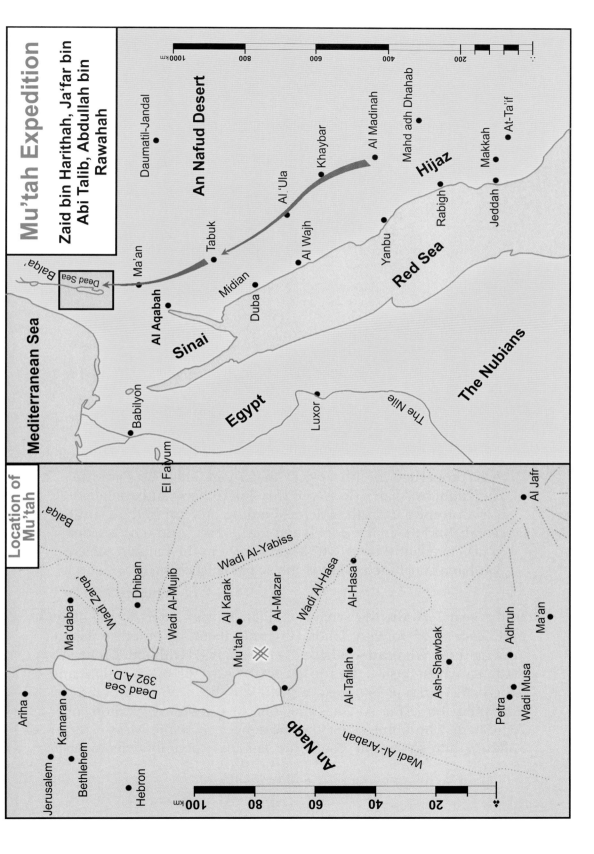

Mu'tah Expedition

Zaid bin Harithah, Ja'far bin Abi Talib, Abdullah bin Rawahah

An Nafud Desert

Daumatil-Jandal

Khaybar

Al 'Ula

Al Madinah

Mahd adh Dhahab

Hijaz

Tabuk

Ma'an

Al Wajh

Midian

Rabigh

Makkah

At-Ta'if

Jeddah

Yanbu

Red Sea

Duba

Al Aqabah

Sinai

Dead Sea

Balqa'

Mediterranean Sea

Babilyon

El Fayum

Egypt

Luxor

The Nile

The Nubians

1000 km
800
600
400
200

Location of Mu'tah

Balqa'

Ariha

Kamaran

Ma'daba

Dhiban

Wadi Zarqa'

Dead Sea 392 A.D.

Wadi Al-Mujib

Wadi Al-Yabiss

Jerusalem

Bethlehem

Hebron

Al Karak

Mu'tah

Al-Mazar

Wadi Al-Hasa

Al-Hasa

Al-Tafilah

Ash-Shawbak

Petra

Adhruh

Wadi Musa

Ma'an

Al Jafr

An Naqb

Wadi Al-'Arabah

100 km
80
60
40
20

Mu'tah Expetition

The Army Of The Umarâ' (Leaders)
(Jumâda Al-Ulah, 8 H)

﴿إِنَّ اللَّهَ اشْتَرَى مِنَ الْمُؤْمِنِينَ أَنفُسَهُمْ وَأَمْوَلَهُم بِأَنَّ لَهُمُ الْجَنَّةَ يُقَٰتِلُونَ فِى سَبِيلِ اللَّهِ فَيَقْتُلُونَ وَيُقْتَلُونَ وَعْدًا عَلَيْهِ حَقًّا فِى التَّوْرَىٰةِ وَالْإِنجِيلِ وَالْقُرْءَانِ وَمَنْ أَوْفَىٰ بِعَهْدِهِ مِنَ اللَّهِ فَاسْتَبْشِرُوا بِبَيْعِكُمُ الَّذِى بَايَعْتُم بِهِۦ وَذَٰلِكَ هُوَ الْفَوْزُ الْعَظِيمُ ﴿١١١﴾﴾

Verily, Allāh has purchased of the believers their lives and their properties for (the price) that theirs shall be Paradise. They fight in Allāh's Cause, so they kill (others) and are killed. It is a promise in truth which is binding on Him in the Taurāt (Torah) and the Injīl (Gospel) and the Qur'ān. And who is truer to his covenant than Allāh? Then rejoice in the bargain which you have concluded. That is the supreme success.

(Qur'ân 9: 111)

In the year 7 H, the Messenger of Allâh ﷺ sent letters to the kings and leaders of foreign lands, inviting them to embrace Islam. Among those who carried those letters was Al-Hârith ibn 'Umair Al-Azdi ؓ, whose task it was to go to the king of Busra Ash-Sham. When Al-Hârith ؓ stopped at Mu'tah, he was confronted by Shurahbil ibn 'Amr Al-Ghassâni, one of Caesar's governors over Ash-Sham. Shurahbil killed the messenger ؓ of the Messenger of Allâh ﷺ, and so the purpose of the Mu'tah expedition was to teach

Shurahbil Al-Ghassâni a lesson.

The Prophet ﷺ assembled an army that consisted of 3000 fighters, and he ﷺ appointed Zaid ibn Hârithah ؓ to be their leader. The Prophet ﷺ knew that it was going to be a dangerous mission, for they were fighting the Romans and not just a small tribe; and so he explained that if Zaid ؓ were to die, then Ja'far ibn Abi Tâlib ؓ should take his place as leader; and that if Ja'far ؓ were to die, then 'Abdullah ibn Rawâhah ؓ should take his place.

The Army of *Al-'Umara'* (Leaders) then marched towards Mu'tah. In terms of numbers, the Muslim army was certainly not an equal match for the opposing army. The Romans were able to assemble in Mut'ah an army of 100,000 fighters, while the Muslim army consisted of a mere 3000 fighters. The battle began, and after the three appointed leaders all were martyred, the banner of leadership was handed over to the 'Sword of Allâh,' Khâlid ibn Al-Walid ؓ, who was able to realize a safe retreat, without suffering any more losses.

Had it not been for the skillful retreat, the entire army would have been destroyed. But when they returned to Al-Madinah, the Muslims said to them, "O you who have taken flight: you have fled (when it was time to fight) in the way of Allâh." Coming to their defense, the Prophet ﷺ then said, "Rather, you are ones who have retreated, and I am your troop [referring to the following verse: "And whoever turns his back to them on such a day unless it be a stratagem of war, or to retreat to a troop (of his own)"]."

﴿وَمَن يُوَلِّهِمْ يَوْمَئِذٍ دُبُرَهُ إِلَّا مُتَحَرِّفًا لِقِتَالٍ أَوْ مُتَحَيِّزًا إِلَىٰ فِئَةٍ فَقَدْ بَآءَ بِغَضَبٍ مِّنَ ٱللَّهِ وَمَأْوَىٰهُ جَهَنَّمُ وَبِئْسَ ٱلْمَصِيرُ ۝ فَلَمْ تَقْتُلُوهُمْ وَلَٰكِنَّ ٱللَّهَ قَتَلَهُمْ وَمَا رَمَيْتَ إِذْ رَمَيْتَ وَلَٰكِنَّ ٱللَّهَ رَمَىٰ وَلِيُبْلِىَ ٱلْمُؤْمِنِينَ مِنْهُ بَلَآءً حَسَنًا إِنَّ ٱللَّهَ سَمِيعٌ عَلِيمٌ ۝﴾

And whoever turns his back to them on such a day — unless it be a stratagem of war, or to retreat to a troop (of his own), — he indeed has drawn upon himself wrath from Allāh. And his abode is Hell, and worst indeed is that destination! You killed them not, but Allāh killed them. And you (Muhammad ﷺ) threw not when you did throw, but Allāh threw, that He might test the believers by a fair trial from Him. Verily, Allāh is All-Hearer, All-Knower.

(Qur'ân 8: 16, 17)

- Ibn Khaldun: 2/40
- Ibn Sa'd: 1/341, 2/128, 3/234
- Ibn Hishâm: 4/8
- At-Tabari: 3/38
- Al-Kâmil Fit-Târikh: 2/158
- 'Uyun Al-Athar: 2/153

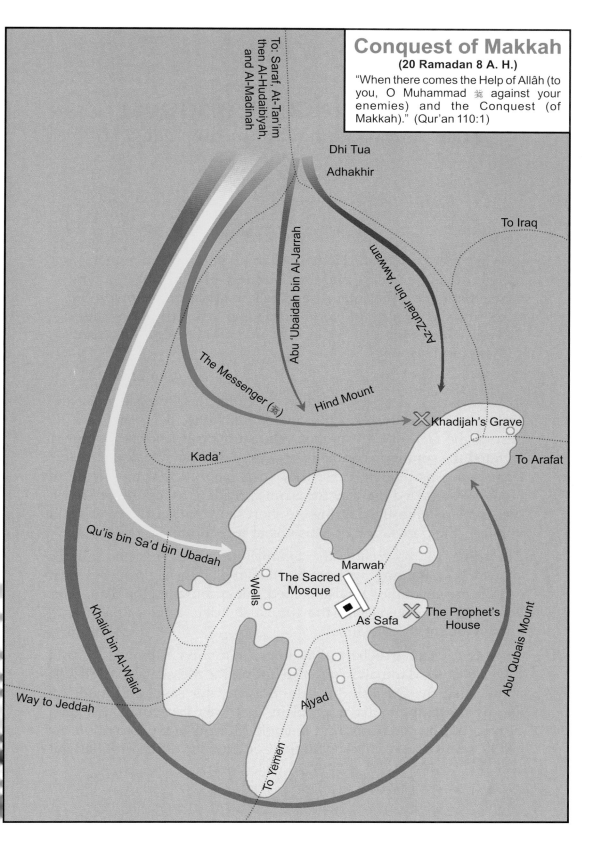

Conquest of Makkah
(20 Ramadan 8 A. H.)

"When there comes the Help of Allâh (to you, O Muhammad ﷺ against your enemies) and the Conquest (of Makkah)." (Qur'an 110:1)

To: Saraf, At-Tan'im then Al-Hudaibiyah, and Al-Madinah

Dhi Tua

Adhakhir

To Iraq

Abu 'Ubaidah bin Al-Jarrah

Az-Zubair bin 'Awwam

The Messenger (ﷺ)

Hind Mount

Khadijah's Grave

Kada'

To Arafat

Qu'is bin Sa'd bin Ubadah

Marwah

The Sacred Mosque

Wells

As Safa

The Prophet's House

Abu Qubais Mount

Khalid bin Al-Walid

Way to Jeddah

Ajyad

To Yemen

The Makkah Conquest
(The 10th of Ramadan, in the year 8 H)

﴿إِذَا جَاءَ نَصْرُ ٱللَّهِ وَٱلْفَتْحُ ١ وَرَأَيْتَ ٱلنَّاسَ يَدْخُلُونَ فِي دِينِ ٱللَّهِ أَفْوَاجًا ٢ فَسَبِّحْ بِحَمْدِ رَبِّكَ وَٱسْتَغْفِرْهُ إِنَّهُ كَانَ تَوَّابًا ٣﴾

When there comes the Help of Allāh (to you, O Muhammad ﷺ against your enemies) and the Conquest (of Makkah). And you see that the people enter Allāh's religion (Islam) in crowds. So, glorify the Praises of your Lord, and ask His forgiveness. Verily, He is the One Who Ever accepts the repentance and Who forgives.

(Qur'ân 110:1-3)

In what was a clear and blatant violation, the Quraish broke the Treaty of Hudaibiyah on the 8th of Ramadan, 8 H; they did so despite the fact that it was they who stubbornly and peremptorily dictated the conditions of the treaty. Why did they break the treaty? Perhaps it was hindsight, for they soon realized that the Treaty of Hudaibiyah paved the way for Islam spreading to different tribes in the Arabian Peninsula. During the short span that the treaty was still in effect, the population of Muslims at least doubled.

According to the treaty, the Quraish promised not to fight or sponsor any fighting against the Muslims or their allies. But then certain leaders of the Quraish helped and encouraged the Banu Bakr tribe to exact revenge on the Khuza'ah tribe, a tribe that was a known ally of the Muslims.

After the act of treachery was done, 'Amr ibn Sâlim Al-Khuzâ'i traveled to Al-Madinah in order to inform the Messenger of Allâh ﷺ about what the Quraish did. Abu Sufyân later came and made an abortive attempt to fix a problem that was caused by his own people, but he could not find a single Muslim to pay attention. At last he said, "I have checked all the Companions of the Prophet, but

I have not seen any nation so submissive to its leader."

The Prophet ﷺ then decided to march towards and take control of Makkah. Hâtib ibn Abi Balta'ah ☺, a true Muslim and one of the participants of the Battle of Badr, made the mistake of trying to send news to the Quraish about the impending arrival of the Muslim army. It was a clear mistake because the Prophet ﷺ was eager to make his arrival a surprise. Regarding Hâtib's mistake, Allâh ﷻ revealed these Verses:

﴿يَٰٓأَيُّهَا ٱلَّذِينَ ءَامَنُوا۟ لَا تَتَّخِذُوا۟ عَدُوِّى وَعَدُوَّكُمْ أَوْلِيَآءَ تُلْقُونَ إِلَيْهِم بِٱلْمَوَدَّةِ وَقَدْ كَفَرُوا۟ بِمَا جَآءَكُم مِّنَ ٱلْحَقِّ يُخْرِجُونَ ٱلرَّسُولَ وَإِيَّاكُمْ أَن تُؤْمِنُوا۟ بِٱللَّهِ رَبِّكُمْ إِن كُنتُمْ خَرَجْتُمْ جِهَٰدًا فِى سَبِيلِى وَٱبْتِغَآءَ مَرْضَاتِى تُسِرُّونَ إِلَيْهِم بِٱلْمَوَدَّةِ وَأَنَا۠ أَعْلَمُ بِمَآ أَخْفَيْتُمْ وَمَآ أَعْلَنتُمْ وَمَن يَفْعَلْهُ مِنكُمْ فَقَدْ ضَلَّ سَوَآءَ ٱلسَّبِيلِ ① إِن يَثْقَفُوكُمْ يَكُونُوا۟ لَكُمْ أَعْدَآءً وَيَبْسُطُوٓا۟ إِلَيْكُمْ أَيْدِيَهُمْ وَأَلْسِنَتَهُم بِٱلسُّوٓءِ وَوَدُّوا۟ لَوْ تَكْفُرُونَ ② لَن تَنفَعَكُمْ أَرْحَامُكُمْ وَلَآ أَوْلَٰدُكُمْ يَوْمَ ٱلْقِيَٰمَةِ يَفْصِلُ بَيْنَكُمْ وَٱللَّهُ بِمَا تَعْمَلُونَ بَصِيرٌ ③﴾

O you who believe! Take not My enemies and your enemies (i.e., disbelievers and polytheists) as friends, showing affection towards them, while they have disbelieved in what has come to you of the truth (i.e., Islamic Monotheism, this Qur'ān, and Muhammad ﷺ), and have driven out the Messenger (Muhammad ﷺ) and yourselves (from your homeland) because you believe in Allāh, your Lord! If you have come forth to strive in My Cause and to seek My Good Pleasure, (then take not these disbelievers and polytheists, as your friends). You show friendship to them in secret, while I am All-Aware of what you conceal and what you reveal. And whosoever of you (Muslims) does that, then indeed he has gone (far) astray from the Straight Path. Should they gain the upper hand over you, they would behave to you as enemies, and stretch forth their hands and their tongues against you with evil, and they desire that you should disbelieve. Neither your relatives nor your children will benefit you on the Day of Resurrection (against Allāh). He will judge between you. And Allāh is All-Seer of what you do.   (Qur'ân 60: 1-3)

The Muslim army that made the journey to Makkah comprised of 10,000 Muslims, a force that was far too great for the inhabitants of Makkah to withstand. When the army reached Dhi Tuwa and Adhâkhir, the Prophet ﷺ sent Az-Zubair ibn Al-'Awâm ؓ to enter Makkah from the north; Khâlid ibn Al-Walid ؓ to enter it from the south; Qais ibn Sa'd ibn 'Ubâdah ؓ to enter it from the east; and Abu 'Ubaidah ibn Al-Jarrâh ؓ to enter it from the direction of Mount Hind, beside which the Muslims were gathered in Al-Hujun with the Prophet ﷺ.

The sheer surprise of the attack stunned the Quraish, making them feel as if they had suddenly been struck with a cold piece of iron. As the Prophet ﷺ entered Makkah as the victor on the 20th of Ramadan, 8 H, he repeatedly recited *Sûrat An-Nasr*:

﴿إِذَا جَآءَ نَصْرُ ٱللَّهِ وَٱلْفَتْحُ ۝ وَرَأَيْتَ ٱلنَّاسَ يَدْخُلُونَ فِي دِينِ ٱللَّهِ أَفْوَاجًا ۝ فَسَبِّحْ بِحَمْدِ رَبِّكَ وَٱسْتَغْفِرْهُ إِنَّهُ كَانَ تَوَّابًا ۝﴾

When there comes the Help of Allāh (to you, O Muhammad ﷺ against your enemies) and the Conquest (of Makkah). And you see that the people enter Allāh's religion (Islam) in crowds. So, glorify the Praises of your Lord, and ask His forgiveness. Verily, He is the One Who Ever accepts the repentance and Who forgives.

(Qur'ân 110: 1-3)

And as he destroyed the idols of the Quraish, he ﷺ recited this Verse:

﴿وَقُلْ جَآءَ ٱلْحَقُّ وَزَهَقَ ٱلْبَاطِلُ إِنَّ ٱلْبَاطِلَ كَانَ زَهُوقًا ۝﴾

And say: "Truth (i.e., Islamic Monotheism or this Qur'ān or *Jihād* against polytheists) has come and *Bātil* (falsehood, i.e., Satan or polytheism) has vanished. Surely, *Bātil* is ever bound to vanish."

(Qur'ân 17: 81)

The victory was significant militarily, to be sure, but it was also significant on another level as well: the Prophet ﷺ now won over the hearts of Quraish's leaders and citizens. The Quraish had tortured and oppressed the Muslims as long as they had lived in Makkah; then they drove them out, forcing them to migrate to Al-Madinah; and then they plotted and waged war against them. At first, they hid in their houses when the Prophet ﷺ entered Makkah. But then the Prophet ﷺ said, "Go forth, for you are the freed ones." After all of the enmity they showed to him, he forgave them. May the peace and blessings of Allâh be upon our Prophet, Muhammad ﷺ. The leaders and citizens of Makkah finally were satisfied, and they finally believed that Islam is the truth. Their acceptance of Islam led to the end of polytheism in the Arabian Peninusula. In the following year (9 H), delegates came from all over the Arabian Peninsula to announce their acceptance of Islam so much so that the year had its name as " the Year of Delegations".

- Ibn Khaldun: 2/42
- Ibn Sa'd: 2/135
- Ibn Hishâm: 4/30
- Al-Bidâyah wan-Nihâyah: 4/285
- At-Tabari: 3/51
- Al-Kâmil Fit-Târikh: 2/163
- 'Uyun Al-Athar: 2/167

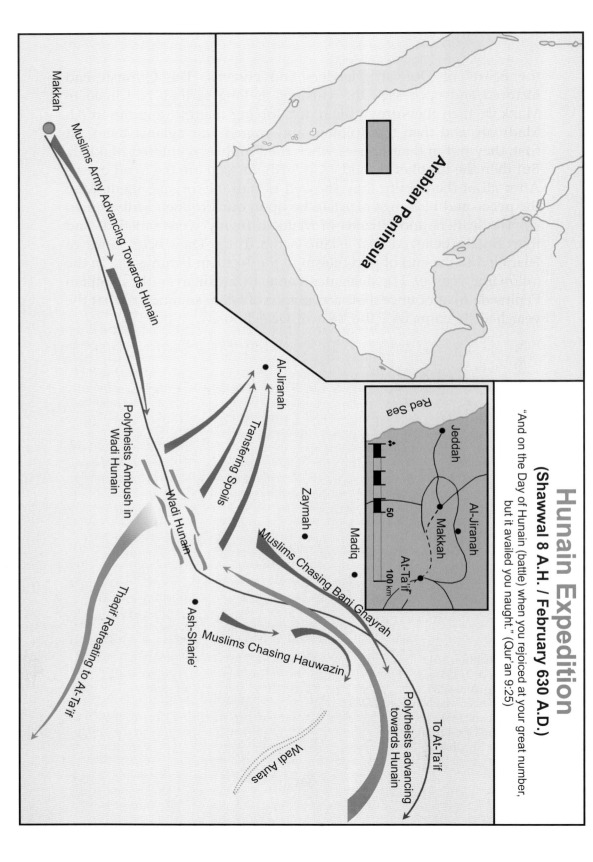

Hunain Expedition
(Shawwal 8 A.H. / February 630 A.D.)

"And on the Day of Hunain (battle) when you rejoiced at your great number, but it availed you naught." (Qur'an 9:25)

Makkah

Muslims Army Advancing Towards Hunain

Polytheists Ambush in Wadi Hunain

Thaqif Retreating to At-Ta'if

Wadi Hunain

Transfering Spoils

Al-Jiranah

Zaymah

Madiq

Muslims Chasing Bani Ghayrah

Ash-Sharie'

Muslims Chasing Hauwazin

Wadi Autas

Polytheists advancing towards Hunain

To At-Ta'if

Arabian Peninsula

Red Sea

Jeddah

Al-Jiranah

Madiq

Makkah

At-Ta'if

50

100 km

Hunain And At-Tâ'if

بِسْمِ اللَّهِ الرَّحْمَنِ الرَّحِيمِ ﴿لَقَدْ نَصَرَكُمُ اللَّهُ فِي مَوَاطِنَ كَثِيرَةٍ وَيَوْمَ حُنَيْنٍ إِذْ أَعْجَبَتْكُمْ كَثْرَتُكُمْ فَلَمْ تُغْنِ عَنكُمْ شَيْئًا وَضَاقَتْ عَلَيْكُمُ الْأَرْضُ بِمَا رَحُبَتْ ثُمَّ وَلَّيْتُم مُّدْبِرِينَ ﴿٢٥﴾ ثُمَّ أَنزَلَ اللَّهُ سَكِينَتَهُ عَلَى رَسُولِهِ وَعَلَى الْمُؤْمِنِينَ وَأَنزَلَ جُنُودًا لَّمْ تَرَوْهَا وَعَذَّبَ الَّذِينَ كَفَرُوا وَذَلِكَ جَزَاءُ الْكَافِرِينَ ﴿٢٦﴾ ثُمَّ يَتُوبُ اللَّهُ مِنْ بَعْدِ ذَلِكَ عَلَى مَن يَشَاءُ وَاللَّهُ غَفُورٌ رَّحِيمٌ ﴿٢٧﴾﴾

Truly, Allāh has given you victory on many battlefields, and on the day of Hunain (battle) when you rejoiced at your great number, but it availed you naught and the earth, vast as it is, was straitened for you, then you turned back in flight. Then Allāh did send down His *Sakīnah* (calmness, tranquillity and reassurance) on the Messenger (Muhammad ﷺ), and on the believers, and sent down forces (angels) which you saw not, and punished the disbelievers. Such is the recompense of disbelievers. Then after that Allāh will accept the repentance of whom He wills. And Allāh is Oft-Forgiving, Most Merciful.

(Qur'ân 9: 25-27)

The tribes of Hawâzin and Thaqif were deeply shaken by the conquest of Makkah (the 20th of Ramadan, 8 H) and the end of polytheism in that region. They felt that, now that the Quraish were defeated, they were going to be the next targets. The leaders of the two tribes agreed to attack Muhammad ﷺ before he attacked them. The leader of Hawâzin, Mâlik ibn 'Auf An-Nasri, assembled a group of fighters from both his tribe and the Thaqif. Other tribes joined with them as well Nasr, Jusham, Sa'd ibn Bakr, and people from Banu Hilâl. Absent from Hawâzin were Ka'b and Kilâb.

The tribe of Banu Jusham brought along with them Duraid ibn As-Simmah, who was 120 years old and had lost his eyesight. They brought him along not to fight, of course, but to rely on his counsel and his deep knowledge of warfare.

Leading the Thaqif tribe was Kinânah ibn 'Abd Yâlil, and by his side was Qârib ibn Al-Aswad ibn Mas'ud ibn Mu'attab. Banu Mâlik was led by Dhul-Khimâr Subai' ibn Al-Hârith and his brother, Ahmar ibn Al-Hârith. But the overall leader of the battle was Mâlik ibn 'Auf An-Nasri. He had brought his army with all their families and the movable property.

Led by Mâlik, the army stopped at a place called Autâs, which was a valley near the homes of the Hawâzin; that is why the battle is also known as the "Battle of Autâs." It is estimated that Mâlik had 20,000 or more fighters with him.

The Prophet ﷺ set out to meet Mâlik's army on the 6th of Shawwâl, in the year 8 H. He had with him 12,000 fighters, 10,000 from his Companions ؓ that took part in the conquering of Makkah, and 2,000 from the 'freed ones' of Makkah.

Based on the counsel of Duraid ibn As-Simmah, Mâlik ibn 'Auf's army waited to ambush the Muslims in the narrow part of the Hunain valley. It was just before *Fajr* time, when the Muslims had reached the heart of the valley, that Mâlik's army ambushed them. Showered by arrows and attacked by horsemen, the Muslim army retreated; but the Messenger of Allâh ﷺ and a number of his Companions ؓ remained firm and protected the backs of their retreating forces. The closest of the Prophet's Companions ؓ then gathered around him, in an attempt to turn defeat into victory. Their efforts then sparked the return of their retreating forces.

﴿لَقَدْ نَصَرَكُمُ ٱللَّهُ فِي مَوَاطِنَ كَثِيرَةٍ وَيَوْمَ حُنَيْنٍ إِذْ أَعْجَبَتْكُمْ كَثْرَتُكُمْ فَلَمْ تُغْنِ عَنكُمْ شَيْئًا وَضَاقَتْ عَلَيْكُمُ ٱلْأَرْضُ بِمَا رَحُبَتْ ثُمَّ وَلَّيْتُم مُّدْبِرِينَ ٢٥ ثُمَّ أَنزَلَ ٱللَّهُ سَكِينَتَهُ عَلَىٰ رَسُولِهِ وَعَلَى ٱلْمُؤْمِنِينَ وَأَنزَلَ جُنُودًا لَّمْ تَرَوْهَا وَعَذَّبَ ٱلَّذِينَ كَفَرُوا وَذَٰلِكَ جَزَآءُ ٱلْكَٰفِرِينَ ٢٦ ثُمَّ يَتُوبُ ٱللَّهُ مِنۢ بَعْدِ ذَٰلِكَ عَلَىٰ مَن يَشَآءُ وَٱللَّهُ غَفُورٌ رَّحِيمٌ ٢٧﴾

Truly, Allāh has given you victory on many battlefields, and on the day of Hunain (battle) when you rejoiced at your great number, but it availed you naught and the earth, vast as it is, was straitened for you, then you turned back in flight. Then Allāh did send down His *Sakīnah* (calmness, tranquillity and reassurance) on the Messenger (Muhammad ﷺ), and on the believers, and sent down forces (angels) which you saw not, and punished the disbelievers. Such is the recompense of disbelievers. Then after that Allāh will accept the repentance of whom He wills. And Allāh is Oft-Forgiving, Most Merciful.

(Qur'ân 9: 25-27)

Now facing defeat, the forces of Hawâzin and Thaqif became both confused and scattered. A number of them, among whom was Mâlik ibn 'Auf, sought refuge in At-Tâ'if, where they sheltered themselves behind a fortress. And a number of them returned to Autâs. To the latter group the Prophet ﷺ sent a unit of fighters that was headed by Abu 'Aamir Al-Ash'ari.

The Prophet ﷺ set out from Hunain to At-Tâ'if, where he besieged Mâlik and his followers for a long time somewhere between 23 and 29 nights. Realizing that they could do nothing about neighboring tribes that had accepted Islam and pledged allegiance to the Prophet ﷺ, Thaqif felt like they were trapped; and their situation worsened when an economic embargo was imposed against them. In Ramadan of the year 9 H, they went to the Prophet ﷺ and announced their acceptance of Islam. And the Prophet ﷺ appointed 'Uhtmân ibn Abi Al-'Aas Ath-Thaqafi ﷺ to be their leader. The first important battle that took place among the Arabs during the Prophet's lifetime was Badr, and the last of them was Hunain. Because these are the most significant of the battles that the Prophet ﷺ fought, they are often juxtaposed in speech, so that people say, "Badr and Hunain."

- Ibn Khaldun: 2/45
- Ibn Hisham: 4/64
- Al-Bidayah wan-Nihayah: 4/322
- At-Tabari: 3/72
- Al-Kamil Fit-Tarikh: 2/177
- 'Uyun Al-Athar: 2/187

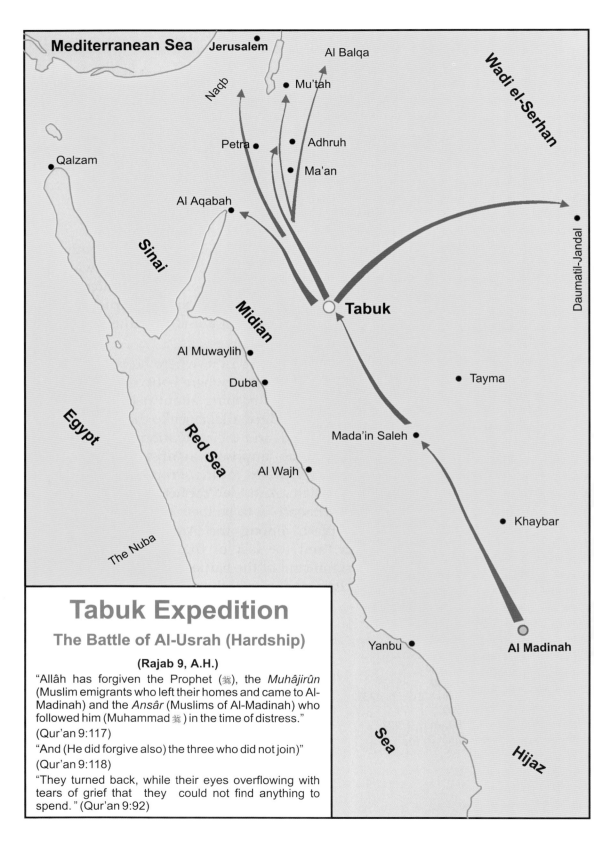

Mediterranean Sea Jerusalem

Al Balqa

Wadi el-Serhan

Naqb

Mu'tah

Petra

Adhruh

Ma'an

Qalzam

Al Aqabah

Sinai

Daumatil-Jandal

Midian

Tabuk

Al Muwaylih

Duba

Tayma

Egypt

Red Sea

Mada'in Saleh

Al Wajh

Khaybar

The Nuba

Tabuk Expedition

The Battle of Al-Usrah (Hardship)

(Rajab 9, A.H.)

"Allâh has forgiven the Prophet (ﷺ), the *Muhâjirûn* (Muslim emigrants who left their homes and came to Al-Madinah) and the *Ansâr* (Muslims of Al-Madinah) who followed him (Muhammad ﷺ) in the time of distress."
(Qur'an 9:117)

"And (He did forgive also) the three who did not join)"
(Qur'an 9:118)

"They turned back, while their eyes overflowing with tears of grief that they could not find anything to spend. " (Qur'an 9:92)

Yanbu

Al Madinah

Sea

Hijaz

Tabûk:
The Battle of Al-'Usrah
(Rajab, 9 H)

﴿لَّقَد تَّابَ ٱللَّهُ عَلَى ٱلنَّبِيِّ وَٱلْمُهَٰجِرِينَ وَٱلْأَنصَارِ ٱلَّذِينَ ٱتَّبَعُوهُ فِى سَاعَةِ ٱلْعُسْرَةِ مِنۢ بَعْدِ مَا كَادَ يَزِيغُ قُلُوبُ فَرِيقٍ مِّنْهُمْ ثُمَّ تَابَ عَلَيْهِمْ إِنَّهُ بِهِمْ رَءُوفٌ رَّحِيمٌ ۝ وَعَلَى ٱلثَّلَٰثَةِ ٱلَّذِينَ خُلِّفُوا۟ حَتَّىٰ إِذَا ضَاقَتْ عَلَيْهِمُ ٱلْأَرْضُ بِمَا رَحُبَتْ وَضَاقَتْ عَلَيْهِمْ أَنفُسُهُمْ وَظَنُّوٓا۟ أَن لَّا مَلْجَأَ مِنَ ٱللَّهِ إِلَّآ إِلَيْهِ ثُمَّ تَابَ عَلَيْهِمْ لِيَتُوبُوٓا۟ إِنَّ ٱللَّهَ هُوَ ٱلتَّوَّابُ ٱلرَّحِيمُ ۝﴾

Allāh has forgiven the Prophet (ﷺ), the *Muhājirūn* (Muslim emigrants who left their homes and came to Al-Madinah) and the *Ansār* (Muslims of Al-Madināh) who followed him (Muhammad ﷺ) in the time of distress (Tabūk expedition), after the hearts of a party of them had nearly deviated (from the Right Path), but He accepted their repentance. Certainly, He is to them full of kindness, Most Merciful. And (He did forgive also) the three who did not join (the Tabūk expedition and whose case was deferred by the Prophet ﷺ for Allāh's Decision) till for them the earth, vast as it is, was straitened and their own selves were straitened to them, and they perceived that there is no fleeing from Allāh, and no refuge but with Him. Then, He forgave them (accepted their repentance), that they might beg for His Pardon (repent to Him). Verily, Allāh is the One Who forgives and accepts repentance, the Most Merciful.

(Qur'ân 9: 117, 118)

News reached the Messenger of Allâh ﷺ about how the Romans were gathering forces in Ash-Sham (Syria and surrounding regions; these areas were then under the control of the Roman Empire), and about the many units that were mobilizing in Al-Balqa (Jordan). In dealing with the threat, the Prophet ﷺ had all but two choices:

1) Wait for them to launch an attack on Al-Madinah.
2) Go to them in what would be a preventive war.

The Messenger of Allâh ﷺ chose the second option, the one that would involve a show of strength and honor. The Prophet ﷺ then announced that they were going out for battle. As described in the above-mentioned verse, it was a time of distress the weather was extremely hot and they were undergoing a period of drought. Because the situation required immediate action, the Prophet ﷺ quickly assembled an army of 30,000 fighters and 10,000 horsemen.

They set out in Rajab, in the year 9 H. They stopped at Tabûk, which was to be their central camp. After the gathered forces of the Romans became scattered and divided, Khâlid ibn Al-Walid ؓ was sent to Daumatil-Jandal. Yuhannah ibn Rau'bah, of 'Ailah (Al-'Aqabah), came to Khâlid ؓ and made a peace pact on the condition that he was to pay a small amount of *Jizyah* to the Muslims. The people of Jarbâ and Adhrah came as well, making a similar agreement.

Here are some of the most important things that took place during the Tabûk expedition:

1) The Muslims set out to fight the Romans, in spite of the drought and the extreme heat:

﴿لَّقَد تَّابَ ٱللَّهُ عَلَى ٱلنَّبِيِّ وَٱلْمُهَٰجِرِينَ وَٱلْأَنصَارِ ٱلَّذِينَ ٱتَّبَعُوهُ فِى سَاعَةِ ٱلْعُسْرَةِ مِنۢ بَعْدِ مَا كَادَ يَزِيغُ قُلُوبُ فَرِيقٍ مِّنْهُمْ ثُمَّ تَابَ عَلَيْهِمْ إِنَّهُۥ بِهِمْ رَءُوفٌ رَّحِيمٌ ﴿١١٧﴾ وَعَلَى ٱلثَّلَٰثَةِ ٱلَّذِينَ خُلِّفُوا حَتَّىٰ إِذَا ضَاقَتْ عَلَيْهِمُ ٱلْأَرْضُ بِمَا رَحُبَتْ وَضَاقَتْ عَلَيْهِمْ أَنفُسُهُمْ وَظَنُّوا أَن لَّا مَلْجَأَ مِنَ ٱللَّهِ إِلَّا إِلَيْهِ ثُمَّ تَابَ عَلَيْهِمْ لِيَتُوبُوا إِنَّ ٱللَّهَ هُوَ ٱلتَّوَّابُ ٱلرَّحِيمُ ﴿١١٨﴾﴾

Allâh has forgiven the Prophet (ﷺ), the *Muhājirūn* (Muslim emigrants who left their homes and came to Al-Madinah) and the *Ansār* (Muslims of Al-Madināh) who followed him (Muhammad ﷺ) in the time of distress (Tabūk expedition), after the hearts of a party of them had nearly deviated (from the Right Path), but He accepted their repentance. Certainly, He is to them full of kindness, Most Merciful. And (He did forgive also) the three who did not join (the Tabūk expedition and whose case was deferred by the Prophet ﷺ for Allāh's Decision) till for them the earth, vast as it is, was straitened and their own selves were straitened to them, and they perceived that there is no fleeing from Allāh, and no refuge but with Him. Then, He forgave them (accepted their repentance), that they might beg for His Pardon (repent to Him). Verily, Allāh is the One Who forgives and accepts repentance, the Most Merciful.

(Qur'ân 9: 117-118)

2) Those who wept: When the Prophet ﷺ made the announcement that people should get ready to depart for the Tabûk expedition, a number of Companions ﷺ came to him and said, "O Messenger of Allâh, carry us (i.e., provide us with mounts so that we can come with you)." He ﷺ said, "By Allâh, I can find no (mounts) to carry you on." They turned back, and their eyes flowed with tears of sincere grief; it was most painful to them that they should have to stay behind from the expedition for the want of mounts and necessary provisions. Allâh ﷻ then revealed this Verse:

﴿وَلَا عَلَى ٱلَّذِينَ إِذَا مَآ أَتَوْكَ لِتَحْمِلَهُمْ قُلْتَ لَآ أَجِدُ مَآ أَحْمِلُكُمْ عَلَيْهِ تَوَلَّوْا۟ وَأَعْيُنُهُمْ تَفِيضُ مِنَ ٱلدَّمْعِ حَزَنًا أَلَّا يَجِدُوا۟ مَا يُنفِقُونَ ﴿٩٢﴾﴾

Nor (is there blame) on those who came to you to be provided with mounts, when you said: "I can find no mounts for you," they turned back, while their eyes overflowing with tears of grief that they could not find anything to spend.

(Qur'ân 9: 92)

Here is a list of those Companions ﷺ whose eyes flowed with tears of grief for not being able to join the expedition:

- From the Banu 'Amr bin 'Auf bin 'Umair clan (from the Ansâr): Sâlim ibn 'Umair ﷺ, Tha'labah ibn Zaid ﷺ,

'Abdullah ibn Mughaffal ⬥, 'Ulbah bin Zaid ⬥, 'Amr bin Al-Hammâm bin Al-Jamuh, Hurmi bin 'Abdullah ⬥, and 'Irbâd ibn Sâriyah Al-Fazâri ⬥.

- From the Bani Wâqif clan: Hirmi bin 'Amr ⬥.

- From Banu Mâzin ibn An-Najjâr: 'Abdur-Rahmân ibn Ka'b ⬥.

- From Bani Al-Mu'alla: Salmân ibn Sakhr ⬥.

- From Banu Hârithah: 'Abdur-Rahmân ibn Yazid ⬥.

- From Banu Salamah: 'Amr ibn 'Anamah ⬥ and 'Abdullah ibn 'Amr Al-Muzani ⬥.

- A number of people from Muqarrin: It is said that they were Ma'qil ⬥, Suwaid ⬥, and An-Nu'mân ⬥; however, it is also said that they were Abu Musa Al-Ash'ari ⬥ and his companions ⬥ from the people of Yemen.

3) Those who stayed behind (The excuse-givers): When the Prophet ﷺ and his Companions ⬥ were preparing to go to Tabûk, a group of Bedouins made excuses to explain why they could not go along for the expedition; but their excuses were weak and unacceptable. Those who excused themselves were a total of 82 men from the Banu Ghifâr tribe. But Allâh ﷻ did not accept their excuses:

﴿لَوْ كَانَ عَرَضًا قَرِيبًا وَسَفَرًا قَاصِدًا لَّٱتَّبَعُوكَ وَلَٰكِنۢ بَعُدَتْ عَلَيْهِمُ ٱلشُّقَّةُ وَسَيَحْلِفُونَ بِٱللَّهِ لَوِ ٱسْتَطَعْنَا لَخَرَجْنَا مَعَكُمْ يُهْلِكُونَ أَنفُسَهُمْ وَٱللَّهُ يَعْلَمُ إِنَّهُمْ لَكَٰذِبُونَ ۝ عَفَا ٱللَّهُ عَنكَ لِمَ أَذِنتَ لَهُمْ حَتَّىٰ يَتَبَيَّنَ لَكَ ٱلَّذِينَ صَدَقُوا۟ وَتَعْلَمَ ٱلْكَٰذِبِينَ ۝ لَا يَسْتَـْٔذِنُكَ ٱلَّذِينَ يُؤْمِنُونَ بِٱللَّهِ وَٱلْيَوْمِ ٱلْءَاخِرِ أَن يُجَٰهِدُوا۟ بِأَمْوَٰلِهِمْ وَأَنفُسِهِمْ وَٱللَّهُ عَلِيمٌۢ بِٱلْمُتَّقِينَ ۝﴾

Had it been a near gain (booty in front of them) and an easy journey, they would have followed you, but the distance (Tabûk expedition) was long for them; and they would swear by Allāh: "If we only could, we would certainly have come

330

forth with you." They destroy their own selves, and Allāh knows that they are surely liars. May Allāh forgive you (O Muhammad ﷺ). Why did you grant them leave (for remaining behind; you should have persisted as regards your order to them to proceed on *Jihād*), until those who told the truth were seen by you in a clear light, and you had known the liars? Those who believe in Allāh and the Last Day would not ask your leave to be exempted from fighting with their properties and their lives; and Allāh is All-Knower of *Al-Muttaqūn* (the pious.

(Qur'ân 9: 42-44)

﴿وَجَآءَ ٱلْمُعَذِّرُونَ مِنَ ٱلْأَعْرَابِ لِيُؤْذَنَ لَهُمْ وَقَعَدَ ٱلَّذِينَ كَذَبُوا۟ ٱللَّهَ وَرَسُولَهُۥ سَيُصِيبُ ٱلَّذِينَ كَفَرُوا۟ مِنْهُمْ عَذَابٌ أَلِيمٌ ٩٠ ﴾

And those who made excuses from the bedouins came (to you, O Prophet ﷺ) asking your permission to exempt them (from the battle), and those who had lied to Allāh and His Messenger (ﷺ) sat at home (without asking the permission for it); a painful torment will seize those of them who disbelieve.

(Qur'ân 9: 90)

4) "The Three that Remained Behind": A few Muslims hesitated in their intention, and despite the fact that they were true, sincere Muslims, they ended up staying behind, a decision that they sincerely regretted later on. They were Ka'b ibn Mâlik ibn Abi Ka'b ﷺ, a brother of Banu Maslamah; Hilâl ibn Umayyah ﷺ, a brother of Banu Wâqif; and Murârah ibn Ar-Rabi' ﷺ, a brother of Banu 'Amr ibn 'Auf. There was a fourth sincere Muslim who lagged behind, Abu Khuthaimah ('Abdullah ibn Khuthaimah Al-Ansâri), a brother of Banu Sâlim ibn 'Auf; but he ended up traveling all alone until he caught up with the Prophet ﷺ and the Muslims at Tabûk. As for the three others mentioned above, they sincerely repented. And when the Muslims returned from At-Tabûk, the three were punished with a kind of punishment that helped to purify their souls. The Muslims were ordered to boycott them to neither greet nor speak to them though the

three were free to go wherever they wanted. Then, after a very difficult period in which they repented their sin, the following Verses were revealed, announcing that Allâh ﷻ had forgiven them:

﴿لَّقَد تَّابَ ٱللَّهُ عَلَى ٱلنَّبِيِّ وَٱلْمُهَٰجِرِينَ وَٱلْأَنصَارِ ٱلَّذِينَ ٱتَّبَعُوهُ فِى سَاعَةِ ٱلْعُسْرَةِ مِنۢ بَعْدِ مَا كَادَ يَزِيغُ قُلُوبُ فَرِيقٍ مِّنْهُمْ ثُمَّ تَابَ عَلَيْهِمْ إِنَّهُۥ بِهِمْ رَءُوفٌ رَّحِيمٌ ۝ وَعَلَى ٱلثَّلَٰثَةِ ٱلَّذِينَ خُلِّفُوا۟ حَتَّىٰٓ إِذَا ضَاقَتْ عَلَيْهِمُ ٱلْأَرْضُ بِمَا رَحُبَتْ وَضَاقَتْ عَلَيْهِمْ أَنفُسُهُمْ وَظَنُّوٓا۟ أَن لَّا مَلْجَأَ مِنَ ٱللَّهِ إِلَّآ إِلَيْهِ ثُمَّ تَابَ عَلَيْهِمْ لِيَتُوبُوٓا۟ إِنَّ ٱللَّهَ هُوَ ٱلتَّوَّابُ ٱلرَّحِيمُ ۝﴾

Allāh has forgiven the Prophet (ﷺ), the *Muhājirūn* (Muslim emigrants who left their homes and came to Al-Madinah) and the *Ansār* (Muslims of Al-Madināh) who followed him (Muhammad ﷺ) in the time of distress (Tabūk expedition), after the hearts of a party of them had nearly deviated (from the Right Path), but He accepted their repentance. Certainly, He is to them full of kindness, Most Merciful. And (He did forgive also) the three who did not join (the Tabūk expedition and whose case was deferred by the Prophet ﷺ for Allāh's Decision) till for them the earth, vast as it is, was straitened and their own selves were straitened to them, and they perceived that there is no fleeing from Allāh, and no refuge but with Him. Then, He forgave them (accepted their repentance), that they might beg for His Pardon (repent to Him). Verily, Allāh is the One Who forgives and accepts repentance, the Most Merciful.

(Qur'ân 9: 117-118)

5) The hypocrites: Hypocrites are those who outwardly manifest Islam but inwardly harbor disbelief. The leader of the hypocrites was 'Abdullah ibn Ubai ibn Salûl, who, before the migration of the Prophet ﷺ, had been nominated to become leader of Yathrib (Al-Madinah).

Not wanting to be found out, and finding that they could create much mischief from within the ranks of the Muslims, the hypocrites mingled freely among them. About the hypocrites, Allâh ﷻ said:

$$﴾ إِنَّ ٱلْمُنَٰفِقِينَ فِى ٱلدَّرْكِ ٱلْأَسْفَلِ مِنَ ٱلنَّارِ وَلَن تَجِدَ لَهُمْ نَصِيرًا ﴿١٤٥﴾ ﴾$$

Verily, the hypocrites will be in the lowest depth (grade) of the Fire; no helper will you find for them.

(Qur'ân 4: 145)

Hudhaifah ibn Al-Yamân ؓ was the holder of the Prophet's secret knowledge regarding the hypocrites, meaning that the Prophet ﷺ told Hudhaifah ؓ and no one else about the identities of the hypocrites. And that is why, when anyone would die after the lifetime of the Prophet ﷺ, 'Umar ؓ would wait to see if Hudhaifah ؓ attended the Funeral Prayer. If Hudhaifah ؓ attended the Funeral Prayer, 'Umar ؓ would come as well; otherwise, 'Umar ؓ would abstain from participating in the Funeral Prayer and in the burial.

$$﴾ فَرِحَ ٱلْمُخَلَّفُونَ بِمَقْعَدِهِمْ خِلَٰفَ رَسُولِ ٱللَّهِ وَكَرِهُوٓا۟ أَن يُجَٰهِدُوا۟ بِأَمْوَٰلِهِمْ وَأَنفُسِهِمْ فِى سَبِيلِ ٱللَّهِ وَقَالُوا۟ لَا تَنفِرُوا۟ فِى ٱلْحَرِّ قُلْ نَارُ جَهَنَّمَ أَشَدُّ حَرًّا لَّوْ كَانُوا۟ يَفْقَهُونَ ﴿٨١﴾ فَلْيَضْحَكُوا۟ قَلِيلًا وَلْيَبْكُوا۟ كَثِيرًا جَزَآءً بِمَا كَانُوا۟ يَكْسِبُونَ ﴿٨٢﴾ ﴾$$

Those who stayed away (from Tabuk expedition) rejoiced in their staying behind the Messenger of Allāh (ﷺ); they hated to strive and fight with their properties and their lives in the Cause of Allāh, and they said: "March not forth in the heat." Say: "The fire of Hell is more intense in heat;" if only they could understand! So let them laugh a little and (they will) cry much as a recompense of what they used to earn (by committing sins).

(Qur'ân 9: 81-82)

6) *Sûrat At-Tawbah*, in which certain points are mentioned in regards to the Tabûk expedition, mentions "*As-Sâbiqun* (literally: the ones who come first or the ones who precede others) *Al-Awwalun* (literally: the first ones) (Qur'ân 9: 100)." Scholars of *Tafsir* disagree about the identities of the *Sâbiqun Al-Awwalun*. It is said that they are those who pledged allegiance to the

333

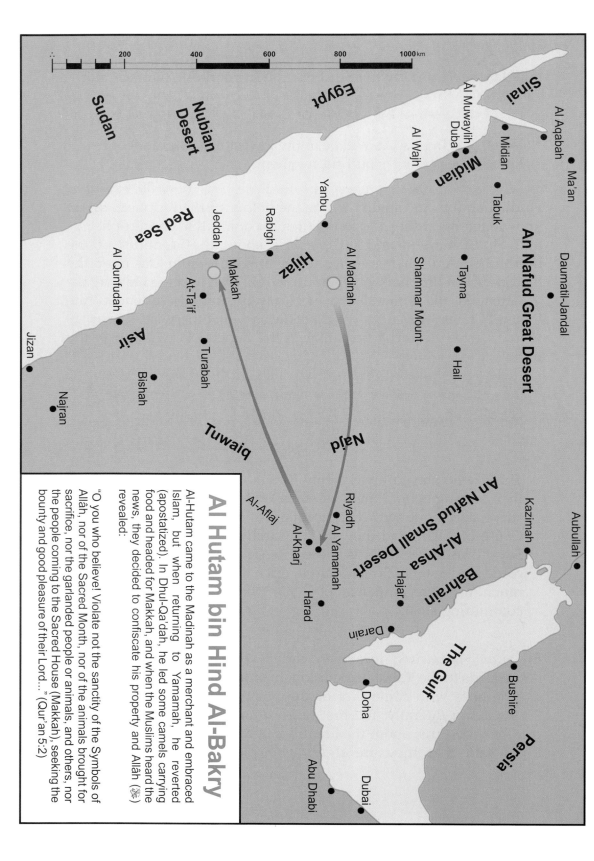

Al Hutam bin Hind Al-Bakry

Al-Hutam came to the Madinah as a merchant and embraced Islam, but when returning to Yamamah, he reverted (apostatized). In Dhul-Qa'dah, he led some camels carrying food and headed for Makkah, and when the Muslims heard the news, they decided to confiscate his property and Allâh (ﷻ) revealed:

"O you who believe! Violate not the sanctity of the Symbols of Allâh, nor of the Sacred Month, nor of the animals brought for sacrifice, nor the garlanded people or animals, and others, nor the people coming to the Sacred House (Makkah), seeking the bounty and good pleasure of their Lord..." (Qur'an 5:2)

Map labels

Sudan

Nubian Desert

Egypt

Sinai

An Nafud Great Desert

Al Aqabah

Ma'an

Daumatil-Jandal

Al Muwaylih
Duba
Midian
Midian
Al Wajh
Tabuk

Yanbu

Rabigh

Red Sea

Jeddah

Makkah

Hijaz

Al Madinah

Shammar Mount

Tayma

Hail

At-Ta'if

Al Qunfudah

Asir

Turabah

Bishah

Jizan

Najran

Tuwaiq

Najd

Al-Aflaj

Al-Kharj

Riyadh

Al Yamamah

Harad

An Nafud Small Desert

Al-Ahsa

Bahrain

Hajar

Kazimah

Aubullah

Bushire

Persia

Darain

The Gulf

Doha

Abu Dhabi

Dubai

200   400   600   800   1000 km

Messenger of Allâh ﷺ in *Bai'atur-Ridwân*, under the tree at Al-Hudaibiyah. Among other views in the matter is that they are the ones who accepted Islam early enough to have prayed towards both *Qiblahs* (Baitul-Maqdis and the Ka'bah) and who participated in the Battles of Badr and Uhud. According to Ar-Râzi, the first ones to migrate and to help (i.e., the *Ansâr*) are those who raced to embrace Islam. But racing to embrace Islam (preceding others) does not necessarily mean racing to migrate. What he is saying, it seems, is that the verse refers both to members of the *Muhâjirun* (those who migrated to Al-Madinah) and the *Ansâr* ('The Helpers': Native dwellers of Al-Madinah who accepted Islam and welcomed those who migrated to their land).

﴿وَٱلسَّٰبِقُونَ ٱلْأَوَّلُونَ مِنَ ٱلْمُهَٰجِرِينَ وَٱلْأَنصَارِ وَٱلَّذِينَ ٱتَّبَعُوهُم بِإِحْسَٰنٍ رَّضِىَ ٱللَّهُ عَنْهُمْ وَرَضُوا۟ عَنْهُ وَأَعَدَّ لَهُمْ جَنَّٰتٍ تَجْرِى تَحْتَهَا ٱلْأَنْهَٰرُ خَٰلِدِينَ فِيهَآ أَبَدًا ذَٰلِكَ ٱلْفَوْزُ ٱلْعَظِيمُ ﴿١٠٠﴾﴾

And the foremost to embrace Islam of the *Muhājirūn* (those who migrated from Makkah to Al-Madinah) and the *Ansār* (the citizens of Al-Madinah who helped and gave aid to the *Muhājirūn*) and also those who followed them exactly (in Faith). Allāh is well-pleased with them as they are well-pleased with Him. He has prepared for them Gardens under which rivers flow (Paradise), to dwell therein forever. That is the supreme success. (Qur'ân 9: 100)

- Ibn Khaldun: 2/44
- Ibn Sa'd: 2/165
- Ibn Hishâm: 4/118
- Usdul-Ghabah: 5/93
- Al-Bidâyah wan-Nihayah: 5/2
- Târikh At-Tabari: 2/102, 3/100
- Tafsir At-Tabari: 6/213, 7/6
- Ruhul-Ma'âni: 6/231
- Fathul-Qadir: 2/393
- AL-Kâmil Fit-Târikh: 2/189
- 'Uyun Al-Athar: 2/216

The Greatest Day
(Dhul-Hijjah 9 A.H.)

"And a declaration from Allâh and His Messenger to mankind on the greatest day (the 10th of Dhul-Hijjah-12th month of Islamic calendar) that Allâh is free from (all) obligations to the Mushrikûn and so is His Messenger. So if you (Mushrikûn) repent, it is better for you..." (Qur'an 9:3)

"Then when you leave 'Arafât, remember Allâh (by glorifying His Praises, i.e., prayers and invocations) at the Mash'aril-Harâm."

(Qur'an 2:198)

Arafat lies 22 km east of Makkah.

Makkah
Sacred House
Al-Hijoun
Jabal Al-Nûr
Ghar Hira
Wadi Ibrahim
Ghar Thawr
Jabal Thawr
Jamarat
Al-Muhassab
Al-Manhar
Jabal Thuqbah
Mina
Bir Al-Mu'iseer
Wadi Ibrahim
Batn Mahhar
Wadi Baz
Al-Muzdalifah
The Standing,
Muzdalifah Mosque
Al-Ababdiyah
Dhabb Way
Jabal Ahdab
Jabal Namirah
Masjid Namirah
Arafat Marks
Wadi 'Aranah
Jabal Khushrum
Jabal Sattar
Jabal Siteer
Wadi Al-Numan
Jabal Ar-Rahmah
Arafat
Jabal Sa'd
Wadi Arafa
Ain Zubaidah
To At-Ta'if
Jabal Al-Qassar

The Greatest Day
(9 H)

﴿بَرَآءَةٌ مِّنَ ٱللَّهِ وَرَسُولِهِۦٓ إِلَى ٱلَّذِينَ عَٰهَدتُّم مِّنَ ٱلْمُشْرِكِينَ ۝ فَسِيحُوا۟ فِى ٱلْأَرْضِ أَرْبَعَةَ أَشْهُرٍ وَٱعْلَمُوٓا۟ أَنَّكُمْ غَيْرُ مُعْجِزِى ٱللَّهِ وَأَنَّ ٱللَّهَ مُخْزِى ٱلْكَٰفِرِينَ ۝ وَأَذَٰنٌ مِّنَ ٱللَّهِ وَرَسُولِهِۦٓ إِلَى ٱلنَّاسِ يَوْمَ ٱلْحَجِّ ٱلْأَكْبَرِ أَنَّ ٱللَّهَ بَرِىٓءٌ مِّنَ ٱلْمُشْرِكِينَ وَرَسُولُهُۥ فَإِن تُبْتُمْ فَهُوَ خَيْرٌ لَّكُمْ وَإِن تَوَلَّيْتُمْ فَٱعْلَمُوٓا۟ أَنَّكُمْ غَيْرُ مُعْجِزِى ٱللَّهِ وَبَشِّرِ ٱلَّذِينَ كَفَرُوا۟ بِعَذَابٍ أَلِيمٍ ۝ إِلَّا ٱلَّذِينَ عَٰهَدتُّم مِّنَ ٱلْمُشْرِكِينَ ثُمَّ لَمْ يَنقُصُوكُمْ شَيْـًٔا وَلَمْ يُظَٰهِرُوا۟ عَلَيْكُمْ أَحَدًا فَأَتِمُّوٓا۟ إِلَيْهِمْ عَهْدَهُمْ إِلَىٰ مُدَّتِهِمْ إِنَّ ٱللَّهَ يُحِبُّ ٱلْمُتَّقِينَ ۝ فَإِذَا ٱنسَلَخَ ٱلْأَشْهُرُ ٱلْحُرُمُ فَٱقْتُلُوا۟ ٱلْمُشْرِكِينَ حَيْثُ وَجَدتُّمُوهُمْ وَخُذُوهُمْ وَٱحْصُرُوهُمْ وَٱقْعُدُوا۟ لَهُمْ كُلَّ مَرْصَدٍ فَإِن تَابُوا۟ وَأَقَامُوا۟ ٱلصَّلَوٰةَ وَءَاتَوُا۟ ٱلزَّكَوٰةَ فَخَلُّوا۟ سَبِيلَهُمْ إِنَّ ٱللَّهَ غَفُورٌ رَّحِيمٌ ۝ وَإِنْ أَحَدٌ مِّنَ ٱلْمُشْرِكِينَ ٱسْتَجَارَكَ فَأَجِرْهُ حَتَّىٰ يَسْمَعَ كَلَٰمَ ٱللَّهِ ثُمَّ أَبْلِغْهُ مَأْمَنَهُۥ ذَٰلِكَ بِأَنَّهُمْ قَوْمٌ لَّا يَعْلَمُونَ ۝ كَيْفَ يَكُونُ لِلْمُشْرِكِينَ عَهْدٌ عِندَ ٱللَّهِ وَعِندَ رَسُولِهِۦٓ إِلَّا ٱلَّذِينَ عَٰهَدتُّمْ عِندَ ٱلْمَسْجِدِ ٱلْحَرَامِ فَمَا ٱسْتَقَٰمُوا۟ لَكُمْ فَٱسْتَقِيمُوا۟ لَهُمْ إِنَّ ٱللَّهَ يُحِبُّ ٱلْمُتَّقِينَ ۝ كَيْفَ وَإِن يَظْهَرُوا۟ عَلَيْكُمْ لَا يَرْقُبُوا۟ فِيكُمْ إِلًّا وَلَا ذِمَّةً يُرْضُونَكُم بِأَفْوَٰهِهِمْ وَتَأْبَىٰ قُلُوبُهُمْ وَأَكْثَرُهُمْ فَٰسِقُونَ ۝ ٱشْتَرَوْا۟ بِـَٔايَٰتِ ٱللَّهِ ثَمَنًا قَلِيلًا فَصَدُّوا۟ عَن سَبِيلِهِۦٓ إِنَّهُمْ سَآءَ مَا كَانُوا۟ يَعْمَلُونَ ۝ لَا يَرْقُبُونَ فِى مُؤْمِنٍ إِلًّا وَلَا ذِمَّةً وَأُو۟لَٰٓئِكَ هُمُ ٱلْمُعْتَدُونَ ۝ فَإِن تَابُوا۟ وَأَقَامُوا۟ ٱلصَّلَوٰةَ وَءَاتَوُا۟ ٱلزَّكَوٰةَ فَإِخْوَٰنُكُمْ فِى ٱلدِّينِ وَنُفَصِّلُ ٱلْءَايَٰتِ لِقَوْمٍ يَعْلَمُونَ ۝ وَإِن نَّكَثُوٓا۟ أَيْمَٰنَهُم مِّنۢ بَعْدِ عَهْدِهِمْ وَطَعَنُوا۟ فِى دِينِكُمْ فَقَٰتِلُوٓا۟ أَئِمَّةَ ٱلْكُفْرِ إِنَّهُمْ لَآ أَيْمَٰنَ لَهُمْ لَعَلَّهُمْ يَنتَهُونَ ۝ أَلَا تُقَٰتِلُونَ قَوْمًا نَّكَثُوٓا۟ أَيْمَٰنَهُمْ وَهَمُّوا۟ بِإِخْرَاجِ ٱلرَّسُولِ وَهُم بَدَءُوكُمْ أَوَّلَ مَرَّةٍ أَتَخْشَوْنَهُمْ فَٱللَّهُ أَحَقُّ أَن تَخْشَوْهُ إِن كُنتُم مُّؤْمِنِينَ ۝ قَٰتِلُوهُمْ يُعَذِّبْهُمُ ٱللَّهُ بِأَيْدِيكُمْ وَيُخْزِهِمْ وَيَنصُرْكُمْ عَلَيْهِمْ وَيَشْفِ صُدُورَ قَوْمٍ مُّؤْمِنِينَ ۝ وَيُذْهِبْ غَيْظَ

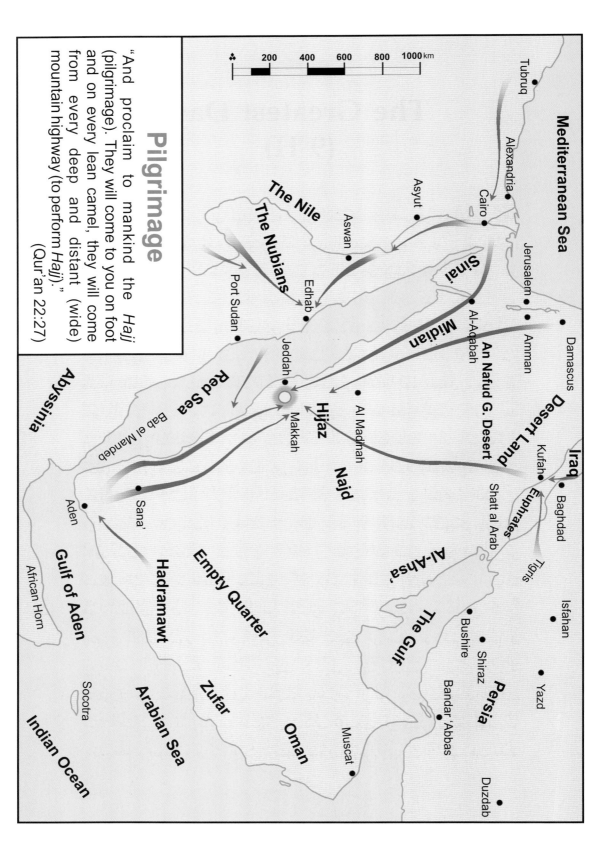

Pilgrimage

"And proclaim to mankind the *Hajj* (pilgrimage). They will come to you on foot and on every lean camel, they will come from every deep and distant (wide) mountain highway (to perform *Hajj*)."

(Qur'an 22:27)

Mediterranean Sea

Tubruq

Alexandria

Asyut

Cairo

Jerusalem

Aswan

Damascus

Amman

The Nile

The Nubians

Sinai

Al-Aqabah

Midian

An Nafud G. Desert

Port Sudan

Edhab

Jeddah

Desert Land

Al Madinah

Hijaz

Makkah

Najd

Kufah

Iraq

Euphrates

Baghdad

Tigris

Shatt al Arab

Red Sea

Bab el Mandeb

Abyssinia

Aden

Sana'

Hadramawt

Empty Quarter

Al-Ahsa'

Isfahan

Bushire

The Gulf

Shiraz

Yazd

Bandar 'Abbas

Persia

African Horn

Gulf of Aden

Socotra

Zufar

Arabian Sea

Oman

Muscat

Duzdab

Indian Ocean

200 400 600 800 1000 km

قُلُوبِهِمْ ۚ وَيَتُوبُ اللَّهُ عَلَىٰ مَن يَشَآءُ ۗ وَاللَّهُ عَلِيمٌ حَكِيمٌ ۝ أَمْ حَسِبْتُمْ أَن تُتْرَكُوا۟ وَلَمَّا يَعْلَمِ اللَّهُ الَّذِينَ جَٰهَدُوا۟ مِنكُمْ وَلَمْ يَتَّخِذُوا۟ مِن دُونِ اللَّهِ وَلَا رَسُولِهِۦ وَلَا الْمُؤْمِنِينَ وَلِيجَةً ۚ وَاللَّهُ خَبِيرٌۢ بِمَا تَعْمَلُونَ ۝ مَا كَانَ لِلْمُشْرِكِينَ أَن يَعْمُرُوا۟ مَسَٰجِدَ اللَّهِ شَٰهِدِينَ عَلَىٰٓ أَنفُسِهِم بِالْكُفْرِ ۚ أُو۟لَٰٓئِكَ حَبِطَتْ أَعْمَٰلُهُمْ وَفِى النَّارِ هُمْ خَٰلِدُونَ ۝ إِنَّمَا يَعْمُرُ مَسَٰجِدَ اللَّهِ مَنْ ءَامَنَ بِاللَّهِ وَالْيَوْمِ الْءَاخِرِ وَأَقَامَ الصَّلَوٰةَ وَءَاتَى الزَّكَوٰةَ وَلَمْ يَخْشَ إِلَّا اللَّهَ ۖ فَعَسَىٰٓ أُو۟لَٰٓئِكَ أَن يَكُونُوا۟ مِنَ الْمُهْتَدِينَ ۝ ۞ أَجَعَلْتُمْ سِقَايَةَ الْحَآجِّ وَعِمَارَةَ الْمَسْجِدِ الْحَرَامِ كَمَنْ ءَامَنَ بِاللَّهِ وَالْيَوْمِ الْءَاخِرِ وَجَٰهَدَ فِى سَبِيلِ اللَّهِ ۚ لَا يَسْتَوُۥنَ عِندَ اللَّهِ ۗ وَاللَّهُ لَا يَهْدِى الْقَوْمَ الظَّٰلِمِينَ ۝ الَّذِينَ ءَامَنُوا۟ وَهَاجَرُوا۟ وَجَٰهَدُوا۟ فِى سَبِيلِ اللَّهِ بِأَمْوَٰلِهِمْ وَأَنفُسِهِمْ أَعْظَمُ دَرَجَةً عِندَ اللَّهِ ۚ وَأُو۟لَٰٓئِكَ هُمُ الْفَآئِزُونَ ۝ يُبَشِّرُهُمْ رَبُّهُم بِرَحْمَةٍ مِّنْهُ وَرِضْوَٰنٍ وَجَنَّٰتٍ لَّهُمْ فِيهَا نَعِيمٌ مُّقِيمٌ ۝ خَٰلِدِينَ فِيهَآ أَبَدًا ۚ إِنَّ اللَّهَ عِندَهُۥٓ أَجْرٌ عَظِيمٌ ۝ يَٰٓأَيُّهَا الَّذِينَ ءَامَنُوا۟ لَا تَتَّخِذُوٓا۟ ءَابَآءَكُمْ وَإِخْوَٰنَكُمْ أَوْلِيَآءَ إِنِ اسْتَحَبُّوا۟ الْكُفْرَ عَلَى الْإِيمَٰنِ ۚ وَمَن يَتَوَلَّهُم مِّنكُمْ فَأُو۟لَٰٓئِكَ هُمُ الظَّٰلِمُونَ ۝ ۞

Freedom from (all) obligations (is declared) from Allāh and His Messenger (ﷺ) to those of the *Mushrikūn* (polytheists, pagans, idolaters, disbelievers in the Oneness of Allāh), with whom you made a treaty. So travel freely (O *Mushrikūn*) for four months (as you will) throughout the land, but know that you cannot escape (from the punishment of) Allāh; and Allāh will disgrace the disbelievers. And a declaration from Allāh and His Messenger (ﷺ) to mankind on the greatest day (the 10th of Dhul-Hijjah — the 12th month of Islamic calendar) that Allāh is free from (all) obligations to the *Mushrikūn* and so is His Messenger (ﷺ). So if you (*Mushrikūn*) repent, it is better for you, but if you turn away, then know that you cannot escape (from the punishment of) Allāh. And give tidings (O Muhammad ﷺ) of a painful torment to those who disbelieve. Except those of the *Mushrikūn* with whom you have a treaty, and who have not subsequently failed you in aught, nor have supported anyone against you. So fulfil their treaty to them for the end of their term. Surely, Allāh loves *Al-*

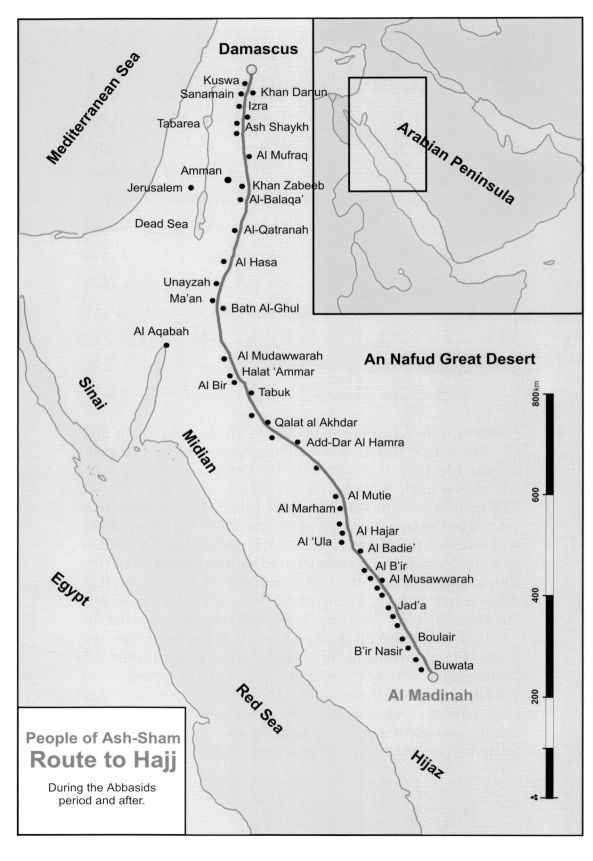

Damascus

Kuswa
Khan Darun
Sanamain
Izra
Tabarea
Ash Shaykh
Al Mufraq
Amman
Khan Zabeeb
Jerusalem
Al-Balaqa'
Dead Sea
Al-Qatranah
Al Hasa
Unayzah
Ma'an
Batn Al-Ghul
Al Aqabah
Al Mudawwarah
Halat 'Ammar
Al Bir
Tabuk
Qalat al Akhdar
Add-Dar Al Hamra
Al Mutie
Al Marham
Al Hajar
Al 'Ula
Al Badie'
Al B'ir
Al Musawwarah
Jad'a
Boulair
B'ir Nasir
Buwata
Al Madinah

Mediterranean Sea

Arabian Peninsula

An Nafud Great Desert

Sinai

Midian

Egypt

Red Sea

Hijaz

800 km
600
400
200

People of Ash-Sham
Route to Hajj

During the Abbasids
period and after.

Muttaqūn (the pious). Then when the Sacred Months (the 1st, 7th, 11th, and 12th months of the Islamic calendar) have passed, then kill the *Mushrikūn* wherever you find them, and capture them and besiege them, and lie in wait for them in every ambush. But if they repent [by rejecting *Shirk* (polytheism) and accept Islamic Monotheism] and perform *As-Salāt* (the prayers), and give *Zakāt* (obligatory charity), then leave their way free. Verily, Allāh is Oft-Forgiving, Most Merciful. And if anyone of the *Mushrikūn* (polytheists, idolaters, pagans, disbelievers in the Oneness of Allāh) seeks your protection then grant him protection so that he may hear the Word of Allāh (the Qur'ān) and then escort him to where he can be secure, that is because they are men who know not. How can there be a covenant with Allāh and with His Messenger (ﷺ) for the *Mushrikūn* (polytheists, idolaters, pagans, disbelievers in the Oneness of Allāh) except those with whom you made a covenant near *Al-Masjid Al-Harām* (at Makkah)? So long as they are true to you, stand you true to them. Verily, Allāh loves *Al-Muttaqūn* (the pious). How (can there be such a covenant with them) that when you are overpowered by them, they regard not the ties, either of kinship or of covenant with you? With (good words from) their mouths they please you, but their hearts are averse to you, and most of them are *Fāsiqūn* (rebellious, disobedient to Allāh). They have purchased with the *Ayāt* (proofs, evidences, Verses, lessons, signs, revelations, etc.) of Allāh a little gain, and they hindered men from His way; evil indeed is that which they used to do. With regard to a believer, they respect not the ties, either of kinship or of covenant! It is they who are the transgressors. But if they repent [by rejecting *Shirk* (polytheism) and accept Islamic Monotheism], perform *As-Salāt* (the prayers) and give *Zakāt* (obligatory charity), then they are your brethren in religion. (In this way) We explain the *Ayāt* (proofs, evidences, Verses, lessons, signs, revelations, etc.) in detail for a people who know. But if they violate their oaths after their covenant, and attack your religion with disapproval and criticism then fight (you) the leaders of disbelief (chiefs of Quraish pagans of

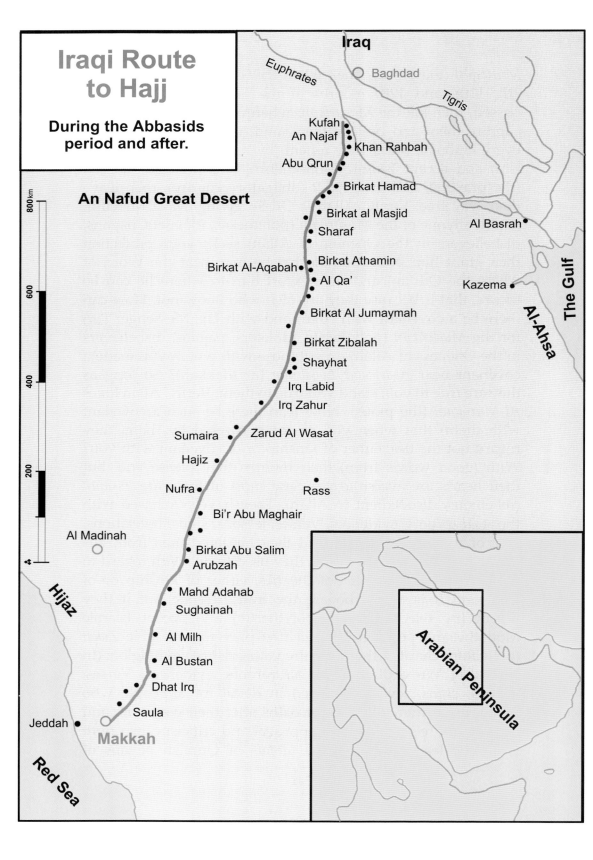

Makkah) — for surely, their oaths are nothing to them — so that they may stop (evil actions). Will you not fight a people (pagans of Makkah) who have violated their oaths and intended to expel the Messenger (ﷺ) while they did attack you first? Do you fear them? Allāh has more right that you should fear Him if you are believers. Fight against them so that Allāh will punish them by your hands and disgrace them and give you victory over them and heal the breasts of a believing people, and remove the anger of their (believers') hearts. Allāh accepts the repentance of whom He wills. Allāh is All-Knowing, All-Wise. Do you think that you shall be left alone while Allāh has not yet tested those among you who have striven hard and fought and have not taken Walījah [(Bitānah — helpers, advisors and consultants from disbelievers, pagans) giving openly to them their secrets] besides Allāh and His Messenger (ﷺ), and the believers. Allāh is Well-Acquainted with what you do. It is not for the Mushrikūn (polytheists, idolaters, pagans, disbelievers in the Oneness of Allāh) to maintain the mosques of Allāh (i.e. to pray and worship Allāh therein, to look after their cleanliness and their building), while they witness against their own selves of disbelief. The works of such are in vain and in Fire shall they abide. The mosques of Allāh shall be maintained only by those who believe in Allāh and the Last Day; perform As-Salāt (the prayers), and give Zakāt (obligatory charity) and fear none but Allāh. It is they who are on true guidance. Do you consider the providing of drinking water for the pilgrims and the maintenance of Al-Masjid Al-Harām (at Makkah) as equal to the one who believes in Allāh and the Last Day, and strives hard and fights in the Cause of Allāh? They are not equal before Allāh. And Allāh guides not those people who are the Zālimūn (polytheists and wrong doers). Those who believed (in the Oneness of Allāh — Islamic Monotheism) and emigrated and strove hard and fought in Allāh's Cause with their wealth and their lives, are far higher in degree with Allāh. They are the successful. Their Lord gives them glad tidings of mercy from Him, and His being pleased (with them), and of Gardens (Paradise) for them

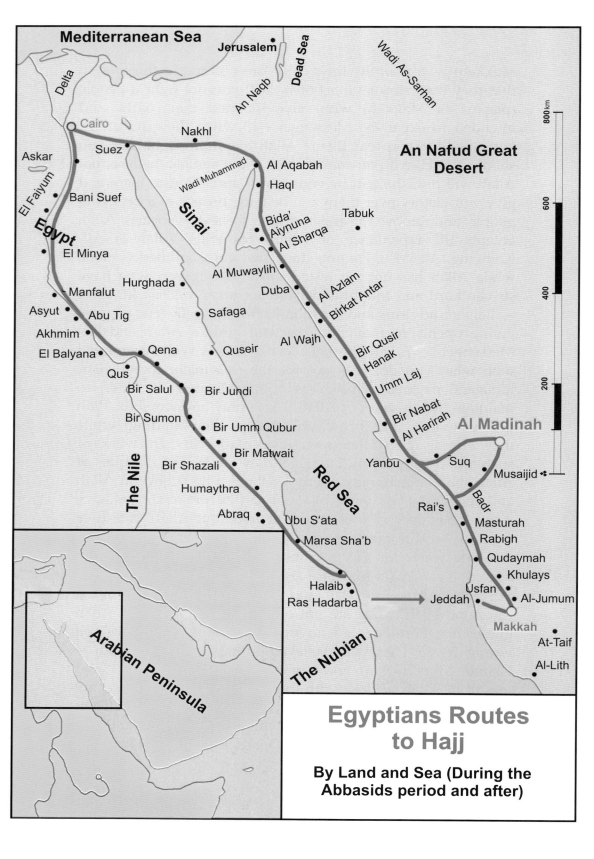

Mediterranean Sea

Jerusalem

Dead Sea

Wadi As-Sarhan

Delta

Cairo

Nakhl

Askar

Suez

An Naqb

El Faiyum

Bani Suef

Wadi Muhammad

Al Aqabah

Haql

An Nafud Great Desert

Egypt

Sinai

El Minya

Bida' Aiynuna

Al Sharqa

Tabuk

Manfalut

Hurghada

Al Muwaylih

Asyut

Abu Tig

Safaga

Duba

Al Azlam

Birkat Antar

Akhmim

Quseir

Al Wajh

Bir Qusir

El Balyana

Qena

Hanak

Qus

Bir Salul

Bir Jundi

Umm Laj

Bir Sumon

Bir Umm Qubur

Bir Nabat

Al Madinah

Al Harirah

The Nile

Bir Matwait

Yanbu

Suq

Bir Shazali

Red Sea

Musaijid

Humaythra

Rai's

Badr

Abraq

Ubu S'ata

Masturah

Marsa Sha'b

Rabigh

Qudaymah

Khulays

Halaib

Usfan

Al-Jumum

Ras Hadarba

Jeddah

Makkah

At-Taif

The Nubian

Al-Lith

Arabian Peninsula

800 km

600

400

200

Egyptians Routes to Hajj

By Land and Sea (During the Abbasids period and after)

wherein are everlasting delights. They will dwell therein forever. Verily, with Allāh is a great reward. O you who believe! Take not as *Auliyā'* (supporters and helpers) your fathers and your brothers if they prefer disbelief to Belief. And whoever of you does so, then he is one of the *Zālimūn* (wrong doers).

(Qur'ân 9: 1-23)

$$ \text{﴿لَيْسَ عَلَيْكُمْ جُنَاحٌ أَن تَبْتَغُوا۟ فَضْلًا مِّن رَّبِّكُمْ ۚ فَإِذَآ أَفَضْتُم مِّنْ عَرَفَٰتٍ فَٱذْكُرُوا۟ ٱللَّهَ عِندَ ٱلْمَشْعَرِ ٱلْحَرَامِ ۖ وَٱذْكُرُوهُ كَمَا هَدَىٰكُمْ وَإِن كُنتُم مِّن قَبْلِهِۦ لَمِنَ ٱلضَّآلِّينَ ﴿١٩٨﴾﴾} $$

There is no sin on you if you seek the bounty of your Lord (during pilgrimage by trading). Then when you leave 'Arafāt, remember Allāh (by glorifying His Praises, i.e., prayers and invocations) at the *Mash'ar-il-Harām*. And remember Him (by invoking Allāh for all good) as He has guided you, and verily, you were, before, of those who were astray.

(Qur'ân 2: 198)

"The Greatest Day" refers to the *Hajj* of *'Arafah*, distinguishing it (The Greater *Hajj*) from *'Umrah*. It is also said that it refers to the Day of *An-Nahr*. It is called the Greater *Hajj* (The Greater Pilgrimage) because *'Umrah* is called the Lesser *Hajj* (The Lesser Pilgrimage). It is also called the Greater *Hajj* because among the pilgrims of that particular *Hajj* was Abu Bakr As-Siddeeq ﷺ.

As for the Farewell Pilgrimage (*Hajjatul-Wida'*), *Hajjatul-Balâgh*, or the Pilgrimage of Islam (*Hajjatul-Islam*), these all refer to the *Hajj* of the year 10 H, the only year in which the Prophet ﷺ performed *Hajj*. There are many important lessons that the Prophet ﷺ taught during that pilgrimage; one of those lessons was that, no matter how rich or poor a person is, and no matter what color a person is, he is inherently equal to all other human beings: the only factor that can make a person superior to others is the level of his *Taqwa* (piety).

After Islam began to spread, there are four major routes people took in traveling from their lands to Makkah for *Hajj* (these routes are

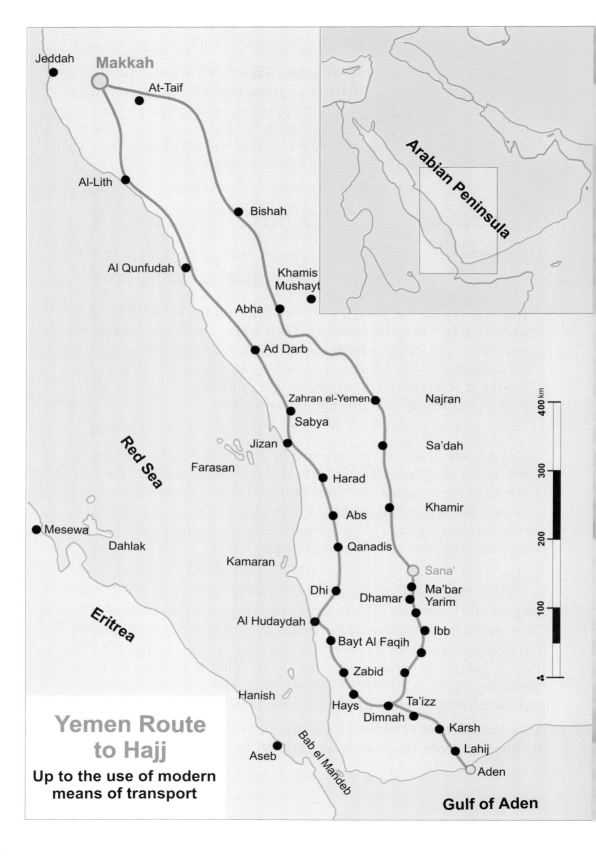

Jeddah

Makkah

At-Taif

Arabian Peninsula

Al-Lith

Bishah

Al Qunfudah

Khamis
Mushayt

Abha

Ad Darb

Zahran el-Yemen

Najran

Sabya

Red Sea

Jizan

Sa'dah

Farasan

Harad

Mesewa

Abs

Khamir

Dahlak

Qanadis

Kamaran

Sana'

Dhi

Ma'bar
Yarim

Dhamar

Eritrea

Al Hudaydah

Ibb

Bayt Al Faqih

Zabid

Hanish

Ta'izz

Hays

Karsh

Dimnah

**Yemen Route
to Hajj**

Lahij

Aseb

Aden

**Up to the use of modern
means of transport**

Gulf of Aden

400 km

300

200

100

outlined in the maps on the following pages):

1) Al-Hajj Ash-Shâmi (Which came through Ash-Sham)
2) Al-Hajj Al-Misri (Which came through Egypt)
3) Al-Hajj Al-'Irâqi (Which came through Iraq)
4) Al-Hajj Al-Yameni (Which came through Yemen)

- Ibn Hishâm: 2/352
- Al-Bidâyah wan-Nihayah: 5/109
- At-Tafsir Al-Munir: 10/102
- Safwatut-Tafâsir: 1/521
- At-Tabari: 3/148
- Al-Kashshâf: 2/246

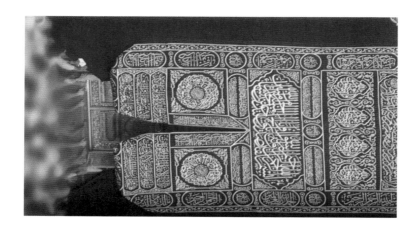

Al-Multazim (Door of the Ka'bah)

Sa'y between As-Safa And Al-Marwah

**Outside view of the burial place of the Prophet (ﷺ)
in Al-Madinah Al-Munawwarah**

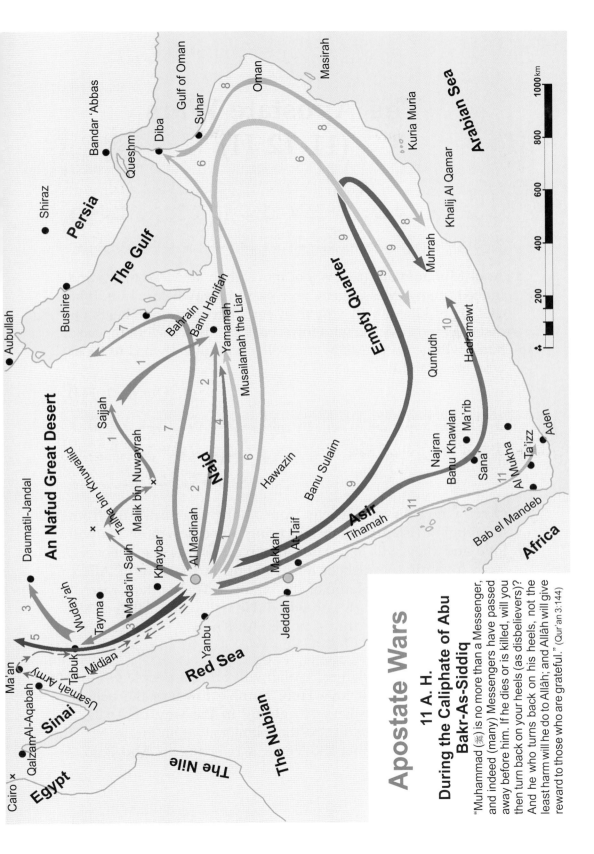

Apostate Wars
11 A. H.
During the Caliphate of Abu Bakr-As-Siddiq

"Muhammad (ﷺ) is no more than a Messenger, and indeed (many) Messengers have passed away before him. If he dies or is killed, will you then turn back on your heels (as disbelievers)? And he who turns back on his heels, not the least harm will he do to Allāh; and Allāh will give reward to those who are grateful." (Qur'an 3:144)

Egypt
Cairo ×
Qalzam Al-Aqabah
Ma'an
Sinai
Usamah Army
Midian
Tabuk
3 Mada'in Salih
Tayma
Wuday'ah
Daumatil-Jandal
An Nafud Great Desert
×
Taher bin Khuwailid
×
Malik bin Nuwayrah
Khaybar
Sajiah
Al Madinah
Yanbu
Red Sea
Jeddah
Makkah
At-Taif
The Nile
The Nubian
Bahrain
Banu Hanifah
Yamamah
Musailamah the Liar
Najd
Hawazin
Banu Sulaim
Asir
Tihamah
Bab el Mandeb
Africa
Al Mukha
Ta'izz
Aden
Sana'
Ma'rib
Banu Khawlan
Najran
Qunfudh
Hadramawt
Empty Quarter
Muhrah
Khalij Al Qamar
Kuria Muria
Arabian Sea
Oman
Masirah
Gulf of Oman
Suhar
Diba
Queshm
Bandar 'Abbas
The Gulf
Bushire
Shiraz
Persia
Aubullah

1000 km
800
600
400
200

The Apostate Wars
(11-12 H)

﴿وَمَا مُحَمَّدٌ إِلَّا رَسُولٌ قَدْ خَلَتْ مِن قَبْلِهِ ٱلرُّسُلُ أَفَإِيْن مَّاتَ أَوْ قُتِلَ ٱنقَلَبْتُمْ عَلَىٰ أَعْقَابِكُمْ وَمَن يَنقَلِبْ عَلَىٰ عَقِبَيْهِ فَلَن يَضُرَّ ٱللَّهَ شَيْئًا وَسَيَجْزِي ٱللَّهُ ٱلشَّـٰكِرِينَ ۝﴾

And Muhammad (ﷺ) is no more than a Messenger, and indeed (many) Messengers have passed away before him. If he dies or is killed, will you then turn back on your heels (as disbelievers)? And he who turns back on his heels, not the least harm will he do to Allāh; and Allāh will give reward to those who are grateful.

(Qur'ân 3: 144)

﴿يَـٰٓأَيُّهَا ٱلَّذِينَ ءَامَنُوا مَن يَرْتَدَّ مِنكُمْ عَن دِينِهِ فَسَوْفَ يَأْتِي ٱللَّهُ بِقَوْمٍ يُحِبُّهُمْ وَيُحِبُّونَهُۥ أَذِلَّةٍ عَلَى ٱلْمُؤْمِنِينَ أَعِزَّةٍ عَلَى ٱلْكَـٰفِرِينَ يُجَـٰهِدُونَ فِي سَبِيلِ ٱللَّهِ وَلَا يَخَافُونَ لَوْمَةَ لَآئِمٍ ذَٰلِكَ فَضْلُ ٱللَّهِ يُؤْتِيهِ مَن يَشَآءُ وَٱللَّهُ وَٰسِعٌ عَلِيمٌ ۝﴾

O you who believe! Whoever from among you turns back from his religion (Islam), Allāh will bring a people whom He will love and they will love Him; humble towards the believers, stern towards the disbelievers, fighting in the way of Allāh, and never fear the blame of the blamers. That is the Grace of Allāh which He bestows on whom He wills. And Allāh is All-Sufficient for His creatures' needs, All-Knower.

(Qur'ân 5: 54)

As for the saying of Allâh ﷻ, "Allâh will bring a people whom He will love and they will love Him; humble towards the believers, stern towards the disbelievers, fighting in the way of Allâh, and never afraid of the blame of the blamers." (Qur'ân 5: 54), the scholars of *Tafsir* say that the Verse is referring to Abu Bakr As-

Siddiq ﷺ and his companions who fought with him against the apostates.

When the Prophet ﷺ died, many Arab tribes apostatized; some of them did so when they refused to pay *Zakât*; and others, when they sided with liars who claimed to be prophets, such as Musailamah Al-Kadhdhâb, Tulaihah Al-Asdi, and Sujâh.

Abu Bakr As-Siddiq ﷺ prepared 11 armies, and he followed their progress closely from Al-Madinah, as if he were seated in a modern-day command center. He was able to keep a close eye on the progress of his armies their comings and goings, their daily battles, their movements and strategy, etc., through military messengers, who went back and forth with messages to and from Abu Bakr ﷺ and the leaders of his armies.

The decisive battle took place in Al-Yamâmah against Musailamah Al-Kaddhâb and his followers. The battle reached its climax in a garden that, from then on, became known as *Hadiqatul-Mawt* (The Garden of Death). It was there that many eminent Companions ﷺ showed wonderful examples of bravery and sacrifice. Musailamah was killed by the sword of 'Abdullah ibn Zaid Al-Ansâri ﷺ and the spear of Wahshi ﷺ. And the main responsibility of leading the Muslims and ending the apostate movement rested on the shoulders of Khâlid ibn Al-Walid ﷺ. After the Muslims were victorious in the Apostate Wars, Abu Bakr As-Siddiq ﷺ began to send armies to conquer Iraq and to free the lands of Ash-Sham, thus bringing people out of the darkness of disbelief and into the light of belief.

- Al-Bidâyah wan-Nihayah: 6/311
- At-Tabari: 2/241
- Al-Kamil Fit-Târikh: 2/231

The Eleven Armies And Leaders
Of The Apostate Wars

S.No.	Leader Of The Army	Destination Of The Army
1	Khâlid ibn Al-Walid 🙵	To Buzâkhah, where Tulaihah ibn Khuwailid Al-Asdi and his followers lived. The army then traveled to Al-Battâh, where Mâlik ibn Nuwairah and his followers lived. Finally, the army proceeded to Al-Yamâmah, to participate in the battle against Musailamah Al-Kaddhâb.
2	'Ikrimah ibn Abi Jahl 🙵	This army, led by 'Ikrimah 🙵, went to Al-Yamâmah, where Musailamah ibn Al-Kaddhâb and his followers lived. 'Ikrimah's army, or unit, was needed to help the greater army of Khâlid ibn Al-Walid 🙵. Afterwards, 'Ikrimah's army moved on to Oman, where Dhut-Tâj, or Laqit ibn Mâlik Al-Azdi lived. They then moved on to Muhrah, to Hadramawt, and then finally to Yemen.
3	'Amr ibn Al-'Aas 🙵	'Amr's army went to Tabûk and Daumatil-Jandal, where the tribes of Qudâ'ah, Di'ah, and Al-Haarith lived.

S.No.	Leader Of The Army	Destination Of The Army
4	Shurahbil ibn Hasanah ﷺ	Following the lead of 'Ikrimah's unit, Shurahbil's unit went to Al-Yamamah, and it too was considered a precautionary and additional unit to the larger Muslim army that was already there. Afterwards, they moved on to Hadramawt.
5	Khâlid ibn Sa'eed ibn Al-'Aas ﷺ	This army traveled to Al-Hamqatain (the highlands of Ash-Sham)
6	Turaifah ibn Hâjiz ﷺ	This army traveled to the east of Makkah and Madinah, to where the tribes of Hawâzin and Banu Sulaim were situated.
7	Al-'Alâ ibn Al-Hadrami ﷺ	Al-'Alâ's army traveled to Bahrain, where Al-Maghrur, Al-Mundhir ibn An-Nau'mân ibn Al-Mundhir, lived.
8	Hudhaifah ibn Mihsan Al-Ghalfâni	Hudhaifah's army traveled to 'Oman (the people of Diba), where Dhut-Tâj, or Laqeet ibn Mâlik Al-Azdi, lived. It then moved on to Muhrah, to Hadramawt, and finally to Yemen.
9	'Arfajah ibn Harthamah Al-Bâriqi	'Arfajah's army first went to Oman then Muhrah, then to Hadramawt, and finally to Yemen.
10	Al-Muhajir ibn Abi Umayyah	This army first went to Yemen; afterwards it went to Kandah and then to Hadramawt.
11	Suwaid ibn Muqarrin Al-Muzani	Suwaid's army went to Tuhâmatul-Yemen and then traveled along the shores of the Red Sea, from Makkah until Bâb Al-Mandib

Appendix

To make this Atlas more comprehensive, I include here a description of places, peoples, and persons that are mentioned either explicitly or implicitly in the Noble Qur'ân and that do not require any map or picture for me to describe them.

﴿وَلَا تُسۡرِفُوٓا﴾

- **"And waste not by extravagance"**

﴿وَهُوَ ٱلَّذِىٓ أَنشَأَ جَنَّٰتٍ مَّعۡرُوشَٰتٍ وَغَيۡرَ مَعۡرُوشَٰتٍ وَٱلنَّخۡلَ وَٱلزَّرۡعَ مُخۡتَلِفًا أُكُلُهُۥ وَٱلزَّيۡتُونَ وَٱلرُّمَّانَ مُتَشَٰبِهًا وَغَيۡرَ مُتَشَٰبِهٍ كُلُوا۟ مِن ثَمَرِهِۦٓ إِذَآ أَثۡمَرَ وَءَاتُوا۟ حَقَّهُۥ يَوۡمَ حَصَادِهِۦ وَلَا تُسۡرِفُوٓا۟ إِنَّهُۥ لَا يُحِبُّ ٱلۡمُسۡرِفِينَ ١٤١﴾

"And it is He Who produces gardens trellised and untrellised, and date-palms, and crops of different shape and taste (its fruits and its seeds) and olives, and pomegranates, similar (in kind) and different (in taste). Eat of their fruit when they ripen, but pay the due thereof (its *Zakât*, according to Allâh's Orders 1/10th or 1/20th) on the day of its harvest, and waste not by extravagance. Verily, He likes not *Al-Musrifun* (those who waste by extravagance)."

(Qur'ân 6: 141)

This was revealed in regards to Thâbit ibn Qais ibn Shammâs, who cut off all of the fruits of his trees and fed them to others; by the time nightfall came, he had no fruits left that he could call his own.

﴿ٱلۡأَبۡتَرُ﴾

- **"He will be cut off"**

﴿إِنَّ شَانِئَكَ هُوَ ٱلۡأَبۡتَرُ ٣﴾

356

"For he who makes you angry (O Muhammad ﷺ, – he will be cut off (from every good thing in this world and in the Hereafter).''

(Qur'ân 108: 3)

This verse was revealed about Al-'Aas ibn Wâ'il. When the Prophet's son Al-Qâsim died, Al-'Aas said the following about the Prophet ﷺ: "Leave him, for he is a man who is cut off: he has no offspring (i.e., he will have no descendents). When he dies, he will no longer be remembered.'' In reality, as we are reminded of in the above verse, it is Al-'Aas who is cut off cut off, from the mercy of Allâh ﷻ.

- **"Abu Lahab"**

﴿تَبَّتْ يَدَآ أَبِى لَهَبٍ وَتَبَّ ۝ مَآ أَغْنَىٰ عَنْهُ مَالُهُ وَمَا كَسَبَ ۝ سَيَصْلَىٰ نَارًا ذَاتَ لَهَبٍ ۝ وَٱمْرَأَتُهُ حَمَّالَةَ ٱلْحَطَبِ ۝ فِى جِيدِهَا حَبْلٌ مِّن مَّسَدِۢ ۝﴾

"Perish the two hands of Abu Lahab (an uncle of the Prophet ﷺ), and perish he! His wealth and his children (etc.) will not benefit him! He will be burnt in a Fire of blazing flames! And his wife too, who carries wood (thorns of Sadan which she used to put on the way of the Prophet ﷺ, or used to slander him). In her neck is a twisted rope of Masad (palm fibre).''

(Qur'ân 111: 1-5)

Abu Lahab's full name is 'Abdul-'Uzza ibn 'Abdul-Muttalib, and he was one of the uncles of the Messenger of Allâh ﷺ. His wife was 'Arwa Umm Jamil, a sister of Abu Sufyân; she was called, as is mentioned in the above verse, the one 'who carries wood.' This, a famous metaphor in the Arabic language, refers to a slanderer. These two – Abu Lahab and 'Arwa showed unmitigated enmity and cruelness to the Messenger of Allâh ﷺ.

- **"Four are Sacred"**

﴿إِنَّ عِدَّةَ ٱلشُّهُورِ عِندَ ٱللَّهِ ٱثۡنَا عَشَرَ شَهۡرًا فِى كِتَٰبِ ٱللَّهِ يَوۡمَ خَلَقَ ٱلسَّمَٰوَٰتِ وَٱلۡأَرۡضَ مِنۡهَآ أَرۡبَعَةٌ حُرُمٌ ذَٰلِكَ ٱلدِّينُ ٱلۡقَيِّمُ فَلَا تَظۡلِمُواْ فِيهِنَّ أَنفُسَكُمۡ وَقَٰتِلُواْ ٱلۡمُشۡرِكِينَ كَآفَّةً كَمَا يُقَٰتِلُونَكُمۡ كَآفَّةً وَٱعۡلَمُوٓاْ أَنَّ ٱللَّهَ مَعَ ٱلۡمُتَّقِينَ ﴿٣٦﴾﴾

"Verily, the number of months with Allâh is twelve months (in a year), so was it ordained by Allâh on the Day when He created the heavens and the earth; of them four are Sacred, (i.e., the 1st, the 7th, the 11th, and the 12th months of the Islamic calendar). That is the right religion, so wrong not yourselves therein, and fight against the Mushrikoon (polytheists, pagans, idolators, disbelievers in the Oneness of Allâh) collectively, as they fight against you collectively. But know that Allâh is with those who are *Al-Muttaqun* (the pious)."

(Qur'ân 9: 36)

These, in their proper order, are the twelve months of the lunar calendar: Muharram, Safar, Rabi' Al-Awwal, Rabi' Ath-Thâni, Jumâda Al-Ulah, Jumâda Ath-Thâniyah, Rajab, Sha'bân, Ramadan, Shawwâl, Dhul-Qa'dah, and Dhul-Hijjah.

As the above-mentioned verse clarifies, four of these months are sacred. They are Dhul-Qa'dah, Dhul-Hijjah, Muharram (these three come one after the other), and Rajab (which is preceded and followed by months that are not from the Sacred Months). These are sacred and inviolable months, months in which people should strive to do more acts of worship, and in which fighting is prohibited, so as to ensure safety for *Hajj* (in the first three of the sacred months) and *'Umrah* (in Rajab).

﴿ٱمۡرَأَتُ فِرۡعَوۡنَ﴾

- **"The wife of Fir'aun"**

﴿وَقَالَتِ ٱمۡرَأَتُ فِرۡعَوۡنَ قُرَّتُ عَيۡنٍ لِّى وَلَكَ لَا تَقۡتُلُوهُ عَسَىٰٓ أَن يَنفَعَنَآ أَوۡ نَتَّخِذَهُۥ وَلَدًا وَهُمۡ لَا يَشۡعُرُونَ ﴿٩﴾﴾

"And the wife of Fir'aun (Pharaoh) said: 'A comfort of the eye for me and for you. Kill him not, perhaps he may be of benefit to us, or we may adopt him as a son.' And they perceive not (the result of that)."

(Qur'ân 28: 9)

Fir'aun's wife was Aasiyah bint Muzâhim, a noble and pious believer, whose heart Allâh ﷻ filled with compassion for Musa ﷺ.

$$﴾قُرَّتُ عَيْنٍ لِّي وَلَكَ لَا تَقْتُلُوهُ عَسَىٰ أَن يَنفَعَنَا أَوۡ نَتَّخِذَهُۥ وَلَدًا﴿$$

"A comfort of the eye for me and for you. Kill him not, perhaps he may be of benefit to us, or we may adopt him as a son."

And Allâh ﷻ honored her with true *Imân* (Faith).

$$أَهْلُ الْمَدِينَةِ الَّتِي اسْتَطْعَمَا أَهْلَهَا$$

• **"The people of a town they asked them for food"**

$$﴾فَانطَلَقَا حَتَّىٰ إِذَآ أَتَيَآ أَهۡلَ قَرۡيَةٍ ٱسۡتَطۡعَمَآ أَهۡلَهَا فَأَبَوۡاْ أَن يُضَيِّفُوهُمَا فَوَجَدَا فِيهَا جِدَارًا يُرِيدُ أَن يَنقَضَّ فَأَقَامَهُۥۖ قَالَ لَوۡ شِئۡتَ لَتَّخَذۡتَ عَلَيۡهِ أَجۡرًا ۝﴿$$

"Then they both proceeded, till, when they came to the people of a town, they asked them for food, but they refused to entertain them. Then they found therein a wall about to collapse and he (Khidr) set it up straight. [Musa (Moses)] said: "If you had wished, surely, you could have taken wages for it!"

(Qur'ân 18: 77)

The name of the town is not mentioned in the above Verse, which is why people differ about which town is being referred to. Some say that it is Antâkiyah; others, that it is Ailah (Al-'Aqabah); others, that it is Tanjah; and yet others, that it is a city in the region of Al-Buhairât Al-Murrah.

The following is taken from Ibn Al-Qayyim's book *Miftâh Dârus-Sa'adah*: "A questioner asked about the name of the town that is referred to in *Sûrat Al-Kahf* (i.e., the above-mentioned Verse). It has been said that it is Ailah (Al-'Aqabah); it has also been said that it is

359

Antâkiyah, or Tanjah, or the meeting of the Gulf of Al-'Aqabah and the Gulf of As-Suweis, or that it is beside Al-Buhairât Al-Murrah. Allâh ﷻ did not mention the name of the town, thus protecting it from being exposed for the quality of miserliness, a quality that is hated by Allâh ﷻ as well as by people. Had Allâh ﷻ mentioned the name of the town, the reputation of being miserly would have stuck to its inhabitants until the Day of Resurrection.

- **"The two seas"**

﴿مَرَجَ ٱلْبَحْرَيْنِ يَلْتَقِيَانِ ۝ بَيْنَهُمَا بَرْزَخٌ لَّا يَبْغِيَانِ ۝﴾

"He has let loosed the two seas (the salt water and the sweet) meeting together. Between them is a barrier which none of them can transgress."

(Qur'ân 55: 19, 20)

Two bodies of water, one salty and one sweet, neighbor one another and even meet, yet they do not mix; there is a barrier between them, so that they do not mix. The same can be said about warm sea currents (such as the Gulf current) and cold currents (such as the Labrador current): the two meet but do not mix with one another.

﴿وَجَآءَ أَهْلُ ٱلْمَدِينَةِ يَسْتَبْشِرُونَ ۝﴾

- **"And the inhabitants of the city came rejoicing (at the news of the young men's arrival)." (Qur'ân 15: 67)**

Coming from the city of Soddom, these, the people of Lot, were rejoicing at the news of Lot's guests; their intention was to commit lewd acts on them.

﴿وَدَخَلَ ٱلْمَدِينَةَ عَلَى حِينِ غَفْلَةٍ مِّنْ أَهْلِهَا﴾

- **"And he entered the city at a time of unawareness of its people;" (Qur'ân 28: 15)**

This is referring to when Musa ﷵ entered either the city of Manf (Memphis) or Heliopolis (The Eye of the Sun), in Egypt.

360

$$\textnormal{﴿إِلَىٰ رَبْوَةٍ ذَاتِ قَرَارٍ وَمَعِينٍ﴾}$$

- **"And We gave them refuge on high ground..." (Qur'ân 23:50)**

This high ground is Jairun (in or near Damascus), though some believe that the verse is referring to a highland area somewhere near or in the land of Jerusalem.

$$\textnormal{﴿رِبِّيُّونَ﴾}$$

- **"Ribbiyun"**

$$\textnormal{﴿وَكَأَيِّن مِّن نَّبِيٍّ قَاتَلَ مَعَهُ رِبِّيُّونَ كَثِيرٌ فَمَا وَهَنُوا لِمَا أَصَابَهُمْ فِي سَبِيلِ اللَّهِ وَمَا ضَعُفُوا}$$
$$\textnormal{وَمَا اسْتَكَانُوا ۗ وَاللَّهُ يُحِبُّ الصَّابِرِينَ ﴿١٤٦﴾﴾}$$

"And many a Prophet (i.e., many from amongst the Prophets) fought (in Allâh's Cause) and along with him (fought) *Ribbiyun* (large bands of religious learned men). But they never lost heart for that which did befall them in Allâh's way, nor did they weaken nor degrade themselves. And Allâh loves *As-Sâbirin* (the patient ones etc.)."

(Qur'ân 3: 146)

Ribbiyun refers to scholars who educate, train, and raise people to higher levels of faith. They are righteous slaves of Allâh, and they are wise, learned men of the religion.

$$\textnormal{﴿زَيْدٌ﴾ (ابْنُ حَارِثَةَ)}$$

- **Zaid ibn Hârithah ﷺ**

$$\textnormal{﴿وَإِذْ تَقُولُ لِلَّذِي أَنْعَمَ اللَّهُ عَلَيْهِ وَأَنْعَمْتَ عَلَيْهِ أَمْسِكْ عَلَيْكَ زَوْجَكَ وَاتَّقِ اللَّهَ وَتُخْفِي فِي}$$
$$\textnormal{نَفْسِكَ مَا اللَّهُ مُبْدِيهِ وَتَخْشَى النَّاسَ وَاللَّهُ أَحَقُّ أَن تَخْشَاهُ ۖ فَلَمَّا قَضَىٰ زَيْدٌ مِّنْهَا وَطَرًا}$$
$$\textnormal{زَوَّجْنَاكَهَا لِكَيْ لَا يَكُونَ عَلَى الْمُؤْمِنِينَ حَرَجٌ فِي أَزْوَاجِ أَدْعِيَائِهِمْ إِذَا قَضَوْا مِنْهُنَّ وَطَرًا ۚ}$$
$$\textnormal{وَكَانَ أَمْرُ اللَّهِ مَفْعُولًا ﴿٣٧﴾﴾}$$

"And (remember) when you said to him (Zaid ibn Hârithah

361

‏, the freed slave of the Prophet ‏ﷺ‏) on whom Allâh has bestowed Grace (by guiding him to Islam) and you (O Muhammad) have done favor (by manumitting him) "Keep your wife to yourself, and fear Allâh." But you did hide in yourself (i.e., what Allâh has already made known to you that He will give her to you in marriage) that which Allâh will make manifest, you did fear the people (i.e., Muhammad ‏ﷺ‏ married the divorced wife of his manumitted slave) whereas Allâh had a better right that you should fear Him. So when Zaid had accomplished his desire from her (i.e., divorced her), We gave her to you in marriage, so that (in future) there may be no difficulty to the believers in respect of (the marriage of) the wives of their adopted sons when the latter have no desire to keep them (i.e., they have divorced them). And Allâh's Command must be fulfilled."

(Qur'ân 33: 37)

﴿لِّلَّذِىٓ أَنۡعَمَ ٱللَّهُ عَلَيۡهِ﴾

"on whom Allâh has bestowed Grace": by guiding Zaid ibn Hârithah to Islam.

﴿وَأَنۡعَمۡتَ عَلَيۡـهِ﴾

"And you (O Muhammad) have done favor (by manumitting him)": By not only emancipating Zaid ‏, but also providing him with a good upbringing.

﴿أَمۡسِكۡ عَلَيۡكَ زَوۡجَكَ﴾

"Keep your wife to yourself": This is referring to Zainab bint Jahsh ‏.

﴿ٱلسَّامِرِىُّ﴾

• **"As-Sâmiri"**

﴿قَالَ فَإِنَّا قَدۡ فَتَنَّا قَوۡمَكَ مِنۢ بَعۡدِكَ وَأَضَلَّهُمُ ٱلسَّامِرِىُّ ٨٥﴾

362

"(Allâh) said: Verily! We have tried your people in your absence, and As-Sâmiri has led them astray."

(Qur'ân 20: 85)

$$﴿قَالُوا۟ مَآ أَخْلَفْنَا مَوْعِدَكَ بِمَلْكِنَا وَلَٰكِنَّا حُمِّلْنَآ أَوْزَارًا مِّن زِينَةِ ٱلْقَوْمِ فَقَذَفْنَٰهَا فَكَذَٰلِكَ أَلْقَى ٱلسَّامِرِىُّ ۝٨٧﴾$$

"They said: We broke not the promise to you, of our own will, but we were made to carry the weight of the ornaments of the [Fir'aun's (Pharaoh's)] people, then we cast them (into the fire), and that was what As-Sâmiri suggested."

(Qur'ân 20: 87)

$$﴿قَالَ فَمَا خَطْبُكَ يَٰسَٰمِرِىُّ ۝٩٥﴾$$

"[Musa (Moses)] said: And what is the matter with you, O Sâmiri (i.e., why did you do so?)?"

(Qur'ân 20: 95)

As-Sâmiri was originally from the town of Bâjarma, which is situated in Syria, beside the Euphrates River, near the city of Ar-Raqqah. After first going to Egypt, As-Sâmiri then moved on to Sinai. He was both a magician and a hypocrite, and he came from a people who worshipped cows. While Musa ﷺ was away, As-Sâmiri gathered some pieces of jewelry and formed a calf out of them. He then invited Musa's people to worship that calf.

$$﴿ٱلسَّدَّيْنِ﴾$$

• "As-Saddain" (The two mountains)"

$$﴿حَتَّىٰٓ إِذَا بَلَغَ بَيْنَ ٱلسَّدَّيْنِ وَجَدَ مِن دُونِهِمَا قَوْمًا لَّا يَكَادُونَ يَفْقَهُونَ قَوْلًا ۝٩٣﴾$$

"Until, when he reached between two mountains, he found, before (near) them (those two mountains), a people who scarcely understood a word."

(Qur'ân 18: 93)

The area referred to above is situated between two huge barriers, where the lands of Mongolia end, not too far from Azerbaijan and Armenia. *As-Saddain* is the dual form for the word *Sadd*, which At-Tabari defined as being a barrier between two things. The meaning in this context is two mountains, between which a barrier was made. It was Dhul-Qarnain who filled up the barrier, in order to prevent the tribes of Ya'jûj and Ma'jûj from creating mischief and plundering neighboring towns and villages. It is said that the *As-Saddân* are situated near the Gate of Gates (Dirband).

﴿وَسَكَنتُمْ فِى مَسَٰكِنِ ٱلَّذِينَ ظَلَمُوٓا۟ أَنفُسَهُمْ﴾

- **"And you dwelt in the dwellings of men who wronged themselves..." (Qur'ân 14: 45)**

Of the various views in the matter, the strongest is that the above verse is referring to the dwellings of Sâlih, in southern Tabûk. The meaning of the verse is: You dwelt in the dwellings of men who wronged themselves and whom we consequently destroyed; will you then not reflect on and learn a lesson from their dwellings?

﴿وَٱلسَّلْوَىٰ﴾

- **"As-Salwa (The quails)"**

﴿وَظَلَّلْنَا عَلَيْكُمُ ٱلْغَمَامَ وَأَنزَلْنَا عَلَيْكُمُ ٱلْمَنَّ وَٱلسَّلْوَىٰ كُلُوا۟ مِن طَيِّبَٰتِ مَا رَزَقْنَٰكُمْ وَمَا ظَلَمُونَا وَلَٰكِن كَانُوٓا۟ أَنفُسَهُمْ يَظْلِمُونَ ۝﴾

"And we shaded you with clouds and sent down on you *Al-Manna* and the quails, (saying): "Each of the good lawful things We have provided for you," (but they rebelled). And they did not wronged Us but they wronged themselves."

(Qur'ân 2: 57)

﴿وَقَطَّعْنَٰهُمُ ٱثْنَتَىْ عَشْرَةَ أَسْبَاطًا أُمَمًا وَأَوْحَيْنَآ إِلَىٰ مُوسَىٰٓ إِذِ ٱسْتَسْقَىٰهُ قَوْمُهُۥٓ أَنِ ٱضْرِب بِّعَصَاكَ ٱلْحَجَرَ فَٱنۢبَجَسَتْ مِنْهُ ٱثْنَتَا عَشْرَةَ عَيْنًا قَدْ عَلِمَ كُلُّ أُنَاسٍ مَّشْرَبَهُمْ وَظَلَّلْنَا عَلَيْهِمُ ٱلْغَمَٰمَ وَأَنزَلْنَا عَلَيْهِمُ ٱلْمَنَّ وَٱلسَّلْوَىٰ كُلُوا۟ مِن طَيِّبَٰتِ مَا رَزَقْنَٰكُمْ وَمَا ظَلَمُونَا وَلَٰكِن كَانُوٓا۟ أَنفُسَهُمْ يَظْلِمُونَ ۝﴾

"And We divided them into 12 tribes (as distinct) nations. We directed Musa (Moses) by inspiration, (saying): 'Strike the stone with your stick,' and there gushed forth out of it 12 springs: each group knew its own place for water. We shaded them with the clouds and sent down upon them *Al-Manna* and the quails (saying): 'Eat of the good things with which We have provided you.' They harmed Us not but they used to harm themselves."

(Qur'ân 7: 160)

﴿يَٰبَنِىٓ إِسۡرَٰٓءِيلَ قَدۡ أَنجَيۡنَٰكُم مِّنۡ عَدُوِّكُمۡ وَوَٰعَدۡنَٰكُمۡ جَانِبَ ٱلطُّورِ ٱلۡأَيۡمَنَ وَنَزَّلۡنَا عَلَيۡكُمُ ٱلۡمَنَّ وَٱلسَّلۡوَىٰ ٨٠﴾

"O Children of Israel! We delivered you from your enemy, and We made it covenants with you on the right side of the Mount, and We sent down to you *Al-Manna* and quails (*As-Salwa*)."

(Qur'ân 20: 80)

As-Salwa is a bird that is actually similar to a quail, and its taste is delicious. The majority of *Tafsir* scholars hold this view.

﴿سَنَسِمُهُ عَلَى ٱلۡخُرۡطُومِ ١٦﴾

- **"We shall brand him over the nose!" (Qur'ân 68: 16)**

This verse was revealed about Al-Walid ibn Al-Mughirah. It means: We shall brand him on his nose, so that he will be known by that disgrace until his death.

﴿طَآئِفَتَانِ﴾

- **"Two parties"**

﴿إِذۡ هَمَّت طَّآئِفَتَانِ مِنكُمۡ أَن تَفۡشَلَا وَٱللَّهُ وَلِيُّهُمَاۗ وَعَلَى ٱللَّهِ فَلۡيَتَوَكَّلِ ٱلۡمُؤۡمِنُونَ ١٢٢﴾

"When two parties from among you were about to lose heart, but Allâh was their *Wali* (Supporter and Protector). And in Allâh should the believers put their trust."

(Qur'ân 3: 122)

The parties referred to in this verse are two *Ansâr* clans: Banu Salamah and Banu Hârithah. These clans almost lost heart; they intended to leave Uhud after the betrayal of 'Abdullah ibn Ubai ibn Salûl, who retreated with one-third of the army. Ibn Salûl said, "For what reason should we kill ourselves and our children!" The two aforementioned clans from the *Ansâr* intended to leave as well, but then Allâh ﷻ protected them, and they remained with the Messenger of Allâh ﷺ.

﴿طَآئِفَتَيۡنِ﴾

- **"Two sects" (Qur'ân 6: 156)**

﴿أَن تَقُولُوٓاْ إِنَّمَآ أُنزِلَ ٱلۡكِتَـٰبُ عَلَىٰ طَآئِفَتَيۡنِ مِن قَبۡلِنَا وَإِن كُنَّا عَن دِرَاسَتِهِمۡ لَغَـٰفِلِينَ ﴿١٥٦﴾﴾

"Lest you (pagan Arabs) should say: The Book was only sent down to two sects before us (the Jews and Christians), and for our part, we were in fact unaware of what they studied."

(Qur'ân 6: 156)

The two sects referred to in this verse are the Jews and the Christians.

﴿وَيَسۡـَٔلُونَكَ عَن ذِى ٱلۡقَرۡنَيۡنِ﴾

- **"And they ask you about Dhul-Qarnain" (Qur'ân 18:83)**

Contrary to what some claim, he is definitely not Alexander of Macedon. Rather, Dhul-Qarnain was a righteous king, who was given both knowledge and wisdom. He was called Dhul-Qarnain (*Qarnain* is the dual form of *Qarn*, which means 'horn'), because he was the king of both eastern lands and western lands. He was a just, Muslim king.

﴿أَلَمۡ تَرَ إِلَى ٱلَّذِى حَآجَّ إِبۡرَٰهِـۧمَ فِى رَبِّهِۦ﴾

- **"Have you not looked at him who disputed with Ibrâhim (Abraham) about his Lord (Allâh)?" (Qur'ân 2: 258)**

It was An-Namrud ibn Kan'ân who disputed with Ibrâhim ﷺ about the existence of Allâh ﷻ.

﴿ٱلَّذِينَ كَفَرُوا۟ بِـَٔايَٰتِنَا﴾

- **"Surely! Those who disbelieved in Our *Ayât* (proofs, evidences, Verses, lessons, signs, revelations, etc.),"** (Qur'ân 4: 56)

This Verse is referring to Al-'Aas ibn Wâil ibn Hâshim As-Sahmi Al-Qurashi, who was from those who mocked and derided the Prophet ﷺ in particular, and the Muslims in general.

﴿أَوْ كَٱلَّذِى مَرَّ عَلَىٰ قَرْيَةٍ وَهِىَ خَاوِيَةٌ﴾

- **"Or like the one who passed by a town and it had tumbled over its roofs."**

﴿أَوْ كَٱلَّذِى مَرَّ عَلَىٰ قَرْيَةٍ وَهِىَ خَاوِيَةٌ عَلَىٰ عُرُوشِهَا قَالَ أَنَّىٰ يُحْىِۦ هَٰذِهِ ٱللَّهُ بَعْدَ مَوْتِهَا فَأَمَاتَهُ ٱللَّهُ مِا۟ئَةَ عَامٍ ثُمَّ بَعَثَهُۥ قَالَ كَمْ لَبِثْتَ قَالَ لَبِثْتُ يَوْمًا أَوْ بَعْضَ يَوْمٍ قَالَ بَل لَّبِثْتَ مِا۟ئَةَ عَامٍ فَٱنظُرْ إِلَىٰ طَعَامِكَ وَشَرَابِكَ لَمْ يَتَسَنَّهْ وَٱنظُرْ إِلَىٰ حِمَارِكَ وَلِنَجْعَلَكَ ءَايَةً لِّلنَّاسِ وَٱنظُرْ إِلَى ٱلْعِظَامِ كَيْفَ نُنشِزُهَا ثُمَّ نَكْسُوهَا لَحْمًا فَلَمَّا تَبَيَّنَ لَهُۥ قَالَ أَعْلَمُ أَنَّ ٱللَّهَ عَلَىٰ كُلِّ شَىْءٍ قَدِيرٌ ٢٥٩﴾

"Or like the one who passed by a town and it had tumbled over its roofs. He said: 'Oh! How will Allâh ever bring it to life after its death?' So Allâh caused him to die for a hundred years, then raised him up (again). He said: 'How long did you remain (dead)?' He (the man) said: '(Perhaps) I remained (dead) a day or part of a day.' He said: 'Nay, you have remained (dead) for a hundred years, look at your food and your drink, they show no change; and look at your donkey! And thus We have made of you a sign for the people. Look at the bones, how We bring them together and clothe them with flesh.' When this was clearly shown to him, he said, 'I know (now) that Allâh is able to do all things'."

(Qur'ân 2: 259)

367

The town mentioned at the beginning of the Verse is Jerusalem (Īliyâ), after it had been brought to ruin by Bukhtanassar.

﴿ٱلَّذِينَ يَبْخَلُونَ﴾

- **"Those who are miserly"**

﴿ٱلَّذِينَ يَبْخَلُونَ وَيَأْمُرُونَ ٱلنَّاسَ بِٱلْبُخْلِ وَيَكْتُمُونَ مَا ءَاتَىٰهُمُ ٱللَّهُ مِن فَضْلِهِۦ وَأَعْتَدْنَا لِلْكَٰفِرِينَ عَذَابًا مُّهِينًا ٣٧﴾

"Those who are miserly and enjoin miserliness on other men and hide what Allâh has bestowed upon them of His Bounties. And We have prepared for the disbelievers a disgraceful torment."

(Qur'ân 4: 37)

This Verse was revealed for a group of Jews, who used to say to the *Ansâr*, "Do not spend your wealth for *Jihad* or for charity."

﴿وَٱلَّذِينَ يَرْمُونَ أَزْوَٰجَهُمْ﴾

- **"And for those who accuse their wives..."** (Qur'ân 24: 6)

An incident between Hilâl ibn Umayyah ﷺ and his wife prompted the revealing of this verse. In the presence of the Prophet ﷺ, Hilâl ﷺ accused his wife of committing adultery with Sharik ibn Sahm ﷺ.

﴿ٱلَّذِينَ يُنَادُونَكَ مِن وَرَآءِ ٱلْحُجُرَٰتِ﴾

- **"Verily! Those who call you from behind the dwellings,"** (Qur'ân 49: 4)

'Uyainah ibn Hisn and Al-Aqra' ibn Hâbis led a delegation of 70 men from Banu Tamim who had all come to see the Messenger of Allâh ﷺ. They came to him at noontime, when he ﷺ was taking his midday nap. They called out from outside, "O Muhammad, come out to us."

﴿وَلَوْ أَنَّهُمْ صَبَرُوا۟ حَتَّىٰ تَخْرُجَ إِلَيْهِمْ لَكَانَ خَيْرًا لَّهُمْ﴾

"And if they had patience till you could come out to them, it would have been better for them."

﴾فَلَوْلَا كَانَتْ قَرْيَةٌ ءَامَنَتْ﴿

- **"Was there any town (community) that believed (after seeing the punishment)..." (Qur'ân 10: 98)**

The town being referred to is Ninawa, the town of Yunus .

﴾قَـٰرُونَ﴿

- **"Qârun"**

﴾إِنَّ قَـٰرُونَ كَانَ مِن قَوْمِ مُوسَىٰ فَبَغَىٰ عَلَيْهِمْ وَءَاتَيْنَـٰهُ مِنَ ٱلْكُنُوزِ مَآ إِنَّ مَفَاتِحَهُ لَتَنُوٓأُ بِٱلْعُصْبَةِ أُوْلِى ٱلْقُوَّةِ إِذْ قَالَ لَهُۥ قَوْمُهُۥ لَا تَفْرَحْ إِنَّ ٱللَّهَ لَا يُحِبُّ ٱلْفَرِحِينَ ٧٦﴿

"Verily, Qârun (Korah) was of Musa's (Moses) people, but he behaved arrogantly towards them. And We gave him of the treasures, that of which the keys would have been a burden to a body of strong men. When his people said to him: Do not be glad (with ungratefulness to Allâh's Favors). Verily! Allâh likes not those who are glad (with ungratefulness to Allâh's Favors)."

(Qur'ân 28: 76)

﴾وَقَـٰرُونَ وَفِرْعَوْنَ وَهَـٰمَـٰنَ وَلَقَدْ جَآءَهُم مُّوسَىٰ بِٱلْبَيِّنَـٰتِ فَٱسْتَكْبَرُواْ فِى ٱلْأَرْضِ وَمَا كَانُواْ سَـٰبِقِينَ ٣٩﴿

"And (We destroyed also) Qârun, (Korah), Fir'aun (Pharaoh), and Hâmân. And indeed Musa (Moses) came to them with clear Âyât (proofs, evidences, Verses, lessons, signs, revelations, etc.), but they were arrogant in the land, yet they could not outstrip Us (escape Our punishment)."

(Qur'ân 29: 40)

﴾إِلَىٰ فِرْعَوْنَ وَهَـٰمَـٰنَ وَقَـٰرُونَ فَقَالُواْ سَـٰحِرٌ كَذَّابٌ ٢٤﴿

"To Fir'aun (Pharaoh), Hâmân, and Qârun (Korah), but they

called (him): "A sorcerer, a liar!''

(Qur'ân 40: 24)

Fir'aun (Pharaoh) was the well-known tyrant, and Hâmân was his minister. And Qârun, the cousin of Musa ﷺ, was an extremely wealthy man. Based on the wealth that Allâh ﷺ blessed him with, Qârûn thought he was superior to others, and so he began to deal with his people in an arrogant and high-handed manner.

﴿ٱلْقُرَى ٱلَّتِي بَرَكْنَا فِيهَا﴾

- **"And the towns which We had blessed,"** (Qur'ân 34: 18)

The area referred to in this verse extends from the lands of Saba' to the towns of Ash-Sham; they are a series of towns that come one after another from Yemen to Ash-Sham. These towns are so close to one another that it is often the case that, while one is in certain areas of one of the towns, one can see the town that is next to it.

﴿ٱلْقَرْيَةِ ٱلَّتِي أُمْطِرَتْ مَطَرَ ٱلسَّوْءِ﴾

- **"The town on which was rained the evil rain."** (Qur'ân 25: 40)

This Verse is referring to the town of Prophet Lot ﷺ, Sodom and Gomorrah. The Quraish would often pass it on their way to doing business in Ash-Sham.

﴿ٱلْقَرْيَةِ ٱلظَّالِمِ أَهْلُهَا﴾

- **"This town whose people are oppressors;"** (Qur'ân 4: 75)

This Verse is referring to Makkah, which remained a land of disbelief until it was conquered in the year 8 H. 'Whose people' refers to the leaders of the Quraish, who prevented the weak Muslims from migrating to Al-Madinah, and who, until the year 8 H, forbade Makkah's inhabitants from openly practicing the religion of Islam.

﴿قَرْيَةً كَانَتْ ءَامِنَةً مُّطْمَئِنَّةً﴾

- **"A township, that dwelt secure and well content."** (Qur'ân

Although it seems obvious that the verse is referring to Makkah, some believe that it is referring to another township that is meant to serve as an example for Makkah. Ar-Râzi said, "This is an example for the people of Makkah, for they lived a life of safety, comfort, and prosperity. Then Allâh ﷻ sent a great blessing to them, Muhammad ﷺ, but they disbelieved in him and inflicted a great deal of harm upon him. And so Allâh ﷻ punished them with drought and hunger for a number of years.

﴿هِيَ أَشَدُّ قُوَّةً مِّن قَرْيَتِكَ﴾

- **"....stronger than your town which has driven you out.."** **(Qur'ân 47: 13)**

There were many evil inhabitants of other townships who were stronger and mightier than the people of Makkah. But the end of all of them was utter destruction.

﴿لِإِيلَـٰفِ قُرَيْشٍ ①﴾

- **"For the taming of the Quraish." (Qur'ân 106: 1)**

Quraish is derived from the word *Al-Qarsh*, which means: gathering together, joining together, and (mutually) profiting.

﴿وَقَلْبُهُ مُطْمَئِنٌّ بِٱلْإِيمَٰنِ﴾

- **"...and whose heart is at rest with Faith;" (Qur'ân 16: 106)**

The polytheists continued to physically torture 'Ammâr ibn Yâsir ﷺ until they succeeded in forcing him to utter words of disbelief. People then began to say, "'Ammaar ﷺ has indeed disbelieved." Knowing that to be utterly untrue, the Prophet ﷺ said, "Indeed,

«إِنَّ عَمَّارًا مُلِيءَ إِيمَانًا مِنْ فَوْقِهِ إِلَى قَدَمِهِ، وَاخْتَلَطَ الْإِيمَانُ بِلَحْمِهِ وَدَمِهِ»

'Ammâr is filled with *Imân* (Faith) from his hairline (his head) until his feet. And *Imân* (Faith) is mixed in his flesh and blood."

After 'Ammâr ﷺ was released by the disbelievers, he ﷺ went to the Prophet ﷺ, crying. The Messenger of Allâh ﷺ asked him,

371

«كَيْفَ تَجِدُ قَلْبَكَ؟»

"What state do you find your heart to be in?"
'Ammâr ☜ answered, "It is at rest with Faith." The Prophet ﷺ said,

«إِنْ عَادُوا فَعُدْ»

"If they return, then do it again (i.e., if, through physical torture, they force you to utter words of disbelief, then comply with their request, but let your heart be at rest with Faith)."

﴿قَوْلَ ٱلَّتِي تُجَٰدِلُكَ﴾

- **"The statement of her that disputes with you"**

﴿قَدْ سَمِعَ ٱللَّهُ قَوْلَ ٱلَّتِي تُجَٰدِلُكَ فِى زَوْجِهَا وَتَشْتَكِىٓ إِلَى ٱللَّهِ وَٱللَّهُ يَسْمَعُ تَحَاوُرَكُمَآ إِنَّ ٱللَّهَ سَمِيعٌۢ بَصِيرٌ ۝ ٱلَّذِينَ يُظَٰهِرُونَ مِنكُم مِّن نِّسَآئِهِم مَّا هُنَّ أُمَّهَٰتِهِمْ إِنْ أُمَّهَٰتُهُمْ إِلَّا ٱلَّٰٓـِٔى وَلَدْنَهُمْ وَإِنَّهُمْ لَيَقُولُونَ مُنكَرًا مِّنَ ٱلْقَوْلِ وَزُورًا وَإِنَّ ٱللَّهَ لَعَفُوٌّ غَفُورٌ ۝ وَٱلَّذِينَ يُظَٰهِرُونَ مِن نِّسَآئِهِمْ ثُمَّ يَعُودُونَ لِمَا قَالُوا فَتَحْرِيرُ رَقَبَةٍ مِّن قَبْلِ أَن يَتَمَآسَّا ذَٰلِكُمْ تُوعَظُونَ بِهِۦ وَٱللَّهُ بِمَا تَعْمَلُونَ خَبِيرٌ ۝ فَمَن لَّمْ يَجِدْ فَصِيَامُ شَهْرَيْنِ مُتَتَابِعَيْنِ مِن قَبْلِ أَن يَتَمَآسَّا فَمَن لَّمْ يَسْتَطِعْ فَإِطْعَامُ سِتِّينَ مِسْكِينًا ذَٰلِكَ لِتُؤْمِنُوا بِٱللَّهِ وَرَسُولِهِۦ وَتِلْكَ حُدُودُ ٱللَّهِ وَلِلْكَٰفِرِينَ عَذَابٌ أَلِيمٌ ۝﴾

"Indeed Allâh has heard the statement of her (Khaulah bint Tha'labah) that disputes with you (O Muhammad ﷺ) concerning her husband (Aus ibn As-Sâmit), and complains to Allâh. And Allâh hears the argument between you both. Verily, Allâh is All-Hearer, All-Seer. Those among you who make their wives unlawful (Az-Zihâr, which is the saying of a husband to his wife: 'You are to me like the back of my mother (i.e., unlawful for me to approach') to them by saying to them "You are like my mother's back." They cannot be their mothers. None can be their mothers except those who gave them birth. And Verily, they utter an ill word and a lie. And verily, Allâh is Oft-Pardoning, Oft-Forgiving. And those who

372

make unlawful to them (their wives) (by *Az-Zihâr*) and wish to free themselves from what they uttered, (the penalty) in that case (is) the freeing of a slave before they touch each other. That is an admonition to you (so that you may not return to such an ill thing). And Allâh is All-Aware of what you do. And he who finds not (the money for freeing a slave) must fast two successive months before they both touch each other. And for him who is unable to do so, he should feed 60 of the Miskeen (poor). That is in order that you may have perfect faith in Allâh and His Messenger. These are the limits set by Allâh. And for disbelievers, there is a painful torment."

(Qur'ân 58: 1-4)

The one who disputed was Khaulah bint Tha'labah ﷺ. She had an argument with her husband, Aus ibn As-Sâmit ﷺ, who said to her, "You are to me like the back of my mother (i.e., 'you are unlawful for me to approach')." When Khaulah ﷺ told the Prophet ﷺ what her husband had said and complained about how he was treating her, Allâh ﷺ revealed the Verse:

$$﴿قَدْ سَمِعَ ٱللَّهُ قَوْلَ ٱلَّتِى تُجَـٰدِلُكَ فِى زَوْجِهَا وَتَشْتَكِىٓ إِلَى ٱللَّهِ﴾$$

> "Indeed Allâh has heard the statement of her that disputes with you concerning her husband,"

The Prophet ﷺ then told her to inform her husband that he had to make atonement for what he said concerning her being forbidden upon him: "Order him to free a slave or to fast two months continuously." She ﷺ said, "He is an old man, and so he cannot fast." The Prophet ﷺ said,

$$«فَلْيُطْعِمْ سِتِّينَ مِسْكِينًا وَسْقًا (سِتُّونَ صَاعًا) مِنْ تَمْرٍ»$$

> "Then let him feed 60 poor people *Wasqan* (A *Wasq* is a form of measurement) of dates."

She ﷺ said, "O Messenger of Allâh, he doesn't have any (dates)." After the Prophet ﷺ said he would give some dates to help for 'Aus's atonement, Khaulah ﷺ promised to do the same. In appreciation of her generous promise, the Prophet ﷺ said,

«قَدْ أَصَبْتِ وَأَحْسَنْتِ، فَاذْهَبِي فَتَصَدَّقِي بِهِ عَنْهُ، ثُمَّ اسْتَوْصِي بِابْنِ عَمِّكِ خَيْرًا»

"You have done what is right; you have done well. So go (now) and give it (the dates) in charity on his behalf. Then treat your cousin well,"

and she of course did as the Prophet ﷺ ordered her to do.

Years later, during his caliphate, 'Umar ibn Al-Khattâb ؓ passed by an old woman. After he stopped to greet her, they started talking to one another. Since 'Umar ؓ was the Caliph, many people would come to him with their problems. One man was at that moment standing and waiting for 'Umar ؓ to finish his conversation with the old woman. Becoming impatient, the man said, "O Leader of the Believers, you are making people wait because of this old woman!" 'Umar ؓ answered, "Woe unto you! Do you know who she is? She is the woman whose complaint Allâh ﷻ heard from above the seven heavens. She ؓ is Khaulah bint Tha'labah ؓ, regarding whom Allâh ﷻ revealed the verse:

﴿قَدْ سَمِعَ ٱللَّهُ قَوْلَ ٱلَّتِي تُجَٰدِلُكَ فِي زَوْجِهَا﴾

"Indeed Allâh has heard the statement of her (Khaulah bint Tha'albah) that disputes with you (O Muhammad ﷺ) concerning her husband (Aus ibn As-Sâmit)."

'Umar ؓ continued: "By Allâh, were she to stand (here) until the night, I would not part from her, except for prayer; and then I would return to her."

﴿فَكَأَيِّن مِّن قَرْيَةٍ أَهْلَكْنَٰهَا وَهِيَ ظَالِمَةٌ﴾

- "And many a township have We destroyed while it was given to wrongdoing," (Qur'ân 22: 45)

Though the word 'township' is used here to convey a general meaning, something more specific is being referred to: a castle that was built by Shaddâd ibn 'Âd ibn Iram.

374

$$﴿وَكَم قَصَمْنَا مِن قَرْيَةٍ كَانَت ظَالِمَةً﴾$$

- "How many a town (community), that were wrongdoers, have We destroyed," (Qur'ân 21: 11)

It is a town called Hadur, and it is situated in Yemen.

$$﴿فَأَخْرَجْنَٰهُم مِّن جَنَّٰتٍ وَعُيُونٍ ٥٧ وَكُنُوزٍ وَمَقَامٍ كَرِيمٍ ٥٨ ﴾$$

- "So, We expelled them from gardens and springs, treasures, and every kind of honorable place." (Qur'ân 26: 57, 58)

Some scholars of *Tafsir* maintain that this verse is referring to the Al-Fayum of Egypt. 'We expelled them' means: We expelled Fir'aun and his people from their gardens and lands that were bordered by flowing rivers; and We expelled them from their beautiful homes and from the places in which they hoarded treasures of gold and silver.

$$﴿عَبَسَ وَتَوَلَّىٰٓ ١ أَن جَآءَهُ ٱلْأَعْمَىٰ ٢ ﴾$$

- "(The Prophet ﷺ) frowned and turned away, because there came to him the blind man." (Qur'ân 80: 1, 2)

This Verse was revealed for 'Abdullah ibn Umm Maktum ؓ, who was blind. He once went to the Messenger of Allâh ﷺ and said, "Teach me from that which Allâh ﷻ has taught you." He then repeated this request, not knowing that the Messenger of Allâh ﷺ was busy inviting important leaders of the Quraish to Islam. Not liking to be cut off in his speech, the Prophet ﷺ frowned and turned away from 'Abdullah ibn Umm Maktum ؓ. Allâh ﷻ then revealed the Verse: "(The Prophet ﷺ) frowned and turned away, because there came to him the blind man." The Messenger of Allâh ﷺ would then say to 'Abdullah ibn Umm Maktum ؓ,

$$«مَرْحَبًا بِمَنْ عَاتَبَنِي فِيهِ رَبِّي، وَيَبْسُطُ لَهُ رِدَاءَهُ»$$

"Welcome, O one about whom my Lord reproached me." In honoring him, the Prophet ﷺ would then extend his robe for him.

﴿عَيْنَ ٱلْقِطْرِ﴾

- "A fount of (molten) brass."

﴿وَلِسُلَيْمَٰنَ ٱلرِّيحَ غُدُوُّهَا شَهْرٌ وَرَوَاحُهَا شَهْرٌ وَأَسَلْنَا لَهُ عَيْنَ ٱلْقِطْرِ وَمِنَ ٱلْجِنِّ مَن يَعْمَلُ بَيْنَ يَدَيْهِ بِإِذْنِ رَبِّهِ وَمَن يَزِغْ مِنْهُمْ عَنْ أَمْرِنَا نُذِقْهُ مِنْ عَذَابِ ٱلسَّعِيرِ ﴿١٢﴾﴾

"And to Solomon (We subjected) the wind, it's morning (stride from sunrise till midnoon) was a month's (journey), and its afternoon (stride from the midday decline of the sun to sunset) was a month's (journey, i.e., in one day he could traveled two months' journey). And We caused a fount of (molten) brass to flow for him, and there were jinns that worked in front of him, by the Leave of his Lord, and whosoever of them turned aside from Our Command, We shall cause him to taste of the torment of the blazing Fire."

(Qur'ân 34: 12)

Allâh ﷻ bestowed these blessings upon Sulaimân ﷺ, just as He ﷻ made steel soft and pliable for Dâwud ﷺ.

﴿ءَاتُونِي زُبَرَ ٱلْحَدِيدِ حَتَّىٰ إِذَا سَاوَىٰ بَيْنَ ٱلصَّدَفَيْنِ قَالَ ٱنفُخُوا۟ حَتَّىٰ إِذَا جَعَلَهُ نَارًا قَالَ ءَاتُونِي أُفْرِغْ عَلَيْهِ قِطْرًا ﴿٩٦﴾﴾

- "Give me pieces (blocks) of iron," then, when he had filled up the gap between the two mountain-cliffs, he said: "Blow," till when he had made it (red as) fire, he said: "Bring me molten copper to pour over it." (Qur'ân 18: 96)

The translation of the Verse is self-explanatory: Dhul-Qarnain was asking for molten iron that he was going to use to make an impenetrable barrier between two mountain cliffs.

﴿لِلْفُقَرَآءِ ٱلْمُهَٰجِرِينَ﴾

- "For the poor emigrants."

﴿لِلْفُقَرَآءِ ٱلْمُهَٰجِرِينَ ٱلَّذِينَ أُخْرِجُوا۟ مِن دِيَٰرِهِمْ وَأَمْوَٰلِهِمْ يَبْتَغُونَ فَضْلًا مِّنَ ٱللَّهِ وَرِضْوَٰنًا

$$\text{وَيَنصُرُونَ ٱللَّهَ وَرَسُولَهُۥٓ أُوْلَٰٓئِكَ هُمُ ٱلصَّٰدِقُونَ} \ (\text{٨})$$

"And there is also a share in this booty) for the poor emigrants, who were expelled from their homes and their property, seeking Bounties from Allâh and to please Him. And helping Allâh (i.e., helping His religion) and His Messenger (Muhammad ﷺ). Such are indeed the truthful (to what they say)."

(Qur'ân 59: 8)

They were the 'People of Suffah,' poor Muslims who migrated to Al-Madinah Al-Munawwarah; these Companions ؓ had neither homes, nor family, nor wealth. They were approximately 400 men who took refuge in a shaded part of the Prophet's Masjid. It is there that they lived and learned their religion. At meal times, the Prophet ﷺ would send groups of them to various Companions ؓ; and some among them would eat with him ﷺ.

$$\text{مُبْتَلِيكُم بِنَهَرٍ}$$

● **"Allâh will try you by a river"**

$$\text{فَلَمَّا فَصَلَ طَالُوتُ بِٱلْجُنُودِ قَالَ إِنَّ ٱللَّهَ مُبْتَلِيكُم بِنَهَرٍ فَمَن شَرِبَ مِنْهُ فَلَيْسَ مِنِّي وَمَن لَّمْ يَطْعَمْهُ فَإِنَّهُ مِنِّيٓ إِلَّا مَنِ ٱغْتَرَفَ غُرْفَةًۢ بِيَدِهِۦۚ فَشَرِبُوا۟ مِنْهُ إِلَّا قَلِيلًا مِّنْهُمْۚ فَلَمَّا جَاوَزَهُ هُوَ وَٱلَّذِينَ ءَامَنُوا۟ مَعَهُۥ قَالُوا۟ لَا طَاقَةَ لَنَا ٱلْيَوْمَ بِجَالُوتَ وَجُنُودِهِۦۚ قَالَ ٱلَّذِينَ يَظُنُّونَ أَنَّهُم مُّلَٰقُوا۟ ٱللَّهِ كَم مِّن فِئَةٍ قَلِيلَةٍ غَلَبَتْ فِئَةً كَثِيرَةًۢ بِإِذْنِ ٱللَّهِۗ وَٱللَّهُ مَعَ ٱلصَّٰبِرِينَ} \ (\text{٢٤٩})$$

"Then when Tâlût (Saul) set out with the Army, he said: 'Verily! Allâh will try you by a river. So whoever drinks thereof, he is not of me, and whoever tastes it not, he is of me, except him who takes (thereof) in the hollow of his hand.' Yet, they drank thereof, all, except a few of them. So when he had crossed it (the river), he and those who believed with him, they said: 'We have no power this day against Jâlût (Goliath) and his hosts.' But those who knew with certainty that they were to meet their Lord, said: 'How often a small group overcame a mighty host by Allâh's Leave?' And Allâh is with *As-Sâbirin* (the patient ones etc.).''

(Qur'ân 2: 249)

The Jordan River (also known as the Shariah River), which runs between Palestine and Jordan, is the intended river in the above-mentioned Verse.

﴿ٱلْمَشْرِقُ وَٱلْمَغْرِبُ﴾

- **"The east and the west"**

﴿وَلِلَّهِ ٱلْمَشْرِقُ وَٱلْمَغْرِبُ فَأَيْنَمَا تُوَلُّوا۟ فَثَمَّ وَجْهُ ٱللَّهِ إِنَّ ٱللَّهَ وَٰسِعٌ عَلِيمٌ ﴿١١٥﴾﴾

"And to Allâh belong the east and the west, so whenever you turn yourselves or your faces there is the Face of Allâh (and He is High above, over His Throne). Surely! Allâh is All-Sufficient for His creatures' needs, All-Knowing.''

(Qur'ân 2: 115)

﴿سَيَقُولُ ٱلسُّفَهَآءُ مِنَ ٱلنَّاسِ مَا وَلَّىٰهُمْ عَن قِبْلَتِهِمُ ٱلَّتِى كَانُوا۟ عَلَيْهَا قُل لِّلَّهِ ٱلْمَشْرِقُ وَٱلْمَغْرِبُ يَهْدِى مَن يَشَآءُ إِلَىٰ صِرَٰطٍ مُّسْتَقِيمٍ ﴿١٤٢﴾﴾

"The fools (pagans, hypocrites, and Jews) among the people will say, 'What has turned them (Muslims) from their *Qiblah* [prayer direction (towards Jerusalem)] to which they were used to face in prayer.' Say, (O Muhammad ﷺ) 'To Allâh belong both, east and the west. He guides whom He wills to a Straight Way'.''

(Qur'ân 2: 142)

﴿لَّيْسَ ٱلْبِرَّ أَن تُوَلُّوا۟ وُجُوهَكُمْ قِبَلَ ٱلْمَشْرِقِ وَٱلْمَغْرِبِ وَلَٰكِنَّ ٱلْبِرَّ مَنْ ءَامَنَ بِٱللَّهِ وَٱلْيَوْمِ ٱلْأَخِرِ وَٱلْمَلَٰٓئِكَةِ وَٱلْكِتَٰبِ وَٱلنَّبِيِّـۧنَ وَءَاتَى ٱلْمَالَ عَلَىٰ حُبِّهِۦ ذَوِى ٱلْقُرْبَىٰ وَٱلْيَتَٰمَىٰ وَٱلْمَسَٰكِينَ وَٱبْنَ ٱلسَّبِيلِ وَٱلسَّآئِلِينَ وَفِى ٱلرِّقَابِ وَأَقَامَ ٱلصَّلَوٰةَ وَءَاتَى ٱلزَّكَوٰةَ وَٱلْمُوفُونَ بِعَهْدِهِمْ إِذَا عَٰهَدُوا۟ وَٱلصَّٰبِرِينَ فِى ٱلْبَأْسَآءِ وَٱلضَّرَّآءِ وَحِينَ ٱلْبَأْسِ أُو۟لَٰٓئِكَ ٱلَّذِينَ صَدَقُوا۟ وَأُو۟لَٰٓئِكَ هُمُ ٱلْمُتَّقُونَ ﴿١٧٧﴾﴾

"It is not *Al-Birr* (piety, righteousness, and each and every act of obedience to Allâh, etc.) that you turn your faces towards east and (or) west (in prayers); but *Al-Birr* is (the quality of) the one who believes in Allâh, the Last Day, the Angels, the Book, the Prophets and gives his wealth, in spite of love for it, to the kinsfolk, to the orphans, and to *Al-Masâkin* (the poor), and to the wayfarer, and to those who ask, and to set slaves free, performs *As-Salât* (Prayer) (*Iqâmatus-Salât*), and gives the *Zakât*, and who fulfill their covenant when they make it, and who are patient in extreme poverty and ailment (disease) and at the time of fighting (during the battles). Such are the people of the truth and they are *Al-Muttaqun* (the pious ones).''

(Qur'ân 2: 177)

﴿أَلَمْ تَرَ إِلَى ٱلَّذِى حَاجَّ إِبْرَٰهِـۧمَ فِى رَبِّهِۦٓ أَنْ ءَاتَىٰهُ ٱللَّهُ ٱلْمُلْكَ إِذْ قَالَ إِبْرَٰهِـۧمُ رَبِّىَ ٱلَّذِى يُحْىِۦ وَيُمِيتُ قَالَ أَنَا۠ أُحْىِۦ وَأُمِيتُ قَالَ إِبْرَٰهِـۧمُ فَإِنَّ ٱللَّهَ يَأْتِى بِٱلشَّمْسِ مِنَ ٱلْمَشْرِقِ فَأْتِ بِهَا مِنَ ٱلْمَغْرِبِ فَبُهِتَ ٱلَّذِى كَفَرَ وَٱللَّهُ لَا يَهْدِى ٱلْقَوْمَ ٱلظَّٰلِمِينَ ﴿٢٥٨﴾﴾

"Have you not looked at him who disputed with Ibrâhim (Abraham) about his Lord (Allâh), because Allâh had given him the kingdom? When Ibrâhim (Abraham) said (to him): 'My Lord (Allâh) is He Who gives life and causes death.' He said, 'I give life and cause death.' Ibrâhim (Abraham) said, 'Verily! Allâh causes the sun to rise from the east; then cause it you to rise from the west.' So the disbeliever was utterly defeated. And Allâh guides not the people, who are *Zâlimun* (wrongdoers, etc.).''

(Qur'ân 2: 258)

﴿قَالَ رَبُّ ٱلْمَشْرِقِ وَٱلْمَغْرِبِ وَمَا بَيْنَهُمَآ إِن كُنتُمْ تَعْقِلُونَ ﴿٢٨﴾﴾

"Musa (Moses) said: "Lord of the east and the west, and all that is between them, if you did but understand!''

(Qur'ân 26: 28)

﴿رَبُّ ٱلْمَشْرِقِ وَٱلْمَغْرِبِ لَآ إِلَٰهَ إِلَّا هُوَ فَٱتَّخِذْهُ وَكِيلًا ﴿٩﴾﴾

"He Alone is) the Lord of the east and the west, *Lâ ilaha illa Huwa* (none has the right to be worshipped but He). So take Him Alone as *Wakil* (Disposer of your affairs)."

(Qur'ân 73: 9)

﴿ رَّبُّ ٱلْمَشْرِقَيْنِ وَرَبُّ ٱلْمَغْرِبَيْنِ ﴿١٧﴾ ﴾

"(He is) the Lord of the two easts (places of sunrise during early summer and early winter) and the Lord of the two wests (places of sunset during early summer and early winter)." (Qur'ân 55: 17)

﴿ وَأَوْرَثْنَا ٱلْقَوْمَ ٱلَّذِينَ كَانُوا۟ يُسْتَضْعَفُونَ مَشَٰرِقَ ٱلْأَرْضِ وَمَغَٰرِبَهَا ٱلَّتِى بَٰرَكْنَا فِيهَا ۖ وَتَمَّتْ كَلِمَتُ رَبِّكَ ٱلْحُسْنَىٰ عَلَىٰ بَنِىٓ إِسْرَٰٓءِيلَ بِمَا صَبَرُوا۟ ۖ وَدَمَّرْنَا مَا كَانَ يَصْنَعُ فِرْعَوْنُ وَقَوْمُهُۥ وَمَا كَانُوا۟ يَعْرِشُونَ ﴿١٣٧﴾ ﴾

"And We made the people who were considered weak to inherit the eastern parts of the land and the western parts thereof which We have blessed. And the fair Word of your Lord was fulfilled for the Children of Israel, because of their endurance. And We destroyed completely all the great works and buildings which Fir'aun (Pharaoh) and his people erected." (Qur'ân 7: 137)

﴿ فَلَآ أُقْسِمُ بِرَبِّ ٱلْمَشَٰرِقِ وَٱلْمَغَٰرِبِ إِنَّا لَقَٰدِرُونَ ﴿٤٠﴾ عَلَىٰٓ أَن نُّبَدِّلَ خَيْرًا مِّنْهُمْ وَمَا نَحْنُ بِمَسْبُوقِينَ ﴿٤١﴾ ﴾

"So I swear by the Lord of all (the 360) points of sunrise and sunset in the east and the west that surely We are Able."

(Qur'ân 70: 40)

The sun, as is observable, rises from two points: a point that we can see in the summer; and a much further off point that we can see in the winter. And the same can be said about the setting of the sun.

﴿ حَتَّىٰٓ إِذَا جَآءَنَا قَالَ يَٰلَيْتَ بَيْنِى وَبَيْنَكَ بُعْدَ ٱلْمَشْرِقَيْنِ فَبِئْسَ ٱلْقَرِينُ ﴿٣٨﴾ ﴾

"Till, when (such a one) comes to Us, he says [to his *Qarin* (Satan/devil companion)] 'Would that between me and you were the distance of the two easts (or the east and west)' – a worst (type of) companion (indeed)!"

(Qur'ân 43: 38)

﴿رَّبُّ ٱلسَّمَٰوَٰتِ وَٱلْأَرْضِ وَمَا بَيْنَهُمَا وَرَبُّ ٱلْمَشَٰرِقِ ٥﴾

"Lord of the heavens and of the earth, and all that is between them, and Lord of every point of the sun's risings. (None has the right to be worshiped but Allâh)."

(Qur'ân 37: 5)

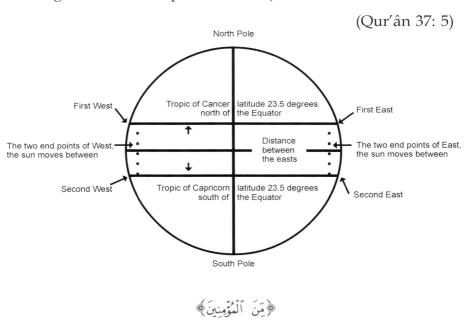

﴿مِّنَ ٱلْمُؤْمِنِينَ﴾

- **"Among the believers are men"**

﴿مِّنَ ٱلْمُؤْمِنِينَ رِجَالٌ صَدَقُوا۟ مَا عَٰهَدُوا۟ ٱللَّهَ عَلَيْهِ فَمِنْهُم مَّن قَضَىٰ نَحْبَهُۥ وَمِنْهُم مَّن يَنتَظِرُ وَمَا بَدَّلُوا۟ تَبْدِيلًا ٢٣﴾

"Among the believers are men who have been true to their covenant with Allâh [i.e., they have gone out for *Jihad* (holy fighting), and showed not their backs to the disbelievers], of them some have fulfilled their obligations (i.e., have been martyred), and some of them are still waiting, but they have never changed (i.e., they never proved treacherous to their

381

covenant which they concluded with Allâh) in the least." (Qur'ân 33: 23)

This verse was revealed for Anas ibn An-Nadr ﷺ, who took part in the Battle of Uhud (Shawwal, 3 H) but not in the Battle of Badr. After the latter battle was finished, Anas ibn An-Nadr ﷺ said, "O Messenger of Allâh, I was absent from the first battle you fought against the polytheists. By Allâh, when Allâh witnesses me fighting the polytheists, Allâh will indeed see what I will do (against them)!" On the day of Uhud, when the Muslims were searching for the corpses of their martyred brothers, they came across the corpse of Anas ibn An-Nadr ﷺ. They found in him over 80 wounds, which were inflicted by swords, spears, and arrows. He ﷺ had so many wounds that it was difficult to recognize him; it was his sister, Ar-Rubayyi'a bint An-Nadr, who identified him, recognizing him by his fingertips.

﴿ وَمِنَ ٱلنَّاسِ مَن يُعْجِبُكَ قَوْلُهُۥ ﴾

- **"And of mankind there is he whose speech may please you (O Muhammad ﷺ) in this worldly life,"** (Qur'ân 2: 204)

This Verse was revealed for Al-Akhnas ibn Shuraiq Ath-Thaqafi. He outwardly manifested Islam, but then, when he came across a field of crops and a number of donkeys that belonged to a group of Muslims, he set fire to the crops and slaughtered the donkeys.

﴿ وَٱلْمُؤَلَّفَةِ قُلُوبُهُمْ ﴾

- **"... and for attracting the hearts of those who have been inclined (towards Islam);"**

﴿ إِنَّمَا ٱلصَّدَقَٰتُ لِلْفُقَرَآءِ وَٱلْمَسَٰكِينِ وَٱلْعَٰمِلِينَ عَلَيْهَا وَٱلْمُؤَلَّفَةِ قُلُوبُهُمْ وَفِى ٱلرِّقَابِ وَٱلْغَٰرِمِينَ وَفِى سَبِيلِ ٱللَّهِ وَٱبْنِ ٱلسَّبِيلِ فَرِيضَةً مِّنَ ٱللَّهِ وَٱللَّهُ عَلِيمٌ حَكِيمٌ ﴾ ﴿ ٦٠ ﴾

"As-Sadaqât (here it means *Zakât*) are only for the *Fuqarâ'* (poor), and *Al-Masâkin* (the poor) and those employed to collect (the funds); and for attracting the hearts of those who have been inclined (towards Islam); and to free the captives; and for those in debt; and for Allâh's Cause (i.e., for *Mujâhidin* – those fighting in the holy wars), and for the wayfarer (a traveler who is cut off from everything); a duty imposed that Allâh. And Allâh is All-Knower, All-Wise.''

(Qur'ân 9: 60)

The Messenger of Allâh ﷺ gave camels to a number of Arab chieftains and leaders, in order to attract their hearts towards Islam. Among those he gave to are the following: Al-Aqra' ibn Hâbis At-Tamimi, Al-'Abbâs ibn Mirdâs As-Sulami, 'Uyainah ibn Hisn Al-Fazâri, Abu Sufyân ibn Harb, Mu'âwiyah ibn Abi Sufyân, Al-Hârith ibn Hishâm ibn Al-Mughirah, Hakim ibn Taliq, Khâlid ibn Asid ibn Abil-'Ais, Sa'id ibn Yurbu' Al-Makhzumi, Safwân ibn Umayyah ibn Khalf Al-Jumahi, Suhail ibn 'Amr, Huwaitib ibn 'Abdul-'Uzza Al-'Aamiri, Hakim ibn Hizâm ibn Khuwailid, Abu Sufyân ibn Al-Hârith ibn 'Abdul-Muttalib, Mâlik ibn 'Auf, and Al-'Alâ' ibn Jâriyah Ath-Thaqafi.

The Messenger of Allâh ﷺ gave 100 camels to each of the above, except for Sa'eed ibn Yurbu' and Huwaitib; he ﷺ gave these two 50 camels each.

﴿وَمِنْهُم مَّن يَقُولُ ٱئْذَن لِّي وَلَا تَفْتِنِّيٓ﴾

- **"And among them is he who says: "Grant me leave (to be exempted from *Jihad*) and put me not into trial.'' (Qur'ân 9: 49)**

This was revealed for Al-Jadd ibn Qais, who was a hypocrite. When the Messenger of Allâh ﷺ told the Muslims to get ready for the Battle of Tabûk, Al-Jadd said, "O Messenger of Allâh, grant me leave to be exempted from *Jihad* and put me not to trial of the Roman women as they are very beautiful.''

﴿عَدُوِّي وَعَدُوَّكُمْ أَوْلِيَآءَ﴾

- **"My enemies and your enemies as friends''**

383

﴿يَٰٓأَيُّهَا ٱلَّذِينَ ءَامَنُوا۟ لَا تَتَّخِذُوا۟ عَدُوِّى وَعَدُوَّكُمْ أَوْلِيَآءَ تُلْقُونَ إِلَيْهِم بِٱلْمَوَدَّةِ وَقَدْ كَفَرُوا۟ بِمَا جَآءَكُم مِّنَ ٱلْحَقِّ يُخْرِجُونَ ٱلرَّسُولَ وَإِيَّاكُمْ أَن تُؤْمِنُوا۟ بِٱللَّهِ رَبِّكُمْ إِن كُنتُمْ خَرَجْتُمْ جِهَٰدًا فِى سَبِيلِى وَٱبْتِغَآءَ مَرْضَاتِى تُسِرُّونَ إِلَيْهِم بِٱلْمَوَدَّةِ وَأَنَا۠ أَعْلَمُ بِمَآ أَخْفَيْتُمْ وَمَآ أَعْلَنتُمْ وَمَن يَفْعَلْهُ مِنكُمْ فَقَدْ ضَلَّ سَوَآءَ ٱلسَّبِيلِ ١ إِن يَثْقَفُوكُمْ يَكُونُوا۟ لَكُمْ أَعْدَآءً وَيَبْسُطُوٓا۟ إِلَيْكُمْ أَيْدِيَهُمْ وَأَلْسِنَتَهُم بِٱلسُّوٓءِ وَوَدُّوا۟ لَوْ تَكْفُرُونَ ٢ لَن تَنفَعَكُمْ أَرْحَامُكُمْ وَلَآ أَوْلَٰدُكُمْ يَوْمَ ٱلْقِيَٰمَةِ يَفْصِلُ بَيْنَكُمْ وَٱللَّهُ بِمَا تَعْمَلُونَ بَصِيرٌ ٣﴾

"O you who believe! Take not My enemies and your enemies (i.e., disbelievers and polytheists, etc.) as friends, showing affection towards them, while they have disbelieved in what has come to you of the truth (i.e., Islamic Monotheism, this Qur'ân, and Muhammad ﷺ), and have driven out the Messenger (Muhammad ﷺ) and yourselves (from your homeland) because you believe in Allâh your Lord! If you have come forth to strive in My Cause and to seek My Good Pleasure, (then take not these disbelievers and polytheists, etc., as your friends). You show friendship to them in secret, while I am All-Aware of what you conceal and what you reveal. And whosoever of you (Muslims) does that, then indeed he has gone (far) astray, (away) from the Straight Path. Should they gain the upper hand over you, they would behave to you as enemies, and stretch forth their hands and their tongues against you with evil, and they desire that you should disbelieve. Neither your relatives nor your children will benefit you on the Day of Resurrection (against Allâh). He will judge between you. And Allâh is the All-Seer of what you do."

(Qur'ân 60: 1-3)

This was revealed in regards to Hâtib ibn Abi Balta'ah ﷺ, who, during the year 8 H, just after the Quraish had violated the terms of the Treaty of Al-Hudaibiyah, sent a letter to the Quraish, informing them that the Muslims were preparing to conquer Makkah.

﴿يَشْرِى نَفْسَهُ ٱبْتِغَآءَ مَرْضَاتِ ٱللَّهِ﴾

- **"And of mankind is he who would sell himself, seeking the Pleasure of Allâh." (Qur'ân 2: 207)**

This was revealed for Suhaib Ar-Rumi ◈ who, when he left Makkah in order to migrate to Al-Madinah, was pursued by certain members of the Quraish. When it became certain that they were going to overtake him, Suhaib ◈ got off of his mount, took out his bow and quiver, and said, "O people of Quraish, you indeed know that I am one of your best archers. By Allâh, you will not reach me until I fire every single arrow that I have with me in my quiver, and then I will begin to fight with my sword. If you want, I will tell you where my wealth is in Makkah, but you will have to then leave me alone." They said, "Yes (we agree to those terms)." When Suhaib ◈ completed his journey and reached Al-Madinah, the Messenger of Allâh ﷺ said, "(Your) trade has been very profitable, O Abu Yahya (i.e., Suhaib), (your) trade has been very profitable."

﴿يُخْرِبُونَ بُيُوتَهُم بِأَيْدِيهِمْ﴾

- **"So they destroyed their own dwellings with their own hands." (Qur'ân 59: 2)**

This was revealed in relation to when the people of Banu An-Nadir were banished from their homes in Al-Madinah.

***

﴿رَبِّ أَوْزِعْنِى أَنْ أَشْكُرَ نِعْمَتَكَ ٱلَّتِى أَنْعَمْتَ عَلَىَّ وَعَلَىٰ وَٰلِدَىَّ وَأَنْ أَعْمَلَ صَٰلِحًا تَرْضَىٰهُ وَأَصْلِحْ لِى فِى ذُرِّيَّتِىٓ إِنِّى تُبْتُ إِلَيْكَ وَإِنِّى مِنَ ٱلْمُسْلِمِينَ ﴿١٥﴾﴾

"My Lord! Grant me the power and ability that I may be grateful for Your Favor which You have bestowed upon me and upon my parents, and that I may do righteous good deeds, such as please You; and make my offspring good. Truly, I have turned to You in repentance, and truly, I am one of the Muslims (submitting to Your Will)."

(Qur'ân 46: 15)

References

— *Asbâb An-Nuzul* [Events that prompted the revelation (of certain Verses from the Qur'ân)], 'Ali ibn Ahmad An-Naisâburi. Dâr-ul-Fikr, Beirut, 1414 h/ 1994.

— *Al-Isti'âb Fi Asmâ Al-Ashâb* (A Comprehensive Study of the Names of Companions), Yusuf ibn 'Abdullah ibn Muhammad Al-Qurtubi. This book consists of the footnotes from *Al-Isâbah Fi Tamyiz As-Sahâbah*.

— *Usdul-Ghâbah Fi Ma'rifatus-Sahâbah* - Another Study of the Prophet's Companions, 'Ali ibn Muhammad Al-Juzari (Ibn Al-Athir). Kitâb Ash-Sha'ab edition, Egypt.

— *Al-Isâbah Fi Tamyiz As-Sahâbah* (Correctly distinguishing the Companions), Shihâb Ad-Deen Ahmad ibn 'Ali Al-'Asqalâni (Ibn Hajr, author of Fathul-Bâri). Beirut (No date is mentioned).

— *Al-'Alâm Khairad-Din* (From the best of the important people of the religion), Az-Zurkali. Dâr-al-'Ilm Lil-Malâyin, Beirut. The 1979 edition.

— *Al-A'lâm Fil-Qur'ân* (Important figures mentioned in the Qur'ân), Al-Fariq Yahya 'Abdullah Al-Mu'allami. Dâr-al-Mu'allami Lin-Nashr, Riyadh, 1414 h/ 1994.

— *Al-Bidâyah wan-Nihâyah* (The Beginning and the End) - famous history book, Ibn Kathir. Maktabah Al-Ma'ârif, Beirut. Second edition, 1974 h.

— *Târikh Ibn Khaldun* (History of Ibn Khaldun). Dâr-al-Bayân edition (date of printing is not mentioned).

— *Târikh At-Tabari* (History of At-Tabari) - Târikh Ar-Rusul wal-Muluk (History of Messengers and Kings). With the addition of critical notes by Muhammad ibn Al-Fadl Ibrâhim. Dâr Al-Ma'arif, Egypt, 1960.

— *Tafsir Ruh Al-Bayân* (*Tafsir*: The Spirit of Explanation), Isma'il Haqqi Al-Barusawi. Dar Al-Fikr, Beirut (no mention of the printing date is made).

— *Tafsir At-Tabari: Jâmai' Al-Bayân Fee Ta'wil Āyil-Qur'ân* (A Comprehensive Explanation of the Meanings of the Qur'ân's Verses), Ibn Jarir At-Tabari, Dar Al-Fikr, Beirut. The 1420 h/1999 edition.

— *Tafsir Al-Fakhr Ar-Râzi: At-Tafsir Al-Kabir wa-Mafâtih Al-Ghaib* [The large *Tafsir* (very literal translation) and the Keys to the Unseen). Imam Fakhr Ad-Deen Muhammad Ar-Râzi. Dar Al-Fikr, Beirut. The 1410 h/1995 edition.

— *Tafsir Al-Qur'ân Al-'Azeem* (Better known as, *Tafsir* Ibn Kathir), Abu Al-Fida Isma'il ibn Kathir Al-Qurashi Ad-Damashqi. Dar-ul-Maktabatul-Hilal, Beirut. First Edition, 1986.

— *Tafsir* Al-Murâghi, Ahmad Mustafa Al-Murâghi. Dar Al-Fikr, Beirut (no mention is made of a printing date).

— *At-Tafsir* Al-Munir, Dr. Wahbah Az-Zuhaili. Dar Al-Fikr, Damascus. First Edition, 1411 h/1991.

— *At-Takmil wal-Itmâm* (literally: The Completion and Finalization), Muhammad ibn 'Ali Al-Ghassâni (Ibn 'Askar). With the addition of critical notes by Hasan Marwah. Dar Al-Fikr, Damascus. First Edition, 1418 h/1997.

— *Dairatul-Ma'ârif Al-Islâmiyyah.* Dar Al-Fikr, Beirut (printing date not mentioned).

— *Ad-Durr Al-Manthur Fit-Tafsir* Bil-Ma'thur [Scattered Pearls in regards to At-*Tafsir* with Al-Ma'thur (i.e., *Tafsir* that is based on narrations, not on opinion)], Jalaal Ad-Deen As-Suyuti. Muas-sasatur-Risâlah, Beirut (printing date not mentioned).

— *Dauwal Al-Islâm* (Countries of Islam), Shamsud-Deen Adh-Dhahabi. With the addition of critical notes by Hasan Marwah. Dâr-ul-Masâdir, Beirut. First Edition, 1999.

— *Ruhul-Ma'âni Fee Tafsir Al-Qur'ân Al-'Azim was-Sab' Al-Mathani,* an explanation of the Noble Qur'ân, Shihab Ad-Deen Mahmud Al-Aalusi Al-Baghdâdi. Dar Al-Fikr, Beirut, 1417 h/1997.

— *Ar-Raud Al-Unuf Fi Tafsir Fi Tafsir* As-Seerah An-Nabawiyyah, book on the Prophet's Biography, Ibn Hishaam Abul-Qaasim ibn 'Abdullah As-Suhaili. Dar Al-Fikr, Beirut (printing date not mentioned).

— *As-Seerah An-Nabawiyyah* (Biography of the Prophet ﷺ), Ibn Hishâm. Dar-ul-Jil, Beirut, 1975 h.

— *Safwatut-Tafasir* (The Choice of *Tafsir* Books), Muhammad 'Ali As-Sâbuni. Dar Al-Fikr, Beirut, 1408 h/1988.

— *At-Tabaqât Al-Kubra*, Ibn Sa'd Az-Zuhri. Darul-Masadir, Beirut (printing date not mentioned).

— *'Uyun Al-Athar Fi Funun Al-Maghâzi was-Shamâil was-Seyar* - basically, a compilation of narrations that have to do with famous battles and famous figures - Ibn Sayyid An-Nas. Dar-ul-Jeel, Beirut. Second Edition, 1974.

— *Fathul-Qadir Al-Jâmi' Baina Fannai-ar-Riwâyah wad-Dirâyah Min 'Ilm At-Tafsir* (Fathul-Qadir: A Comprehensive Study of the Narration-Based and the Inference-Based Approaches to the Science of *Tafsir*), Muhammad ibn 'Ali Ash-Shawkani. Dar Al-Fikr, Beirut, 1403 h/1983.

— *Futuh Al-Buldân* (Conquering of the Lands), Abul-Hasan Ahmad ibn Yahya Al-Baladhiri. Al-Maktabah At-Tijariyyah Al-Kubra, Egypt, 1959.

— *Al-Qâmus Al-Islami* (Islamic Dictionary), Ahmad 'Atiyyatullah. Maktabah An-Nahdah Al-Misriyyah, 1390 h/1970.

— *Qisas Al-Anbiya': Al-'Arâis* (Stories of the Prophets), Ahmad ibn Muhammad ibn Ibrâhim An-Naisaburi, who is more well known by the name, Ath-Tha'labi. Dar Al-Fikr, Beirut, 1420 h/ 2000.

— *Qisas Al-Qur'ân Minal-Qur'ân wal-Athar* [Stories of the Qur'ân from the Qur'ân and Narrations (Narrations that expand on or explain those stories)], Abul-Fida Al-Hafiz Ibn Kathir Ad-Dimashqi. Dar Al-Fikr, Beirut. Third Edition, 1418 h/1998.

— *Qisas Al-Anbiy'* (Stories of the Prophets), Abu Ja'far Muhammad ibn Jarir At-Tabari. Dar Al-Fikr, Beirut, 1409 h/1989.

— *Qisas Al-Anbiya'* (Stories of the Prophets), 'Abdul-Wahhab An-Najjâr. Dar Al-Fikr, Beirut (printing date not mentioned).

— *Al-Kâmil Fit-Târikh* (A Complete Account of History), Ibn Al-Athir Al-Juzari. Idâratut-Tibâ'ah Al-Muniriyyah, Cairo, 1348 h.

— *Kitâb Al-Asnâm* (Book of Idols), Hisham ibn Muhammad As-Sâ'ib Al-Kalbi. With the addition of critical notes by Dr. Muhammad 'Abdul-Qadir Ahmad and Ahmad Muhammad 'Abid. Maktabah An-Nahdah Al-Misriyyah (printing date not mentioned).

— *Kitâb Ar-Raud Al-Ma'târ Fee Khabaril-Aqtâr* - subject matter: history of many lands - Muhammad ibn 'Abdul-Mun'im Al-Humairi. With the addition of critical notes by Dr. Ihsân 'Abbâs. Muassasah Nâsir Ath-Thaqafiyyah, 2980.

— *Al-Kashâf 'An Haqâiq At-Tanzil wa-'Uyun Al-Aqawil Fi Wujuh-at-Ta'wil* - well-known book of *Tafsir* - Az-Zamakhshari. Dar-ul-Fikr, Beirut (printing date not mentioned).

— *Lubâb At-Ta'wil Fi Ma'âni At-Tanzil* (The Core of Interpretation Regarding the Meanings of Revelation), or better known as,

Tafsir Al-Khâzin, 'Ali ibn Muhammad ibn Ibrâhim Al-Baghdadi, who is well known by the name, Al-Khazin. Dar Al-Fikr, Beirut (Printing date not mentioned).

— *Mukhtasar Târikh Damashq* (A Summary of the History of Damascus), by Ibn Asâkir, and summarized by Ibn Manzur. Dar Al-Fikr, Damascus. First Edition was published in 1984, and the latest edition was published in 1988.

— *Muruj Adh-Dhahab wa-Ma'âdin Al-Jauhar*, 'Ali ibn Al-Husain ibn 'Ali Al-Mas'udi. Dar Al-Fikr, Beirut. Fifth Edition, 1393 h, 1973.

— *Mo'jam Al-Buldaan* (Lexicon of Countries), Shihaab-ud-Deen Yaaqoot Al-Hamawee. Daar As-Sâdir, Beirut, 1398 h, 1977.

— *Al-Mo'jam Al-Mufahris Li-Alfâz Al-Qur'ân Al-Karim* - an index of the words used in the Qur'ân - Muhammad Fuâd 'Abdul-Bâqi. Dar Al-Fikr, Beirut, 1401 h/ 1981.

— *Al-Mo'jam Al-Mufahris Li-Ma'âni Al-Qur'ân Al-Karim*, Muhammad Bassâm Az-Zain and Muhammad 'Adnân Salim. Dar Al-Fikr Al-Mu'asir, Beirut. Second Edition, 1417 h/1996.

— *Al-Mausu'ah Al-Yamaniyyah* (Encyclopedia of Yemen), Mu'assasatul-'Afif Ath-Thaqâfiyyah, San'a. First Edition, 1412 h/1992.

— *Hidâyatul-Bayân Fee Tafsir Al-Qur'ân* (A Guided Explanation in regards to the *Tafsir* of the Qur'ân), Râshid 'Abdullah Al-Farhân. Printed and published by the Faculty of Islamic Da'wah, Tripoli, 1993.

— *Al-Wafâ Bi-Ahwâl Al-Mustafa* - deals with the life of the Prophet ﷺ - Abul-Farj 'Abdur-Rahmân ibn Al-Jawzi. Dar-ul-Kutub Al-Hadithah, Egypt. First Edition, 1386 h/1966.

Tema Nason was b[orn] [of immigrant]
Jewish parents who [...] [...]. She
studied economics at Brooklyn College and
the University of Chicago, worked as a factory
worker, union representative and government
economist, and earned an M.A. in creative
writing from the Johns Hopkins University.
She began writing fiction after the birth of her
fifth child.

Tema Nason is the author of a collection of
short stories, *A Stranger Here, Myself. Ethel*, her
first published novel, was written while she
was in residence at the Bunting Institute, Radcliffe and Brandeis University, where she is
currently Research Associate in the Sociology
Department. She now lives in Boston.

ETHEL

A Novel About
ETHEL ROSENBERG

TEMA NASON

FONTANA/Collins

Note

An extract from the song 'Blue Moon' by Richard Rodgers and Lorenz Hart is reproduced by permission of EMI, United Partnership Ltd, London WC2H 0EA, © 1934, Robbins Music Corp., USA. In Australasia, © 1934, renewed 1952, Metro-Goldwyn-Mayer Inc. Used by permission of CPP/Belwin Inc. and International Music Publications. In Canada, © 1934 (Renewed 1961, 1962) Metro-Goldwyn-Mayer Inc. Assigned to Robbins Music Corporation. All Rights of Robbins Music Corporation. Assigned to EMI Catalogue Partnership. All Rights controlled and administered by EMI Robbins Catalog, Inc. International Copyright secured. All Rights reserved. Used by permission.

An extract from 'Love, Your Magic Spell Is Everywhere', words by Elsie Janis, is used by kind permission of Redwood Music Limited, 14 New Burlington Street, London W1X 2LR.

Inside front cover photograph appears by courtesy of AP/Wide World Photos. Inside back cover, copyright © 1953 by The New York Times Company. Reprinted by permission.

First published by William Collins Sons & Co. Ltd 1990
First issued in Fontana Paperbacks 1990
Copyright © Tema Nason 1990

Printed and bound in Great Britain by
William Collins Sons & Co. Ltd, Glasgow

For my Mother, Bella Czernitzski Stein
(1885–1959),
and
my Father, Gerson Stein
(1882–1958),
who dreamt the dreams
that made this book possible

Author's Note

I reach beyond the laboratory brain.
                                    HENRY JAMES

Novelists are, after all, mystery story writers, not always searching for solutions to crimes, true, but rather to enter the maze of the human personality, approach the elusive truth of another human being.

In this seven-year pursuit, I did extensive research, steeped myself in the record and in the period in which Ethel Rosenberg lived, relied on available information, written and oral, to provide the necessary and important clues. Ultimately, however, intuition and an informed imagination were the trusty bloodhounds leading the way.

The entire text of this fictional autobiography, including Ethel Rosenberg's diaries and letters, is a work of the imagination except for the summary legal history of the Rosenberg case. I've used both real and fictional characters to uncover and tell her story. I've recorded what I imagine Ethel Rosenberg's opinion would have been about the other real participants in the trial, without intending to suggest that this is a factual report. In effect, unofficially and posthumously, I have appointed myself her ghost writer.

This novel seeks to apprehend a reality, her reality, not conceivable except through fiction. In giving her a voice I have enabled her to make a case for her own innocence. I leave it to the reader to decide.

                                                        T.N.

I

MARCH 6, 1951

The trial of Julius and Ethel Rosenberg begins in the Federal Courthouse in New York City. Husband and wife plead innocent to charges that they conspired with David Greenglass, her younger brother, to supply information to the Soviet Union about atomic bomb research at Los Alamos. Stating that he was working through another co-conspirator, Soviet Vice Consul A. Yakolev, Harry Gold testifies that he was sent to Albuquerque, New Mexico, in June 1945 to pick up the information from Greenglass. Gold states that he told Greenglass, 'Julius sent me', produced half of a Jello boxtop and received the information. Greenglass testifies that, in September 1945, he sketched the atom bomb for Julius and wrote a description of it which Ethel typed.

MARCH 29

After one day of deliberation, the jury finds the Rosenbergs and Greenglass guilty of conspiring to commit espionage.

APRIL 5

Judge Irving Kaufman sentences the Rosenbergs to die in the electric chair on May 21, 1951. David Greenglass is sentenced to fifteen years. Ruth Greenglass, his wife, a self-confessed co-conspirator who testified for the prosecution, remains free.

APRIL 11

Ethel Rosenberg is suddenly transferred to the Death House at Sing Sing Prison, Ossining, NY.

From this solitary cell longing for the scent of lilacs in Central Park, locked in this dark womb, I will speak out.

To say that my spirit cannot be chained to these grey walls or beaten into silence; it is free to roam out there and explore, free to see and report back, to bring home the Word that will free me ... and others.

ONE

APRIL 1951

I'm one of the World's Great Dreamers. Along with Marx, Moses, Lincoln ... also God. It's only recently that I've discovered this important fact about myself. If they ever make up another list – like the Seven Wonders of the World? – *then I should be on it*. Yes, definitely. I belong. Because when I get into that golden chariot, I ride the skies like a rainbow. Oh, the thrill and the beauty of it! But the funny thing, no, it's not so funny, I'm beginning to realize it's really very odd, at the time I'm up there, I don't know that, it all seems so natural, so real ...

... like here now in solitary – the Death House at Sing Sing – sometimes I feel as though it's all happening to me in a play, and I'm in the audience watching myself perform behind bars. Sometimes I'm so angry I shake – or is it fear? – and yet part of me sits back and watches it happen as though it's happening to someone else, a woman I once knew and haven't seen in years.

Yesterday we're sitting in the Visitors' Room separated by that damn wire screen and we're discussing our brief to the US Circuit Court of Appeals, and I say to Manny, that's Emmanuel Bloch, our lawyer and best friend, the only lawyer in the whole of New York City with guts enough to take our case, Manny, I say to him, I'm trying to understand why I'm here.

'Traitors!' Judge Kaufman screams at us that day in court. I'll never forget it. 'Gave away the secret of the atom bomb to the Russians. Responsible for 50,000 deaths in Korea, maybe more! I consider your crime worse than murder.'

Me a traitor? Ettie Greenglass from Seward Park High? *Mata Hari* was a traitor, that's who ... she was so beautiful,

Greta Garbo up there on the screen ...

Right away Manny's impatient with me. 'Ethel,' he says in that indulgent, yet chastising voice he gets from his uncle, the rabbi. 'I don't follow you. Why are you off on that tangent today when we have this appeal to discuss? When I saw Julie yesterday in New York, he said to be sure to talk it over with you – there are only three days left to file.' And he zips open his case and shuffles some papers like he's got to be doing something with his hands. He's upset. The paper shuffling I recognize from the courtroom. But this time he's upset, because this time I've dared to say to him what I've never dared to say out loud before, so I don't continue with what's on my mind. But I look at myself in this *schmatteh*, and I ask myself, what am I doing here, Ethel Rosenberg in a housecoat like an old bathrobe and bedroom slippers two sizes too large, when I should be home fixing dinner for Julie and the kids. How scared they must be! So little, so young to be away from us. *How did all this happen to me? How did I get from my kitchen here?*

I suppose 1945 was the crucial year for us ... and for the world. So much is crowded in – Roosevelt dies, we drop the atom bomb, the war ends ... so much else happens ...

Of course, Ma's main concern is that the war should be over before her Dovey gets sent overseas. That's her number one reason for winning the war. Bernie's overseas, too, stationed in England, but somehow she worries less about him.

In a letter we receive from Dovey before Thanksgiving in '44, he writes that he's been assigned to a secret project with a return address care of a post office in Santa Fe, New Mexico. Also that his training as a machinist is turning out to be very valuable. So maybe they'll keep him there for the duration. When I mention this to Ma, she looks towards heaven and says, '*Gottenu*, it should only happen!'

Anyhow, when Ruth goes out there for their anniversary

soon after, she comes back and says the same thing, that Dovey's on a very important secret assignment. More than that she can't tell us. And she raises her eyebrows to accentuate just how important.

When he's home on leave in January they come over for dinner one night. Dovey really looks good. He's lost that jowly look and trimmed down to fit into his corporal's uniform, with a fresh shave, and a new peppy stride, not his usual slouch. The uniform, too, gives him an air of authority he's enjoying, you can see it, he's a lot more self-confident.

'So, how's it going?' Julie asks him, and taps his waistline. 'You're looking very fit. You like it out there?'

'Fine, fine,' he says. 'Yeah, it's the good life, sun all the time, not like back here ... I miss Ratner's and Marty's corned beef, though.'

'So we'll send you packages,' I say, 'not corned beef, but salami'll travel.' I can't help smiling at him, I'm so happy to see him, and looking so well. He's a good kid, that Dovey. After all Ma's worries and mine, too, he's turning out okay.

'Ran into Benny,' he says, 'haven't seen him since I left for basic.'

'What's he have to say?' Julie asks.

'Nothing much, except that most of the guys've been drafted. Jackie's overseas flying bombers ... Arnold's gone ... killed taking off from an airstrip in the Pacific.' He looks scared.

'How come Benny's around?'

'Bad knee,' he says. 'You know how he is – always a guy who tried to get out of doing anything. Even in the Young Communist League ... big talker, but that's all.'

As we're sitting there, I'm thinking that the console table Julie bought on sale at Macy's really comes in handy when we have company like this. With the leaf down, the four of us can sit comfortably around it, not like before with that shaky card table.

'That was a wonderful meal, Ettie,' Dovey says opening the

11

top button of his pants. From the pocket of his khaki shirt, he takes out a long cigar, removes the band, nips it carefully with a clipper, and lights up. He's the picture of contentment.

So it was worth using up all our ration points to serve steak, and butter with the rolls, I'm thinking, also that the chocolate éclairs with whipped cream went over big.

Ruth brushes at the smoke and looks annoyed. She always looks annoyed when the four of us get together. Don't ask me why. Quite a change in her since they got married. Before that, sweet as honey.

I get up to put some water on for coffee.

'So what are you doing?' Julie asks him.

David smiles, 'I can't tell you.'

'What d'ya mean?'

'Just that, Julie, I can't tell you. *Top secret*.'

He puffs away and the room fills with the smell of the smoke.

'Pfuiey!' I say. 'Boy, that cigar stinks. Hey, when did you take up cigars?'

'Why don't you lay off him?' Ruth snaps at me. 'I'm sick of you picking on him!'

'Picking on him? What are you talking about? When?'

'Now.' And she gets that mean look on her face like an angry cat.

So I say, 'Hey, Dovey, you know I was only kidding.'

'Yeah, but lay off. I'm not a kid any more, Ettie. Sometimes you forget. And call me David. Forget this Dovey stuff.'

'I'm sorry.'

He tips back the kitchen chair against the wall, inhales, and gives a good puff right in our faces. '*Top secret*,' he repeats, then closes his mouth as though it's been sealed tight by orders.

Julie and I have to smile at each other, the way he hams it up. *Top Secret!* Because you can see he's dying to let us know how important the work is, you can just see it. Between puffs, gradually, he drops hints, and more hints – 'working

12

on high explosives' ... puff puff ... 'could end the war sooner' ... puff puff ... 'super secret' ... long puff ... 'You should only know the famous scientists who are working there!', this time he rolls his eyes and moves his head from side to side. He's so thrilled to be in on something like this, all hush hush, and yet he can't stand not to be able to talk about it to us, to brag a little, that's his nature. '*Los Alamos*,' he says. '*Top secret.*' Why shouldn't he feel great? He's doing important work for the war effort, and for the first time in his life, Ma's not hanging over him – or Ruth either. Only in her letters can she tell him to change his socks and wipe the snot off his nose! And he doesn't have to listen.

'Are the Russians in on it?' I'm thinking of the thousands who died at Stalingrad, and Pa's *shtetl* near the Polish border – how the Germans made them all march out into a field and then, one by one, shot them down.

'I don't know,' he says, 'but I've heard a few guys speaking with an English accent.'

'I hope so,' says Julie. 'Why shouldn't they be? We're all in this together ... it would be the best thing for world peace.'

Talked? Sure we talked ... or rather, we *schmoozed* ... the way you do when you sit around the table after dinner with the family, catching up with each other ... little bits of news you forgot to put in letters about a cousin or a friend, discussing the war, how it's going, and our hopes for afterwards. We ask him some questions – like what it's like out there – sure, like anybody would.

Ruth breaks in to say she wants to come out there to be with him. 'Could I live on the base?' she wants to know.

'No,' he says, 'only the top brass and scientists can have their families with them.'

'So where could I stay?' she asks, getting that whine in her voice.

'Probably Albuquerque,' he says. 'It's further away than Santa Fe but I hear housing isn't so tight.'

He goes on to tell us that he's working as a machinist in

13

one of the labs building models from blueprints the scientists bring, 'very close precision work ... and I got a bastard for a foreman, he's riding me all the time.' Which sounds like the old Dovey – always griping that someone's got it in for him.

Anyway, that's how we talked that night, and Dovey's the biggest talker ... how he's going to do this and that after the war, oh, that brother of mine feels important for the first time in his life. We all agree that it'll be wonderful to live in a peaceful world again ... and that if the Soviet Union and the US go on being friendly allies, there's so much hope for the world *this time*. We talked, yes, but never the way Dovey and Ruth testified at the trial.

Manny is coming through the static in my head. ' ... so that's the situation as I see it. You and Julie,' he goes poof, 'are like two straws in heavy political winds. We've got a very tough fight on our hands, Ettie.'

'I know that. I know that.' He's getting to me today. He shakes his head as though he hasn't heard me. 'Just about every newspaper is for the death sentence. "Completely justified," that's the *St Louis Post Dispatch*. The *Atlanta Constitution* congratulated Judge Kaufman. And the Jewish organizations are behind him too. And we need money ... '

'Manny, *please*, not today.' Maybe my face convinces him. When I saw myself this morning in the tin mirror, my skin's like old parchment. 'Why did they rush me here? What's their hurry? Is that the usual?'

'No, not at all.' He's appalled, too.

'And Julie stays in New York?'

'I've already filed a petition testing the legality of your transfer.'

'Whatever you do, Manny, please, don't let them transfer Julie here. It's horrible.'

He waves his hands helplessly. 'We'll do what we can.'

TWO

JUNE 1931

You know, when I walked off the stage that night, the night of our senior play, with that applause ringing in my ears, *that* was the happiest moment of my life. I looked into the future and it was shining gold. Put it first on that other list, I tell myself, *The Ten Best Moments of My Life*. Number two on that list I guess would be the night I met Julie, though I wouldn't want him to know that, he'd be hurt. It's funny, since they shipped me here after the trial – *is it only a week?* – and I'm alone all the time, I notice I've become a great one for lists. I'm making lists of all kinds to give to Manny, to Julie, to his mother for the boys ... some others like *The Ten Best Books I've Read* ... *My Favourite Movie Stars* ... also a daily schedule so that I can plan my activities for the day ... Activities, now that's a joke. Still, there's something about writing down number one, number two, number three that's clear and settled and I like that, especially here where time drags from one day to the next and nothing happens in between. Like an ageing horse pulling a heavy load.

But that night – June 13, 1931 – will I ever forget it? That night is definitely number one on my list. By far. The audience and me are like one. They're out there and inside of me and I'm filled with such happiness like never before. This is me, Ettie Greenglass, up there on the stage and they're applauding *me*, and it's not even curtain call, but the second act, that scene where I tell my stepmother to go to hell; I put everything I had into that scene. It felt like I was pure electricity. It's the kind of applause that you know makes the palms sting, they're clapping so hard.

Afterwards, backstage, everyone's hugging and kissing me and telling me how great I was ... and they should sign me up for Hollywood, and I tell you, I'm riding that chariot and it doesn't even curve down, it just goes up, up in the sky like a straight line into infinity. Mama and Papa come backstage, and she gives me a big hug and says she's *takeh* proud of me, and I looked so beautiful up there. 'How your eyes were flashing,' she says, 'and how you stood even. You looked taller and different somehow. I tell you, Ethel,' she says, 'you were like a different girl.' What's the matter, I almost say, what's the matter you don't like me the way I am? But I shut up before I say it. What's the use of starting something right there on the happiest night of my life?

Papa hugs me, too, and he says to me, 'Tonight you were an actress – for real.' And in his quiet smile, I know he's happy for me, and he doesn't have to say more, only with his satisfied eyes. Sam didn't come, of course, it's only his kid sister in a high school play, nothing important, but Bernie and Dovey come, and they're sweet, you can tell they're proud of me, too. What a night! Then Papa says, 'We've got to celebrate, Ettie, the whole family. Let's go get some ice-cream, whadya say?'

But there's supposed to be a big cast party afterwards and I say, 'Thanks, Pop, but let's do it another night,' and he says gently, 'Sure, any time,' but then we never get around to it.

So the whole gang goes to Marchiony's, that's on Grand Street near Clinton – on the lower East Side – Dutch treat, all of us, backstage crew and all, and order ice-cream sodas or sundaes. I have mine with two scoops, one chocolate, the other maple walnut, with lots of hot fudge and nuts and whipped cream on top. Those were the days when they really piled it on, too, the real thing and not the kind that comes in a spray can. I squeeze into a booth with three of the guys in the cast. What were their names again? The only one I remember for sure is Ziggy – and he shoves in next to me though he barely makes it, his belly keeps rubbing against the table, but he's joking and kibbitzing and has everyone laughing. Everything he says is hysterical. I don't know when

I've laughed so much, I'm actually crying from laughing so hard and the mascara from the play is running. Even in those days, Ziggy was a terrific comedian, his mouth would twitch a couple of times and you knew he was off and running. And could he put away that ice-cream! Kidding around all the time, Ziggy, clowning and eating, that's what he loved to do best. And Arthur who handled ticket sales is there, too, he's sitting opposite us and he purses his lips as though he's looking down at the whole stupid business, you know that nose in the air look, how we're sitting there laughing our heads off. Somehow it must have made him feel superior. I hear he became a successful CPA. It figures. Later on a partner in a big firm that handled a lot of accounts in fur. Rochelle, who played the mother, once told me that when I ran into her in Woolworth's. Michael was around two then, so it must've been around 1945, because he was still in his stroller and making a fuss as usual about having to stay in it while she and I were talking. I had to promise him a box of animal crackers if he'd sit still.

Anyhow, Rochelle asks me, 'Why didn't you come to the reunion?' What could I say, that we didn't have the money, not even a lousy five dollars for two tickets to the Grand Ballroom on Second Avenue? ... forgetting a new dress and shoes ... and a shirt for Julie ... what it cost ... so I made some excuse, we had some place else to go, and she says, 'Too bad, all of Seward Park was there ... people asked for you ... Ziggy, too, he asked had anyone heard ... you know he's making it ... this summer in the Catskills he played at Kutcher's Country Club and now he's opening in a club down in the Village. I think we'll go see him. Are you interested?'

I shake my head. Why try to explain?

'Success hasn't gone to his head like with some others,' she goes on with a little bite in her voice. 'The nice thing is, Ethel, he's still a good guy, still wears the same size hat, still kibbitzes around like he used to. Only a little fatter. Remember?'

Did I remember? Suddenly that cast party's coming back to me and I can see it clearly like it's lit up on the stage.

I'm sitting with Arthur on the couch, that's later when somebody suggested going to the Eagles clubroom; it's a basement apartment they rent on Christopher Street. So, very casually, as we're talking, he puts his arm on the back of the couch, then still very casually, he's really very funny about it, probably saw it in a movie, he casually drops his arm down around my shoulder. I remember it's an old couch with the springs bursting through because then when he suddenly leans over and kisses me, I feel myself being pushed against the springs and I say, it hurts, and he looks like I've insulted him and I start to giggle, not you, you dope, the springs in the couch. Oh, he says, and straightens his tie and collar, smooths down his hair and stands up. He's so uncomfortable and red, I'm not sure he's ever kissed any girl before – and it's my first time, too, and all I can remember is the springs hurting me as though Mom's there reminding me, only a kiss, remember, nothing more, you want to disgrace us? So I stand up, too, and just then Ziggy comes over and flops down in our place. 'Hey, Ethel,' he says, 'come sit down,' and he pulls at the hem of my dress, 'I got something to show you,' and makes a grab for his fly – and everyone's watching and laughing so I laugh, too, and thumb my nose at him and he pulls me down and says, 'Relax, kid, it won't hurt.' I know he's only kidding.

'So what's next for you, Ethel?' He turns to me serious now. 'You gonna give it a try?'

'Are you?'

'Yeah, sure, might as well.'

'I don't know, Ziggy, my family, mostly my mother, turns purple when I mention going on the stage.'

'So what's the difference? They're not you.'

'I know that, but still ... '

'Listen, you got nothing to lose. I'll tell you what, I worked

18

for a while with the settlement house group, there's a guy there, the director, Joe Polovoy, he's good. This guy's having a rough time earning a living right now on Broadway so he's taken this job with the Clark Players and it pays the rent. But he's a pro – and you could learn a lot from him. Tell him I sent you.'

I don't know why, but suddenly I feel very shy with Ziggy. It's like he's up there already and I'm still down here looking up at him. 'Look, it's different for me.' I try to explain. 'I guess I can do it in a high school play all right, but in that situation? You know the other actors and all, they know so much more and they're probably a lot older.'

'So what! How old are you anyway?'

'Well, almost sixteen ... next September.'

He seems surprised, I don't think he realized that; he must have been eighteen already. Ziggy always seemed older than the rest of us somehow, like he was born old. Anyhow, his expression changes and he says, 'Yeah, well listen, you gotta try ... there's no other way to make it, Ethel ... listen, I think you have real talent. You were great up there tonight, I mean it, they loved you.'

He really said that to me, Zero Mostel himself. I have to remind myself. He wasn't just kidding me. That's what made it such a wonderful night, all that applause and then Ziggy telling me I had real talent, he used just those words, not just talent, but *real* talent, I mean that says something, doesn't it?

Then Arthur comes back and wants to know if he can walk me home and I say, sure, not knowing what else to say, and Ziggy just says, 'Nice talking to you, Ethel, if I don't see you again after graduation, lotsa luck!'

'You, too,' I say, wishing I hadn't said yes to Arthur so quickly. I want to talk some more with Ziggy – he's so clear about it, as though he's figured out what's right for him and what he has to do to get into show business. I could learn from him, I tell myself, maybe we could do it together. But he's already gotten himself up – he must have weighed over

19

two hundred even then – and lumbers away like a friendly black bear. What a guy – and what a great night!

Of course, Arthur talks non-stop about himself all the way to my house. He's starting a night course in business and accounting at City College downtown right after graduation. He already has a job after school in an office near 23rd Street and he figures he can take courses at night and get his degree in seven years. Then he can take the exam for CPA. Boy, he's got it all figured out to the last decimal place and to me it's *chutzpah*. This is June 1931, all those people out there selling apples, I've seen them myself, and this guy thinks he's got his life all neatly laid out and arranged. Naturally Ma says, when he starts coming round, 'That Arthur's a smart young man, he'll go places, mark my words.'

Anyhow, Arthur keeps yacking away and I stop listening and just hear Ziggy in my head the rest of the way home. At our stoop, he pecks me on the cheek and says, 'Listen, I'll call you tomorrow, maybe we can go to the movies. Okay?' I want to say, don't bother, but I just smile up at him, because I'm up in that chariot travelling seventy miles an hour.

'That you?' Ma yells when she hears my key.

'Yeah. Go to sleep, Ma, I'm home.'

I can't fall asleep for a long time thinking about what happens after graduation. I'm scared, too, but mostly excited ... maybe someday my name will be up there in lights ... It can happen. I tell myself I'll have to dream up something better; I remember thinking, Ethel Greenglass isn't a name for a star.

THREE

JUNE 1931

Of course the next morning, it's raining outside, and we're back to the old familiar story: Go get a job!

Ma comes in while I'm in the kitchen fixing myself hot chocolate before going to school. It's Regents' Week, the last day, and I still have French and American History to take. I'm conjugating verbs under my breath, and my head's ringing with dates. Her bathrobe's open and her pink cotton nightgown's showing. Under the nightgown, you can see the outline of her breasts flopping down on her belly.

She sits down at the table with her coffee and looks me over. 'Did you know Elsie from upstairs has a job already?' My mother, the Inquiring Reporter for the *Daily News*, is on my case first thing in the morning.

'Yeah, she told me the other day.' My throat's shutting down and I start to get up.

'Why are you rushing away? The minute I start to talk sense to you – you're out the door. Why didn't you take stenography and typing like I told you time and time again?'

She shakes her finger at me. 'You're like your father. You don't want to look ahead, you don't want to talk about it. If it weren't for me, do you know where we'd be? Out on the street. Like those other families you see out there. You think it can't happen to us? You think your father makes enough money for us to live on? Believe me, if it weren't for me mopping the halls and the stairs and cleaning the stinkin' toilets in this *verdammten* building ... you think Farber'd let us stay? Look at my hands!'

And she shoves them under my nose. I'm sick – they're red and cracked and swollen and the nails are broken down to nothing.

21

Just then Dovey comes in. He's only eight and his face still has the cute roundness of a little boy – my Robby looks a little like him, especially around the eyes, I think. For a moment both of us look at him with pleasure, how the sun polishes his hair into golden ringlets. His clean white shirt already has spots because he always gets dressed first and then he slaps some water on his face – that's my Dovey! There's a line that starts at one ear and runs under his jaw to the other ear, and it separates the face that he washes from the neck he never touches. Right away Ma is on her feet. 'Nu Dovele – breakfast, mein Kind? A little cereal?'

While she's busy fixing oatmeal for him, I get myself out of there.

So I graduate from Seward Park High School in June 1931. 1931, not two years after the stock market crash. Not that I understood what that meant at the time. Who knew about stocks in my family? But then no one in my family jumped out of the window after the crash either.

The history books refer to it as the heart of the Depression. I'd say it was just the opposite. No heart. And that was the beginning of my real education.

It's only now, twenty years later, that I can see it all clearly. Would you believe it, when I graduated, the Almanac, the senior yearbook, predicted that in 1950 Ethel Greenglass would be the leading actress in the country? And that Ziggy Mostel would be a Rembrandt or a comedian? Can you believe it? At least he made it. But for me, even the words now sound like they're in a foreign language.

Of course, when I graduated, we still had hope. This one was going to college and that one, too. At least that's what they said in the yearbook ... City College, Hunter, Columbia, Barnard ... Boy, did I want to go to Barnard! It sounded so high-tone up there on 116th Street and Broadway. One day I took the Broadway–Seventh Avenue express up there and walked around the campus. It was a whole new world, the

22

girls looked so well dressed and ritzy, from homes where the family all sat down to dinner together and the table was set in advance. In our house, Ma kept an oilcloth on the kitchen table, except on the Sabbath, and somebody was always getting up or sitting down, and Ma usually ate standing up afterwards. The brick buildings there had vines climbing up them, with trees around, and there was a high iron picket fence surrounding the college. No boys – which surprised me, but I figured they're nearby at Columbia so I'll meet them – and I don't think I saw a single Jewish girl there either, or if she was Jewish, she didn't look it. It seemed like an unfriendly place; still, I almost went into the one building that looked like the main one to ask about scholarships, but then I lost my nerve. *What's the use*, I asked myself.

So I walked over to Riverside Drive and sat down on a bench overlooking the Hudson and pictured myself going to college up here. Even the air smelled different. And the sounds were different – a boat whistle, some birds calling out to each other, and cars whizzing by. Maybe I'd meet a guy who had a roadster with a rumble seat and belonged to a fraternity. If you'd asked me why that mattered, I couldn't have told you, except that that meant college to me. All I knew was from the movies I'd seen where it was Rah, Rah, Rah, and the Big Football weekend – that, and necking in the rumble seat. Thinking about it now, I can't believe I ever wanted those things. But really it was something else – I wanted to be let into that world, the world of books and knowledge and professors who talked to their students after class and helped them find the answers to Life. There was so much I wanted to know, there was a whole world out there I knew nothing about. I would have given anything for that ticket of admission. I even wrote 'College bound – Barnard' on the *Almanac* form for 'Future Plans'. To me, it meant moving on, not getting stuck down here on the East Side for the rest of my life. I'll get out of here yet, I promised myself, I can do it. I'll work hard and I'll go to night school … and …

I don't say anything when I get home. Ma's sitting on the stoop talking to Mrs Schwartz and hardly looks up. These days we're not saying much to each other. But Dovey must have noticed something because he comes over and snuggles against me as I sit there at the kitchen table, feeling low, beat. He doesn't say anything, just snuggles close and I hug him. He's a good kid.

FOUR

APRIL 1951

From Julie, by way of Manny, I received this today. He says Julie worries about me being here alone in Sing Sing without him. 'Tell him not to, I'm managing.' Not true, but I have mounted it on a frame made from the cardboard backing to a pad of paper, and now it's taped to the prison bars next to the snapshots of the children. It's from Jeremiah:

> Do not break down before them
> Lest I break you before them
> I make you this day
> A fortified city,
> And an iron pillar
> Against the whole land –
> Against Judah's kings and officers,
> And against its priests and citizens.
> They will attack you,
> But they shall not overcome you:
> For I am with you – declares the Lord – to save
> You.

'Anything new on the appeal yet?' I ask.

'No, it's too soon.'

'I keep worrying about the boys, Manny.'

'They're fine, they're just fine,' he repeats in that pseudo-hearty voice.

How can they be fine, I'm thinking, with the two of us in prison – not even the same one. Keep us apart – that way they figure they'll break me.

After it got started, the FBI investigation and all that followed – David's arrest in June 1950, Julie's in July, then mine in August – we never had a chance, privately, I mean, the two of us by ourselves, to discuss what's happening to us. The way a husband and a wife need to. What should we do under such extraordinary circumstances to protect ourselves? To make sure that our legal rights aren't being violated? And to make proper arrangements for Michael and Robby, naturally our big concern. They're only seven and three, and we're brutally torn away from them – first Julie, then me. Suddenly, in less than a month, it's as though they've been orphaned. Last November, Manny had to move them out of Ma's to the Hebrew Children's Home in the Bronx. Ma threatened to dump them at the nearest police station if we didn't get them off her hands. I tell you, the way the whole thing was handled, it had to be deliberate. And then setting bail for each of us at $100,000.

Things are happening so fast, my head's swimming. In fact it's only when we're arraigned in October that the whole extent of the charges against us even becomes clear to me. Spies for the Russians. Incredible! And somehow they drag Marty Sobell into it and put him on trial with us, too. He's an old classmate of Julie's at CCNY, also an engineer. He's charged with conspiracy in connection with the spy ring Julie is supposedly masterminding, but not with the Los Alamos business.

Not that it makes any more sense than before. It's like a giant octopus, some place out there, invisible at first, hovering over us, that's closing in with its tentacles. And suddenly, we're in its clutches.

The only time we talked alone, even semi-private, was in the police van on the way to court for arraignment, crowded in next to the other prisoners.

'What do we do, Julie?' I ask him.

'Only one thing – we're innocent, aren't we? So that's what we say.'

'Yes, of course.'

'So that settles it.'

26

And I knew he was right.

Over and over again, I've asked myself, what could we have done differently. I mean when it first came up. But then it never showed its real face until it was too late. Like a cancer that starts out with a cough, maybe at first, along with a cold – so why should you immediately suspect cancer? You don't. You say, that damn cold is hanging on; two weeks later, a month later, you're still saying, this stupid cough won't go away.

FIVE

JULY–AUGUST 1931

That summer, right after graduation, Ma starts in on me. 'Go to business school, at least.' I shut my ears and go my own way. Even Arthur, who used to drop in on his way home from class, would be at me to register for a business course. 'It's the only way, take it from me.'

For him, maybe, but not for me. I'd signed up like Ziggy suggested with the Clark Players at the settlement house which is practically around the corner. And all I can think about is acting. Maybe even singing in musical comedies or operettas.

Once I buy *Variety* and read it all through. The big news on page one is all about *Of Thee I Sing*, BRILLIANT MUSICAL WINS PULITZER PRIZE. I'd never heard of it before, but it's so exciting to be reading about show business in the same paper all the actors are reading. Headlines like SMASH HIT/REUNION IN VIENNA/CO-STARS LUNT AND FONTANNE, or MOURNING BECOMES ELECTRA/O'NEILL'S LATEST BREAKS RECORDS.

All this is happening up around Times Square and Broadway. I know I'll make it there yet. The only live theatre I've gone to was once the Yiddish Art Theatre at Proctor's Fifth Avenue in 1929. The play is *Jew Süss* by Feuchtwanger and I enjoy it, but still it's not the way I imagined it uptown. The actors with the yarmulkes and long dark beards all speak a thick Yiddish and carry on like crazy waving their hands and screaming at each other. This can't be good acting, I tell myself, the theatre to me means in English. English is the language of Shakespeare.

These days, how I wait for rehearsals to start. My heart's already beating faster, as the gang drifts in after supper, after work, and then we rehearse late, maybe until midnight. It's a small auditorium, seats only a hundred and fifty or so, and we have very little money for costumes or props, but to me it's the Theatre. It's where I live my real life; the rest is just something I go through the motions of doing so I can be here at night.

Mornings I'm exhausted, but still I get up early and go out looking for work – to employment agencies, banks, stores, factories, you name it, I go there. Every place the answer's the same. No, no openings.

So three months go by, a lot of nickels for carfare down the drain and still no job. It's getting to me, and Ma is at me the minute I walk in the door. '*Nu* – any luck today?'

'No.' And I start to go to my room, but she stops me. Sometimes I feel she asks just to rub it in. Sometimes I wish I didn't have to go home and face her. I dream of running away. I could take a tramp steamer to Tahiti ... The only other place I can think of is Brooklyn. That's running away? On the subway to Brighton Beach where I'd go live with Tante Rosie?

Sooner or later Ma must figure I'll give in, and I do, but not until after that day at Bloomfeld's on 14th Street. It happens through an ad in the *News* for a sales clerk in this five and dime. So I get all dressed up in a pleated skirt and white blouse, wear my only pair of silk stockings without a run, and high heels, and put my hair up so I look older, at least nineteen. Some rouge, too, though Ma doesn't like it when I put on make-up.

The first thing I notice when I get to Bloomfeld's is the crowd surrounding the store next to Hearn's Department Store. At first I suppose some kind of sale is going on, everyone's pushing and shoving to get in the door and the crowd's all over. There are police around swinging their sticks like a warning. Then a thin guy with no hair and wire glasses comes out and yells, 'The job's filled, the job's filled.' There's an angry sound, like a dog's growl that seems to come from everyone's throat and suddenly the crowd's pushing for real. I hear the sound of glass breaking and a woman's scream, 'Oh, my eye, my eye,' and suddenly a blast of water hits my back and I turn and catch it full force on my face from the hose a fireman's pointing at me. The force almost knocks me over. Imagine, they connected the fire hoses to the hydrants and turned them on us! I hear women crying and men cursing. I break away from the crowd, people are scattering in all directions knocking each other over, and I run all the way to the subway station at Union Square. I'm wet and cold and shivering, and I go home, people sitting next to me on the train staring. I don't care. The tears stay frozen inside me for a long time.

Right then and there I decide I have to go to business school. Maybe in six months, things'll pick up, that's what President Hoover's saying, and besides, I'll have some business training.

That experience at Bloomfeld's changed my life. Sure I'd heard stories before ... about the bosses, how they treated the workers ... I mean, Reva used to grab me in the school cafeteria and give me long lectures about how come I wasn't active protesting and demonstrating. But at the time, it all sounded like slogans and it had nothing to do with my life as an actress ... Though when I go and visit Tante Rosie in Brighton Beach she talks union to me, and how bad conditions are in her shop – even though she's afraid that it'll all get back to her Mr G, that's her boss. Here she's living in an apartment he pays for and at the same time, she's talking union. Full of contradictions, that's how people are, I've learned.

Thinking about it now, her telling me about it wasn't the same as having that water hit my back.

SIX

1932

The school, the Excelsior Business School, is over a dry-cleaner's on 34th Street near Eighth Avenue.

Since classes are over at one, without telling my mother I'm trying to audition for parts on Broadway. Nothing comes of it, but it does make me feel like I'm in the theatre, or at least, on my way, though most of the time I can't even get past the receptionist. So the Clark Players are still my answer.

In the few months I'm with them, I've already played two different roles: a maid in *Maid's Night Out* – three lines right at the opening, something like, 'I'll see you tomorrow morning, Madam,' real chirpy. In the next play, *Poppies Grow in Flanders*, I play the sweetheart of a soldier in France. It's one small scene where she gets the telegram informing her that he's been killed in action, and she shrieks hysterically. That's all. Exit.

It turns out that Joe Polovoy, the director, never mind what Ziggy said about him, is not that great, and besides, he has his favourites. There's a redhead with a big bust who always gets the leads and I've been noticing that they always leave together. Slowly, too slowly, I'm learning about life, but it goes against everything I've believed up to now, and I'm always concerned that maybe, maybe I'm misinterpreting these things, that maybe he's just seeing her to the subway. I hate to believe that if you sleep with the director you get the lead. Besides, I just can't see myself getting ahead that way. Not with 34-inch hips and a 30-inch bust.

For a short time, I'm even considering studying accounting at City College downtown, but then I know it's not what I really want to do. It would've come in handy when Julie started his machine shop. But then he always told me I was the greatest in everything. Julie was the first person I met

31

who gave me some self-confidence, outside of Tante Rosie, Papa's sister. She was always on my side, too, but I used to figure, she's a relative, so her opinion doesn't count.

At home, things go on as usual. Which means money is always a problem. Worries and arguments. That's their life, I'm thinking. I want mine to be different. In Pa, there's always a little sadness, a little disappointment, it's there in his lips, in the corners, when he's not smiling. But also he accepts how things are because he seems to know there's no other way. He goes his own way, working long hours in his shop – which is really the front room in our apartment with a separate entrance – and likes to *schmooze* with his customers – which makes Ma very angry with him for wasting his time – and he reads the entire *Jewish Forward* every day after dinner.

With Ma, it's different. She fights with life like it's something personal between them. When Pa tries to calm her down, she turns on him like he's the one responsible for everything wrong. Sometimes when she's been on my back, I'll go into the shop and just sit there for a while watching Pa as he's fixing a broken sewing machine. His pale-brown hair has turned straw white while nobody noticed. There's something soothing I find about his slow, deliberate hand movements, carefully examining what's wrong, figuring out how to fix it. And his patience never seems to run out. Once or twice he might come over and stroke my hair gently, maybe say, '*Nu, scheine Mädel, was sagt's du?*' ('What do you have to say?'), expecting no answer, there's none, and we both know it. I always feel better afterwards.

Now my brother Sam has a terrible temper. When he gets angry, he'll say anything that comes into his head, no matter how it hurts you. And sometimes it seems as though he and Ma are running the family instead of Pa. In season he's working as a presser in a shop which makes ladies' blouses and which is strictly non-union. By this time, Sam's making pretty good money considering the times – though each time

32

he's laid off in slack season, he uses up all his savings. And he's going with some girl for four months now, which is serious. None of this pleases my mother. While Sam and I don't get along well, still I can see it from his point of view. I think it's the money he contributes at home that's making the trouble. 'What's your rush?' Ma asks whenever he mentions this girl.

Anyhow, one night there's a big fight between them – maybe it's about this – and Sam goes storming out of the house as though the police are after him. I don't hear, I don't want to hear, what it's all about. So I stay in my room until the door slams.

Pretty soon Ma comes into my room and she sinks down on the bed. Her walk is heavy as though lifting and putting down each foot is too much for her. 'I'm tired,' she says. 'Ya heard him? I should've washed out his mouth with soap when he was little, maybe he wouldn't have the nerve to talk to me like that. Can you believe it? What words he used?'

I don't say anything. And she's quiet looking down at her hands as though she's seeing them for the first time and they're not hers. Then she lies back on the pillow. I start to tiptoe out, thinking maybe she'll fall asleep, she looks very tired, and pale, too – no colour, though usually her cheeks are bright red and you can see the little veins underneath the skin – when she says in a different kind of voice, a weak voice, I've never heard it like that before, 'Stay with me, Etteleh.' Ma never asks like that, so she takes me by surprise, and I sit down near her on a chair. One hand, very rough, is hanging down off the bed and I pick it up. She holds mine very tightly and I'm surprised how cold hers is. Clammy. It frightens me. I never think that anything can happen to Ma. Soon she's snoring and the colour gradually returns to her face. Every so often her head shakes as though she's arguing with someone in her sleep. But after a while even her snores quiet down and a flush spreads across her cheeks and she's sleeping quietly with her mouth partly open. I sit there a long time

33

holding her hand and it feels good.

I'm reminded how one morning early, when I was maybe seven or eight, I came downstairs and it was empty in the kitchen. No one was there. Ma hadn't yelled up to me, 'What's keepin' yuh?', the fire hadn't been stoked, the milk brought in from the window box, even the mousetrap is empty, the cheese gone. It frightened me. Where's Ma? She was always there, sitting with her elbows on the table, resting her head in her hands, hair uncombed, hairpins poking out, and drinking her coffee. How she loved her morning coffee! The sight of her always reassured me even if she wouldn't look up. At least all was normal in my life. So where is she, I wondered.

I hurried down to their room, a small dark room without a window, the doorway without a door, only a long dark rumpled cloth hanging from a rod covered the opening, and I peeped in. No sounds, only a curious silence as if earlier sounds had been silenced. Under the feather quilt, Pa's asleep, like a child with his mouth open, lying on his side. Even Dovey, who's usually standing up in his crib, soaking wet, is asleep, clutching his ragged blanket, and his thumb's in his mouth. I love the sight of that boy! Since he was born and I was seven, I've helped take care of him. Over in the corner Ma's standing, naked, getting dressed. I've never seen her this way before and I'm fascinated – and repelled. Her thick puffy skin is ashen as she struggles to get into her corset, and every few tries, she stops and massages her fingers. That's her ar-tri-tis that she always complains about as though it's a living trouble in her life, like her children and the rent collector. 'Dr Feinkuchen says "live with it" – *a choleryeh ahf 'em*,' she curses. 'Better he should live with it!' She's hooking her high-waisted corset stiffened with stays, sucking in her loose belly with the belly button swimming in fat, and shoving in the flesh like it's the *kishke* of some unkosher animal. As I'm watching, she works her way up the row of metal hooks and eyes to the top ones then sinks down

34

on the wobbly chair behind her. A few heavy sighs and as she stands up again, the fat above her waist rolls over on to the corset like a creamy ruffled peplum. I can't take my eyes off those huge breasts hanging down almost to her waist like the udder of a cow I once saw being milked in the Bronx children's zoo. Hers are plump with large brown circles around the big nipples. A strand of memory tightens in my head. She begins to tug on the laces again, tightening the corset even more until there are no more ripples or bulges left. After she double knots the ends and tucks them into her corset, her abdomen resembles a large peach-coloured cylinder. Then on her shoulders she hangs the heavy broad straps of her long brassière, lifting and pouring her breasts into each cup like so much cotton wadding; tilting slightly forward, she begins again to work with the brassière's hooks and eyes in the back. From the way she bites on her upper lip, it's as though it's painful for her to reach behind.

I want to rush in and say, 'Ma, let me do it for you.' But something holds me back, a whisper, don't. She'll be furious with me, that much I sense, though I'm not sure why and too confused by what I've seen to comprehend the surge of my own feelings.

Then she straightens up and all the bulges are gone except around the armpits where the tight straps bite into her shoulders and the flesh hangs out. In the coarse grey light, she resembles a big white mammal with high rounded breasts and long black shimmering hair. Again, she sinks down heavily on to the chair, drooping her head so that the dark hair covers her face, and her full body hides the chair. She's like a seated statue. Overcome with a sudden longing I can't name, still I watch her.

She must go through this in reverse, I'm thinking, unhooking and untying every night before falling exhausted into bed, and I can picture the red marks inflicted on her flesh by nightfall.

Silently I drop the curtain and return to the kitchen, pick

35

up the empty coal bucket near the cold stove, and start down the basement stairs. I want reddish-blue plumes of fire dancing in the stove when she comes in.

SEVEN

MAY 1951

One look at Manny's face today and I knew. Petition denied. So here I stay.

But it's amazing how you can get used to almost anything. Almost. I remember returning to the Women's House of Detention after Kaufman sentenced us. And Pauline, my neighbour in the next cell, said to me, 'You're so strong, Ethel. I could never handle it knowing what's ahead.' In my heart I felt the same. And yet here I am, a month later.

'How's Julie taking it?'

'He's doing okay. He really is. But he wants to be here with you, and listen, before you say anything, I agree. His set-up there is almost as bad as yours here – he's kept in isolation, away from the other prisoners and not allowed to exercise. And you know how important that is to him. Besides, he misses you very much. At least this way maybe you'll get to see each other. I'm working on it right now.'

'I miss him.' I'm embarrassed to tell Manny how much. Some nights I bury my head in the pillow, I don't want the matron to hear me and then I think, why not. In the morning, the pillowcase is damp.

1931

One night at rehearsal I hear several of the girls talking about Amateur Night at Loew's on Delancey. Gloria, who always plays someone with a dialect – anyhow she's telling them about a girlfriend who won first prize there singing that famous aria from *Carmen*. We're all in the dressing-room which isn't much bigger than a closet down in the basement. This evening we're starting rehearsals on a new play, *Green Stockings* – it's about Ursula, an English spinster who wears green cotton lisle stockings while her younger sister Beryl, that's me, insists on wearing sheer silk hose, black, no less, and therefore ends up marrying the man she's in love with! That's the kind of junk Joe Polovoy picks!

My all time favourite, though, is *The Valiant*. Was it in 1935? That's a wonderful role I had – the condemned man's sister. I still remember some of the lines and sometimes I recite them to myself even now.

Anyhow, hearing about her friend really starts me thinking maybe that's the answer for me, too, I mean Amateur Night, rather than trying out for parts on Broadway. So far, I've gotten nowhere.

I've seen the posters in front of Loew's advertising it for Thursday nights. Wednesday nights are Bingo and Tuesday free dishes.

The next afternoon I make a point to stop in at Loew's on my way home from business school. First, though, I go into Woolworth's and buy myself some red earrings. I figure everything helps and it's only a twenty cent investment in my future. Then I stop at the box office and ask the cashier for the manager.

'I want to speak to him about Amateur Night.' Can she spot how nervous I am?

After a few questions Mr McNeill says, 'Be here at seven next Thursday and I'll give you final instructions. Wear something bright and snappy that looks good from out front – and high heels, too, so at least they can see you.' He smiles to show he's only kidding.

That Thursday I don't say a word at home. I figure I'll put on the dress and make-up at the theatre. I *know* I'll get an argument if Ma sees me in the dress. It's a red satin with rhinestone buttons down the front that I bought at Klein's with the five dollars Tante Rosie gave me for graduation. You should hear Ma on the subject of actresses! As it is, she practically spits out this word, *cur-veh*. I think it means prostitute. It's funny how she's accepted my acting with the

38

Clark Players, though she never comes to a performance. But even mention the word theatre, or vaudeville, to her and she yells, 'Nice Jewish girls don't go on the stage and never mind telling me about Celia Adler and Molly Picon. Don't go comparing yourself to them.'

So I tell her I'm going over to Frieda's, that we have a scene to rehearse.

'Again? What's with all this rehearsing lately? Just remember, you gotta get up early!'

'Don't worry,' I tell her, wishing I didn't have to lie, that I could tell her the truth. Because the truth is I'm scared stiff.

The first three contestants – a tap dancer, a juggler and a funny man who's not so funny with his cracks about kikes and dagoes – are booed off the stage and I'm waiting to go on next. My heart's in my mouth and I'm wishing at this moment that I'd never heard of this stupid Amateur Night and that I could say a magic word and make myself vanish.

But there's no escape. 'Break a leg,' someone says and I stumble forward. Everything out front is a blur. The stage is enormous. I don't see faces, only a blur. What's more, I'm right behind the footlights and I feel as though I'm going to faint. I tell myself, with your luck, you'll fall into the pit and you *will* break a leg. Something inside of me, a steel rod, is holding me up, not me. There are holes in my palms from my fingernails digging in, I can feel them, and my feet are standing in cold water. I open my mouth. Nothing comes out. My mouth feels as though it's been wandering in the Sahara for months.

The music slides to a halt and tries again. Still nothing happens. The third time when the orchestra blares the opening chords, someone in the back yells, 'Well, if you're going to jump, sister, then jump!' And in the balcony, some Bronx cheers. If only Ma were out there rooting for me!

Maybe she is, I imagine. Maybe for once she's out there rooting for me – and I'll show her I can do it. I'll show her. The orchestra opens with the vamp once more and this time when I open my mouth the notes come out and I'm singing – for real. It's very quiet out there and I sense their sudden attention as though my voice has taken them by surprise. It sounds good and clean and sweet and sure of itself. I do some business with my hands. I'll show them, I'll show them all – Ma, and Sam, and the relatives and neighbours, all of them. I'm singing away and my breath is coming fine and I'm free and I'm up there alone and not frightened any more and suddenly I know what I'm doing, just like when I'm up there on the stage acting, it's as though the switch inside has been flicked on and the electricity flows through me. I'm okay now, I'm O-Kay, all I want to do is go on singing, I don't want to stop, just go on and on. Other songs are coming into my head – how about 'Ciribiribbin' if they want an encore? But the orchestra swings into the last notes and I finish up on a high C. The audience is very quiet.

Then the applause breaks on my ears – like a wave at Coney Island. What a thrill! 'More, more!' someone's yelling out, and my heart's fluttering. McNeill who's watching from the wings opposite shakes his head and motions 'No'. So I go out for another bow, though if he'd let me I'd have gone on singing.

And you know what? I win first prize. 'Overwhelmingly, the first prize winner,' that's exactly how McNeill announces it when he hands me the prize, five dollars in a fancy embossed envelope. And next week I get the chance to compete with other winners at Loew's on 86th and Lexington.

You've done it, you've actually done it, I keep telling myself all the way home. I'm singing 'Life's Just a Bowl of Cherries' as I skip down Sheriff Street and everyone's staring at me like I'm crazy. But I don't care.

EIGHT

1932

Now that I'm on the Amateur Night circuit, the big question is, what do I do about my mother.

For several weeks now, I've been waking up in the middle of the night, just lying there, my mind's going a mile a minute. All the night noises come in on me. A cough that sounds serious, high heels clicking along by herself, the howl of an ambulance. They're lonely sounds, even the rattle of the train *schlepping* over the Williamsburg Bridge. Locals don't rush like expresses. After a while, the light sneaks past the dark-green shades and the trucks with big heavy tyres rumble by.

Papa, I don't worry about. He won't like it, but he'll say it once and let it go at that. But my mother won't let up. I know her.

Yet I can't keep it from her much longer. It's killing me, lying about where I'm going, and then keeping quiet about it afterwards, no matter how it turned out. Twice more I've won – once a second prize for three dollars and another time a third prize for two.

There's so much I want to tell her about this whole new world of show business and I have to keep it bottled up inside. Those nights when I win are like wine in my blood. Half dreaming, half running down Sheriff Street, I'm up in my chariot bound for Broadway. Move over, Fanny Brice, here I come!

A few nights later I win second prize at Loew's 86th Street, and when I try to sneak in quietly, there's Ma like a watchdog at the kitchen table with a *glassele* tea in front of her. As soon as she hears me unlocking the door, her fingers start thrumming on the oilcloth.

Before I can even take off my coat, she says, 'So – so what do you have to say for yourself, light of my eyes?' Somehow the kitchen seems extra bright, like they put in bigger light bulbs. I look up – a hundred, a hundred and fifty watts? Two hundred? – I have this dizzy sensation that her question's hanging from a long cord like the ceiling light, and it's swinging back and forth between us. Water from the ice box drips into the metal pan beneath slowly, one drop at a time ... drop ... drop, steady like a metronome ... and upstairs, voices are rising and falling like background music in a movie, but not for a scene like this. She's swelling with anger, her eyes get bigger, buggier, yet I'm glued to that spot.

There's something about my mother I've never been able to figure out. When I'm with her, I always feel cancelled out. It's not her size, because we're both about five feet, more her solidness that feels like she's looming over me whether she's sitting or standing up. Maybe because she's thick in the waist with a broad fleshy back and shoulders. It's something in her voice, too, and the way she looks at me, inspecting, taking me apart, and putting me together again, thinner, taller, turning me into something I'm not. Each time I'd say to myself, even when I'm older and married already, I won't let her do this to me, I'll stand up to her. Five minutes with her – okay, so I'm exaggerating – and I'm running to the bathroom or the refrigerator – anything to get away from her.

So this particular evening she repeats, 'So, my *tzatske*, what do you have to say for yourself?' Suddenly she stands up and the chair topples over. She grabs me by the back of the head and jerks it back hard. My eyes fill up, but I don't say a word. She's hurting me, but that's not what really hurts.

'So, my *scheine Kind* with the rouge,' she says, 'and that black junk on your eyes – you think I don't see what you're up to – all those nights when you're sneaking out with a paper bag under your arm! What kind of mother do you think I am? You think I'll let you fall into the sewer? You *curveh* you! Streetwalker! You think that's the kind of mother

42

I am?' Her face explodes into flames. 'For this I'm working day and night? *Tell me!*'

'Ma!' I cry out, shaking like a leaf. 'Please listen to me.'

'Listen to a *curveh*? Go, go get yourself a permit from the Tsarist police!'

Her face is purple, I swear, and any minute I'm afraid she'll have a heart attack like her sister. For five years now she's been warning me not to excite her.

'Okay Ma,' I'm pleading, 'I'll tell you – it's really nothing, nothing at all.'

'Nothing?' she's mocking me.

'It's just ... I'm entering Amateur Nights at Loew's, that's all. I'm singing in their amateur contests. It's nothing to get upset about ... believe me ... '

She's standing there, watching me. Believing me? Who knows? At least she lets go of my hair.

I back away. 'And I won some money. Tonight – three dollars. Look, you can have it.' I go for my pocketbook. My throat hurts.

'All this you're hiding from me?' Her voice is cooling down.

I'm breathing easier. 'Let me tell you about it ... how it happened.'

We sit down at the table, and then I excuse myself and get up for a drink of water. The water slides down my throat, easing it open.

'You're hungry?' She motions to the icebox.

I shake my head.

Just then Sam walks in. He's got these small sharp eyes that size up a situation immediately and he turns to walk out again, but she motions him, sit down. He doesn't want to, but she repeats, 'Sit down!' and he does. 'I want you should listen. Ettie's got something very in-ter-esting to tell us about.'

'Sam ... I was going to tell her ...' I turn to him. For once be on my side, I'm praying.

Anyhow, I start all over again, slowly. They both hear me

43

out, for once, although Sam interrupts me every so often, impatient as usual. 'Get on with it.' 'Just tell us, did you win?' 'What happened exactly?'

By the time I finish, it's late, maybe after one. There they sit, the two of them. So what's the verdict, ladies and gentlemen of the jury? Guilty or not guilty?

Sam plants his palms on the kitchen table and shoves away on his chair. '*Nu*,' he says, 'I'm beat. Let's go to bed. Tomorrow we can talk about it.'

My legs are still wobbly as I go up the stairs. My head's pounding. I swallow two aspirins, don't bother to wash, and crawl into bed.

From that night on, while Ma's not exactly singing with joy when I leave the house all dressed up in the red satin, at least there are no more dirty digs or suspicious looks from her.

For a couple of months there, my enthusiasm for the theatre runs high. In school while I'm adding columns in bookkeeping, I'm already picturing my name up there in lights. ETHEL GREENGLASS? No! ELAINE GREEN? GWENDOLYN GASTON? So-so. SHEILA SHANE? Maybe a little too Irish? Something more catchy, glamorous. No wonder Mr Horowitz finds so many mistakes in my work. 'Ethel,' he warns me sorrowfully, 'a bookkeeper you'll never be.'

Oh, I'm enthusiastic about the theatre all right, and I still have plans, big ones, I'm not giving up, no way. But there's a little problem to solve first – like finding a job. This is January 1932, remember?

Business school ends on a Friday with a small white diploma printed in heavy black letters that certifies that Ethel Greenglass satisfactorily completed a business course, and a handshake from Mr Balducci, the director. It's in his office and two of us are finishing up – a girl called Janice, from the Upper West Side, and me.

So it's goodbye, Excelsior, upward and onward. I clean out

my desk and leave. 'Keep in touch,' Janice smiles, but doesn't offer her address. So much for my college days.

At home I examine my one good pair of high heels that I can use for job-hunting. They're black leather pumps and I polish them every morning with Griffen's natural cream, but inside I keep changing the cardboard.

Tante Rosie gives me a pretty white blouse of hers and a good pair of white gloves. 'Rinse them out every night in a little Ivory,' she says, 'and you'll look like a lady. And don't ever let them treat you cheap. Get off on the right foot with the bosses, that's very important, and just tend to business.'

Funny she should say that; Ma always spoke of Rosie as an example of the worst that can happen to you, the absolute worst. Living in sin. Yet to me she was always the loveliest and kindest person I've ever known besides my father, and in fact, so much like him. I loved her like she was my own mother – in some ways she was much nicer, though I feel guilty about saying that. When she died ...

Anyhow, every morning I'm back to the HELP WANTED section. After the first week, I go out at night around ten to buy the early editions of the *Daily News* and *Mirror* so I can get a head start in the morning. Unfortunately, at least a million others have the same bright idea, so there's always a line no matter how early I get there. Like tickets for the World Series. And then the pushing and the fights and arguments that break out, everyone's so irritable and worn down – who can blame them? – probably hungry, too.

Usually before they ever get to me in the queue, they've hired someone else. By the time I take the subway home, my feet are killing me. I walk as much as possible to save on carfare, but it's a cold winter and I can still feel that wind cutting across my cheeks. Sometimes we're allowed inside the building, other times, nothing doing.

A week goes by like this, two, three, four, by now I'm getting desperate. '*Nu?*' Like a sentinel, Ma is always standing there at the door with that look – hope? fear? anger? I shake my head and run up to my room. I don't want to cry in front of her. After a while, I get up from the bed, wash my eyes, put on some powder and go out, over to Frieda's or the settlement house, anywhere just to get out of the house.

NINE

MAY 1951

In my dreamer's head all this time, I've pictured our first meeting here, over and over again. Before all this happened, Julie and I had never been apart for more than a day – from the night we met. So it'll go like this – entering from opposite ends of the room, shyly we'll stand there a minute, just taking each other in – *finally, finally, it's happening* – and then rush into each other's arms and kiss passionately, not letting go ... feeling whole again and, finally, alone together.

But these are only bad stage directions. Instead, there's Manny, busy digging out papers from his messy overloaded briefcase, and a matron, the dried-up one who never looks at me directly and speaks to me only in monosyllables. Yesterday I overheard her tell one of the others that we'd got what we deserved. 'Those dirty rotten spies!' So all we have is a quick embarrassed kiss in front of these two.

Oh, Julie, back here now, how I hunger for the physical warmth of you, such a fleeting moment together, and not this image that vanishes right out of my hands when I try to hold on to it. Though when the guard brings you in, you're still my Julie, with that special light in your eyes for me, eager, youthful, your head, as usual, slightly ahead of your body as though to see better ... probably, you still forget to clean your glasses. I always had to remind you when you complained that you needed new ones. But then when you stoop to kiss me, I see the white waxen pallor, and a sudden twitch that jerks your shoulder, your eye.

Your arms around me, thinner yet warm and loving, are so comforting, so familiar. Your arms spell home, the only home I have. For the first time in almost a year, I feel safe and stop trembling inside. Remember our friend, Sheila, who had a

Mexican chihuahua, a small trembling handful, and I couldn't understand why his trembling never stopped? Now I do.

There's so much to cover in so short a time – and Manny's waiting for us – as he reminds us several times. 'What do you think?' Sharply he taps his pen on the table. 'This Jack Jones, with a small machine shop like yours, has made you an offer. So that's one thing we have to discuss. The other is some good news about your mother, Julie – Sophie is feeling better, her blood pressure has dropped twenty points and the doctor cut down on her medication. She's thinking maybe now she can help out with the boys. Maybe she'll rent a larger apartment, get someone in to help her ... '

Yet I can't seem to concentrate on these important matters. Instead I'm thinking, *What does Julie see when he looks at me? When will this nightmare end?* And with a rising panic, *Will we ever go free out of here so we can all be together?* ... and that chair, that dreadful electric chair is in front of my eyes again, all those wires and leather straps that have never left my thoughts since that last terrible day in court. As soon as Kaufman spoke those fateful vindictive words, this dark vision, like a blindfold, moved into place, and it won't move aside, except momentarily, for anything or anyone else. And there are nights here, Julie, when try as I may to imagine you in bed with me, losing ourselves in our love and passion, that instrument of death intrudes between us.

So, Julie, even while you keep looking at me across the table, as though to say, this once let's forget Manny, and the jail, and our sons, and what lies ahead, *block it all out*, your eyes plead with me, *Ethel sweetheart, just be there for me* ... and I want to be there for you, only you, more than anything ... The truth is ... *I can't do it.* My own fear is more pressing, more demanding and overpowering, and I can smile at you with my lips and my eyes saying *I love you* – and I do, I do – but something's happening inside me, Julie, so slowly I haven't even been aware of it until this moment, and

48

I tremble at the thought that I've been moving away from you all these months – fear and I have a rendezvous these days – sitting there today with you at the other end of that long table, I realized that this recognition first came to me when we drove into Sing Sing only weeks ago. As soon as I got out of the car still handcuffed to the deputy, I sensed an enveloping quiet as though the prison of necessity drew its high electrified walls tightly about itself to make a world of its own – and that in some deeply significant, but still obscure way, I would have to leave you – and the children – in entering the enclosure, and make a world of my own – or I would not survive a single day here.

'Does that make sense to you, my dearest Julie?' I wanted to cry out today. 'Can you understand that I have to leave you, my darling, though I don't want to – for I can't survive my own pain coupled with your pain and the children's that I experience like my own, and all the fear and pain of standing by helplessly while those sinister men manhandle our children and our lives ... and that electric chair looms in front of my eyes ... like the gas chamber ... '

TEN

FEBRUARY 1932

The first thing I do in going for an interview at National Packing – which is right in the heart of the garment district – is to get lost. No kidding. I'm furious with myself. This girl I met at the Clark Players, her name's Angela Farcione – well, she's the one who told me about the job. But she warned me, 'Be there no later than nine. He's very particular about that.'

So here I come into this old dilapidated building on 36th, off Seventh. The elevator is just as old and dirty as the building and the doors take for ever to close. A short fat man with the eyes of a lizard chomping on a big fat cigar gets on, followed by two other guys, busy talking to each other. They're carrying heavy sample cases, salesmen types with manicured fingernails and the strong smell of shaving lotion.

'What floor d'ye want, girlie?' the fat guy asks me.

I don't like this girlie stuff. But I answer him anyway. 'Four.'

The elevator creaks all the way up like it has a bad heart. When the door finally opens at four, he pushes his way out with me right behind him, and starts down this long narrow corridor with rich dark mahogany halfway up the walls. But it's all scratched up. FUCK YOU! someone has gouged out. BOSSES STINK! This guy keeps moving ahead with his shoulders hunched up and his head down like a prizefighter. The tails of his tight-fitting jacket bounce off his big fat behind and his white socks show.

At the frosted glass door with National NY Packing and Shipping printed in large capital letters, he goes in and I follow.

'Good morning, Mr Kantrowitz,' gushes this older dame

50

with lots of rouge, earphones and a frizzy permanent.

He signals hello while shoving back his hat. He swings by her and I'm left standing there like I don't exist. The operator goes back to the switchboard. 'Good morning, National Packing. What can I do for you? Just a moment puh-leez,' and she keeps on chewing gum and plugging and unplugging wires and jotting messages, never looking up. 'He just came in,' she answers in this genteel singsong. 'I'll ring him for you.' To me she says nothing. Obviously, she's trying to sound classy, but everything about her says Delancey Street. Finally, I speak up. My voice shakes as I ask, 'Is Mr Kantrowitz in? Angela Farcione – she works here? She told me there's a part-time opening for a shipping clerk, she said to ask for him?'

'I don't know anything about it,' and she shakes her head.

'Would you please ask him?' At least I don't run out. And boy, do I want to!

The board buzzes and she's busy again for another few minutes. Finally she buzzes him for me. 'Yes,' she says into the phone and tells me, 'You can go in now.'

His office smells from all the corned-beef sandwiches he must've eaten, but at least there's a window. He's got a big old desk piled up with papers, bills and receipts in pink and blue. And in one corner, there's a family picture taken with his wife and four daughters, all with the same round moon face and dark dots for eyes.

By this time, I've gone through a few interviews so I handle myself a little better than I used to.

He asks me a few questions. I tell him I'm eighteen, that I took a business course at Seward Park and that since then I've been working for Seligman and Cohen on 37th off Broadway, and that I was laid off last week. They're a big outfit I looked up in the phone book, and I'm praying he's too busy to check up on me.

'So, it's slow for them, too?' he says and looks a little happier. He doesn't say another word to me, but lets out a

51

yell, 'Fannie!' and this short girl with a dark moustache comes hurrying in from the other room with a smile right out of a Colgate toothpaste ad.

'Yes, Mr Kantrowitz?'

'Try her out.' She motions to me to follow her. In the other room, there are six girls crowded in who take one look at me and continue with what they're doing, which looks like billing and filing. Fannie takes me over to her desk and I sit down at the typewriter. I'm nervous as a cat, but it's a Remington like at Excelsior so I manage to turn out some decent copy fast. She says in a kindly voice, the first I'd heard there, 'You're okay, you can handle it. Just don't let him push you around,' she adds. I'm surprised at that, but she's whispering, so I know she's afraid of him, too.

Back in his office, he says to me, 'Okay, you're hired for part-time work. We pay one rate – thirty-five cents an hour – that's it! You start Monday. Be here at eight-thirty sharp. One minute late and we start docking you. One other thing – I'll need you to work nights and weekends in rush season, so don't give me any *meises* about a boyfriend waiting for you or your mother expecting you home for dinner. I've heard them all and I don't buy.'

Which means he's not paying overtime. If I'm lucky, I'll make about six, seven dollars a week, depending, of course, on how many hours I get to work.

Ten cents a day carfare, I figure, and if I bring my own lunch, then I'll have about five, six dollars left. Not much, but more than I'm making now, which is zero, plus what I'm putting out for carfare. So I figure I'll be ahead. And maybe Ma'll lay off me.

That Monday, I still remember the date, February 2nd, 1932, I start work. A wind straight from the North Pole comes tearing around the corner. As I come out of the subway, my breath freezes into wisps, icy patches glitter on the sidewalk, and a man goes chasing down the street after his hat, watching with a foolish expression as it ends up under a truck. Pages of a newspaper sweep by and one wraps itself round my leg. I envy the few women going by with warm fur collars. One of the first things I'm going to do, I decide, is to save up for a new winter coat.

At 34th and Seventh, waiting for the light to change, is a black Ford roadster with a window sticker that says:

> Coolidge Blew the Whistle
> Mellon Rang the Bell
> Hoover pulled the Throttle
> And the Country Went to Hell.

When I come in, Fannie again takes charge of me and I'm glad. She seems nice. Still all day long, I'm nervous. What if Mr Kantrowitz should check on my references and fire me on the spot!

'Come with me,' says Fannie after showing me where to put my things. I brought my lunch – a salami sandwich and an apple – and I hope the others do. I don't want to stick out like a greenhorn and already I'm regretting the salami which is smelling up the place. Maybe tomorrow I'll bring American cheese.

So she takes me into a large room with a lot of people working away, both men and women, and she explains, 'You start out here writing receipts for the packages as they go by on that moving belt. You'll work next to the fellow who assembles and ties them into one big package – like teamwork,' she adds. 'Listen, don't miss even one package because that causes a terrible mix-up. See. See how they're doing it. Watch that girl over there in the grey smock?' She's talking to me, though, like in a first-grade reader, *See Jack, See Jill*. That bothers me. She points to this Hannah and introduces us. 'An oldtimer,' she says like it's a gold star next to her name. The sleeves of Hannah's smock are shoved up and you can see the cords in her forearm swell as she grips the pencil and scribbles away like crazy, never

53

stopping because the belt's moving so fast.

'Ethel? That's your name?' this Hannah asks me. She sounds like from the Old Country. 'Listen I'll tell you something, don't get your hopes up. Three years I'm here already still doing the same *verdammten* job.'

Fannie points to the fellow working alongside Hannah. 'Watch them, how they do it,' she says, so I watch. Hannah calls out the number on the receipt she's written, then he marks it down on the package with a black crayon while she straightens up for a moment and sighs. 'Next!' She calls out a number and starts writing again. All day long that's what I'll be doing.

'See in here we take care only of shipping. Loebel himself started this business – the first of its kind. One hundred and forty-seven employees,' she adds proudly.

What's it to her, I wonder. As far as I'm concerned, all I see is hands flying, packages, big, small, all sizes, moving along the belt, and more packages piled up on push trucks nearby, and people hustling. Nobody's standing still, that's for sure.

Fannie continues in that sweet voice, I never heard her sound any different, no matter what. 'Wherever the merchandise has to go, we ship it. Suppose a dress manufacturer has to ship to Texas, California and Colombia – that's in South America,' she adds for my benefit, for Ettie Greenglass who won the geography medal in eighth grade, 'well, all those separate orders, already wrapped, come here, and we have to figure out the fastest and cheapest way to deliver. Then we route according.'

You can tell, she enjoys explaining like a teacher. I'm not that interested. I'm busy looking at the people – seems like they never get out in the sun. Everyone around us is working their guts out, I'm thinking, for what! For thirty-five cents an hour, like me? I'll have to work a week to make what I make on Amateur Night for one song if I win. And what's she making – a dime more?

ELEVEN

MARCH 1932

After the first couple of weeks, I get the hang of it and my life settles down. Most of the girls are older than me. Mixed in with their conversations about clothes and fellows and dates are jokes I don't catch on to at first, mostly about the foremen, Larry and Carl, who try to get you off in a corner. 'Has he pulled it on you yet?' a tall girl with a heavy underlip asks me when someone makes a crack that Carl's at it again. 'What do you mean?' I ask her. I'm so dumb about these things, but right away from the giggles and smirks on their faces, I get the point. The trouble is I'm not even sure what to do, so finally a few days later I get up the nerve to ask.

'Oh, let him take a feel,' this one girl, Laura, laughs. She's a big fat girl who seems to disappear a lot.

'Oh you!' giggles Miriam, who's even smaller than I am.

'So – so what's so wrong about having a little fun while you're working?' Laura demands angrily, and then laughs, a little too loudly, I think.

I'm beginning to feel more comfortable around all of them, and when Laura asks me about myself, I open up and tell her about my ambition to go on the stage. 'But don't tell the others.' I suddenly feel foolish.

'Yeah sure – but would you sing for us some time? I'd really like to hear you.'

'Sure, some time,' I say, putting it off.

That first time sticks out in my mind. It's mid-afternoon on a Friday, and that sense of tiredness, and at the same time, looking forward to the weekend, is in the air. So nobody's making a move to get back to work after break, especially since Carl isn't around. Someone mentions listening to the Amateur programme on WJZ the night before. 'Some of them are really good,' she says, 'especially this one girl who imitated Kate Smith ... ' and without thinking, I blurt out, 'Oh, I've been on it.'

'You're kidding,' says this other new girl.

'No, I'm not.'

Suddenly I'm annoyed that just by looking at me, she decides I can't sing. Sure it's true that I don't look like much in my work clothes. Some of the girls really like to dress up, even for work. But I don't care, so I wear this old skirt every day with a faded blouse and a stretched-out navy cardigan that's worn at the elbows. It's comfortable and warm in a building where they hardly send up any heat.

Anyhow, Laura turns around and says to me, 'How about it, Ethel – you said you'd sing for us some time, so how about today, whaddya say?' Several girls start chanting, 'We want Ethel, we want Ethel.'

And it's like they're daring me to do it, so I climb up on one of the tables and smile. 'Okay, you win.'

Everyone moves back a little and the room gets very quiet. I open with my favourite, 'The Indian Love Call'. At first, my throat's tight, but as soon as I see the expression of surprise – and pleasure – on their faces, it loosens up. That's the pay-off. I hold the last note for a few seconds longer, and when I finish, they burst into applause. 'More, more!'

Miriam calls out, 'Star Dust', and after that, someone asks for another one, and by this time, some of the men drift over, and Fannie comes out of the office, and everyone's listening, and it feels great. I can see there's a different look in their eyes and everyone keeps quiet until I finish. Then I get an ovation with clapping and stamping, even a few whistles from the men. I feel just great. I'm right up there in my chariot.

From that time on, people in the place, fellows and girls, they all know me by name. 'You should hear Ethel sing!' one says to another as I walk by – and I love it.

*

56

About a week later, Fannie, who's always very friendly, comes by.

'How's it going?'

'Not bad.'

'Listen,' she lowers her voice, 'can you come to my house for supper next Friday? I live with my older sister – and I'd like you to meet her.'

I'm so surprised, I don't know what to say. Actually I have a rehearsal that particular night. The Players are doing this new one, *Shop Girls*, and I have the female lead. It's a juicy part, the biggest yet, and I'm all excited. We're supposed to get the scripts and run through the lines on Friday. So I say, 'I'd love to,' and I put a lot of expression into it, 'but I can't, I have a rehearsal that night.'

'Oh, that's too bad. I really want you to meet Celia – my sister – and that's the one night she's usually home. The other nights she's always out at ... I mean, she's usually busy. I'll tell you what – I'll find out what other nights are good for her, and I'll let you know.'

'I'd love to come!'

So the following Tuesday, it turns out Celia will be home and I'm invited. I figure a green plant would be all right, so I buy one and bring it with me, and right from work, we go to their apartment in Brooklyn, someplace around Eastern Parkway not far from the Brooklyn Museum. They live in a very nice four-storey walk-up, maybe not the most classy neighbourhood, but it's a big improvement over Sheriff Street. No pushcarts, no stables, no manure, no rotten vegetables along the kerb. They even have their own bathroom with a shower and bathtub right in the apartment.

By the time we reach the fourth floor carrying groceries, we're out of breath. So it's a pleasure to come into this nice clean apartment. There's a plushy wine-coloured velvet sofa and two green chairs upholstered in damask, and some books, magazines like the *Saturday Evening Post* and *Collier's*, and one that's new to me, *New Masses* – and lots of plants. I'm pleased I brought one, too. It's a warm cosy room with drapes and a console radio against one wall with a large framed photograph of a woman on top. Also there's a dark upright piano in the foyer.

While I'm standing around in the kitchen watching, Fannie starts preparing the hamburgers. I offer to help, but she says no, not necessary, just keep her company.

Just as I'm thinking she probably gets lonely here by herself if Celia's out so much, the downstairs buzzer sounds. 'That's her,' she says and her face lights up as she hurries into the hall to buzz back. It must be nice to have an older sister, I'm thinking.

'Hello everybody!' Celia calls out. Right away you can see the difference between them. Fannie has this look in her eyes that asks you to be nice to her, but not this one. Oh no. She's the exact opposite. One look from those brown eyes, and you know she's Somebody, and expects to be treated that way. Amazing how all of this gets said in a kind of shorthand. If only I could learn how! But then Fannie hasn't learned from her either.

In appearance, they're so different, too; Celia's a good head taller than Fannie, on the statuesque side with muscular calves like a dancer. And she carries herself like one, too, shoulders back, head up. She has a sallow complexion where Fannie's all peaches and cream, and a sharp jaw. But then lots of brownish gold hair that sends out sparks. It's piled up in a sleek upsweep like Rosalind Russell used to wear, and later Fannie tells me that her sister goes to a beauty parlour every week. It must be very expensive.

Several weeks later, Joe, in the shop, who knows them and sees we're getting friendly, tells me that they're really stepsisters – same mother, different fathers, and that Celia's older than Fannie. So, in a way, she's almost like Fannie's mother. You can see that Celia's someone who's right out there in the world, dealing with people, and she's accustomed to being treated with respect. I can even picture her having a lover, maybe more than one. In some ways, she's the kind of woman I'd like to be.

Right away we're talking; she's friendly, but you know that she's a very busy lady who has to have a good reason for everything she does. I also feel that I'm being looked over, though for what I can't guess, which makes me a little uncomfortable. And Fannie, too, I notice, treats her almost like a guest, and waits on her.

While we're setting the table which is now covered with a tablecloth which Fannie embroidered in red and black cross-stitch, Celia changes from the gabardine tailored suit she had on into a pretty rose-coloured flannel robe. And while the hamburgers are broiling, we sit in the living-room and the two of them sip wine. They offer me some, too, but I shake my head. At home, we only drink it for the holidays.

'Celia always enjoys a glass of wine before dinner,' Fannie explains, as though she's uncomfortable with her sister's American ways, and yet proud of them, too.

'Well, how do you like it at National? What do they have you doing?' Celia asks in that slightly husky voice, almost like an actress. 'Fannie tells me you just recently started there.' She reaches for a cigarette from a pack near her plate and offers me one.

I shake my head again, and feel like such a baby. Yet that's all I need with the way Ma feels about smoking. She'd smell it on my breath.

'Well,' I stall, 'I'm just learning the ropes ... right now clerking ... writing receipts ... ' and I laugh uncomfortably. She's not impressed, that's clear.

'So, how do you feel about conditions in the shop?' she asks and wipes her mouth daintily with a napkin. A slight film clings to the hair above her lip, almost turning it into a moustache.

What do I say? Aside from disliking the work itself and the pressure to keep up, I hadn't thought much about it. Work to me is work, and you can't bargain with it. Try it and you'll be out on your ear and I've had enough of job-hunting to last me a lifetime. Still I'd feel stupid saying just that. So I act like I'm thinking about it. 'I guess I wish I made more money.'

'Of course, you're right. I keep telling Fannie that Loebel, the owner – Kantrowitz, his brother-in-law, is just his messenger boy – is a bastard of the first order.' Fannie's getting red in the face, but Celia's keeping her eyes on me. 'We hear he's as bad as Max Kaminsky and Izzy Drusoff, the two biggest bastards in the industry.'

She's telling Fannie an incident from her shop, something about going to the boss with a complaint for someone. So the boss got angry and walked out on her, and now she'll have to discuss it with the whole shop committee.

'Celia works for I. Shapiro, they're a big dress manufacturer with an expensive line that retails for fifty dollars and up in Saks Fifth Avenue,' Fannie explains to me. 'She's an operator and also a shop steward.'

'So we'll meet with Shapiro on Thursday and his brother-in-law damn well better not be there,' she adds. 'I can't stand that bastard. I think he figures that if he cries enough, we'll accept a wage cut. Drop dead!'

'How do you know all this?'

She smiles like the cat who just swallowed a canary. 'Oh, because we have friends, very good friends in the front office.'

It turns out to be a nice evening after all and when I leave, I feel a lot more comfortable around them, especially Celia, than when I came in.

TWELVE

MAY 1951

Funny coincidence. A letter from Celia today. Haven't heard from her in years. She's living in North Carolina, small town, married, doesn't say much more, just that she's very sorry about what happened and when she comes into New York she wants to visit me.

Sure, why not?

APRIL 1934

Sometimes it's hard for me to remember how I felt in those days. Incredible how old I feel now, like all the life juices have been squeezed out of me, and yet I was so young and alive then. *As though I had for ever and everything could be mine.*

Always with new situations, or people, my mind would go on like that; *this* was going to change my life, *this, this was it, this* new thing, a job, a part in a play, or a party where I'd meet my one true love, like Cinderella at the ball, and *this* would turn my life, now lived in suspension, into the Real Thing. The kind of life I was waiting for … that was coming to me … for which secretly I knew I was intended … and not to end up like my mother with her shopping bag searching for life's bargains on pushcarts! And yet it never quite happened like that, well maybe with Julie when we met that first night, but frankly speaking, even that never quite lived up to what I had imagined, it was more something we invented between us because like most young people, we wanted so desperately to be in love. Like Claudette Colbert and Clark Gable, like Norma Shearer and Robert Taylor. We really believed those modern fairy tales, certainly I must have, deep down, though we all used to kid about Hollywood and its phoney happy endings, pretending not to believe in them, all the time desperately wishing for them to come true. If it could happen on the screen, then why not in real life?

In time, of course, my life did begin to change slowly, but I was always impatient. Let's get on with it. Around the corner, *it* – whatever it was – was waiting there for me.

And so it was when I started at National. At first, big expectations, big disappointments. I came home every night and flung myself on the bed and cried. *This was what my life was going to be for ever after?* Writing receipts for packages? Like a machine? Writing receipts – that's all? Rushing like crazy so my hand hurt for hours afterwards?

After the first few weeks, I settled into the new job, the routine of going to work, even if it wasn't the steady nine to five secretarial job I had expected. Actually, a lot of things changed in the country during the time I worked at National – Hoover was out, thank God, and Roosevelt was in. You could just see the hope on the faces around you, especially after the bank holiday when Roosevelt came in. I remember how upset Ma and Pa were at first with no money in the house – but people got through that week somehow, the butcher let you charge, someone could spare a dollar ... that's how.

I was now a working girl, bringing home a paycheque, me and thousands like me in New York City – bookkeepers, secretaries, typists, clerks, even factory workers. Fresh in the morning, all made up, we'd get on the subway with our lunch bags and ride the crowded train, hanging on to the straps, getting pushed and shoved around, a man getting too close, and finally getting to work, and after a long hard day, getting back on the subway – all packed in like sardines in rush hour, and going home so we could get up the next day and start in all over again. Life,, I've discovered, always boils down to the daily routine, it doesn't matter whether it's school or work –

or later on, home with Julie and the kids. Or here ... And all the time I'm yearning for excitement, for theatre lights, and fame. To do one outstanding thing and fill my life with – an effulgence. Once I saw that word in a novel and when I looked it up in *Webster's Dictionary*, I said, *that's* what I want. A radiant brilliance, a splendour. I want my life to be filled with effulgence. Just once even. Ironic, yes?

So work became what I did during the day – and evenings were when I came alive. Like Cinderella at the ball.

As it works out, I'm averaging about seven dollars a week and I have to work whatever hours Kantrowitz or Fannie want me. But from what I make, I'm saving up to buy first a winter coat and then a piano. To have my own piano, that's my dream.

There's a picture of myself taken about that time, I found it in an old box of mementoes before the arrest – how old was I there? Seventeen? Eighteen? I know it was taken on a picnic to the Palisades with a group of girls from Seward Park who kept in touch after graduation. It was early in April, the ground was still wet in the woods and sprouts of skunk cabbage were coming up. Roosevelt had already been president for over a year and we were talking about what changes he'd made as we hiked along. The air smelled so sweet and full of spring and I wanted so much to be there with a boy holding hands and walking in the woods. Still it was good.

'Things in the country are looking up, the *Times* editorial said,' and Gittel who'd been student president in high school quoted some employment and wage statistics.

'At least they're not going down,' Frieda said. She went on to talk about the new job she'd just started as a typist in an employment agency which paid a little better than the last one. 'Thank God, I'm out of that bakery,' she added. 'If one more *yenta* said to me, "*Ta-keh* it's fresh baked from today, you're sure?" I'd have let her have it!'

'Frieda, just wait until you have to deal with three bosses, all Mr Impossible,' Shirley said. 'Sixteen hours a day is what I need for each of them.' Personally I think she liked being exploited, she was always the complaining type.

'I'll take three bosses any day to those women on the Grand Concourse,' Frieda laughed.

Things *were* looking up a little at that time. Even Ma seemed a little less worried. She admitted to me that Papa was doing a little better in the shop; at least he could collect from some of his customers. 'But not enough to live on,' she quickly added. My mother always operated on the theory that you never tell God how well off you are because he'll take it away immediately. Things were a little calmer around the house. Sam and I were both bringing in a little money. The NRA code in men's clothing raised the hourly rate in his shop even though his boss was still screaming how FDR personally was forcing him into bankruptcy. But orders were picking up and Sam was still seeing his girl, Dorothy. They'd announced their engagement with a little party her parents gave in February.

So on this picture I was referring to, there are six of us, Frieda, Lillian, Sarah, Gittel, Shirley and me – and to me now, that Ettie looks so young, so frighteningly young. I guess I *was* the youngest. I used to pin up my hair with bobby pins to look older when I started working, but in this picture it's down to my shoulders. And about that time, I also started to wear lipstick, no matter what my mother said. But I still look so small and flatchested next to the others, especially Frieda who was so much taller and more developed. 'More developed,' that's the way we used to refer to girls who wore brassières.

I'm thinking, even though I'm standing next to Frieda in the picture, so I look like I'm part of the group, I never felt that way inside. Inside I always felt different, separated from them, though I envied them, my best friends, and though I wanted so badly to be one of them, yet a part of me said, No, you're different, there's a different life ahead for you, be glad of it; they'll get married and have children and live out their lives in a predictable way and you won't – something more's ahead for you – and it'll be different. People will know about you some day. Maybe it was because of the prediction the *Almanac* printed about me – 'America's leading actress in 1950'. But no, that dream of mine started long before. At times, it felt as though my life was passing by as I waited just for it to happen. My heart would quicken as I imagined it. One day, my Fate was going to walk up to me and say, Here I am, and we'd link arms and be off together.

THIRTEEN

MAY 1951

A gloomy day! And although it's already late May, it's raining too hard for me even to walk outside in the 'courtyard', and my mind won't let up worrying about the boys, especially Robby – he's so little. *How could they do such a thing to our family?*

Since I haven't seen them anyplace else but at home, I can't seem to visualize them, that they're just living someplace else right now, that's all. Though Manny keeps reassuring me that they're okay, *Ethel, believe me*, to me it still feels like they've vanished from the face of the earth. You know those clocks that show you the time simultaneously in Paris, Tokyo, Moscow and Hawaii? Well, to me, they always seemed a fake. I can't take it all in, that life is going on right now in all these different cities. My imagination can't juggle all these balls at the same time. So this is the same kind of feeling. Which is very strange when they've been in my thoughts ever since Michael was born back in 1943. Since before that even. Three months pregnant and already I'm getting anxious. I want so much to be a good mother, which, to me, means not like my own mother. Because I'm convinced the good mother *is* the key to raising children, the one all important person. And, by now, my copy of Dr Spock's book on baby and child care is all worn out. There was a point where I practically changed diapers with one hand while reading directions from the book with the other.

Since last August – though it hardly seems possible – I haven't heard my sons laugh ... or touched them, or even seen them. At first, we thought it would be better this way, that we'd be coming home soon, and they wouldn't have to come to prison to see us. What an impression it would make on young children! But now I know it's worse – there's a great big gaping hole in our lives. We have just got to see each other, no matter what, and I've asked Manny to get busy on this.

There are times here when I get positively frantic. Where are my babies? Why are they keeping me away from them? And I'm so scared that something terrible has happened to them, and they're not telling me. I try to quiet myself by reciting the facts – Michael and Robby are safe, they're safe, I repeat to myself, you know that for a fact. And I've received two of Michael's letters, each word printed so carefully, even a drawing from Robby – two small kids and a big empty sky. But still a couple of days ago, I started to shake so badly thinking about them that I had to ask Molly to come and stand there close by, right next to the bars and talk to me. 'Say something, anything,' I tell her, 'just keep talking to me so I can hear your voice.' And she does. I can't remember all she says because she talks for quite a while, pats my hand through the bars until the shaking stops, and I fall exhausted on my cot. As I'm falling asleep, I remember she's telling me the story of Moses from the Bible and how Pharaoh's daughter found him, this little baby crying in the bulrushes, and brought him back to the palace and took care of him, and he was safe.

That heartpinching fear is creeping over me again ... and slowly I'm discovering that when you can't live with now, you can always lose yourself in the past ...

1935

So we're rehearsing this new one, a one-acter called *The Valiant*.

At the first rehearsal, Irv, Polovoy's assistant, hands out the parts. I start to skim through, mostly for my lines. A laugh a minute, I'm thinking. Why does he pick them like this? Picture this – the scene opens on a miserable rainy night in the Warden's office in the State Prison in Wethersfield, Connecticut. It's almost midnight, time for an execution. Depressing right off the bat? And the cast includes such lighthearted characters as the lead, Jim Dyke, a convicted murderer, who's about to die at midnight, the warden and the prison chaplain. And then there's me – cast as the young girl in search of her long-lost brother. Will he turn out to be Jim Dyke? And is that his *real* name? I just know the audience is going to love this one! That's entertainment? With all that's going on in the world, they come to the theatre for this?

'Okay cast!' Polovoy claps his hands and motions to the four of us to sit in a circle. Jerry, who's playing the prisoner, Dyke, raises his eyebrows at me as though to say, *What's with him?*

'Listen, let's discuss what the play's about,' says Polovoy.

How about that! Jerry signals with his lips. Polovoy has never done that in his life before, I mean discuss a play with the cast. Always, it's put your feet there, or here, or exit upper left, no, not that way, do it this way, my way. That's all he's ever concerned with – do this, do that. Directions. Naturally, he reminds me of my mother.

He continues, 'You see, Middlemaas, the playwright, is dealing with a very important theme here – death. Facing death. Accepting it, one's mortality.' And his voice drops melodramatically, and he sits there for a few moments reflecting, resting his arms on his thighs. 'Is he saying' – now he's staring far off into space – 'that how one faces death is a measure of that person? Is it the ultimate test? Facing death with grace?' His eyes drop.

We all look at each other. Frankly, I'm a little lost. I've never given it much thought; to me death is something way off in the distance. Right now, I have a lot more important things to worry about. And probably so do the others. I can understand maybe if you have a sick mother or father or some other close relative. But otherwise, you don't just sit yourself down and speculate about death as a big abstract philosophical question. I don't even think it's natural.

'What we have here is a real moral conflict,' he continues. 'It's clear that the prisoner is concealing something – undoubtedly, his real identity. Why? Why would a man not want others to know who he really is – especially since he will die in a few hours? The warden and the chaplain are troubled; what's he hiding, the warden is wondering. And the priest is concerned about his salvation. But the prisoner isn't. "I'm going to die with a clear conscience," he tells them and he means it. And then the young girl comes in, sent by her sick mother – hoping and yet fearful that this man, this convicted murderer, will turn out to be her beloved brother, the big brother with whom she played, recited Shakespeare, feeding each other lines from *Romeo and Juliet* when they were children. Dyke denies it, the whole thing, that he's ever heard of Shakespeare even, and yet he's touched by her love for that long-lost brother and her desire to find him.'

As he's talking, the whole situation still seems too remote to me – a convicted murderer and a girl looking for her brother – what does it have to do with my life? With anything in my experience? As yet, it has no meaning for me.

But as he continues, suddenly it strikes me, supposing something were to happen to Dovey! Not that it would, I quickly reassure myself. Somehow even thinking about it seems like I'm tempting the fates.

But still, just suppose ... maybe he disappears and we don't know where he is, we don't hear from him, nothing. For days, years ... I mean, children *do* disappear, get kidnapped. Look at the Lindberghs, what happened with their baby, even if they're so rich and famous, still it didn't protect them from what happened. What an awful thing – or maybe gypsies – and then years later, you read about someone – and there's something, a resemblance, and you get your hopes up again – and I just start imagining how I would feel if

Dovey disappeared or something – and the whole play takes on a different meaning for me. I'm all ears now.

'So then Dyke sends her off with a heartbreaking story about this brother of hers, that he was a buddy of Dyke's in World War One and that he actually died a glorious hero in battle. He must figure that any family can swallow that one more easily than a murderer. And he gives her some money to take to her mother. Of course, by the end, the audience knows that he really is the man she's searching for.

'And then after she leaves – get this, he recites those famous lines from *Julius Caesar*.' Polovoy pauses to make sure he's got our full attention and then he stands up and gives it everything he's got.

'Cowards die many times before their deaths;
The Valiant never taste of death but once.'

No one says anything after he finishes, just genuine applause. Then we all sit there silently. The ending hits you hard.

After a few more minutes, Polovoy straightens up and says, 'Suppose we stop now and you can give it some more thought. It's a big one all right. Okay? We'll talk about it again at rehearsal on Wednesday.'

The next few nights after dinner, I'm up in my room studying my part. Josephine Paris, a small-town girl from Ohio. It's a challenge all right. What would I know about someone like that? Someone who enters in a cheap navy-blue suit with a starched white sailor collar. Who ever owned a suit? I'm not clear how he wants her played. She's only eighteen. What a frightening experience for her going by herself to a prison on a dark rainy night searching for a brother she isn't even sure is alive or that she'll recognize ... just going on hope, on a long chance. I still remember the phrase he uses to describe her, 'a spiritual aloofness from the modern world'. What does he mean by that?

Is she supposed to be very unsophisticated and naïve? What a horrible situation to be in! I can't imagine myself going on such a mission. How does she manage? What does she hold on to? Look at her situation – her father's dead, her mother's supposed to be very sick, and her brother – if that's who this man is – is going to die. Otherwise he's still missing in action. What does she have to look forward to at eighteen – left all by herself, alone in the world? Somehow, it seems to me she's got to have something to keep her going – some inner belief, that's the only thing that would make sense. She has to believe in something. Maybe she's religious? Is that what he means by 'spiritual'?

Now the prisoner has that ... that inner quality. That's made clear from the moment he walks onstage. But for her, it's different, she's still seeking; something has to happen during their scene together.

I start to think about them – now his future's settled, he has no choice, to live or die. But suppose he had such a choice offered to him, suppose the warden says to him, 'Tell us the truth about yourself and we'll get the death sentence commuted.' What would he do then?

Anyhow, Dyke's role is very convincing. He makes you believe in him and he wins your sympathy even though he's a confessed murderer. Mainly because he has this iron determination not to reveal his identity, and that's admirable. That more than anything else becomes his life line. For him, there's only one way to go and that's what he's doing – dying on his own terms.

As I'm thinking about it, it hits me. Of course! By the time Josephine leaves, she's learned the truth. She's figured out that he's her brother all right. But by now, she's also determined not to let him know that. She *wants* him to die believing he's succeeded in protecting his family, and that they won't remember him as a murderer. Young as she is, she understands that. That's his source of strength. And her strength then must come from protecting his. That's it!

71

They're in this together; she knows it though he never will.

And the audience has to understand this, too, by the time the curtain drops.

Now that I grasp what's involved here, I feel the goose-pimples rising on my arms. The trouble is – I don't know if I can put it across.

How I wish I had more experience!

FOURTEEN

1935

At Wednesday's rehearsal, Polovoy's got some good suggestions, particularly in that last scene, which is a real tearjerker. Dyke and the girl are alone in the warden's office and he's just given her an envelope with the money. He tells her to give it to her mother, in memory of her brother.

Just as he's saying goodbye, she looks at him tenderly and says – wait, I remember it goes like this, 'Goodbye – and thank you.' She holds out her hand to him. 'You've done more for me – and mother – than I could possibly tell you. And – and I'm so sorry for you, so *truly* sorry. Is there anything I could do?'

At first he won't say, but then he gives in and tells her how lonesome he is tonight, that she's the first girl he's seen in months. 'I'd forgotten how much like angels women look.'

At this point she gazes at him, and then she understands, she flushes, and moves into his outstretched arms.

Now picture this – when Jerry, who's all of six feet two, bends down to kiss me, who's all of five feet, we're standing sideways, and I'm staring obliquely out at the audience while he's facing upstage. So he bends down and kisses me right under my left ear – and then catches himself and switches to my forehead, gently kisses it twice – which is what the script calls for.

Suddenly it hits me. Of course! I practically smack my head as the idea hits me.

'Listen Jerry,' I turn to him, 'why did you kiss me behind the ear?'

He blushes red as a beet and everyone laughs because they know Jerry has just come back from spending his honeymoon at Grossingers.

'C'mon Ethel, cut it out,' he gets annoyed, 'I wasn't making a pass at you.'

'I didn't say you were. I just want to know why you played it that way?'

'To be perfectly honest,' and he blushes again, 'that's where I like to kiss my wife.'

Everyone snickers again, and this time, he laughs, too. But, of course, it makes sense.

So as soon as he says that, I get the answer. 'Listen, I've got a great idea,' I tell Polovoy. 'You see, Dyke starts to do that with Josephine, and then he catches himself, remembering that's a familiar intimate gesture from the old days, so instead he pulls back and gently touches his lips to her forehead.'

Polovoy nods. 'So?'

'So – involuntarily, however, Josephine, too, responds in the old familiar way,' I continue, 'and her hand starts to move up to stroke his hair. But then she catches herself and drops it. The audience sees this gesture behind his back, but he doesn't. For her, that first kiss and her automatic response are enough. Now she's convinced he's her brother. So she smiles at him, trying to carry it off as best she can, but her quavery voice almost gives her away as she's saying goodbye.

'He picks up on that. "What is it?" he asks.

'"N ... nothing," Josephine answers. "If only I could have – have said it to him just once more for goodbye." He urges her to do so, so she quotes those famous lines from *Romeo and Juliet*, hoping he'll finish them after all:

> 'Good-night, good-night! parting is such sweet
> sorrow
> That I shall say good-night till it be morrow.

'Now here it gets tricky,' I continue, 'because he says nothing so she starts towards the anteroom with tears in her eyes. Remember, her face is turned towards the audience when she claps her hand forcefully across her mouth as though to prevent herself from crying out his name. And the anguish on her face, which he can't see, tells the audience the truth – that he is her brother and she knows it. She also realizes that his greatest desire, no, his greatest need at this moment, facing his execution, is to convince her he's not the man she's looking for. *She and her mother are not to know.* That's his guiding star.

'In a moment of gathering strength, she decides to go along with his decision. That last anguished look on her face has to say it all.'

Polovoy says nothing, just looks dubious when I finish. Nevertheless he says after a few moments, 'Go ahead, give it a try.'

So Jerry and I play it just that way. He's wonderful. And when it comes to that last anguished look, I tell you, I'm practically dragging myself off stage, as I leave him for the last time.

Polovoy comes rushing up on the stage while the others are still applauding. He grabs me in a bear hug. 'That's just terrific. Just beautiful, Ethel,' he says. 'I wasn't looking for so much subtlety. You're a real pro. What a performance! Congratulations!' And we smile and shake hands.

Ziggy would be proud of me now, I'm thinking.

Ma said she wasn't coming. More than that she wouldn't say.

I don't even argue, we've been over the same ground so many times before. But Papa, who's drinking tea with his head buried in the *Jewish Forward*, says quietly, 'Listen Ettie, be sure you save two tickets for me. Rosie'll come, she told me. You think Dovey would understand it? Maybe I'll bring him, too.'

Just then Dovey himself comes in and I'm struck by how fast he's growing – wider, broad like in Ma's family, but also taller. Already he's as tall as Papa. His face is still very round with those rosy cheeks like apples, with those plump white hands and boyish knickers and the high socks he never pulls up properly so they're always falling down. I really love the sight of him, there's something so young and sweet about him. In two years, he'll be Bar Mitzvahed. I remember so clearly when he was born. Ma was sick with a fever for a week afterwards and I took care of him. At seven, for me it was like having a live doll – handling him, so tiny and helpless, watching him sleep, his little fingers giving a twitch.

He's got the icebox open, searching.

'You want something?' Ma asks him.

'I'll see, Ma – I'll look around,' he answers. He loves to fix himself a sandwich on an onion roll, so he takes out the cream cheese and lox with a Spanish onion and the milk bottle. He also finds some black olives and a half-sour pickle, and that's quite a sandwich he fixes. Then he sits down at the table with Papa and me. Ma's finishing the dishes.

How that boy loves eating and listening. He himself never says much, but he likes to hang around and listen, sort of soaking up what's going on around the house. His grades in school aren't good – and it's always a bad time around the house when he comes home with his report card. Then he likes to sit in my room to get away from Ma because she really lets him have it. I guess he worries her.

Sometimes he comes into my room just to hear me rehearse, or help me memorize lines. Then we both get into the spirit of the play and it's fun.

But at times I worry, too, because Bernie can take care of himself, but Dovey ... I don't know. He doesn't seem to have interests or hobbies, even play sports, like other kids his age in the neighbourhood, and I worry what he'll do when he grows up and I'm married and out of the house.

The phone rings and it's Fannie.

'How's it going?' she wants to know.

'Okay, though we're still working on some last-minute changes. You're coming tomorrow night? And Celia, too?'

'Oh sure, we wouldn't miss it for the world.'

I'm so glad they're coming, it makes up for Ma.

This Friday night, they'll all be there – Papa and Dovey, and Tante Rosie, and Fannie and Celia, so I'm doubly excited ... and nervous ...

Talk about elation – pure unadulterated elation! That's me when the curtain rings down. For a moment before the applause breaks, I'm still in the Warden's office, caught in the pain of saying goodbye, and yet that flame of pure joy, too, that I can withstand the pain and not cry out.

And then the next moment, the applause! I'm back with the audience, as though lifted up on their shoulders, and I'm not up there alone.

I've never heard such applause before. For the play, for Jerry and for me. I forget how many times we go back for bows. Inside I'm shaking, it's such a profound experience. The audience loves us and won't let us go.

There are flowers brought to me on stage, a big basket of coral, yellow and white chrysanthemums. From Polovoy with a card: 'You made the play yours! What a triumph! Love and best wishes, Joe.' For the rest of the night, I'm up there in my chariot riding the heavens as though they declared a moratorium on Newton's Law.

And Fannie and Celia squeeze in backstage, even though it's mobbed afterwards – and they, too, bring me flowers, a bouquet of American Beauty roses – my first ever. And they're so excited for me, kissing and hugging me. And Papa and Tante Rosie are beaming, and Dovey tugs at the sleeve of a man standing next to him and says, 'Hey, Mister.' He points with his thumb at me, 'She's my sister.'

At that moment, my happiness is complete.

FIFTEEN

JUNE 1951

Today I'm in here and not out there. *A fact.*

I see the sky in here only through a slice of glass high above my head with the sun warming it tepidly late in the afternoon. *A fact.*

Therefore, I must be facing west in here ... towards the setting sun. *A fact.*

Nine months I'm in prison locked up like an animal. *A fact.*

And as I say nine months – a measurable time surely, long enough to conceive and give birth to our third child, maybe a girl – why does it seem like for ever? That's not *a fact.*

And Ma was in here today to remind me strictly of *facts.*

Her feet tell me she's coming. There's something implacable about her tread in those black Dr Posner arch-support shoes with room enough for her bunions – heavy-footed, just so, each step, just so many inches, placed right here, and not over there, with a certainty that's invincible. As though she never questions her movements, her decisions, herself.

So I'm waiting. In the Visitors' Room. Locked in a two by four cell. Separated by a wire screen from the cubicle in which Ma will sit. Facing me. Like in *The Valiant*, when the sister comes looking for her long-lost brother, now a convicted murderer. Only now I'm the defendant.

I'm always alone. There are six cubicle-cells, and yet right now, all are empty. I think they don't want any of the other prisoners to see me or know I'm here. Because I'm always alone. Even at services. I'm brought in before the men, and seated off to one side in the back, and hidden behind a heavy opaque screen. As though I were an orangutan or Typhoid

Mary. But they can't stop me from joining in on the hymns!

I haven't seen her since the trial when she dressed up all in black and sat next to Ruth, and they kept whispering to each other in that way people have when they're trying to reinforce their own self-righteousness by fuelling the other's. I made sure to avoid looking in their direction when I was on the witness stand. And afterwards she never came near me. Not to the House of Detention before I was transferred here. Not even a word that she was sorry about the verdict or Judge Kaufman's sentence. Nothing.

That's always been her inimitable way of showing me she's very angry with me. I know her so well. A heavy-footed silence. Like the humidity on a hot summer's day. Invisible, but oppressive and unrelenting.

They're coming closer. Molly's walk I recognize, too. She's a sprightly energetic woman with dusty brown hair and a tight permanent, and if there were something else to do in Ossining, I'm sure she'd prefer it. Guarding people like animals in a zoo would not be her first choice. We've never talked about it, but with her love of flowers and her children, and the grandchild that's coming next month – the first and her daughter's almost thirty! – I know it without her telling me. But she does it, anyway, because having no choice, she accepts her lot with grace. Ma's different – she makes light things heavy and heavy things heavier.

Last week Molly brought me a handful of anemones and petunias in shades of purple and lavender. A city girl like me wouldn't have known the names except she told me – and when she added that their house was on a small plot running alongside the railroad tracks, I knew why she grew anemones and wears a little enamelled pin in the shape of a daisy on her uniform.

They're almost here, I hear those quick flying steps of Molly's, two for each of Ma's, like a light-hearted arpeggio set against sombre chords in the bass.

Ma's in black again. Only her hair's whiter. Pulled back

79

tighter, like a scrubwoman's. And those bristly black brows that refuse to yield to age.

'You are going to die in the electric chair in here,' she informs me calmly, inscrutably, like a messenger from God. These few words from a woman who has always used two words for one, sometimes three, speaking quickly, emphatically.

She can say those words calmly. I can't. To me, it's not yet a fact, but a possibility. *Something will happen at the last minute.* I believe that. I have to believe that. And then she points a finger at me that's bent into a hook by arthritis. 'You'll burn, Ettie,' and her voice gets hectic and flushed, and her eyes bulge, 'unless you tell them, "You're right – whatever you say I did, I did," she says, "You're right and David is telling the truth." Lie, if you have to,' she pounds away at me, 'repeat after them, "Yes we did all those evil things – the devil be cursed, but now forgive me, I'm sorry. *Rebeynu shel oylem.* Have Mercy! Let me live and be a mother to my children."'

Her final words, as I feel the cold spray of saliva through the wire screen, 'Go on your knees if you have to, but live!'

She leaves me, to go out there. And I'm left in here – in pieces. The guilt! Oh the guilt! From her, there is no appeal. She's always the prosecutor, the judge and the jury. What's worse, from her I've inherited the same legal apparatus – along with being the actual defendant in this case. Call it a gene, a transplant, whatever you call it, the result is the same.

How do you fight it, that overwhelming, life-sucking guilt? It's what I'm hearing in my head after she leaves. Guilt talking! The shadow skulking within. The only one who never leaves me.

Guilt. Sodden, like layers and layers of wet paper towels slapped on your face and left there.

Guilt. That rotten taste in your mouth that no amount of brushing with toothpaste will make go away.

Guilt. All those silences filled with accusations.

Those silent accusations heard back at birth go deep,

cutting wounds that remain unsutured, bleeding. Oh the pain when I hear Ma in my head saying imperiously, 'You are betraying me – as you did that night when you sneaked out of the house to go singing at a benefit, and what happened? You caught pneumonia – and who had to take care of you? Me! Not your Julie, not that *boychik* – sure he came to visit you, your new boyfriend (finally you had a boyfriend), and brought you a book. Big sport! A second-hand book!' (He brought me Steinbeck's *Tortilla Flat*.) 'But who filled the tea kettle for steam day and night and called the doctor and sat with you while you coughed your lungs out?'

She's still talking in my head. 'That's what mothers do for their children. Protect them. Guard their lives – and that's what I'm trying to do for you – keep you alive for your children, and you won't listen to me! Watch out, Ettie, I tell you, you don't listen to me, terrible things are gonna happen.'

What, I stop and ask her, what could be worse than what's happened?

'Never mind,' she answers in my head, 'you'll see – terrible things.'

Raising a spectre for me that cuts off all air, noxious, suffocating, like the red-yellowish sulphur dust I once saw rising out of a factory stack near the New Jersey Turnpike, nightmarish against the black starless sky. We were coming back from a performance with the Major Bowes Amateur Hour troupe in Perth Amboy. 'Quick, close the windows,' a saxophonist named Arnie yelled, 'or we'll all be asphyxiated.'

How do I say to her – and myself – yes, I want to live, with all my heart I want to live, to be all that a mother can be to her children, to see them grow into fine happy human beings, their lives full of satisfying plans and accomplishments, married, with children of their own. And yet something in me stubbornly speaks against this. If this is the only reason *why* you choose to live, it says to me, if this is how you choose to live, with lies, by lies, then you will die, if not in the electric chair, then by quietly and obscenely dribbling away your gift of life. Will you choose a life sentence out there?

SIXTEEN

1935

Reality slapped me in the face the next morning.

'I see you finally decided to show up,' sings out Marie, the telephone operator and official watchdog, as I come rushing in. What a comedown, from leading lady to shipping clerk in less than twenty-four hours. 'Kantrowitz won't like it, especially today. He's in one of his moods,' and she waggles her finger at me like a second-grade teacher.

Frankly I don't know what it was that I was expecting. To be greeted like there are rave reviews in the morning papers? Hailed as a rising young actress? Flash announcements on WNYC? Who knows? All I do know is that here I am in this stinking locker-room and suddenly it hits me like a punch in the stomach – *nothing's really changed in my life*. I'm right back here, in my everyday work clothes, mousy drab insignificant Ettie Greenglass, silently putting her lunch away as usual. About the only thing that's changed since I started working here is that I sometimes buy a bacon, lettuce and tomato sandwich on white toast at the deli down the street instead of bringing a salami sandwich from home.

This morning I'm feeling like Cinderella must've on the day after. *Here I am back in the kitchen*, she's saying to herself, right back scrubbing floors. Last night, maybe it didn't even happen, maybe I imagined it all ... *the ball, the prince, the pumpkin, the glass slipper ... all a fairy-tale, that's what it is*. Just then her stepsisters come in, tracking mud all over the wet linoleum and she looks around her and says, '*Yeah, maybe the other stuff never happened, but these two, they're still for real.*'

Maybe some girls have it easier, I don't know. Like Janet Gaynor? Remember her? In that musical, *On the Sunny Side of the Street*? With that sweet little-girl look that's so appealing?

That charming irresistible cleft in her chin that wiggles so bravely when she's struggling not to cry? So that men want to take her in their arms and protect her? That should only happen to me!

Forget it, I say to myself, experience has taught me not to expect that. By now I should know better. Just concentrate on staying out of Kantrowitz's way. Today I can see he's like a raging bull. And when that happens, Fannie gets that worried look and she goes up to him and gently pats his arm, saying, 'Easy now, Mr Kantrowitz, remember your blood pressure.' And for a moment there, you can see the veins in his temple subsiding, but then, something else, almost anything, the next minute, sets him off.

And when I get to my station, Tony, the guy I work with, he's in a rotten mood, too. No 'Hiya sweetheart!' today. Usually we'll kid around, he'll break into a song, maybe from *La Traviata* or Puccini. One of those happy-go-lucky kids with pomade on his hair and five cents in his pocket. What I've discovered is that these Italian kids really love opera, and listening to him, I've gotten the yen to study singing, too. Really train my voice professionally. I've been asking around and someone told me about an opera singer from Milan who's teaching at Carnegie Hall Studios and not too expensive. I'm saving up to start lessons, maybe in a couple of months.

Suddenly Tony lets out a scream that tears your heart out. He's holding up his left hand and blood's pouring out of it like it's water. He goes dead white. I see he's sliced his index finger with the razor knife – right down to the bone. I grab a towel from someone and wrap it around, but it soaks right through. Carl tries a tourniquet, but nothing helps, the blood's all over, so Carl says, 'Let's go to the French Hospital, Tony, it's the closest.' Poor kid, he's still trying to act brave in front of everybody, and refuses any help as they leave.

Meanwhile, Kantrowitz, who acts like everything that happens is being done to him personally on purpose, is ready to explode. Screaming directions, he puts in a new guy to work with me – a real smart-alecky kid, this Joey. All morning he keeps making cracks to me, smutty ones that I could do without. We're working like crazy, because the packages are piling up and every other minute, Kantrowitz is hollering, 'Speed it up, you dummies, move it!'

Thank God for Fannie! About an hour later when I'm feeling like my head's gonna burst, she stops by for a moment. 'You were terrific last night, really!' she says and shakes her head admiringly. 'Listen, can you come for dinner tomorrow night? Celia and I couldn't get over you!'

Believe me, that helps.

SEVENTEEN

JUNE 1935

That Friday night, it's early in June, I find out about their mother. In all the time I've known them, they've never said a word to me about her before. All I know is that they're stepsisters and that Celia, who's older than Fannie, is from their mother's first marriage.

It all comes about because of a remark I make. There's this picture of a beautiful young woman in a fancy gilt frame on the console radio, which I've often noticed though I've never asked about it. Probably because I assume it's their mother and also because there are no other family photos around. Since they don't bring it up, I don't. Still, she must be someone very special, I figure.

But this particular evening I stop to examine the picture more closely, struck by her fine features and that mysterious Slavic cast to her cheeks, the thick dark hair that's simply parted in the middle and draped about her face and shoulders like a black veil. It's her eyes, though, that hold me, they're so alive with intelligence, regarding you, considering you, were you worth her while. Like Celia's.

'What beautiful hair,' I say, unable to express more.

'Can you picture it burning?' says Celia softly, so softly that I turn towards her to hear better.

'Burning?' I repeat, not sure I'm hearing right.

'Right, burning,' she answers in that same soft voice that doesn't go with what she's saying.

Fannie, who's sitting in a chair nearby, jumps up like a Jack in the box, darts over to the window and stares out, while Celia comes over to where I'm standing still holding the picture. Something about her face has changed – a tighter set to her lips? Or is it that her jaw juts out more? I don't know exactly, only that it's set in harsher lines.

I wait.

And then she begins. 'Have you ever heard of the Triangle Company?' She's interrogating me in that slightly arrogant tone.

I shake my head. I'm not sure I like this turn.

'Are either of your parents, your father or your mother, in the garment trade?'

'No.'

'So – so no wonder, so, of course, you wouldn't know.' She shakes her head as though regretting my ignorance and looks at me with her mother's eyes.

'When did it all happen?'

In a small choked voice, Fannie pleads with her. 'Not now, Celia. *Please*. We'll be eating soon – I have a nice meal ready – barley soup, baked fish, honey cake – all the things you always like.'

Celia shakes her head at her and continues speaking to me. 'Sit down. I want you to know.'

Slowly, thoughtfully, choosing her words, she continues, 'In that picture, she's seventeen, my mother. Beautiful, yes? Spirited, you can tell.'

I nod.

Then she speaks with the pressure building like water shooting out from a hose. I can picture her at a union meeting whipping up her audience. 'Let me tell you about her, who she was, my mother. Clara Bernstein Kolchin was the youngest of five when they came here, her family, from a small town in Poland. Someplace on the border, a *shtetl* bounced back and forth between Russia and Poland like a rubber ball, my mother used to say. Her father had come here two years before and found work as a cutter. She was only nine and small for her age and seasick the whole time.

'Oh yes, also she told us how good it felt when, at last, after those twelve awful days, on rough seas down in steerage packed on top of each other, the ship sails into New York

Harbour and they run up on deck, smelling like animals, and ahead they see the big lady with the spikes in her head and the lamp in her hand that lights up at night! The Statue of Liberty! Such an excitement inside her.

'So she starts school and all, and then at thirteen, her father dies from hasty consumption – that's TB, that's what they used to call it because it strikes so quickly. One night, it's bitter cold, raining and nasty, and he comes home from work late and his feet get soaking wet. Two months later he's dead. Just like that.

'So at thirteen – young, yes? But not the youngest! There were eight-, nine-, ten-year-olds working there, too, only the boss hides them when the inspectors come around – she goes to work at Triangle, learning to be an operator on ladies' shirtwaists. At first, it's hard for her, her hands are so clumsy and she keeps making mistakes. The foreman yells at her, "You stupid animal, you! When will you learn!" And sometimes the needle goes right through her finger, but she learns to bind it up quickly with a strip of cloth and to go on sewing. It's either learn quickly, or else ... so she learns quickly. By the time she's sixteen, she's making five dollars a week. It means starting at seven-thirty in the morning and finishing maybe six, six-thirty at night. In the busy season, she works until nine. Also they work on Saturdays, and when you're told on Saturday afternoon by a notice in the elevator, "If you don't come in on Sunday, don't bother to come on Monday," you report on Sunday, too. No time and a half, no double time, no paid holidays. The only thing extra they get from the bosses is a little apple pie around dinnertime if they have to work later, like a small turnover. "This big," she'd show us holding up a small ashtray. "And boy did it taste good to us!"

'At first, when some of the girls in the shop start talking seriously about organizing a local of the International Ladies Garment Workers Union, not just going along with the company union, she's very frightened, but then she begins to realize it's the only way, especially when the company fires a lot of the girls – a hundred and fifty, imagine, who stupidly tell the bosses they joined the new union. One person alone, she sees for herself, doesn't stand a chance. It's like a reformatory at Triangle. All the relatives of the owners are there all the time, watching, running the place. You can't go to the toilet without one of them checking how long you take. If you come in a little late – maybe the elevator's slow in coming – you lose half a day's pay. So who can fight them alone? Plenty of girls out there looking for work, they remind you as if you didn't know already.

'So my mother joins the union and becomes very active. Young as she is, eighteen, they come to respect her for her intelligence and courage. She's a good speaker and she's not intimidated by the older workers, already beaten down.

'When a strike's called at Triangle, my mother's right there marching on the picket line with the other women. The company hires prostitutes, imagine that, to stand at the factory doors and fight with the pickets so the scabs can sneak by. So she gets beaten up by the police – her arm's broken – while protesting this and she's hauled off to jail.

'Her arm's still in a sling the night of the big meeting called at Cooper Union. It's a bad night, sleet and rain, yet a big crowd shows up. Lots of speakers already – but no action taken. "Let's not rush into anything," they're saying. And it's getting late.

'My father told us about it, how he's in the audience sitting with her when she says to him, "Jacob, I must go up there," and she walks towards the platform, head up, erect. And young as she is, beautiful in every way, she's not afraid.

'The crowd sees her and shouts, "Clara, Clara, we want Clara." There are those who know her already and others who've heard so much about her.

'She waits on the platform, not saying a word, poised, watching the crowd as they settle down. Even the coughing stops. Though it's late, her voice is fresh and strong as she speaks to them in fluent Yiddish.

' "I'm a working woman," she says, "one of those on strike today at Triangle against unbearable conditions, because I'm fed up with suffering. I'm tired of listening to those who tell us to be patient. What do they know, what my life is like at Triangle? Sixty hours a week, sometimes more, sitting on a hard wooden box all day next to my machine, and for that, I have to pay the boss twenty-five cents a week? For that wooden crate? I want a chair with a back so my own won't hurt so much at night. I shouldn't have to pay a cent for it or for the needle I use in the machine or the electricity that runs the machine. The bosses should provide all this." And the crowd roars yes. "I want safer conditions in the shop against fire and accidents – fire escapes that don't end at the sixth floor when it's a ten-storey building, and doors that open out, not in – what kind of door is that? *And why are they kept locked?* Yet every time our shop committee raises these reasonable demands with the owners, they say it's impossible, they simply can't afford it – what, to unlock the doors?" The crowd laughs with her. "And besides it's the way everyone operates in the industry. Aha! Now we're hearing the truth.

' "So I say to you here tonight, if they can stick together and find strength to use against us, we must stick together and find the strength to fight them. *And win*."

'When the cheering dies down, she continues, "I offer the chairman a resolution that a general strike in the industry be called now."

'Instantly the crowd's on its feet. Everyone's yelling, yes! yes! yes! waving hats, handkerchiefs, anything they can grab – and slapping each other on the back.

'After a demonstration that goes on for five minutes or more, Feigenbaum, the chairman, calls for a vote, and it's unanimous. And that's how the first big shirtwaist strike begins.'

The room is darkening quickly now – the way it does at sunset when the days first begin to get longer – and Fannie's still at the window. She hasn't moved all this time.

'So what happened?' I prompt her.

'What happened?' Celia repeats after a long silence, and her voice sounds like it's coming from an empty place inside. She speaks quickly now, as though eager to get it over with.

'Everyone said it was an important victory for the shirtwaist operators. Sure, they won a few concessions ... but not enough. She'd just gone back to work – 1911, Fannie was only a year old – when the fire broke out at Triangle late on a Saturday afternoon. A beautiful May day, children riding their tricycles on the sidewalk below. It spread so quickly that the firemen were helpless when they finally arrived. And just what my mother worried about ... happened ... the women couldn't get out of the doors so they ran to the windows. She was trapped outside on a ledge high up with the others and she waved her handkerchief at the firemen as they were raising their ladders. But the ladder could only reach as far as the sixth floor and she stopped waving as her skirt caught fire. She leaped for the top of the ladder, almost thirty feet below ... missed ... They said her body landed on top of the others nine storeys down on the ground.'

Fannie goes into the other room. I hear the tap water running.

'One hundred and forty-six women died in that fire. Trapped like animals in a burning barn,' Celia finishes up. 'And yet the bosses were acquitted. Only afterwards the city passes a new up-to-date fire ordinance.' She sits there for a few more minutes in the dark room, and I can hear her heavy uneven breathing, but it's too dark to see her face. Then she leaves, too.

EIGHTEEN

JUNE 1935

From that time on, life in the shop takes on a different meaning for me. Celia's face stays with me, the lines that were put there by anger and a rockbottom determination to say no to all the things that are wrong in life.

When I come into work the next morning, Tony's back. The doctor had to amputate his finger – Carl never told us that – and it's all covered with a big bandage and he can't work fast like he used to. Seymour next to me mutters, 'If Kantrowitz weren't such a son of a bitch, Tony'd still have his finger.' A look passes between us. It's a long time before I hear Tony sing again.

She's smart, that Celia, I tell myself later in the morning as I'm writing receipts, rushing, rushing, always rushing, that Celia knows the score. What's more, I admire the way she uses her head and doesn't bother to hide it like some other women around here, batting their eyelashes like they didn't have a brain. *As for you, Ettie Greenglass, you're still a big kid, still a dreamer, and even at twenty, you can't see what's going on right in front of your eyes.* No, because all I've been thinking of is making it big on the Major Bowes Amateur Night Show. Right now I'm in a travelling company of his that plays small towns in New Jersey on weekends. Supposedly we're all winners from his radio show. What a laugh! I'm one of the few who was actually on the show and won a third prize.

What a cheap bastard this guy Bowes turns out to be! His show attracts all these hopeful amateurs, all kinds of performers from mimics and bell ringers to country musicians who walk in with their jugs and washboards. Serious musicians, too, good ones. And each one of us is hoping for that once in a lifetime break. And yet all you get as a finalist is ten bucks and a dinner before the show. An assistant producer once told me Bowes was taking home fifteen, twenty, maybe twenty-five thousand a week! And that's in 1935! But we're all dreamers – *if it can happen to one person, why not to me?*

The only one whose dream comes true? Frank Sinatra. He gets his start on the show singing with a group that calls itself the Hoboken Four. I pass him once in the hall ... skinny kid with a big Adam's apple.

Anyhow, as I'm eating my tuna sandwich and observing the others, it hits me that after three years here, with the exception of Fannie, I feel no connection with anyone in the shop. To me they're just all these people with whom I work and with whom I have nothing much in common. Some I like, like Laura and Tony and Milly. And others I don't, and it annoys me that they're always either complaining or teasing each other or getting into the stupidest arguments.

Today, somehow, all those things don't matter as much. Like Sonia's false teeth that look mail order, or Jennie's constipation which she always mentions, God knows why. Or Hannah, the *yenteh*, who has this way of grabbing my arm and asking, 'So when are you getting married already?'

Laura and Miriam, who are sitting nearby, are talking about their steady boyfriends, and don't think that doesn't bother me. No one has even asked me out. But maybe that's because I'm so different from the other girls; I'm always busy with work and acting and taking singing lessons, and last week, I was finally accepted by the Schola Cantorum – that's really important to me, it's this well-known choir in New York and they told me I'm the youngest. All I know is if I don't follow a tight schedule, nothing'll happen.

Some of the older women opposite are talking about their kids. Ida's daughter is going with a nice fellow, *takeh* a good match, she says, a fellow with a civil service job. Esther, a widow, chips in with how her son's starting at City College. 'A real smart *bocher*,' she says proudly. Listening to them, I'm envious; sons go to college, why not me?

Just because I'm me, Ethel Greenglass, that doesn't automatically mean that I don't deserve more than this lousy job that pays peanuts. To be stuck in a stinking rotten shop for the rest of my life. There are things I know I can do that are locked inside me now. And I don't want them to stay locked up for ever.

'I hope we finish a little earlier today,' Sarah's saying. 'My little one couldn't go to school this morning – poor kid, she was throwing up all night long and I asked my next-door neighbour to keep an eye on her. I hated to leave her. But what can you do?'

'I know how you feel,' agrees Esther.

'Thank God no pneumonia or mastoids so far this winter. Last year she – ' and quickly Sarah puts in, 'Better I should bite my tongue,' frightened by her own words. Don't take anything for granted, that's what she's really saying. *Anything good is always in jeopardy, that's how life is.* I used to get like that at times, too, when I'd look at Julie and the kids around the table at night, or when they'd jump into bed with us on Sunday mornings. Or going to Coney Island once on a Sunday, with Michael and Robby so excited, they're bouncing up and down on the seat and the other passengers are smiling at them, they're so cute. It's the first time for them, and Julie turns to me with such an expression of love in his eyes, Look, look, he's saying, what we've got, and he takes my hand in his and we ride the rest of the way to Stillwell Avenue, the last stop. *Don't take this away from me*, I remember thinking.

About three an argument breaks out between Abe, one of the older men whose job it is to keep us supplied with twine and wrapping paper, and Carl, the foreman, who's been drinking all day. His breath would kill an elephant. Abe's asking for time off the next day to take his wife who's sick to the clinic at Bellevue. He's a nice man, a little slow sometimes so Carl's always on his back. Also maybe because he wears a *yarmulke* and speaks mostly in Yiddish. Reminds me a little of my father.

'Vy can't I take the morning off?' Abe asks him. 'Mine vife has diabetes, and her doctor refuses to take care of her until the bill is paid. So vat ken I do? Let her die?'

'Listen, you kike, I need you here tomorrow and I don't give a damn what happens to your wife,' Carl fires back. 'Get someone else to take her. You show up tomorrow or don't bother coming in any more. And that's that!'

Abe, his head down, is about to walk away when Sonia, an oldtime socialist from Russia, takes his arm sympathetically. 'Wait, Abe,' she says, 'let me speak to him. Listen, Carl, give the guy a break, you can take on look at him and see how worried sick he is. Sonny usually helps him out when it gets busy. So why can't he take his place tomorrow? Be a good guy.'

By this time, several others have gathered around, including Milly, an older woman who wears her shoes cut out to make room for her bunions. 'Yah,' she says, 'it's against the law for a man to have a sick wife? C'mon, give him a break.'

Carl's face is getting redder and redder. He knows he's wrong because he's allowed others to do this, but this time, he must be afraid of losing face if he backs down.

'I said no and I mean it. Now, all of you, get back to work.' Carl's eyes are red and mean and he weaves a little.

'But Carl,' says Sonia, still trying to talk to him as though he were a reasonable human being.

All of a sudden he's in a rage and starts screaming at all of us, 'Get back to work this minute, and as for you, Sonia, get your ass out of here now, you and your kike buddy Abe. I'll tell Fannie to have your pay envelope ready to pick up on the way out.' And he exits.

All of us are standing there, mouths open, still shocked. Abe can't believe it. His lips – small and round for a man – pucker as though he's about to cry. He takes a few steps towards his locker, stops, shakes his head and stares down at his hands hanging empty at his side. Sonia is about to yell something at Carl, but she shuts up, but not before I hear her mutter, 'I'll get you yet for this, you son of a bitch! You Cossack you!' and she stalks out with her smock flying out behind her like a streamer from a plane.

We all know there's no point in appealing to Kantrowitz. He always backs up the foreman no matter what.

As I'm elbowing my way on to the train during rush hour, I'm still furious with how one, two, three, Abe and Sonia are out, just like that. No protection. No appeal. Carl's word is law. And nobody spoke up for them. *And where were you*, I ask myself, sick at heart. For I'm ashamed of myself, that's the truth.

NINETEEN

1935

With Fannie and Celia, I'm like one of the family, more at home with them than in my own. In mine, no one's interested in me or the things that I'm discovering. Read a book? Forget it, says Ma, girls shouldn't waste their time on foolishness, the same with going to a concert. Through Celia and Fannie, though, I'm discovering the real New York, not that narrow slice I'm trapped in. Sometimes on a Sunday, we go to the Brooklyn Museum, or else I meet them at the Met, though Celia hates all that travelling on her day off, so often she stays home and Fannie and I go. Then it's more like being with a girlfriend. When Celia's with us, I'm a little overawed by her and it's not just that she's older, it's something about her. Like wanting to measure up to her standards, though it's not in any particular way, more like an attitude, a way of looking at things that she assumes is clear to everyone.

Best of all is going to the theatre on Broadway. The first time, I remember, is a Saturday matinée when it's the slow season and we're waiting for the autumn orders to start up in another couple of weeks. So Fannie says to me, 'How about going to see *Awake and Sing*? Celia saw it the other night and she says it's really something we should see. You interested?'

'How much are tickets?' I ask her first.

'Matinées are always cheaper. I'll find out.'

It turns out that if we sit in the top balcony, it's fifty-five cents, so I say, I'm all for it.

I fall in love, that afternoon, in the darkened theatre, with Ralph, with Jules Garfield (later on, in the movies, it became John) who plays Ralph, the rebellious son. The play's all about a Jewish family in the Bronx, and it's like seeing my own mother up there on the stage – though her name happens to be Bessie Berger and Stella Adler plays her to a tee. How this woman tries to run everyone's life! Substitute Tessie for Bessie and you've got my mother! Even the expressions she uses. *Wait, wait, when it's too late, you'll remember how you sucked away a mother's life ... When you're walking in my funeral procession ...*

It's funny, why do I fall in love with Ralph? Because I love the shape of his shaggy head with the thick dark hair, and the way he walks and talks, cocky, idealistic, yet sensitive to the core – and there's so much energy busting to come out of him – and you know at the end he'll use it to good purpose, that he has dreams of his own and he intends to make them come true. *So life shouldn't be printed on dollar bills*, he says. Suddenly, I want so much to be part of that, to be with a man who has that spirit and in some way, like through the umbilical cord, it'll be transmitted to me. We'll do it together.

But also, Ralph reminds me of me – of all the things I want out of life, too, but the difference is he talks up and fights back while I clam up. What does he want more than anything? A pair of white shoes! And me? A warm winter coat, but most of all, that there should be someone, one person, who understands and says, sure, you can dream, it's okay, and not always be standing over me, shaking a finger and insisting, give it up, give it up, it's not for you. I don't want my life printed on dollar bills either.

I suppose in his own quiet way, Pa tries, but he knows so little about the world out there, the way I'm seeing it. He's never worked in a shop with other people all day long, only here in that front room where he sits and fixes other people's sewing machines while he watches the world go by. I don't think he's ever gone anywhere on his own, just out of curiosity, to see what's out there. Once he arrived in New York, somehow his journey ended, right here on Sheriff Street. It's as though his feet carried him this far and no further. He put down his bundles and stayed. But I want more.

Someday, I promise myself, I'll fall in love with someone like Ralph, a man like Jules Garfield, with ideas, with dreams. Together we'll make them come true.

TWENTY

JULY 1951

Here I've been counting the minutes, yet when Dr Singer walks into the Visitors' Room, this burning sensation like spilt acid hits my gut. How dare he desert me! For almost a year. The man I had really come to trust. And when I needed him so badly, all that time in the House of Detention waiting for the trial, he never came. Now, of course, I know all this isn't rational, it's not his fault, but the anger's still there.

You'd never know it, though, because I smile and say, 'It's good to see you again, Dr Singer, it's been a long time.' And I motion for him to sit down in the cubicle facing me as though I'm in my own home.

'You're looking well.' He smiles like he's pleased to see me.

'I am?' That takes me by surprise. Because I feel so ... so dingy ... that's a funny word to use, isn't it? A wall's dingy, an undershirt, sure. But a person? So that's how I see myself? Interesting – because I remember telling him last time I saw him I felt mousy. From mousy to dingy in less than a year. I'm making progress.

'I wondered about you,' he says, 'when you cancelled that last appointment, was it August 13th? Why you never got back to me?' My heart jumps, it's good to hear him say that. 'I asked the answering service. "That's all she said," they told me, " 'Sorry, I have to cancel our appointment.' " And then you never called back,' he continues, clasping his hands. There's that chunky class ring on his right hand, I've never been able to make out where it's from. Probably De Witt Clinton High. Like a lot of the guys at City College I met.

'Are you?' he asks me.

'Am I what?'

'Angry with me?'

'Of course not! Why would I be angry?'

'You never called back,' he says to me. 'That's so strange, I thought, she's never done that before, I wonder why ... and then a day later, I read about your arrest in the paper. I was so sorry. I thought you might want to be in touch, but that maybe you were angry with me?'

'Me? Oh no ... never ... not with you,' I say, and now I mean it because just the sight of that warm round friendly face and his kind eyes looking at me with genuine concern through those thick lenses makes me feel better already. 'It's just I wasn't thinking very clearly then ... to be honest with you, I guess I just didn't want you involved in this mess or for you to get hurt by it in any way. But now I hope I'll be seeing you here regularly. I've missed our sessions so much.'

'Well, it's been approved by the prison psychiatrist,' he says. 'But did you know I tried to see you at the Women's House of Detention?'

'You did?' I'm dumbfounded.

'Sure, didn't anyone tell you? At the front office, they said they would ... yes, I went there a couple of days after your arrest, and when I told them who I was, they said only close relatives and your lawyer were allowed to see you, but they'd give you a message.'

'Those lousy bastards! Never a word to me. And it would have meant so much! I tell you, Dr Singer, there are days in here when I'm so angry – it's like being throttled at the throat with rage – that I begin to think maybe I belong in a padded cell. That's how furious I get, and when I hear you say that! I'm ready to yell and scream and pound the bars.'

'That's not such a bad idea,' he says. 'Try it.'

As we're talking face to face, I'm feeling a sense of release. Hearing that familiar voice, I'm back in his office, and he's in that familiar rocking chair, a sturdy reliable man slowly rocking back and forth, contentedly puffing on his pipe, the one with the thick bowl carved out of burl wood bought someplace in the Orient when he was stationed there during

101

the war. He once told me that. The rest of the time he listened. Three times a week I used to go like clockwork to his office, and there he was, always ready to help me understand myself a bit better ... why I'm so anxious all the time, so down on myself like I'm never good enough. Sometimes I felt guilty about spending the money on myself, ten dollars a session he charged, but one thing I knew, I had to go.

But the first time was so different.

1949

On the phone, he says, 'One o'clock on Tuesday. Can you make it then, Mrs Rosenberg?' and gives me the address. The Jewish Board of Guardians insisted I see a psychiatrist and gave me his name. 'You need some help, too,' the social worker said, 'not just Michael.'

'Can't I see you, too?' I ask her.

'No, each of you needs your own therapist.'

'How come we can't talk together with you like a family?'

'It's just not done that way,' she answers me, growing impatient.

So I'm getting ready for this first appointment with Dr Singer, I figure a good impression is important. It's the summer of 1949 and I'm putting my shoes on in a hurry. Last night I polished them and ironed the dress. Suddenly I'm so tired, all down my arms and legs, so goddam tired ... always rushing. I have to be there at one and I had to make arrangements for the kids, and I haven't even told Julie yet. Who else goes to a psychiatrist? No one I know. Maybe this Dr Singer will tell me I'm okay, I don't need to see him ... that's what I'm hoping.

This shoe in my hand? It's a white open-toe sandal with a double strap, I'm really looking at it for the first time. On the innersole, it's stamped Macy's M.D. Arch-Support Shoes, and on the side, 7B. After three years, you can hardly make it out. These shoes, I say to myself, reveal more about you, Ethel, than all the dreams still floating around in your head. Take a good hard look at them, kid. Yours droop. Like it's too much trouble to stand up straight, and they've been polished so many times with Griffen's white liquid polish that it's all caked into the cracks. That's what he'll see, Ethel ... a short, mousy, overweight housewife with no money to spend on herself, not that glamorous woman who sings on in your head ... 'I'm A Dreamer, Aren't We All?' ... take a good look at yourself in the bureau mirror, see how dumpy you look, even in the new white cotton with the blue polka dots from Ohrbach's up on Union Square. Face it, that full gathered skirt down to your ankles isn't for you, even if the salesgirl said it was the New Look, from Dior or some French designer. 'It's all they're showing,' she says. Yeah, I'm thinking, anything that'll make people part with their money, but on me it's not right. Still I buy it because I'm in a hurry. Dr Singer points to a large easy chair that's slipcovered in a beige and rust stretchknit. Then he settles into a wooden rocker opposite me, fools with his pipe for a few minutes until it's lit, then sits back and says nothing. So I fold my hands in my lap and smile – at him, at the room, what's the difference. I'm waiting. But my heart's going as though I'd just run the hundred yard dash.

So this is a real live psychiatrist, I'm thinking. One thing's for sure, he's nothing like I expected. He's not more than thirty, and he certainly doesn't resemble any psychiatrist I've seen in the movies – dark-bearded, wearing a pinstripe suit with a knitted vest and white shirt, with heavy tortoiseshell glasses and a heavy accent. Straight from Vienna and Dr Freud.

Finally, he says, 'How can I help you?'

'They ... the Jewish Board of Guardians ... they referred me to you. I'm having problems with my son, Michael.' I want to bite my nails, but that wouldn't look right. 'It's not my own idea.'

'I understand,' he says.

Then he rocks some more, slowly, steadily, while I'm sitting there like a dummy. Suddenly I'm crying and he keeps on rocking. I fumble in my purse for a tissue and he stops long enough to hand me one.

'Do you want to tell me a little about yourself? Just a few facts I'll be needing.'

I swallow hard and begin. 'I'm married and I have two sons. Michael, who's six, and Robby, who's only two. We waited four years.'

'I see.'

'I had a hard time after he was born ... Back problems and he was sick a lot, too ... Michael, I mean ... Michael's why I'm here ... he was a colicky baby ... I never got enough sleep ... I mean ... '

He nods like he knows from his own experience what it's like to have a baby crying a lot, especially at night.

'So I guess that started it ... I mean, I probably didn't respond to his needs like I should've. Y'know?'

'What's the problem now?'

I start to cry again. He rocks some more.

'They tell me ... the social worker, y'know ... he's been seeing her for a while now ... that I've botched it ... ' Now I'm crying even harder. 'With both of them ... that I've spoiled Michael, too permissive, no limits, and Robby I've babied too much ... I dunno ... ' Inside, I'm shaking like a leaf.

'We'll have to talk some more about this ... raising children isn't easy, Mrs Rosenberg. I'm sorry, we'll have to stop now. Shall we set up another appointment?' He looks at the black leather book on his desk. 'Thursday. Is two convenient for you?'

'No, I have to be home by the time Michael gets out. A little earlier, maybe?'

'One o'clock then?'

'Okay.' Is he any good, I'm wondering, he's not that busy.

As I stand up, I notice in the ashtray nearby how many tissues I've used up. I suppose some people smoke instead. 'I really try hard, y'know, Dr Singer?' The tears are back again.

'I know that, Mrs Rosenberg.'

On my way out, I notice the lobby is cool and kind of gloomy with lots of dark marble and wood panelling. An old building. No one's around. I see myself in the ornate gilt mirror hanging over a black lacquered chest near the door. Nothing about me has changed. Strange how one's experiences don't show. Except maybe for my eyes – all red from crying. Will the kids notice, ask questions, say something to Julie? I hope not. Dr Singer suggested three visits before we make a decision. That I liked.

As I walk out, a young blonde woman and a much older, grey-haired man are going in. An affair? His secretary maybe? My imagination wanders. For a moment I wish I could look like that – slim, blonde, a *shikse* and beautiful. But I remind myself, in the Party you don't think like that.

On the ride home, my head's pounding in time with the train, and I feel like I'm getting another migraine. The nausea's coming, always the first sign.

TWENTY-ONE

JULY 1951

When I was seeing Dr Singer in his office, he once asked me if there had ever been a time in my life when I felt really good about myself.

I had to think about that one. Then I said, 'I guess when I was working and very active in the union.'

1935

1935! A lot's happening in the world and finally I open my eyes. Twenty years old and I begin to see the world for what it is, and not just the stuff of my dreams. It's the year Italy invades Ethiopia and Senator Huey Long is assassinated. Celia says he was a fascist and the newspaper quotes him as once saying, 'Sure, we'll have fascism in America, only it'll come wrapped in the American flag.' Smart man!

I'm learning, but I'm a slow learner. As one of the World's Great Dreamers, there are some things I don't want to believe. That people are people. It's as simple as that, though it's hard for me to accept even now, here in Sing Sing. But it's true. For instance, why are so many liberals and Jews being intimidated by the Communist witchhunt? And how about the Party? Where are they in our hour of need? When the stakes are so high?

Recalling my entrenched innocence and basic optimism – don't all dreamers have to be optimists? – I realize I must have believed even back then, in 1935, that whatever I was involved in, the outcome was crucial to my future. But in those days, my future was spelled out in lights on marquees. Front page headlines I didn't anticipate.

And yet, I'm beginning to see that everything that happens, each small decision you make, is nothing more than taking a step in a certain direction.

Like when I meet Murray. He's one of these guys you like on sight, friendly and warm, someone you feel you can count on, and what's more, you know he likes you for you. No ulterior motives. Mostly it's his eyes, very blue and lively, and the dimples, unexpected in a man, but nice. We hit it off immediately.

The way I meet him is through Celia at one of their Friday night dinners. 'You'll like him,' she predicts, 'and I've told him about you. He wants to meet you.'

He shows up just as we finish clearing the table for dessert, and grins when Fannie brings in the chocolate éclairs from Duberman's. 'I can't wait!' he says and claps his hands like a kid at his birthday party when they bring in the cake all lit up. I'm the same way. While they're talking, I'm eating, very slowly, making each spoonful of the creamy filling last as long as possible.

Afterwards, Celia and Murray go into the living-room and Fannie and I do the dishes. The two of them must be arguing because every so often her voice gets shrill and stubborn and then he must say something that calms her down. As I'm putting things away, I notice again how nicely Fannie has everything arranged in that kitchen. Philo-dendron and rubber plants on the window, a clean linen tablecloth, a place for everything in the cupboards, not like in ours. Someday I'll have my own kitchen, I promise myself. One time Pa came in when I was sweeping up the mess from the night before, and he says to me, 'You're a sweetheart,' and gives me a kiss on the cheek. I give him a big hug. Standing in the kitchen – it's late afternoon when the sun comes in – he's not much taller than me, and he has these nice rosy cheeks like he just came off the boat, and sparkly eyes, even when things aren't so hot. The boys always loved their *Zayde Barnett*, he always had chewing gum in his pockets and pennies for them. And when he died in 1948 ... I miss you, Pa ... still do.

'So I hear from Celia you're not too happy with the way things are going at National,' Murray says to me as we join them. Fannie's already told me in the kitchen that he's married with two kids.

'Well, three years in February I'm working there and I just got a five cents raise. I guess that says it.'

'That's just what we're talking about.'

'So what can we do? I'm told that there's not even a union for our shop, only for those in manufacturing.'

'You're absolutely right,' he breaks in, 'that's just what the AFL leadership has realized, that you people in shipping have no union to represent you. Now that's gotta change ... with Roosevelt and the Wagner Act, now we can do something about it, get organized. After all, you and I both know that shipping is very important to the manufacturers. Without it, their hands are tied. *Kaput!* Strategically, it has real importance.' He nods like he's agreeing with himself. That's one of his quirks I discover and it's kinda cute. Sometimes, though, he'll sit there cleaning his fingernails when we're talking and that's not so cute.

'So how are we supposed to go about it?' I ask. 'I mean get organized?' What he's saying makes sense.

Murray grins at me, his blue eyes snapping, and he unbuttons his collar and loosens his tie. 'I was hoping you'd ask just that question,' and starts to fill me in.

'Listen,' he says, 'we're setting up an organizing committee and I'd like you to come to our first meeting. There'll be a few others from National and from the other shipping outfits, also the shipping clerks from manufacturing. It's next Thursday, in fact – why don't you come with Celia?'

I wonder about Fannie, why she isn't going with us, but then on the way home, I realize why. She's a supervisory employee, and Murray said they're not included.

108

By now, I'm so busy with organizing that I have to let other things ride. I drop out of the Major Bowes troupe, maybe it's a mistake, because shortly after that, in March 1935, the show goes on a national hook-up for Chase and Sanborn on NBC.

Anyhow, working at it day after day, things start to happen. Not in a vacuum, of course. The newspapers are full of news about the workers organizing – all over the country. It's like the word has gone out, *you can do it, go ahead, get moving*. So it's happening right here in our shop, you can just feel the momentum, and in rubber, and in the auto plants in Michigan, and way out on the West Coast with Harry Bridges and the dock workers leading the way – I once stood next to him at a meeting in Madison Square Garden.

Anyhow Tony signs up after we talk about it a few times and I fill him in on the campaign and who's in on it. Also Dora and Miriam and Angela. But we all have to be very careful because it seems as though Kantrowitz has his ears all over the place – he'll come up behind you and suddenly you turn around and there he is with a little smirk on his face. 'Enough with the talk,' he says, and even if we're not talking union, I'm uneasy. Even the walls start having ears. I remember once in the locker-room while eating lunch, some of us who are members are whispering about tomorrow night's agenda when Lobelia, one of the few Negro women working there (she's supposed to be the sister of Loebel's wife's cleaning woman), comes by. And Judy, feeling good, I suppose, about having just signed up the day before, impulsively blurts, 'Hey, Lobelia, how about joining the union?' And Lobelia, a tall busty woman with thin ankles so she looks like a crane, stares her right in the eye and says, 'Listen, 'round heah, not only don' yah talk union, yah don' think it.'

The others look scared and fall back, and she marches on.

I'll never forget that. She's about forty and grew up, she once told me, on a sharecropper's farm in Georgia. I can understand why she's so frightened and yet it makes me mad – to see someone so intimidated. But that's what the system does to you. I see it also among some of the others, how reluctant they are to take that one step, sign a membership card, even when the law now says it's okay, and they want to. Maybe the older ones are still back in Russia afraid of the Cossacks and the Tsarist police, what Ma always comes back to in her memories. Still, a few of the leaders in the shop are oldtimers, socialists going way back, and they're wonderful and inspiring. It burns me up when those of us born here don't have more courage to stand up for ourselves and what we believe in.

Now I'm hoping Lobelia won't tell her sister. You never know whom you can trust, though I don't think she'll tell somehow. Slowly I'm trying to build faith in the workers. Of course, the Party stresses it later on, still, I've learned through my own experience, that you can't have an across-the-board faith in everyone just because they're members of the proletariat. Julie and I used to argue about that. He wants to trust everyone, it must make him feel more comfortable around people – besides, he always had that religious bent going back to his Yeshiva days. 'You have to believe in people, Ethel,' he'd scold me sometimes, 'at least, the ones on our side. The proletariat.' Honestly, I don't know ... after what Dovey, my own brother, did ... and Ruth ... my sister-in-law ... my mother ... whom *can* I trust?

Anyhow, so within a few weeks, about 60 per cent of the shop has signed up. Murray's wild with excitement. It's almost beyond my own expectations, too, and I have to hang on, not get carried away; otherwise, I'll be up in that chariot and off into the wild blue yonder in no time flat.

Of course, most are what I call coat-tail hanger-onners. Always it comes down to a few hard workers, it always works that way, coming down to a handful and always the same ones who are willing to do the scut work. Forget the chiefs, I tell you, it's the Indians who show up night after night at the local, like myself, to do the hard work that has to get done; we bring a sandwich and grab a coffee downstairs, and discuss the daily developments, and where do we go from here. I really become good at writing and running off leaflets, so after a while, the others automatically say, 'Well, Ethel can take care of that,' and I feel good about it, needed.

Nights after a meeting when I go home, I can't sleep. I'm so excited about what's discussed, what we're planning. Finally we reach the point where we have a list of six concrete demands. But Robert – one of the older men – he keeps throwing in monkey wrenches, suggesting qualifying clauses and complicated arrangements for piece work that won't work. Sometimes Murray has to rule him out of order.

In drawing up our demands, we're still like scared rabbits. If it weren't for Murray, we wouldn't even have the nerve to ask for a minimum wage of twenty-three dollars and two weeks' vacation with pay, and paid legal holidays. Moshe, one of the greenhorns, is convinced our demands are so out of line that Kantrowitz will immediately fire all of us. 'He can't – don't forget the government is behind us. Moshe,' Murray patiently points out, 'it's always better to ask for more than we expect to get, not less. That way, you got somethin' to bargain with, give away if you hafta.'

'Looks like we'll have to show all of them we mean business,' says Murray addressing a large local meeting called at the Hotel Delano because so many are dissatisfied and saying so out loud. All twenty of us from National agree, because we've just come from Loebel's office. Now, from what Murray says, it's obvious all the bosses have gotten together and decided on a unified strategy. They've purposely got us tied up in negotiations. Keep stalling. These jerks are inexperienced, give 'em enough time and their union'll fall apart.

'All of you in shipping are getting the same damn

runaround,' Murray tells us. 'It's time to stop it. Now! Why should the shipping clerks be the stepchildren of the industry?'

And just like that he calls for a strike vote after first reading a letter of approval from William Green, the president of the AFL.

'Will someone offer a resolution to go on strike?' he asks.

Tony's hand shoots up, the one minus a finger. 'I make the motion that Local 19953, the Ladies Apparel Shipping Clerks, call a strike and ask all our brothers and sisters in the garment industry to join us in a sympathy strike.'

'Will someone second the motion?'

'I second the motion, Mr Chairman,' I hear myself saying.

'All in favour?'

'Aye! Aye!' Everyone's on their feet. 'Strike! Strike!' They're cheering.

'Any opposed?' Even Robert, for once, keeps his mouth shut.

'Our membership has unanimously voted to go on strike!' Murray booms out and raises his fist high in the air.

Impulsively I start singing, '*Solidarity for ever, solidarity for ever, solidarity for ever, for the union makes us strong.*' And everyone joins in. What a moment!

TWENTY-TWO

AUGUST 1935

On August 27, 1935, we all go out on strike.

Murray asked me to get to strike headquarters – which is at Christ Church on West 36th – earlier than the others. 'That way you can help me get things lined up.'

'Sure, be glad to.'

He's already there when I rush in, breathless, but neatly dressed. 'It's important,' he'd told us. 'We want the crowd to see you striking for a living wage, not begging for a handout.'

Good old New York, hot and muggy as usual. A short thunderstorm the night before hasn't done a thing to cool it off, and I'm feeling a little nauseous, anyway. Mom contributed by giving me a big argument before I left the house. 'Stay out of it,' she butts in as I'm making last-minute arrangements on the phone with Celia. 'Don't get mixed up with these troublemakers.' Finally I get out with her still going a mile a minute.

Among the first who show up? Robert, of course. Right away he's offering suggestions that won't work and getting on everyone's nerves. Murray gives him something to do that gets him out of the way.

Soon others start showing up. Lots of nervous giggles. This is it! The girls, that is; the men are punching each other on the shoulder, the hearty stuff. 'Hey, Sam!' 'Hey Izzy!' 'Howsa boy? Ready for a little action?' 'Yeah,' rubbing his hands together eagerly, 'but my wife, she ain't so happy about it.'

In less than an hour, 36th Street is packed with people – I can't believe my eyes – hundreds and hundreds are gathering outside the church and more come pouring in every minute. Everywhere hands are reaching out for signs and leaflets as

Murray repeats last-minute instructions. 'Just stay calm no matter what,' he warns us, 'otherwise, we're playing right into their hands. They'll try to provoke us so they can go for an injunction to stop the picketing. Whatever you do, don't lose your head. Remember, they'll do their damnedest!

'Also be prepared for the scabs and guards they'll bring in from Pinkerton's or Bergoff's ... strikebusters! Bums hired for this lousy business right off the street, from the flophouses on the Bowery – they'll stop at nothing. They're the scum – prison records, manslaughter, armed robbery, nice things like that – and they're armed with clubs, blackjacks, knives,' he's speaking slowly so it sinks in, 'and guns ... loaded. They're going to fight us with every weapon they've got. So watch out, everybody!

'One more thing,' he says and then gives us the bad news. 'Our parade down Broadway this afternoon is cancelled.'

'Oh!' moans the crowd.

When he adds, 'The police refused to give us a permit,' the crowd boos long and loud.

'They can't get away with this,' some yell out.

He cups his hands like a microphone and yells back, 'You're damn right! But that's how much influence the bosses have!' The crowd's getting angrier. He's getting to them. 'But we're still not giving up, we're working on it, you can bet your life!' Now he has them cheering. For me, it's an indescribable feeling – to be part of all this and the real strength and fierce determination I read on all the faces around me.

As we head out to our shops, Murray suggests a song. 'C'mon everyone, let's show 'em the kind of spirit we have. Ethel, you've got the voice, suppose you lead off?'

So I call out loud and clear, 'Okay everybody, here goes: *On the line, on the line, come and picket on the picket line. We'll win our fight, our fight for the right, on the picket, picket line.*' We go marching down 36th Street swinging our arms and singing with gusto.

We get to National a few minutes before Loebel and Kantrowitz arrive with the rest of their *mishpocha*. There's our picket line, over one hundred strong, confronting them with big signs: ON STRIKE! NATIONAL UNFAIR TO WORKERS! LADIES APPAREL SHIPPING CLERKS UNION, LOCAL 19953, AFL. And we sock it to them right off: 'We want a living wage, we want a living wage!' Kantrowitz chomping on his cigar looks mad enough to play Edward G. Robinson in *Little Caesar*. He's about to snarl something at us when Loebel, looking slick like he just left the barber's chair, grabs his arms and hustles him inside.

In a few more minutes, Carl and Larry show up. Carl's got this ghoulish grin pinned on his face as he cuts through our line and Larry keeps his eyes glued to the sidewalk. The other foremen arrive soon after in squad formation. When Fannie goes through, I pretend not to see her. For now, it's better that way.

About a half hour later, Lobelia, her dark skin shining with the heat, shows up. She doesn't say a word, picks up a sign, and takes her place in the line. Later, we happen to meet at the coffee shop up the street.

'How ya' doing, Ethel?' she asks, warmer and friendlier than she's ever been.

'Excited – aren't you?'

She surprises me a second time. 'Scared,' she says, 'but Ah'm heah, ain't I?'

'Good for you.'

'My husban' ... he give me a big argument this mornin'. He ain't workin' and he's scared what's gonna happen – fool tried to keep me from comin' ... ' and she points to a large bandage above her right eyebrow, 'threw frying pan clear cross room – caught me heah – five stitches they put in at Harlem Hospital, but Ah'm heah.' She's hurting all right, but something's boiling up in her, and it's good to see it happening.

And that's how it's going, like a current of electricity that's passing between all of us. My mind's racing ahead with ideas. So far, we've managed to stop all deliveries. Nothing's moving on 36th Street, and the sidewalk in front of National is piled up with packages toppling over. Truckdrivers are refusing to cross the picket line. Great, no loading or unloading. Same thing with the Building Service Employees Union. In ours, everyone going up to National has to walk up seven flights. Serves them right; what's more, it's happening all over the garment district.

All day long, we're taking turns picketing, two hours on and a half hour off. It's very lively, with songs and slogans, and clapping hands as we march around. Most people going by are friendly and encouraging. 'Hey, we're with you!' or 'Give it to them!' 'Stick by your guns!' And then this little old lady comes by – like somebody's grandmother with white hair in a bun? – out of the blue, she grabs my hand holding out a leaflet and gives it a hard twist. 'You can take it and shove it!' she barks at me, and sedately walks on. I burst out laughing. People!

Every so often someone from headquarters comes by to fill us in on the latest. Lots of turmoil and excitement. No word yet on the parade, but they're saying eighty-five employers have already asked for a settlement. Wow! On the first day! 'Did y'hear that? Maybe the strike'll be over in a couple of days.' Everyone's hugging and kissing each other, and it's like a holiday from work.

Suddenly there's a commotion as a scab goes by with a loaded pushrack. Usually the streets around here are filled with these moving racks, loaded with clothes, and they're colourful, especially towards summer. But today this is the first. Right after him, moving fast, come about fifty of our guys, and when they catch up with him, he disappears from view. In a few seconds, this kid breaks through the ring of men like Al Capone's after him and heads for Ninth Avenue dodging traffic like crazy. The pushrack's knocked over, and in the gutter are all these blouses in a red, white and blue print. The colours of the American flag, I'm thinking, and the sight upsets me. Deliveries have got to be stopped, I know that, it's the only way – still, it's disturbing.

By afternoon, you can feel the tension in the air. Now the cops, lots of them, are around patrolling, swinging their clubs. 'Keep moving!' they're ordering bystanders, each time edging in a little closer on us. But our picket line holds.

Across the street, these four models are coming out of a building, dressed to the teeth. What grabs my eye is that each one's wearing a warm winter outfit. In 95 degree heat? A yellow cab pulls up in front of them. I hand Angie my sign and run across to take a good look. They're busy talking to each other and oblivious to what's going on right in front of their eyes. This tall redhead in a gorgeous green velvet suit with a great big egg of a diamond on her left hand, looks heavier to me than most of these skinny models I've seen around, and the same with the other three. Sure enough, sticking out from under her skirt are two other hems, a blue and a red. The other three – the same thing. As they climb into the cab, I call out, 'Don't scab – join us!' But they're still busy talking, and the cab pulls away. What's it like to be so beautiful, I ask myself.

The next day, the paper reports that some manufacturers sent out models wearing three or four garments by cab to deliver to the fancy uptown department stores like Saks and Bergdorf's. But more important, though, is the big headline: '14,000 SHIPPING CLERKS STRIKE – PARALYSE MIDTOWN TRAFFIC'. Terrific!

Late in the day, Capital Dress – on the floor above us – also tries a fast one. They send out armed guards, about six, along with scabbing truckers to get their packages out, quickly, one, two, three, so that we'll be caught flatfooted. When our members plant themselves in the way, this one short guard who looks like he's right out of San Quentin? Well, he pulls a gun on them. Everyone stiffens but this one Negro guy near him who's delivering coffee and sandwiches in the

117

neighbourhood. He makes a grab for the gun. In the struggle, it goes off and the bullet hits this scrawny kid, still in knickers, who's working as a messenger for Western Union. Poor kid! He's only watching from the sidelines, and his face goes white and he collapses on the pavement. Someone calls for an ambulance and the police move in. 'Break it up, break it up!' and they're swinging their clubs at us, but we won't give way. Thank God, it turns out to be only a flesh wound.

The next day, Celia shows me this picture – maybe in the *Daily Worker* – there are four young guys playing mandolins and guitars and a few couples dancing closely during a big strike somewhere in Georgia. The headline says: 'STRIKERS TRY TO BAR FINKS S APPROACH TO MILL BY DANCING'. So sweet and young they look. Maybe a couple of them are really in love.

And like me, they must have believed it's possible to conduct a peaceful strike and win without getting into violence.

TWENTY-THREE

AUGUST 1935

The next evening, after a big rally at the Met, with speakers and songs, we're marching up Eighth Avenue, about two hundred and fifty of us, still feeling elated. Suddenly I miss having Fannie with Celia and me, she's so much part of National and it feels strange for her not to be there, too. Celia, though, has been spending a lot of time with us, and she touches my shoulder. 'How ya' doin'?' she asks and I nod, okay, and smile. I know I belong right here, right in with all these shipping clerks, that something important's happening in America and I'm part of it.

In front of us, some strikers drop out of line and stop at a delivery truck pulled up to the kerb where two men are handing down raincoats to three others on the ground. Our guys approach them talking friendly, 'Hey, cut it out, fellows, you don't want to work against us! We're all in this together.'

'Scram!' yells this fat guy with a brush of hair like a porcupine. 'Tell 'em to beat it, Mushie, who the hell do they think they are?'

'Scram, you little bastards, go home to your mudder and suck tit!' snarls this Mushie, a bruiser with a big nose bashed down on his face.

Herbie, one of our guys known for his hot temper, snaps around and takes a swing at him. Mushie ducks and swings back hard, and catches him below the belt. Herb rolls over on the ground moaning.

'Let's get 'em!' calls Seymour behind me and rushes over to the truck followed by some more guys. One of the guards pulls out a blackjack and wallops Seymour over the head. Another punches him in the face and cuts him right under the eye. By now, there are so many fighting I can't see much except guys wrestling, swinging, and suddenly there's a shot. Our guys fall back. 'Move!' barks this big gorilla with his head shaved like a convict, standing up on the truck. 'Or I'll let you pricks have it!'

Sirens as six police cars, one after the other, come roaring up. Some more cops come running from around the corner. It's like in a movie, only this is for real, and I can't take it in, that one minute we're marching peacefully and singing with strength and unity and the next there's this scramble of bodies, fists and screams. A man's black shoe goes flying by. A cop drags a man along the ground who's holding a bloody handkerchief to his nose. 'He broke it, he broke it!' he's moaning, and the cop throws him in the patrol car like a sack of potatoes and tells the driver, 'Wait, there are some more of them damn Commies to haul to St Vincent's.'

'Fucking bastards!' says the driver and spits out the window. 'Just the night I've got tickets for the fight at the Garden! Wouldn't you know it!'

Celia grabs my arm and says, 'Keep walking. Let's get to headquarters and see what's doing.'

When we walk into the church, at one long table, a lot of the wives are fixing baloney sandwiches. Murray's circulating, keeping an eye on things, and he spots us. 'The guys are going out in cabs around the neighbourhood to keep the picket lines going so the bastards won't try to sneak in deliveries during the night, and we're going out to hand out sandwiches and drinks. Want to come along, Ethel?'

'Sure,' and I grab some sandwiches and start putting them in brown paper bags.

In the dark streets, so quiet in comparison to the daytime, our people gather in little groups around entrances. You can see their cigarettes going. A few sit in doorways catching a quick nap while the others keep watch. Like sentry duty, except that the distant boom of guns is missing.

The sun's especially hot that Thursday a week later, and even the little dark hairs on my forearm are sweaty as we march up and down in front of National carrying the signs and chanting slogans.

The strike's dragging on and the heat's getting to me. Twice already I've taken aspirins. Radio cars and lots more cops are patrolling the area and they're getting meaner and freer with their clubs. From the radical and alien squads, someone says. Tough cookies. Ten days already – and there's no end in sight.

Around two, Murray shows up. 'Hey Ethel, can you take a break?'

'Sure.' And I turn my sign over to Sonia.

As we head for some coffee, a small plane flies overhead, trailing a streamer: 'DON'T SCAB AGAINST THE SHIPPING CLERKS'.

'Hey, that's a nifty idea, Murray. Yours?'

'Yeah, you have to come up with something new all the time – it's important to keep the spirit up.'

'I know – it's beginning to get to me, too.'

'That's why we have to come up with some new ideas. See, the main thing is that we're still not getting the support I counted on from the other unions. You can see for yourself what's happened with the Teamsters,' and he mutters something under his breath not meant for my ears.

'Right after the first day, suddenly they're not co-operating. You think that's accidental?' His eyebrows shoot up. 'You'll learn, Ethel, someone high up – maybe the head of the local even? – got "schmeared" by the employers, don't kid yourself, there are a lot of finks right in the unions.' He stabs his fork into the counter.

'Hey Mister, take it easy!' says the counterman, and Murray looks up startled, and grins back.

'You're right,' he says. 'How about a refill?' and hands over his cup. 'Anyhow, as for Dubinsky and the Garment Workers, it's strictly politics with them. Right now they're holding back.'

121

'You're very angry with them.'

'You bet your life I am! These guys promised all-out support before we ever talked strike. Whadya think? That we'd have tried it without that? We'd have to be crazy! Wait, they're going to need us one day, too. Don't forget — fourteen thousand on strike ain't peanuts! -- and then they can go whistle! It's all about who's going to be in control ... politics,' he mutters and stares moodily out of the window where we're sitting. Since I don't know what he's referring to, I keep quiet and look out, too.

Outside three young girls are walking by with their arms around each other's waists and keeping in step with each other. Reminds me of the time when my girlfriends and I went on that picnic to Palisades Park. How differently I saw life then. Only three years ago.

'Hey Murray, I've got an idea, it just came to me,' I speak up. 'How about all the girls lying down right in the street so the trucks can't get by? That should stop them. Whaddya think?'

He looks up at me, starts to shake his head, and changes his mind, just like that. That's Murray. 'Terri-fic!' he says and slaps his hand down on the counter. 'Instead of a sitdown, we'll have a liedown. What an inspiration! That's gonna work. Wait — you'll see!' And he springs up, grabs my hand, and pulls me after him.

'Hey buddy, you ain't paid,' yells the counterman. Murray flips him a quarter and we run out.

In a half-hour, we've got it all arranged. Several of the guys get out there, and hold up their hands like traffic cops, right in front of the one-way traffic, while we spread out our raincoats, newspapers, anything handy, on the ground. And then a bunch of us girls just lie down full length right there, blocking the street so not even a bike can get by. The truck driver stuck in front of us is shaking his head — he can't believe it. I check my skirt, it's okay, my knees are covered. I'm feeling great and I start singing, *There once was a union*

122

maid, who never was afraid of finks … ' and the others join in. '*Oh,
you can't frighten me, I'm sticking to the union, I'm sticking to the
union …* '

We're singing away when in a couple of minutes a radio
car comes shrieking, but we won't budge. So the cops come
charging down the street blowing their whistles. People stop
to see what's going on and between the singing, whistles
going, horns blaring, and the racket of the crowd cheering us
on, there's quite a commotion.

Before I know what's happening, this big beefy cop yells at
me, 'Get up! What's a kid like you doing here? G'wan home!'

Angie, lying next to me, pokes me: Don't answer,
whatever you do. We'd decided that in advance, that way
they couldn't accuse us of using foul language and throw us
in jail.

'Get up, you stupid broad, damn you, didn't you hear me!'
he's roaring, and I lie there like a store window dummy. As I
look up to the seventh floor, there's Loebel's white head at
the window looking down.

The cop bends over swinging his club at me, he grabs my
shoulder in an iron grip and hauls me up. 'You fucking Jew
Commies, why don't you go back where you belong! In
Germany they know how to treat your kind. Hitler's got the
right idea!'

My ears ring with anger and I swing at him with all my
might and catch the big fat slob right on the cheek. He's not
expecting it, and even I can feel the sharp pain go zinging up
my arm.

'Why you fucking bitch!' He's purple like a neon light and
strikes me again and again with his club on the head and
shoulders as I'm trying to cover my face with my hands, but
it's no use. The pain's pounding inside my whole body, but I
manage to twist out of his grip by grabbing his other hand in
my mouth and biting down hard. Before I can get away, he
kicks me and I hit the pavement hard. My hands are
bleeding, my face, too. My head's spinning in all colours, but

most of all, it's my back – it's throbbing so bad I can't stand it, and I can't get up. Tony runs over and lifts me up and half-carries me to the sidewalk and lays me down very carefully.

But I won't give that Nazi the satisfaction of seeing me cry.

At St Vincent's they tell me, 'Just a little sprain. Use a heating pad for a few days and rest.' 'Try hot showers,' says the young jerk of an intern. *Where do I find one, Doctor*, I want to ask him. *Not where I live on Sheriff Street.* Then they book me and three others on charges of disorderly conduct at the police station, which is already filled with other strikers held on these trumped-up charges. The local's lawyer puts up our bail – one thousand dollars for each of us – and the sergeant tells us we can leave. I can barely make it to the subway.

By the time I get home, it's after midnight, I haven't eaten yet and I'm half-dead with the pain. When I go into that stinking hall toilet, and stare in the patchy mirror, a stranger looks back at me. The girl who left home that morning isn't there any more. One sleeve is torn loose where the cop grabbed me, and I see beginning the same angry lines that are stamped around Celia's mouth.

Finally my eyes are open.

TWENTY-FOUR

SEPTEMBER 1935

At my suggestion, the next day we move to 37th Street and use the same tactics. Again, there's a big commotion, with truck drivers honking like crazy, lots of thugs and cops swarming all over the place, fights, arrests, the whole works. In fact, an emergency first aid station gets set up in the church and all day, strikers are coming in – or getting carried in – with all kinds of injuries.

During a break, Lobelia finds me and says, 'Hey, Ethel, I have to talk to you.'

'Sure,' I tell her. 'What's up?'

'Well, I found these in our hallway this morning,' and she pulls out a pair of handcuffs from her pocketbook.

'So?'

'So, I've got an idea I want to try out on you. How about handcuffing me to a lamppost – as a protest. It'll attract attention to our strike, even if the cops try to stop me. It'll take time for them to cut me loose. Meanwhile, I can get my two cents in.'

'Would you be willing to do that?' She continues to amaze me.

'Sure. Why not!' and she tosses me the key. 'Now chain me to the nearest lamppost.'

Naturally, as soon as she calls out good and loud, 'Don't scab – join the strike!' people start gathering and a crowd collects.

In front of me is this guy with baggy pants. Now I've never liked men with pants that droop. It's as though they feel they don't quite fit into them, a man's pants, I mean. And sure enough, before anyone can stop him, this guy darts out and viciously starts clobbering Lobelia with the butt of a revolver

125

he pulls from inside his jacket. All the while he's cursing her. 'You black bitch! This'll teach you to stay where you belong – down South picking cotton!'

'Help! Help!' Suddenly not a single cop's around. She's bleeding heavily from a deep gash on her forehead and her eyes are closed. I beg Murray to let me go to the hospital with her, but he insists I stick around.

'We need you here,' he says and sends Angie instead. I lean against the wall trying not to puke.

Every half-hour or so I'm calling the emergency room at St Vincent's. The only answer I get is this cold voice saying, 'The patient's condition is unchanged.' I can't help feeling that in some way, she got dragged into all this because of me, and I feel so badly, so responsible for what happened to her.

As I'm returning from my last try, Murray suggests I arrange for flying squadrons of women to spread out to the other streets. What I really want is to run someplace and hide. But I tell him, 'Listen, I've heard some are just flinging themselves in front of trucks, right and left. That's dangerous.'

'You're right,' he says, 'but it works.'

So I get busy and, fortunately, the women I recruit listen to me so we cut out all the crazy daredevil stuff. I could never go along with doing anything that's foolish and dangerous.

Things quiet down a little after that and around lunchtime, Murray gets hold of a soap box and speaks to the crowd that collects. Most look like garment workers, and it's touching to see the oldtimers listening thoughtfully, some still with the long beards and *yarmulkes*. 'Listen,' he says, 'let me tell you why we've been forced to go on strike and to tie up the garment industry this way. Because the bosses don't want to hear nothing about us, how we can't live on fourteen bucks a week and feed our families, and pay the rent, too. "It's not our business," they tell us. Because they don't want to hear about nothing but their own profits.

'These brave girls are risking their lives. If the bosses are

126

hellbent on breaking our strike and starving us out, well, we're even more determined that we're going to win!' Lots of cheers at this. 'And we need your help!

'Remember,' he winds up, 'what President Roosevelt said at his inauguration, "The only thing we have to fear is fear itself – nameless, unreasoning, unjustified terror which paralyses needed effort to convert retreat into advance."'

The crowd gives him a big hand, and when he steps down, someone from behind suddenly hoists me up, and there I am in front of maybe three, four hundred people. From the waist down, I'm jelly.

In all my life, I've never spoken at a large meeting like this one, only our shop. Still looking at their upturned faces, I tell myself, Celia and Murray, they believe in me, there's no turning back. Always I've been so afraid of finding myself out there in front, by myself, alone. Except on the stage. Playing a part. But that's different. Maybe that's what you have to do, though, I tell myself, break loose, take the lead and expect others to follow. Still I'm scared stiff. Murray nods encouragingly and says, 'Give it to them. Knock 'em dead!'

'I'm so angry,' I start out saying, 'about what they're pulling on us that if they put me in the lobby of that tall building right now,' and I point to the spire of the Empire State Building off there glittering in the sun, 'my anger would blow it up, like dynamite. Those dirty bastards!' I've never talked that way in my life before. 'Where do they get off, pushing us around this way and treating us like dirt under their feet!' The crowd's right in there with me yelling support. 'Do you know how many of our people have been hurt seriously – and arrested? All because we're asking for a living wage and decent working conditions, and a union to represent us? All because they want to go on living in fancy houses with carpets and gardens and servants and Cadillacs while we should work for nothing, not enough to put bread on the table? Is that fair, I ask you? Is that what America's about? That the rich should get richer and the poor poorer?

'Do you know that one of our strikers, Lobelia Huntington, suffered a serious concussion of the brain this morning? That this courageous working woman, who supports her family with three small kids and a husband out of work, is in the hospital right now *unconscious*? For what? Because she handcuffed herself to a lamppost and appealed for support for our strike! For our legitimate demands! For this terrible crime, a thug hired by the bosses beat her over the head with his revolver until she collapsed!' My eyes fill with tears, but I hold on. 'They think they can break our spirit this way. They've shown us they mean business. Dirty business! Well, we mean business, too.' And I stop, and wait, pacing myself now. I'm getting the hang of it. 'Something in me won't stand for this way of dealing with us any more. It's gone on too long already. And I know something in you, the same anger that charges me today like a battery, is not going to let them get away with it any more. I say, we have to fight them together. Our cause is just and right. With our combined strength and determination, we'll win.'

Boy, did the crowd cheer!

TWENTY-FIVE

JULY 1951

Finish up already about the strike, I tell myself – about Tony and Murray and Angie – and Lobelia – and all the others who stuck their necks out. And the lousy bosses and police, and the blood and violence, and worst of all, as it turned out, the unsuspected treachery.

Amazing how I haven't thought about it in years. It all happened before I met Julie. So you see, I've known it before ... betrayal ... David and Ruth ... they're not the first. Still, my own brother?

Maybe I want to stay right there – in that special moment with the sense of strength we all felt when we were united fighting together. That period of my life had such sweetness and innocence and excitement. Why not? So much happened. And so much more was promised – for the country and for me. And somehow, it was all tied in together. At twenty, what could be sweeter than the discovery for me – the most important, I suppose, for anyone – who Ethel Greenglass was, and what was going to be her real contribution in life?

For the first time, I discovered that what I had to say carried weight with other people – working people – not like at home. That I could speak to them in a way that they would listen – not only listen, but also hear me, and be stirred into action. That, somehow, my words expressed their experiences and feelings and hopes and fears, and better than they could say it for themselves; and then it was as though they knew what they had to do, too, for themselves.

From that time on, I didn't want to be an actress, or even a singer, except when it would help the workers. That was only acting a part written by another, or singing someone else's song. I wanted to be a union leader.

And what did I learn subsequently? Which I wish I didn't have to learn? Maybe a little scepticism. More about people than I wish to know or believe, but it's the kind of basic, vital information I can't brush aside any more when I'm here on Death Row. Like why isn't the Party doing more for us? And why did Judge Kaufman hand down the death sentence? The first time in our nation's history in peacetime! What's in it for him? Court of Appeals? Supreme Court? And Saypol and Cohn and Brownell — what's their price? And the man with the bulldog face, J. Edgar Hoover himself?

1935

What happened with the strike? I'll make it short. Sure, the strike got settled and we returned to work. But a lot happened before that.

First, Lobelia. 'It's all right, Ethel, it's all right,' she keeps saying when I visit her at Bellevue. 'Why do you keep saying it's all your fault? Ah'm the one who comes up with the handcuff business. So why do you have to take all the credit?' She glares at me.

'I know, I know,' I start to say, then look at her bandaged head and choke up.

Three months in and out of the hospital, with infections and double vision, not to mention the constant headaches. She and her family have to go on relief for a while, the union sends them a small weekly cheque. Finally they move so many times, I lose touch. I've often wondered what's happened to her.

And something else happens while the strike is in its second week. Murray invites a few of us, along with Celia, to meet at Ratner's, this great dairy restaurant on Delancey Street. 'C'mon, it's on me!' Anyhow, the six of us are sitting towards the back having our first good meal in weeks and kidding around when guess who should walk in? Kantrowitz and Robert! Together! Kantrowitz says something to the waiter who takes them to a table that's out of the way. I poke

Murray because he's got his back to them. 'In a few minutes, turn around and look over to your right.'

'Goddamit! I figured that bastard for a fink,' he says turning back, 'I just wasn't sure.' And he starts that jabbing motion with his fork. The others catch on, and one by one, take a good look over there.

When we get up to leave, Murray says with a grin, 'Let's be sure to stop and say hello to our friends.' Both rats shrivel in their seats as we come by and give 'em a big hello.

'Fancy meeting you here,' says Murray whacking Robert across the back so hard that you can hear it across the room, and we walk out laughing.

After that, no one sees Robert around any more, though there are all sorts of stories circulating; the one most repeated – maybe because it's so satisfying – is that a week later he landed in Bellevue after getting beat up in a dark alley someplace.

Of course what finally brings an end to the strike is that the big customers are making noises about switching to manufacturers in other cities. It says so in the *New York Times*.

So after a lot more haggling and two weeks of picketing and violence and arrests with no paycheques coming in for us, a settlement is reached. Big deal! We end up going back to work for fifteen bucks a week – for a forty-four hour week! And at National, there's no union recognition because Loebel holds out. That's the bone that sticks in our throats. We know it means trouble ahead. And that's exactly what happens. Because management is determined to break our union and starts right in to set up a company union.

On October 11, only four weeks after the strike is settled, I'm fired.

There's spittle on Kantrowitz's lips the whole time he's screaming at me, 'Fannie tells me you ... ' His mouth's spinning it out like a silkworm. Silk he isn't, but a worm – yes!

'Why, what have I done? Tell me!' I'm trying to get a word in edgewise while Kantrowitz's screaming bloody murder.

'Get your things – all of you – and get out!' Nine of us, fired like that, on the spot. No warnings, no explanation, nothing.

'Tell me! Why pick on us? The whole shop stopped work yesterday when Carl fired Goldblatt. It was clear he was only trying to provoke Goldblatt just so he could fire him. It's so unfair, Mr Kantrowitz,' I say. 'Jack's been here longer than anyone else, and he and Carl have always gotten along great until he joins the union. Then suddenly Carl's picking on him all the time, nothing he does is right. And you know as well as I do that Fannie assured us yesterday that if we went back to work and finished up, you'd discuss the whole matter with us in the morning. So that's what we did. *We had her word*. She must've talked to you about it first. So what happens instead? You come in here this morning and the first words out of your mouth? "You're fired! You, you, and you!" Just like that. Why? What'd she tell you? And why did she give us your promise if you didn't intend to keep it? And she knew that, too, didn't she? *Why did she do it then?* That's what I don't understand. Why are you both pulling this on us?' I still can't believe it!

He's sputtering and fuming and looking everywhere, but not at us, and Fannie's backing away as though she's trying to vanish into a corner. There's a frightened look on her face, and yet something else, more fleeting, complex – it puzzles me, and I put it aside for now. Funny, how it comes back to me again when I see it on Ruth Greenglass's face when she's up on the witness stand. That knife edge of pleasure? A glimpse of malice?

I'm standing there, still dazed and repeating mechanically, 'Why are you picking on me? Why us? Fannie *knows* I finished up my work before joining in the protest. So why me? Tell us!'

'I don't have to give you a reason! You! You!' Any minute he'll blow up like a steam engine. 'Get out of here! All of you.

Especially you, Ethel, a nice girl like you when you started out here – I gave you your first job – you know that as well as I do – and this is how you repay me? You should know better than to get sucked in by these troublemakers. *Paskyudnicks!* You think they have your best interests at heart? Wait, you'll find out different. They're only out to stir up trouble in the shop. Look what's happened already!' He's pacing up and down and his big fat behind's wagging with anger.

'And now you're making trouble for the other girls. I see what you're up to – don't think I don't, whispering and talking against us, behind my back – don't think I didn't see you talking to Lobelia, firing her up, too – a fine woman – her sister still comes every Friday to clean for us like clockwork and every time she cries about what's happened to her sister because she got mixed up with your kind. That's how you help the workers? That's your big contribution? Who talked you into joining? Which one are you sleeping with? Goldblatt? Tony?'

I'm watching the saliva from his lips drip slowly on to his shirt.

'Who? You should be ashamed of yourself – a nice Jewish girl like you!' And then he points to the old man, Ostritzer, an oldtime socialist, who's standing there with his once-powerful arms crossed against his barrel chest, his wise eyes so wrinkled and sad – he's the one who fled from the pogroms. 'That one?' he points.

That's when I leave.

I'll never forget the look on Fannie's face as I walk by her on my way out. Like a broken doll. My best friend, I'm thinking, and all the time, you were on his side, playing informer.

That night when I come home after the shop meeting, Murray calls right away to discuss what to do next (we decide to file a suit with the National Labour Relations Board). I slump on the couch and turn on the radio. Our first, a Zenith table model. Sam bought it for Ma and Pa for their twenty-fifth anniversary last January. Gabriel Heatter's on with the news. I don't know what I'm hearing or thinking – just this whirring sound inside my head like a helicopter propeller going. I remember once going to Floyd Bennett Airport with Julie, watching one land, and thinking how I wouldn't like to be the pilot listening to that racket.

Ma says something to me, maybe, 'Did you eat yet?' I nod. Who remembers?

Celia calls the next day. Fannie feels very badly about the whole business, she says. What she did was to come home and get into bed, just went to her room and stayed there.

'How could you do it?' Celia asks her later.

Fannie turns her face to the wall. Celia can hardly hear her. 'He loves me. He's good to me. I'm not like you or Ethel ... strong.'

'How long have you been carrying on with him?' Celia insists on knowing.

'Four years.' She pulls the covers over her head.

'Get out!' Celia grabs the covers off her and throws them on the floor.

'I could've hit her right then and there,' she tells me, 'but I managed to say, "This is my apartment – I found it and I pay two-thirds of the rent and you'd better find another place to live damn quick. I want you out, y'hear me!"'

'Where'll I go?' She's crying like a lost kid at Coney Island.

'Why don't you go live with your lover, Mr Big Shot? If he's so important to you, more important than anyone or anything else!'

'I can't. He won't leave his wife.'

'Oho, so that's how it is. Then that's your problem, not mine. Just get yourself the hell out of here – and stay away from me. And the quicker the better!' Celia repeats all this to me and we both feel the pain.

By the time the NLRB comes up with a decision nine months later – in June 1936 – ordering all of us reinstated with retroactive back pay, I've finally landed another job after months of looking. Without references, it's not easy. All this time when I'm out of work, 'You shoulda listened to me!' becomes like a broken record around the house.

The figures they give in their decision are accurate. During the whole time, I earned all of twenty-four dollars in six months! Which also includes winning twenty bucks at Amateur Nights.

Murray shows me the decision – and I get a big kick out of going to the 42nd Street Public Library to read it for myself. Volume one, Page 1,009. Sure enough, there's my name in black and white.

The NLRB also rules that Loebel was out to break the union, and was prepared to replace it with an inside organization. So we're completely vindicated. Much good it does because by then those of us fired have found jobs elsewhere, and the whole spirit in the shop is broken. I never want to go back there – or see her face again.

Frieda gets married that June – a big wedding, the works. Flowers, a band playing *kazatzkis*, *kishke*, wine, lots of little kids running around, and she looks happy in her bridal gown. Nice guy, someone in her class at night school, CCNY downtown, and I go to the ceremony although I'm a little hurt she didn't ask me to be a bridesmaid. And I have to admit I envy her. Such an easy way out. Sure, she'll keep on working for a while. But then she plans to stop and have kids and stay home and take care of them. And that's what it's going to be like for her.

And suddenly I've had it! Enough with the struggling to become Someone. Why am I kidding myself – first an actress, then a singer, and now a union leader! It doesn't seem so important any more. What am I supposed to do with myself on Saturday nights when my girlfriends go out with their steady boyfriends? Occasionally this big important union leader plays a benefit or goes to a union dance or a movie with a girlfriend who isn't dating at the moment. But so far, I'm twenty-one and no one has even asked for my telephone number! Maybe Ma's right, after all. 'Find yourself a nice fella and get married,' she keeps telling me, and gives me all the neighbourhood statistics. Such news doesn't exactly gladden my heart.

I just don't know. And even though Celia seems the same, maybe just a little sadder, and Murray, too, he's doing okay working for the ILGWU – and also the others from the shop – somehow I can't accept any of them as unconditionally as before. How do I *know*? Maybe they, too, have their own reasons for being friends with me. And also I don't want to end up like either Fannie or Celia – either betraying a cause because I'm desperate for a man, or living alone in an apartment and just working for the cause. Celia, Fannie once confided in me, had lovers; younger guys who came into the movement always gravitated to her, but they came and went, and nobody stuck around for very long. 'I think she intimidates them,' Fannie added thoughtfully.

Altogether I'm very mixed up. I can no longer tell who's who and what's what. And what's right for me.

And yet even now in this stinking cage with the roaches acting like it's their property, I still flush with excitement remembering how satisfying it was to fight back ... and the beautiful strength of my anger put to use.

TWENTY-SIX

JULY 1951

Even in prison, it's possible to be happy. It surprises me that I can feel this way, but today, it's true. Today is Friday, our day to see each other, Julie and me, and each time they bring him in, my heart jumps. Even with a wire screen and bars between us as he sits outside my cell, his lips and eyes and voice keep telling me, I love you, and that means everything to me, because I have to live on that ration, our one hour together, for a whole week. And towards the end of the week – on Wednesdays and Thursdays, Dark Wednesday and Black Thursday, that's how I've come to think of them – my supply starts running out and my spirits drop precipitously. Drained, empty, shrivelled ... that's me, but just saying those words affects my happy mood today, so I'll stop.

Instead I'm listening. In my head, I'm hearing the song I heard this morning during my walk outside in the 'courtyard'. I couldn't see the bird, there are no trees, only the bare concrete that separates the Death House from the high wired fence, so where it perches or how, I don't know. But I heard five notes, repeated at frequent intervals like this ... duh ... dah dah dah dah ... and now I'm trying to figure it out. Is it C FFFF or C GGGG. Suddenly it's become important to know this one simple fact – F or G. But I have no piano to try them out on, no bird book to consult – so the notes keep sounding in my head, duh ... dah dah dah dah keeping me company with a cheerful refrain.

This morning I was wrestling with fear again while taking this walk. Inside, though you'd never know it, I'm quivering like a coward, a jelly mould in the shape of a woman. There are so many insurmountable obstacles to our freedom. They keep growing in my head until I feel like they'll burst right through my thick skull.

And then I hear that mysterious bird sing out 'duh ... dah dah dah dah', reminding me to have hope. That's what I really live on – hope and our love for each other and our children. And my shoulders relax and I take a deep breath and go on walking. Maybe that *is* the answer, keep walking – and now I'm happy and getting ready to see Julie. I won't have to force a smile, it's there on my lips.

1936–7

I remember writing in my diary on New Year's Eve, 1936: 'Something wonderful happened to me tonight. I don't understand it yet, or what it all means, all I know is that something wonderful – and important in my life – happened tonight.' Then I turned out the light and fell asleep and in the dream I'm wearing that beautiful white dress with the veil from the bride's role with the Clark Players – and this old hag of a woman tries to rip it off me, and I run away.

It's a rotten night to be going out – wet snow on top of leftover slush, and I've got a cold hanging on that's kept me out of work for two days and I'm still coughing so it catches deep in my chest. Ma's at the kitchen table with her coffee as usual, and she says, 'Tonight you're not going anywhere, New Year's Eve or not, forget it! Pneumonia you need? Tonight you stay home!'

'Ma!' I'm twenty-one and she still treats me like a baby. 'They're expecting me. I'm supposed to sing at this big benefit for the NMU tonight. They're counting on me, it's a dance for their strike fund.'

'How much they payin' you?' right away she asks.

'That's not the point, it's not for money, I'm doing it because I believe in what they're for – better conditions for the maritime workers.'

'Tonight you stay home,' she orders and stands guard by the door. There are these little black hairs growing out from

138

her chin, and I want to pluck them out with a tweezer. Instead I go up to my room.

If I'm going, I should leave in five minutes – it's now 7.15. Outside the snow's piling up and people are sloshing along hunched and miserable as though the snow's creeping inside their collars. And me – I'm on the edge of the bed biting my nails and tense as a cat. Why? Because I'm letting them down – it feels like the whole union movement is counting on me and I'm letting them down.

At 7.50 I can't stand it any more. Ma's gone upstairs to *schmooze* with Mrs Eisenstadt. From a hook on the door, I grab my old red dress from Loew's Amateur Nights, now a little tighter, slap on some make-up, mascara, rouge, lipstick, dab on perfume – Houbigant's from Woolworth's in a tiny bottle that says 'Paris' – cover my head with a shawl and sneak out.

By the time I get to the union hall, my head's wet with snow, and Benny, the MC, is sore as hell with me. 'You're late!' First words out of his mouth. For this I knock myself out? 'You go on in ten minutes. Give Louie, the leader, your music.'

Music? Oh my God! I forgot. Can you believe it?

'Is Schamie around?' Usually he can fake it.

'Who?'

'Schamie – the pianist. He knows my songs and he promised he'd come.'

'Well, no one by that name's been around,' he snorts, tapping his foot. '*Nu?* Yes or no?'

I look around. So far only a small crowd dancing self-consciously, the way couples do when there are only a few out there – you know, the fancy steps, in and out, with the big circles and dips and twirls. In the soft rosy light, as the vocalist moans, 'Blue Moon, you saw me standing alone,' the girls all look pretty gazing into the guys' eyes, and I feel washed out. At the back, more people are buying tickets at the door, and a couple of big hefty guys are moving around to keep order. The crowd's not the same as you'd see at one of our local's dances – they're much bigger and tougher looking.

'Benny?' I ask him. 'Let me go on a little later – around ten. Maybe more people? Besides I need time to warm up ... my throat's tight.'

'Can't do!' he snaps, picking at a pimple on his chin. 'We have others – big names – showing up later.'

I want to laugh or something, the whole thing's ludicrous, me pleading with him and this guy picking at his pimples.

'Maybe even Zero Mostel,' he lets drop, kinda snotty. 'He said he'd try, if he can get away from his club date.'

Ziggy? That really throws me. I'd like to see him – and yet five years have made such a big difference in our lives. He's getting to be a name in small clubs around the Village, also the Borscht Belt. Silly, but I still buy *Variety* just for kicks, and even Walter Winchell mentioned him recently in his column.

And me? I'm still a shipping clerk. Still living at home. Do I really want to see him?

Do I really want to see him? Good question. I don't know. All I do know is that my heart's beating double time and I want to stay and go at the same time.

'Okay, okay, I'll go on in ten minutes.' I might as well get it over with. So, after Benny gives me the usual, 'Let's give this little girl a big hand!' and a few sympathetic souls pitch in, I do my spot – a medley of songs starting out with, 'Love, your magic spell is everywhere. Love, I knew you well and found you fair.' What do I know about love? Again, I have this wild desire to laugh. What I *do* know is, my voice's scratchy, the back-up from the band is lousy, and I want out. The crowd applauds politely. Boy, that's the kiss of death, every performer can recognize it, when the crowd is just being nice because they feel sorry for you.

I stumble off and run towards the Ladies' Room. I'm standing right outside it, facing the door, not knowing what

140

to do with myself. If I go inside, they'll see me cry, and right away, want to know what it's all about – you know how girls are? – and I don't want to talk or explain, just cry! Just cry because I'm so damn tired of always being so brave. Nothing, but nothing's gone right. Damn that Schamie! He promised me! This is the second time he's pulled something like this on me, not showing up, and it's the last time. Damn it! I'm entitled to cry if I want to! I just don't want anyone to see me.

Anyhow, someone taps me from behind. 'You have a very sweet voice,' he says, and tells me how much he enjoyed my singing. When I look around, he turns out to be rather nice, slim and dark, boyish, with curly hair, on the tall side, wearing glasses, with his head leading the rest of him, the way it is sometimes with nearsighted people. But nice. And that's when I really start to bawl. In front of a stranger? I can't believe it myself.

'What's the matter?' he keeps asking me, stooping down a little, and I, like a fool, only cry harder. 'Did I say something wrong?' Later on, he tells me he wasn't too surprised because he has three sisters and they do things like that all the time.

He's got a gentle manner and a moustache. I suspect he wants to look older. His name's Julie – Julius Rosenberg – and he goes to City College uptown, a subway trip he hates, he says, because he gets nauseated every time. Same thing in cars. Also, dark eyes, not romantic with long lashes like Robert Taylor, but soft and gentle like Henry Fonda's.

By this time we're sitting near the back of the hall talking away and it's amazing how we agree on so many things right away. Like working for a better world. He tells me about Tom Mooney and the Scottsboro boys and that's how he became interested in politics. I hadn't really paid much attention before to all this, too tied up with what's going on in my own shop. His shoulder's close to mine, almost touching.

And when we get up to dance, I leave my bag there on the chairs so we can return. He's not a good dancer, probably too shy, and he moves stiffly, self-consciously doing the box steps like he probably only practised at home with his sisters, concentrating on taking big square steps while holding me loosely. Also, you can see him counting in his head, one, two, three, four, hesitating a beat each time. I love to dance and I feel the rhythm inside but I'm holding back, fitting my own steps to his.

The next one's a fast Lindy Hop, something from Harry James. 'Too fast for me, this one,' he smiles. 'Let's sit it out.'

By now, it's almost eleven and though the crowd's bigger, some are leaving because it's become a real storm out there. But by now, I simply don't care, it's so nice to be here with Julie. The band goes into a loud ba-rumph, and the spotlights jump around. Benny outdoes himself with the introduction and suddenly there's Ziggy. He skips on, just like always, and gets a big hand. He's smiling and bowing, and the crowd loves him right away. A real pro.

The same old Ziggy – fat and clowning and funny as hell – and a wash of relief passes over me. The sweetness is still there. His jokes are topical, a lot political – kidding Roosevelt and Eleanor and the New Deal, Alf Landon and the capitalists – and he moves back and forth across the stage with a restless energy that radiates from that big body of his which is so surprisingly graceful. And those lips that laugh with you and those small sharp eyes that take it all in and just laugh back at the world like a good friend. He was such a help to all of us in that senior play! Always a high-class performer. And he still is, only a lot more polished and sure of himself.

Lots of applause and whistles and feet stamping and people crowding around him shaking hands, eager for his attention. Both of us agree he's the greatest! I don't mention that I know him from high school, because, after all, I figure a celebrity like Ziggy wouldn't want to be bothered by a kid he knew way back in school. He'd be polite, sure, but it might be embarrassing, too, if he doesn't remember my name or something.

When the band swings into 'Auld Lang Syne' at midnight,

shyly Julie kisses me on the cheek and my heart speeds up. He asks to take me home and it turns out that we're practically neighbours, only a few blocks apart, and that he went to Seward Park, too, and graduated a couple of years after me. I'm a little embarrassed to discover he's younger than me – about two and a half years? – but it doesn't seem to bother him a bit.

When we get to my house, it's impossible to stand and talk with the snow blowing hard, though we both want to. As though we understand each other right away. I've never felt that way before with any other fellow.

So reluctantly we say goodnight and he holds my hand a minute.

'I'm so excited,' I scribble in my diary. 'He said he'd call me and maybe we can go to a movie, though he said he had to tell me right away that he has no money because he's a student and not working.'

'It's okay,' I told him, 'I always go out Dutch treat, and I'm working – finally.' So I tell him about our strike and the NLRB. He's very interested because he's taking a course in Labour Relations as part of the requirement for becoming an electrical engineer. Not that he expects to go into management – never! – quite the opposite, but still it's required.

What an exciting night! I wrote.

A couple of weeks later, I recorded: 'I find myself thinking about him so much – and he tells me the same thing, that since we've met, that's all he can think about, too. He'll be sitting in the library trying to do a math problem and suddenly, he's drawing a picture of me – or writing me a note. Sometimes I receive three letters from him in one day!'

Two days after we meet, I receive a letter from him, a love letter, my first ever, telling me what I already knew. 'We're meant for each other, that much I know. Your Julie.'

From the first day I brought Julie home, I knew it was no go. Not with my mother. My father – he'd accept. He had too many other things to worry about, besides, what difference did it make? I'd get married – and he'd have grandchildren. What else mattered? My father really loved me, and he wanted for me whatever I wanted for myself. But not my mother. She recognized in Julie a vein of steel beneath that quiet sweet manner. Long before I did. And that streak's not for her.

In no time at all, in spite of Mama's attitude, we're a couple. We do everything together, except when he goes to college and I go to work. Life opens up for me with Julie. Political meetings, demonstrations. Other things, too. There are lots of things to do in New York with a fellow that you just don't do with a girlfriend. That summer of 1937 – there's music in Lewisohn Stadium on hot summer nights, sitting on stone benches drinking Cokes and hearing Beethoven or Brahms or Mozart ... with Julie I'm discovering classical music. Then suddenly there's an aeroplane directly overhead, always at 9.15, drowning out the music. Then just as suddenly it's gone and the ecstasy we're sharing is restored. Life will be this way, too, I'm thinking, interruptions, yes, but then back to normal, and 'normal' to me meant happiness full time. Someday. Isn't that what you believe when you're young?

Julie's always telling me how wonderful I am, in every way, how much he looks forward to being with me, how everything I do – and how I do it, with such forethought and planning – pleases him. Like a hummingbird, he says to me one day as we're watching one in the birdhouse at the Bronx Zoo. He's never known a girl like me – so bright and pretty and talented on top of being a warm and loving person who's also socially conscious. We both agree that's very important.

Well, it's almost too embarrassing ... But I love it, especially since he's the first one. And maybe he's not so experienced with girls either?

And I think he's great, too. I love everything about him. Take his hands. They're large and square with long tapering fingers, and when he works with anything mechanical, they're very competent and graceful. He gets into the habit of going in to visit my father in his shop, and more and more, gives him a hand. I can see that Pa really appreciates this, especially since none of my brothers will pitch in at all. What the two of them talk about I don't know, because whenever I walk in it's quiet, and they're busy with some piece of equipment, but it's a restful quiet.

In the kitchen, it's very different. Usually Ma ignores him, and he's aware of it, but he's so good-natured, he never says a thing to me about it and he's always polite. She'll wait till the last minute before inviting him for dinner. 'Oh, you're still here?' she says. 'So you might as well eat with us.' Usually he refuses this gracious invitation, but once in a great while, he'll stay to please me. But he always returns after dinner, and I'll type up a term paper or some report he has to hand in while he's studying. We go up to my room where my typewriter is, but I always make sure to leave the door wide open. That way, Ma keeps quiet.

The only thing about him I don't care for – is he wears white socks. He explains it to me that it's because he worries about picking up athlete's foot ever since he got it once in the college pool. And on these little things, he's a stickler. Easy going as he is, when he gets stubborn, you can't budge him.

TWENTY-SEVEN

AUGUST 1951

Today the children are coming. With Manny. My hands are shaking. In fifteen minutes ... Will I see it in their faces, that I've changed, that I'm not like their Mommy any more? If only I had a scarf, something pretty ... I haven't seen them in a year. Twelve months. Not since that day last August when I left home to testify before the Grand Jury. And never came home again. I was so frightened ... Julie was already in jail ... and yet so unprepared for what happened ... I never even made arrangements for the kids. The day before? – we're riding up in the elevator together? – I ask my next-door neighbour's daughter, a kid of fifteen whose mind is obviously elsewhere, to babysit with them until I get home. 'For how long?' she wants to know, and right away adds, 'I'll have to ask Mom.' Everyone in the building knows about us.

'It shouldn't take too long,' I tell her. 'I'll be back, maybe three, four o'clock – dinnertime at the latest.' Fortunately, Ida, her mother, is still one of the three people in Knickerbocker Village who say hello to me, so later, the kid knocks and says, okay.

My lips suck up the bright red lipstick Julie's sister, Lena, brought me on Saturday. And the children are now with his mother. What a relief! But it's so ironic. Julie's family, they're like my own to me, and mine is like the enemy!

'Raise the mirror just a little, Molly?' (She's the nice one, on the daytime shift.) 'Thanks, that's much better.'

Today she brought me some chocolate chip cookies she baked. It feels good to exchange a smile with another human being. There's this new habit I've developed, a nasty one, wetting my upper lip repeatedly with the tip of my tongue. But it's because I feel so dried out, inside and out – no kisses, no man's hand caressing the back of my neck. Nothing. Some days it feels as though I'm neuter gender, as though I've never been a woman ... a woman in bed with a man, a woman with a full rounded stomach and a baby that thrashed around inside sometimes with the whisper of a butterfly. Some days I'm just an empty vessel, fragile, afraid of being tipped over and never righted again.

My hair – how I always hated its bushiness. I wish they'd let me have some bobby pins, it would help, especially with that haircut the prison barber gave me. Barber? More like a butcher! When Julie put his hand on it the first time I wanted to say to him, 'Never mind, I'm not like that at all, you know, inside I'm fine and silky and smooth' ... That's when he told me I felt like a rose petal.

The first thing Michael says when I'm brought into the Visitors' Room: 'Mommy, you look smaller.'

'And you look bigger, both of you. Just look at you!' I have lots of things prepared to say, but all I want to do is hold them close. That's all. Feel their bodies safely within my arms, their ribs so tender against my breasts, and console the neediness in their eyes. Yet I don't want to swoop down on them. Michael's trying so hard to be a 'big boy', and the little one's watching him for his cues. So I stop myself and say the first thing that comes into my head, 'Hey Michael, that's a great baseball cap you're wearing. Since when've you become a Dodgers fan?'

'Manny bought them for us last Sunday, but Robby lost his someplace.'

'I did not,' says Robby and his pale-pink lips pucker and the tears well up in his big brown eyes. Michael loves him so, and yet, there's still the other side of him, the competition. Maybe when they're away from me, only the protective side comes out.

'Come and see what I have for you,' and I spread out my 'collection' on the table. For months now, on my daily walk

147

outside, I've been collecting insects – flies, mosquitoes, ants, caterpillars, centipedes, a bumblebee that died on its back, two monarch butterflies (Molly looked it up for me, she has an encyclopaedia at home), and several I've captured right in my cell. Julie kids about it, how he headhunts every night, a 'regular massacre of roaches,' he writes to me. But I don't see it as funny. My fear is that I'll find them crawling on my pillow at night, or that one might crawl into my mouth while I'm sleeping. Maybe that's why I sleep restlessly? I've killed a few, and here they are, preserved for my sons. 'Someday,' I promise them, 'we'll have to go to the Museum of Natural History and see if they have a collection as good as mine.'

Intently they're examining the bugs, and I'm eating my boys up with my eyes – *new haircuts* ... and *their ears stick out big and naked* ... *Michael's teeth are coming in fine* ... *I used to worry that his thumb-sucking would affect them* ... *they're white and straight, though* ... *but Robby's not brushing* ... *must remind Julie's mother* ... I'm making mental notes for Manny ... *they must have play materials so they'll play quietly in the morning and not awaken Sophie* ... *she's been complaining* ... *buy Plasticene, cookie cutters, magic slate, new crayons and plenty of paper, rubber cars* ... *let's see* ... *a few simple jigsaw puzzles from Playschool for Robby* ... *use the little money left over from selling off the shop* ...

When they're through examining the bugs, Michael seats himself in a chair between Manny and me, slaps his thighs as though to say, let's get down to business, and asks me in a matter-of-fact tone, 'Ethel, how are you going to die?'

'Wait a second, Michael, who says we're going to die?'

'Grandma Tessie.'

'What does she know? Nothing! Now you listen to me. We live in the United States of America and when people are unjustly convicted, there are legal protections guaranteed to them based on our Constitution and the Bill of Rights. Do you hear me? And I want you to know we're just beginning to fight. So don't you for a minute believe her! Right now, we're appealing to the Circuit Court of Appeals ... and that's only the first step.'

Michael's listening attentively, taking it all in, his eyes on my face unmoving, but the little one's getting restless and climbs into my lap. Molly, who's accompanied me this time, comes over with a lollipop for Robby.

'I don't wanna red one,' sulks the poor kid. What other choices does he have in his life right now? 'Ain't you gotta green one?' She digs into her pocket for a green one and he's busy with it for the next few minutes. When she offers Michael one, he shakes his head impatiently and resumes questioning me.

'But suppose, Ethel, just suppose, they won't change their decision?'

'Look, Michael, Daddy and I both believe that if it ever gets as far as the Supreme Court, they'll reverse the decision without a question.'

'But just suppose ... so then, how are you going to die?'

I've braced myself for this question for weeks and I manage to answer in the same matter-of-fact voice as his. 'The electric chair.' Knowing Michael as I do, I know he won't let me off the hook. He wants answers, that boy, and I have to give them to him. Secretly I hoped that maybe he'd wait until he saw Julie, but I also knew I'd be the one he'd ask.

'Is there an electric chair here?' he continues.

'Yes.'

Since this nightmare began, I've discovered one trait of mine that's been useful, that at moments like this, I'm suddenly very calm – like the eye of a storm. Only later, much later, am I overcome by the urgency of the pain and despair. For the moment I'm okay. My voice doesn't tremble, my eyes don't fill.

And neither do Michael's. I'm proud of him. Maybe I haven't botched it after all.

'Well,' he says, concluding the business part of the visit, 'I

149

want to tell you about the baseball game Manny took us to last Sunday ... ' and suddenly he's a child again, talking rapidly, excitedly about the game, how the Dodgers won in the ninth, and all the *chazerei* – hot dogs, soda, popcorn and ice-cream – Manny let them have.

'Didn't you feel sick afterwards, Michael?'

'Naw!' and he pulls on his baseball cap like he's just pitched a no hit innings and gets up from the chair. Standing, he's suddenly a little boy in pants a size too big for him doing his best because he's got a younger brother to look out for.

I'm not expecting the reaction so soon. Molly, who knows me well already, says, 'I'm afraid it's time ... '

As they're all getting ready to leave, Michael turns to me and with a stern look on his face, says, 'I still want you to kiss me goodnight and put me to bed, not Grandma Sophie.'

'Someday soon, Michael darling ... I live for that, too.' So young and trying so hard to be grown-up. That's what really breaks my heart. That he's forced to grow up so quickly, before his time. What will it do to him later on? And if I have to leave them?

I get down on my knees and hug him, and then the little one runs over and says, 'Me, too, Mommy, me, too.' So the three of us hug and kiss. Their delicious warmth and sweet children's smell makes me cry, though I've promised myself that I absolutely won't.

Michael reaches into the pocket of his jacket for a tissue and wipes my eyes. 'Don't cry, Ethel, it's going to be all right. I'm going to study and be a lawyer and get you and Daddy out of here.'

FEBRUARY 25, 1952

The convictions of Julius and Ethel Rosenberg are upheld by the United States Circuit Court of Appeals, Judge Jerome Frank writing the unanimous opinion.

TWENTY-EIGHT

FEBRUARY 1952

Manny brought me the news today. The United States Court of Appeals voted to uphold our conviction. Judges Swain, Chase and Frank voting.

However, he is optimistic. Given Judge Frank's tactfully stated reservation in writing the opinion – about the severity of the death sentence and that the evidence came almost entirely from accomplices – Manny believes the Supreme Court will agree to review our case. God, I hope so.

I want to go home.

There's no place to run to … Our apartment is vacated, empty … the children gone from there … and Julie's in here. Home is Sing Sing. I never thought of it that way before.

APRIL 1952

Today is my first anniversary in Sing Sing. April 11, 1952. No cards, no flowers. How come?

Guess I'll just have to wait for my birthday. September 28, I'll be thirty-seven. At least I know I'll be around that long because our Supreme Court appeal is still ahead. *You've got to believe*, I say to myself, *that they'll accept the case for review*. Nine men, and all our hopes rest with them.

What's it like to be in prison? Because by now I'm a veteran. Like most people, you ask not because you ever expect to be in there yourself, it's just idle curiosity, the same kind that buys tickets to the sideshows in Coney Island. Funny, I used to feel that way, too, that it was something that happened to other people, never me. Me in the same category with pickpockets and murderers? Or run over by a hit and run driver, bleeding to death on the street with a crowd and an ambulance and a picture spread across the front pages of the *Daily News*? That'll never be me, you think. Or take the Dreyfus case. Sacco–Vanzetti? To me those were courtroom dramas about heroic figures. Victims of political persecution. Even Jesus, I suppose. And their names have a heroic ring I never associate with myself or prison life and just plain doing time.

Suddenly I'm cast in that part myself. Big headlines. Handcuffs on Julie's wrists so that when he tries to put his arms around me, first he has to raise them in the air, then stiffly lower them to embrace me. How strange! Initially the shock makes everything seem unreal. Even when I'm hanging laundry on the steel bars at the back of my cell in those first days ... or hit a homer playing punchball at the House of Detention on the roof enclosed with chicken wire. Just like at Seward Park? It's still like I'm in a play. When I look out of the window in my cell, it's Greenwich Avenue, just another street in New York. Could be I'm looking out of my own apartment window, right? *Nothing's happened for real*, I can tell myself.

Because I still can't believe it! I'm in prison accused of typing up atomic information to be passed to the Russians? Using my beat-up Remington portable that I bought second-hand for twelve dollars from Evelyne March who worked next to me at National? I remember her name because it's scratched into the green metal case, and the *e* and *o* jump when you strike them, so the typing always looks sloppy. But I never got around to having it fixed. It's one of the few personal items I have here with me. And now when I'm typing Julie a letter, at the same address as mine, 354 Hunter Street, Ossining, NY, and he's only thirty yards away in the same building – ah, but there are steel plates and bars and concrete walls between us – I shake myself to remind me – it's for *real*, all right, this *is* our home, and not Knickerbocker

Village or Sheriff Street when he came to study while I typed his reports with the door open so Ma wouldn't think we're doing something dirty.

So the only way it's become real to me is gradually – by living the life of a prisoner hour by hour, day by day, cruel night by night. Seeing our children for the first time in a year *inside* the prison. Seeing Dr Singer for the first time in ten months *inside* the prison. Seeing Julie once a week for an hour when we've always been so close. Slowly I've begun to accept the *reality that I'm locked in* and everyone else in my life, except Julie, is out there *on the outside*. Only the two of us can truly understand what it's like to be in here all the time.

At first you react to the newness – the new situation, new place, new people – on a first come, first served basis – like Ethel, the entertainer, or the goodhearted soul concerned only about the others – when I have an audience. It's only after the newness wears off and I'm transferred here to Sing Sing, without Julie even for the first five weeks, that the truth, the long unending irrefutable unbudgeable truth of this hideous nightmare I'm in, comes home to me. It hits me finally – only because it's continuously being driven home to me by the deadly unvarying monotony of the daily life in prison – eating in my cell, defecating in my cell, masturbating in my cell, typing, reading, pacing, talking to myself, talking to the walls – always with two empty cells alongside. *I'm all alone.* The unconscious fear I've lived with since birth, Dr Singer says. Worthless. Abandoned. My golden chariot and the bright rainbow have vanished, and search as I may, I can't find them anywhere, only the small patch of sky through the small high window that approximates the time of day and the weather.

If I had an appointment book – busy lady that I am – I'd block in my appointments weekly in advance. In order of importance, I'd pencil in:

On Wednesdays (it used to be Fridays) – 1–2 p.m. – Julie. The highlight of my week.

On Saturdays – 1–2 p.m. – Dr Singer. Sometimes he runs into traffic and he's late so we have only thirty minutes instead of a fifty-minute hour, still I always enter it as from 1–2 p.m.

On Thursdays – Manny comes, but the time of his visit varies from week to week, so I mark a big question mark on the page and spend the day waiting. And when he finally arrives, sometimes late afternoon, with a million reasons why he's late, and they're all valid, he brings enough problems in his attaché case to occupy my thoughts for the rest of the week, and more. Usually they involve the children (along with the legal roadblocks we're facing) and our frustrated attempts to provide them with a decent loving home and the attention they need to survive and grow up like other children whose parents don't sit in the Death House. Fat chance!

Fridays – I leave open because that's the day I write to Julie, after Manny's visit – to prepare him for the things we have to talk about when we see each other on Wednesday. So much I can't put into the letter because everything we write and say to each other is read or monitored, and there's always a matron around when we visit. So I struggle with myself, *what should I mention, what should I keep to myself?* Lately, more and more, I keep things to myself, personal thoughts I don't even want to share with Julie any more. That's new for me. Some hostile thoughts even. That's natural, Dr Singer says, for everyone. For me? With Julie? Never before. At times, I find myself getting so angry with him – and I don't know why.

And the children, of course, when Manny finds the time to bring them. What joy to see them! They bring life in with them, and as they kiss me I fondle them – my fingers are so hungry – the very fragrance of the outside on their breath overcomes the smell of death in here embedded in the mouldy dankness of the rough stone walls. And only they, they alone in their beauty can banish it.

'Look Mom, I can stand on my head.' This, Michael shows me on the threadbare rug in the counsel room. Robby tries it, too, and flops laughing and I, with delight, laugh with them.

And then, occasionally, the unexpected visitors. Julie's sister, or my brother, Bernie. Sam never. Also Ma never comes. On that I can count. She came only once to deliver her ultimatum: '*Tell them, tell them anything, but get yourself out of here.*' She had spoken her piece. What other reason then to come back?

To tell me she's sorry that such a terrible thing has happened to Julie and me?

To hold my hand and pat my shoulder and offer me a tissue when I cry?

To listen to me as I talk my heart out to her?

To hold me in her arms and let me bury my head on her breast and say, 'It's okay, Etteleh, my darling one, it's okay – I'm praying everything will turn out all right'? Even when she has her own doubts and I have mine. But maybe that's what I need to hear from her. Then I'd know she really cares, and then, only then, could we share those doubts.

To promise me that she'll help out, look after the boys, too, share it with Sophie, give them comfort and love, since they can't have ours right now. Cuddle Robby for me – he needs it so badly – and take Michael, the Big One (how hard it must be for him!), to the zoo, buy him an ice-cream cone, a Coke and a hot dog and listen as he pours out what happened in school today, share his excitement that the earth revolves around the sun, that there are other planets like the earth up there – 'Can you imagine that, Ma?' – and his eyes shine with the wonder of it so listening you feel that child's excitement again, that there's a bigger world out there with oxcarts and rickshaws and planes that fly faster than sound – and people dying of tsetse fly bites in Africa, and Aborigines in Australia, and gold mining in South Africa. I recall my acronym in fourth grade for remembering the important facts about that country:

go-ld in *Jo*-hannesburg, *di*-amonds in *Ki*-mberly.

What acronyms will Michael invent to remember all he has to learn for himself with no mother or father at his side?

Like: *Don't Trust Anyone – not even your own family.* DTA – sounds like a government agency, the SEC or the NLRB – or the FBI. Some joke!

In my mother's milk as I sucked at her breast already there was a bitter taste, and that bitterness floods my heart as I sit here crying.

TWENTY-NINE

MAY 1952

Julie keeps telling me how brave I am – in his letters, when we see each other too briefly on Wednesdays – what a source of strength I am for him, for all of us, and each time he says it, I feel myself being sapped, drained; how I wish he wouldn't say it to me. How can I tell him how frightened I am, how rapidly my heart beats every time I open the door to that chamber and the bats fly out with an eerie whistle, their black wings brushing my face. How tightly I've tried to lock that door and yet how quickly it springs open. Little things – a date on today's newspaper, May 14, 1952, stabs me – a year from now maybe I won't be here to read it, or a letter from Michael with a crayon drawing of 'My Family' – Robby so small and hanging on to his big brother's hand, Julie and I way off to the other side. How sad and different from the one he did two years ago in kindergarten when we all stood together, our hands on the boys' shoulders.

Who will be there for him next year to enjoy and encourage him? I don't know – and the dam in me overflows with the tears I can't let Julie or anyone else see, even the rabbi, a pleasant man, but guarded, never reaching out like Manny, or like Dr Singer. And yet when this mood seizes me, I say over and over again to myself, Trust yourself and your own definition of *brave*. *That to be brave is to allow yourself to hope*. This I must believe or life becomes bleakly impossible.

I need you, Julie, oh, how I need you – to lean on, and yet I've never dared say that to you. Right from the start, I was the one you turned to, and now I lack the courage to tell you the truth. *You are stronger than I* – you believe with an unshakeable ardour, and I don't, at least not in the same way. I question, I question, over and over again, *why am I here, why have I chosen this path? How will I stick it out?* This far I have come, and I must admit to myself that this far, I *have* made a choice – I will not join Dovey and 'confess' to save my life – and yet I continue to struggle with these questions, and until I know the answers for myself – are there any? – I cannot sustain anyone else with my courage. Not only does it waver and tilt, but it's in short supply and I need every ounce of it for myself.

Julie, my darling, if only I dared send this letter, instead of the one I've just handed to the matron intended to bolster your spirits. Maybe it would be the beginning of truth between us.

1937

I can't help making comparisons the first time Julie takes me up to City College. Up there on 138th and Amsterdam. On a Thursday – it must've been the spring of 1937 – I call in sick so I can go to classes with him. I still want to see what college is really like. Also because there's a rally for the Spanish Loyalists afterwards.

A bunch of kids, I size them up as, what do they know? Some puny, with smooth pink cheeks like they haven't even started to shave. Where could they have learned what I've had to learn the hard way? For them, the answers are still in the books. And yet there's something in me, stubborn, that wants to know what they know.

Funny, all I remember about City now is how the entrance, it's littered with leaflets; all colours, pink, blue, yellow, white, like after a parade. Julie refuses several from different students as we enter the campus. 'Second International!' he mutters, shaking his head at the guy. 'Trotskyites, no way!' and brushes another guy's arm away.

'Why?' I ask him.

160

Again he shakes his head. 'I'll explain later.' But to a third guy who greets him like an old buddy, he says, 'Tomorrow I'll be here, Swifty,' and his leaflet he accepts.

During calculus and mechanical drawing I get restless, but then we go to Modern European History and that's exciting. History was always one of my favourite subjects, but here it's taught on a much higher level, not just dates and wars. The professor – he later got in trouble as a Communist during the Rapp–Coudert investigation of the City Colleges in 1941 when this small-time McCarthy committee makes waves – anyhow, he talks about Martin Luther and the Protestant Reformation and how closely the two were linked with the economic changes from a feudal to an industrial economy, and he mentions names like Max Weber and Thorstein Veblen, and Karl Marx, and it's the first time I realize that Marx is studied in universities and that when Celia and Murray mention his name and *Das Kapital*, he isn't just someone quoted by a Party official in the *Daily Worker*.

Afterwards we have lunch in the Alcove. That's how they all refer to it. It's an area shaped like a horseshoe, off the main lunchroom, kinda dark, with a table and benches, and the table's covered with literature – all kinds, pamphlets, leaflets, very political. Julie makes sure I understand that it's Alcove two, not one, because that's where all the Leftist dissenters collect. He says it scornfully – the Socialists, Trotskyites, and other names I never heard of, like Lovestonites. It's clear, though, that there's no love lost between these two Alcoves. Anyhow, two's where Julie's friends meet and they all get so excited arguing that, it seems to me, they're not doing much listening to each other.

'Does this go on every day?' I ask him.

'Oh sure, we always have so much to discuss and hammer out – what's our position on current issues. Right now, of course, it's to bring pressure to lift the embargo on Spain – and to work for a united front ... You really have to be sure of your facts with these guys ... many times I have to go and look something up. Otherwise, someone's sure to stop you cold. Some of the brightest guys in City are sitting right here. And being in engineering ... ' and he looks down at his hands a minute and then up at me, ' ... is sorta a drawback ... sometimes, I think I'd like to get into this, y'know political activity full-time.'

That takes me by surprise. However, this isn't the time to discuss it. So I ask him, 'Who's the big guy, quiet, with the thick moustache, sitting there listening and when he speaks, everyone stops and listens?'

'That's William.'

'So who's he?'

'He's the head of the YCL.'

'You elected him?' I'm thinking of our local.

'Not exactly. He's appointed from downtown.' He drops it, so I drop it.

Though I still look like a kid at twenty-one, inside I feel so much older than these boys. They're arguing about class war and exploitation by the bosses. Well, I'm living it, fellows, and I'd like to interrupt and tell you a few things. But I'm nobody here. They're polite all right, but after all, I'm only Julie's girl. Right? Because I work in a shop and I don't go to Hunter College? Because I haven't read all the right books? And I can't quote Lenin? To them, it's all theories and ideas, arguing about the smallest points of difference as though the earth itself would stop rotating on its axis if someone's interpretation's incorrect. So what! Myself, I can't get excited. Who's to say what's correct?

Finally I can't help myself and I mutter to Julie, 'You're all talking about revolution and the workers' uprisings like it's all going to happen here tomorrow, but you're not dealing with the workers like I am – seeing the practical considerations people have to weigh. "What's it going to mean in my paycheque?" "Will I lose my job?" That's all they really want to know.'

Julie's shushing me, 'All right, all right,' but I won't stop.

162

'You wanna know something?' My voice's getting louder, but I don't care any more. 'The people I work with? They don't give a damn about the uprising of the miners in Asturias or how much the workers in a tyre factory in Novgorod upped their production because they're so happy living in a Socialist state!'

'You don't know what the hell you're talking about!' interrupts this fat sloppy guy next to me in a vest with no jacket or tie. He stops licking his ice-cream cone long enough to announce in an accent like an English butler, 'The workers do understand and care!'

Everyone within fifty yards looks up.

'Listen,' I talk back, 'they'll talk, sure, lots, even say the right things – how they're for peace and things like that, but when it comes to the bottom line – signing up with the union or going out on strike, they only care about what it's going to mean to them in their next pay envelope. And if you can't deliver? Forget it!' And I slap my hand on the table like I'm at a union meeting.

'You're all wet!' He takes a few more licks like he can't leave the stuff alone, and goes on. The others are watching us. 'Besides, it's our job to educate them,' he says cocking a sophisticated eyebrow at me. Like William Powell, only on him it looks plain silly.

Big shot! His superior attitude infuriates me. Snot nose!

'If you think so, you come to Bell where I work and you talk to them about joining the Abraham Lincoln Brigade and see how far you get!'

'Oh yes?' he jabs.

'Yeah!' I snap back and feel much better.

Afterwards, Julie's annoyed with me. 'Why'd you get into an argument with Hughie?'

'What kind of a name is that, Hughie?'

'He's English, and really an authority on Marx and Engels. His grandfather once met Marx ... '

'So? Maybe his grandfather did, and maybe this jerk knows it all ... but he doesn't know beans about the workers in my shop. That's where I know the situation better 'n he.'

He's unhappy with me, that's for sure. Hughie has them all intimidated because he can quote chapter and verse, but to me that's not nearly as important as knowing how to work with people, to get them involved and committed to action. Going on strike is a hell of a lot different than participating in a campus rally, I once said to Julie – thinking of Lobelia and the price she paid.

'Stay close,' Julie says hanging on to my hand as we approach the Loyalist rally which is off to one side of the campus with signs and banners all around, 'I don't want to lose you.' He presses his arm against my shoulder as I look up at him.

'I don't want to lose you.' And we smile at each other in the way you do when you've turned your heart over to someone else and you know it's in good hands. There's always a light far back in his eyes – they're a warm greyish-green – that moves forward when he smiles at me. Just that makes me feel good again and I can't believe that I'm thinking the same thoughts that so many other girls have – Frieda, Blanche, girls at work – all words I found so ordinary, so mundane. This is the language of love? Even those songs on the radio – 'The Touch of Your Lips', 'I Only Have Eyes For You', 'The Way You Look Tonight', 'That Old Feeling'. That's how you sound when you're in love? Me, I used to think of Shakespeare and *Romeo and Juliet*, and Byron, and Keats. Surely your tongue becomes more inventive. But no, those same words come to my own lips. I love him so much. I find myself noticing his hands when he gestures in moments of great seriousness – or the fit of his jacket, how mansize his shoulders look from the back – though sometimes I have to remind him to straighten up, he gets that Talmudic stoop. Basically, you know, Julie is a very serious guy. Sometimes I wish he saw things with a little more humour, but given his political commitment, he can't kid about it, like I'll do sometimes. The funny contradictions in people that amuse me? Well, him they irritate.

It all becomes obvious a few days later when we're spending a Sunday afternoon in Central Park.

'Do you think so?' he asks after first telling me about his Hebrew schoolteacher, whom he admired so much, and how Mr Sopher on the day of his graduation from the Downtown Talmud Torah – 1931 it was – told him what a fine man he was becoming – but maybe a little too idealistic and sincere for this world? 'I felt bad, even though I was valedictorian,' he says thoughtfully.

Picture us sitting on the grass after wandering around the zoo eating peanuts and feeding them to the animals. Anyhow, I remember being fascinated by the giraffe. How lofty his expression – and those wonderful markings. I hadn't realized how tall he was, with such an overall view of the jungle. He's better built for survival than the lion, I thought, or is it more important to stand your ground and fight?

Anyhow, Julie's stretched out on his back with his head in my lap and still talking. 'Sopher thought I was taking the teachings of Isaiah and Jeremiah too literally ... ' He sounds uncertain. Usually he speaks with such conviction. 'You know, Rashi also believed in them. He –'

'Who's he?' I interrupt.

'A very important Talmudic scholar, a rabbi who lived in the Middle Ages and wrote a very important commentary on the Torah. Even today, he's studied and quoted. In his writings, he tried to interpret the Torah in practical, everyday terms. Like Isaiah and Jeremiah, he, too, believed in helping the underdog and fighting for social justice. Also that there's a reason and a purpose for everything that happens in men's lives and in the history of nations – even if we don't understand it at the time. And that justice will triumph – that's right out of Isaiah. I don't know, though. Watching what's going on these days in the world, what good can come of it?'

'What's bothering you, Julie?'

'The guys in the YCL? Sometimes they get on my back. "Forget all the Hebrew School crap!" Al, or that guy William you met the other day? – they sneer at me. Like they insist my views are very naïve, tainted by a narrow sectarianism, that I see things only as a Jew, rather than as a Marxist who's been handed a scientific method for analysing history, you know, dialectical materialism. Not only that, but a systematic approach towards really building a better world. "Forget this religious crap – you know what Marx said, that religion is the opiate of the people," Al said to me the other night. Sometimes I feel caught in the middle ... '

'Listen,' I tell him, 'I want to read more of this stuff you're talking about – dialectical materialism, all of that.'

'Good,' he says, 'I'll bring over some books tonight.'

But after letting off a little more steam, he comes back to Mr Sopher. 'So tell me, do you think he's right about me?'

'Have you ever gone back to visit this Mr Sopher?' I ask. 'Sounds like he meant a lot to you.'

'No,' he says with no expression, 'what for?'

And yet all the years he spent going to *cheder* and *Talmud Torah* have left their mark on him. There's something of the prophet in Julie. In that sense, we're very different. I went there three times and disliked it, the whole atmosphere, the foreignness of it, and said to myself, eight years old I was – all this doesn't make sense to me, and never went back. But his soul, I believe, still yearns to connect with the teachings of those days, though in political discussions he'll quote Marx, not Isaiah.

I'm stroking his dark hair, stroking it back from his forehead where it always falls impetuously, and his forehead seems very white and surprisingly soft for a man's. Why do I say 'surprisingly soft' – when his is the only man's forehead I've ever stroked? Big expert on men, that's me. One guy, that's all I ever wanted. Maybe I'm different from other women. Anyhow, Dovey's I touched, of course, yes, but he was a little boy and sometimes when he went on crying too long in his crib – he was the kind of kid who'd scream and rattle the crib rather than just climb out like Bernie. And Ma would say to me, '*Geh, geh*, go to him and see what's wrong.' So I used to put my palm on his forehead to check whether it was warm, too warm to be 'normal'. That's how I learned to tell 'temperature'. 'He's got no "temperature", Ma,' I'd say.

'All right, so get him out!' she'd yell back.

And I'd lift him out – chubby, four, five already and quite a *peckele*. Anyhow, his forehead was soft – like Michael's and Robby's. But Julie's is a surprise. Somehow I thought a man's would feel different, maybe rougher.

He's still staring up at the sky as though waiting for my answer. And I'm still stroking his hair, and considering what to say.

'No, my darling,' I say, putting my arms around him and bending over to kiss him on the lips – he has soft full lips, too – 'I like you just the way you are.'

THIRTY

MAY 1952

'Guess what? Today I got married.'

Dr Singer hasn't taken off his coat yet and he looks at me like I've gone stir crazy since last week's visit.

'No, it's not what you think – just that I live in my head so much these days! I'm back there again ... June 18th, 1939, thirteen years ago next month. Such a relief to talk to you about it instead of myself. That's what solitary is doing to me, I'm continually on the witness stand, my head won't stop cross-examining me: Why did you do this instead of that ... If only ... '

'I suppose everyone asks themselves this at some time or other in their life,' he murmurs.

'Yes, but their answers aren't so crucial. There's so much at stake here ... and so much pressure on me to give in ... '

'Why don't you keep a journal – write down your thoughts,' he suggests, 'instead of letting it all spin around in your head?'

Good idea – I'm going to try it.

' ... about our wedding, Dr Singer, there's nothing to tell. Julie graduated and we got married ... that's it. Our only gift was a seven-piece cocktail set from Julie's Uncle Joe who was in the business – six glasses and a martini mixer – just what we needed. No wedding picture.

'But there's a photo taken the summer of '42 at Budd Lake, NJ that I put up in my cell along with the children's. Julie's sitting tailor fashion on the grass, smiling, his eyes half closed against the sun, and I'm on my knees right behind him, my face close to his with both arms resting around his shoulders. When Julie's sister, Ethel, saw it, she said, "Look at you ... you're always touching. Isn't that sweet?" And it was. Those were the good days, Julie's working for the US Signal Corps right here in New York, and we'd just moved into our first apartment. No furniture, only a few borrowed things, but we would've been happy sleeping on the floor.

'It's funny, how in my head, time has a way of rushing up after that. Like a movie speeded up in the projection room. No more dreaming about the future and the guy you hope to meet. Now you're living it. We had good times together whatever we did, though he's only making $2,000 as a junior engineer.

'Fights? Sure we had them. But I loved him and he loved me. *That's all that matters*, we always said to each other. It was like a faith we practised together.'

1944

One night, it must've been in the autumn of 1944, there's a party for which I dig up that old red-sequinned dress. It's even tighter, but Julie says, 'Sex-y ... mmmh, come 'ere,' mugging it with heavy breathing and a roll of his eyes. So I wear it.

It's at the Grossmans' downstairs, a fund-raiser for the Soviet–American Friendship Council. We all pitch in, the Levinsons bring cold cuts, we supply chips and nuts, the Parettis coffee and cake, and everyone brings their own wine.

It's good to see so many familiar faces again. Sonny Carp, a classmate of Julie's, greets us at the door. 'Did you hear the latest? How the Russians are pushing back the Germans?' He's still in uniform, looking twenty pounds lighter and standing up straighter. Proudly he tells us how his plane was shot down over Denmark, and he's rescued by the underground and smuggled out in a small boat to England and flown home for rest and rehabilitation. Sheila, his wife, hangs on to his arm, her eyes can't let go of his face. To have him home safe!

The Grossmans have great records – all the old familiars, *Peat Bog Soldiers*, *Meadowland*, *No Pasaran*, some of Paul Robeson's. We're singing along getting loud and raucous. Also there's a pile of Glenn Miller and Artie Shaw and Tommy Dorsey, even Spike Jones, so the dancing starts. I'm so glad to get out of the house, first evening since we've had Michael, and I'm still nervous about leaving him with a sitter.

Ruth offers to sit. 'While David's in New Mexico,' she says it so proudly, 'there's nothing to do ... I might as well sit in your apartment as ours.' Always now when she refers to David, a letter or a call, she'll add, 'from *New Mexico*.' Since he was shipped there in August, and everything's very hush-hush, it's become his mark of distinction, and therefore hers.

So I accept, though I don't like taking favours from her. I just have this feeling that some day she's going to call them all in – with interest. Don't ask me why. Maybe it's her attitude, how she's always knocking someone, also she plays up to Ma, always hanging around her in the kitchen, talking, the two of them, and sometimes they shut up when I walk in. Sure it bothers me.

Anyhow, I wander over to where Julie's with a group of guys discussing what's ahead after the war. And he's repeating everything we've said to each other at different times when we're talking seriously about ourselves and the future. How optimistic he is, that there'll be a whole new spirit of friendship and cooperation between the Soviets and ourselves because of how well we're cooperating now – and how the Russians' heroic struggle against Hitler on the Eastern front has cemented our alliance.

All I'm hearing though, is 'we' or 'I', never once, 'Ethel said ... ' Somehow I feel cancelled out, and yet, I realize, that's how we've become. Two parts of a whole. We.

So does it really matter? I ask myself. It's no big deal.

By the time we get home, a little high, happy, I forget the whole thing ... we fall on the bed and make love.

1947

One time – this is much later on, after Robby's born in 1947 – I'm lying stretched out on the bed in the living-room – that's where we slept, on a sofabed – when Julie comes in. Right away he asks, 'What's for dinner?'

'There's no dinner.'

'No dinner?'

'No dinner. You heard me right. I'm sick of fixing dinner, taking care of the baby. I'm sick of the whole damn business. I'm sick of trying, always trying to be something I'm not. I just can't be a good mother like they tell you ... '

'That's not so,' he interrupts.

'Listen to me, I'm trying to tell you something important ... to me ... I'm not cut out for it, I lose my patience, I scream ... '

'So what?' he says. 'My mother did.'

'But Julie ... you're not supposed to ... and Michael's driving me crazy with his eating. Ham sandwiches ... that's all he'll eat. Did you ever! And I have to watch him every minute with the baby.' And I burst out crying.

His eyes look empty and he rests his head in his hands. 'Look, what's really bothering you?'

'I just got through telling you and you're asking me – like I haven't opened my mouth! How can I explain – it's like I'm playing a part all the time – the good mother – and inside I feel just the opposite – angry and resentful and cheated somehow. And my mother's no help. All she ever does is criticize.'

'So stop her!'

'Yeah, that's easy for you to say!'

'And there's no one to talk to ... these women in the

171

project, like Rosalie in the next building, all she knows is, "What do you use to wax your floors?" And "My windows are filthy," how many rags she uses, and half and half ammonia and water. This is what my whole life's about? With a few more bucks – already that's all they think about ... getting a TV. Sometimes I feel as though there's no hope, people get bought off so easily, they forget so quickly what it's been like. Nor do they want to be reminded. Mention working for peace – and already you're a Commie ... '

'So don't get discouraged ... look, I'll go out and get something from the deli and bring it back ... You want me to?'

'I don't give a damn! Don't talk to me about food.' I'm getting angrier. 'I'm trying to tell you something.'

'How about the baby?' he says. 'Has he eaten yet? I hear him stirring. Should I check?'

'Why do you ask me every damn thing?' I snap. 'Do whatever you want!'

Now he's finally angry and maybe I'm getting a kick out of it. I'm so sick of that patient voice – like water dripping on a stone.

'You're always telling me every damn thing I'm supposed to do with Michael and Robby,' suddenly he's roaring. 'You're the expert. Okay, so be the expert. But now you decide, *figure it out for yourself*, and I'm supposed to shift gears just like that!' He's cracking his knuckles and pacing the room. 'Ethel, listen, really you don't let me, not for a sec –'

'Cut it out, Julie! Don't jump on me, I warn you.'

He goes out for a few minutes and when he walks back in, he's zipping up his fly. 'Ethel,' he says in that quiet pacifying voice that has the edge of steel in it, 'don't warn me. Listen – you're upset, I can see –'

'Damn right I'm upset, any fool can see that!'

He comes over and strokes my hair. I start to cry.

'Oh, I don't know what I want, Julie – just a relief, some fun, a day off ... You're away so much ... always the shop, the shop ... and I'm here alone with the kids ... can't even go to the bathroom without hearing Michael yell, Ma! I tell ya, I'm getting constipated.'

'So tell me what I can do to help. Let me ... shift over ... '

And I move over to make room for him on the sofabed and he holds me close. 'Just hold me ... '

He kisses my cheek and the tears, wetting them with his kisses. I smell his salty male smell, his armpits. We lie there just that way for a while and I must've dozed off because when Robby cries, I awake with a start.

'What should I feed him?' He's still holding me tight.

'Open some jars – lamb, peas and carrots, apricot – and be sure to heat the bottle and check his diaper, okay?'

I doze off again. When I awaken there's Julie with a kitchen towel slung across his forearm like a waiter and he bows from the hip. 'Madame, your meal is ready.'

THIRTY-ONE

JULY 1952

Last visit Dr Singer suggested keeping a journal. Today is Day 1.

> Loss need not be
> instant, all at once,
> It can happen, molecule by
> molecule,
> Then a cell, two or
> more – clumping,
> separating, dying off.

That's how it must've happened with me, looking back. There's no one moment, no one incident, no one quarrel, no one hour of love that entices you into submitting – afterwards, maybe in the kitchen, or in the living-room, or on the street crossing against traffic – in the mind and spirit where it happens, the real site ... The insidious thing about loss – the reason I hate it so – is it's *invisible*, you cannot mark the day on a calendar, like an appointment, and say, yes, that's the day it happened, I surrender and say to myself, 'Well, that's life.'

Gradually, seeing Dr Singer week after week, starting in 1949, it all comes out, how I've been so afraid of saying no to Michael, how I'm so confused though I can talk a good line right out of Dr Spock's book, how I'll let Michael get away with murder while I'm being patient, patient, explaining, reasoning ... and then suddenly I see red.

Before Robby was born, it wasn't so bad yet. With one I

could manage, give him all the attention he wanted and still be patient and loving, just like the books say. Though I miss work and union activities, and being out in the world doing the full-time volunteer work I did early in the war at the East Side Defence Council.

These days when Julie leaves in the morning, I feel a pang of envy. Stop it, I tell myself, this *is* the life for a woman, staying home and raising a family, and damn it, you just better be content with it. Other women are, you can see it right here in Knickerbocker Village – so it's just you and your silly high-school ambitions. First an actress and singer – maybe even a musical comedy star. Remember the time you even imagined being chosen this month's Miss Subways? And then you had to be a union leader. Forget it! Instead I take a course on How To Be a Good Mother.

Every morning I get up resolved to be a Good Mother. Every night I review the day by writing down what happened, record my actions with Michael – and score myself accordingly. Usually I'm flunking. But the next day, like it's always New Year's, I get up, resolved to try again.

Things only get much worse. He climbs into the crib with the baby, grabs his rattles and bops him on the head. I have to watch him all the time. If I have to run down to the laundry I can't leave him alone with the baby. When I'm nursing Robby, right into my lap he climbs, the baby nursing on one side, and he's on the other saying, 'Ethel' – he always calls me Ethel – 'tell me a story, sing me a song.' He loves *Ballads for Americans* and *Irene*. Once he wanted a diaper put on – four years old in a diaper!

One time when we're visiting at Uncle Joe's house, Michael starts fooling around with his cousin's violin and he won't listen when I tell him to stop. Finally I give him a slap on the bottom and he yells, 'I wish you were dead!' To me that's not so terrible – you're supposed to let them vent their feelings, but to Uncle Joe! A kid should talk like that to his mother! So he starts toward Michael saying, 'If you were mine, I'd –'

'He's not yours!' I yell, 'and I'll break your arm if you lay a finger on him!'

Joe stops and looks at me like he can't believe what he's just heard, but he lets go of Michael fast. True we're never invited back there again, but so what!

Even Julie's older sister kids me about being a mother thirty-six hours a day. I won't use babysitters – it's not just that money is so tight, but also, I don't trust them. Except for very special occasions, like once Julie's union has this party at Café Society Downtown and Ziggy's the featured entertainer. Naturally I want to go and Julie's sister offers to sit.

We had a great evening. Some of Julie's classmates, Morty Sobell, Max Elitcher and Sonny Carp, sit at our table and we all kid around like old times. Ziggy's funnier than ever, and does a take-off of this isolationist Senator – Phineas T. Pellagra. When he's told about the Japs bombing Pearl Harbor, the Senator snaps, 'What the hell was Hawaii doing in the Pacific anyway?'

Afterwards when the applause dies down, Julie urges me to go and say hello to Ziggy backstage.

'What for?' I say.

Anyhow, getting back to my problems with Michael. It all comes to a head one day on Delancey Street when I'm walking the baby in his carriage and Michael's riding alongside on his tricycle. Louise, my neighbour, and I are talking, so naturally my head's turned towards her and suddenly, the carriage is wrenched out of my hands and almost topples over. The baby is screaming his lungs out.

What's happened is that Michael rode his tricycle right in front of the carriage – just like that! Luckily the baby didn't get hurt. But still ... 'Michael, why did you do that?' My heart's still pumping away.

'Well, I had to get your attention somehow,' he says. And at that moment, I hate him, that after all my efforts to give him attention and love, he'd do such a thing. Later on, I realize, of course, how frightened he must've been, too.

But that I could feel such anger for my own child frightens me. It seems unnatural.

That night, after Robby's in his crib, I try to reason with Michael. If I can somehow get through to him, we'll straighten it all out.

But he keeps repeating, 'Ethel, you just weren't listening to me. I had to make you.'

'Why?'

'There was something I had to show you in the toy-store window.'

'Couldn't it wait?'

'No!'

We keep going in circles like this and I'm getting more and more upset and before I know it, I grab him and wallop him as hard as I can with a wooden mixing spoon that's suddenly in my hand and he's screaming bloody murder. Me – who swore I'd never hit a kid of mine. I drop the spoon and sink to the floor with him in my arms, both of us sobbing.

By the time Julie comes home, we're practically asleep right there on the floor.

Next morning I say to Julie as I'm pouring him coffee, 'Julie,' I say, 'I've got to get help with Michael. It can't go on this way any more.'

'Why, what's happened?'

'Never mind,' I say, 'I have to.'

THIRTY-TWO

1937–8

Of course, I have my doubts. *What if ... and suppose ...* And it's at night that they all come zooming in on me. When I suddenly awaken as though shaken awake by someone at an agreed-upon time, and the prison bars remind me where I am, then I can almost see them like the silhouettes of birds flying across the moon, dark and foreboding. Spectres of decisions made, some that were never laid to rest, even now. Like I wanted to go on working even when we got married and had a family, so I say to Julie, 'Why wait? Let's get married now. Somehow we'll manage.'

He's all for it, he wants to as much as I do. But his father's against it. Now I like Harry, his father, but he has some very old-fashioned ideas. 'A husband works and a wife stays home,' he announces when Julie brings it up. 'Makes no difference, she's smart or not, home is where she belongs. With the kids.' His wife, Sophie, never questions this, so why should he.

So Julie goes along. 'Why upset him?' he tells me. 'Let's wait it out.' So we wait, all the time wanting each other so badly. I'm his first girl, and he's for me, the first. Together we're learning from each other. But with Ma standing guard like a dragon, we have to settle for stolen moments, shy delicious moments where we hastily fumble for each other, clumsy, not like in those slow tender love scenes you see in the movies. But still it's ecstasy, even in a dark hallway, or a married friend's apartment, twice on the roof of our building, and once under the boardwalk in Brighton on a hot starless night with the smell of the ocean and damp sand left in our clothes. Feeling guilty afterwards, at least, I did, and probably Julie, too. But liberated – and proud of it.

Decisions. There are lots of them I'm making after I meet Julie.

So much is happening in the world – 1937, '38 – and we're caught right up in it along with everyone else.

Every day big black headlines; it's frightening how Franco's army is gaining in Spain, Hitler's grabbing more and more of Europe – the Saar, Austria, and finally, in September of 1938, Neville Chamberlain flies all the way to Munich to hand him Czechoslovakia on a silver platter. The newspapers describe how crowds of adoring Germans with swastika buttons in their lapels wait outside his hotel for hours to greet him like he's the quarterback at the Rose Bowl who scored the winning touchdown! What the Czechs must have felt, though! Sold out, like cattle for the slaughter! Handed over like a trophy!

Every morning now you can hear the Nazi goosestep across the front page. And on the radio at night, there's H.V. Kaltenborn reporting on Hitler's latest demands and threats of force. Roosevelt's talking peace, while, we find out later, he's arming us for war. Oh yes, there's a lot of doubletalk by everyone, except Hitler. In *Mein Kampf*, which Julie and I both read, he said exactly what he meant. The trouble is, no one believed him then. All this time, England and France are saying 'hands off' in Spain, which is like giving the fascists the go-ahead signal. Myself, I could never understand how the British could get more excited about the Prince of Wales and his love affair with Mrs Wally Simpson than what's going on in the world. What difference does it make who sleeps in Buckingham Palace? Julie told me that Kipling once said that you could turn Satan himself loose in London, and the only thing the British would do would be to invite him to dinner.

I remember sitting there looking at a photo of Spanish women learning to shoot rifles – and crying. Women caring so much that they wanted to fight right alongside the men.

Have I ever felt that way? Yes, at the moment when that cop's beating me up, I wanted a gun in my hand so bad – so I could let him have it! It shocks me to say it, but it's the truth.

'Julie,' I say, 'let's go to that Loyalist rally tonight at the Mecca Temple, and I'll skip rehearsal.'

'You're sure?' He knows how seriously I take rehearsals.

'Yes, I'm sure.'

By the time we get there, the hall's already crowded. André Malraux, the French writer – only a few weeks after fighting in the Battle of Guadalajara. I'm eager to hear him.

People are still milling around trying to find seats. Julie spots a guy he knows way over on the side with a couple of empty seats next to him. So we squeeze past the whole row of knees; people in New York will never make room for you, they just look annoyed. Julie's friend tells us that lots of celebrities are coming, writers, artists, entertainers, professors. Two couples go by, very sophisticated, laughing about something private, and one of the women who looks like a movie actress in a beautiful beaver coat smiles down at me. What's she thinking, I'm wondering. Does she see me as a poor working girl? An exploited member of the proletariat? Dowdy? Oppressed? Somehow I wish I stood out more – with looks, style, clothes, even though this is very bourgeois in our crowd and I'd be ashamed to admit it to anyone, even Julie. Outside of that red-sequinned dress, I've never worn anything that would draw attention to me. Neat, but inconspicuous, that's me. Strictly the mousy type. Except for Julie. If you listen to him, I'm a raving beauty. It should only happen!

Anyhow, out comes the MC. With tonight's headlines, he's serious right off – tells us it's looking bad for the Loyalists, more bombings, more bloodshed. And to please give generously when they pass around the collection boxes. He also mentions all the prominent sponsors, people like Dorothy Thompson, Lillian Hellman, Archibald MacLeish, even Benny Goodman and Paul Muni. And James Cagney. When Malraux finally comes on after some more speakers, I can't take my eyes off him. If Jules (John) Garfield is the first man I fall in love with – aside from Julie – then Malraux is the second! Here's a man, not just an actor on stage, who's doing something very courageous about his beliefs – piloting a plane for the Loyalists. And that's what's important to me. To believe in something – that's all well and good, but to carry those beliefs into action – *that's the kind of courage I truly admire*.

In his dark suit and tie, at first it's hard to imagine him a flyer just returned from battle, but as he goes on speaking, I can just picture him at the controls of an old creaky bomber pursued by the Nazi Junkers. He's so fiery and passionate, it's contagious.

'The Republic did not come out of nowhere,' he starts out by saying, 'the anger of the Spanish people has been building for many years – fuelled by the greed and corruption of those in power. The Church collaborating with the monarchy and the rich. The peasants have been cheated out of their vineyards and homes, the workers forced to live in abject poverty, all this while the Church and their rich and powerful friends flourish, grow richer and more powerful.

'So now, after all these years of oppression, the Spanish people, no matter what their label – anarchist, liberal, Republican, trade unionist, communist or socialist – even pacifist! – they're all fighting for one thing – for their own duly elected government. It's their government and, for the first time in their lives, it offers them a chance for a better life. *Man cannot live without hope!*' I agree, wholeheartedly I agree, and my heart's warming up.

'This is truly a people's war, make no mistake, it's not just two opposing armies. And think of your own Civil War, how important it was that you settled it among yourselves without foreign intervention.' And he tells us how after the battle in Barcelona, the flower vendors in the streets threw their roses and poppies on the empty bloodstained stretchers going by, and men and women together cried.

'You have only to be there to truly understand, to really experience what the Spanish people are fighting for.

It's their very lives and the lives of their children. They need our help! Now!'

And he describes how one of their planes, from the International Brigade, crashed high up in the snow-covered mountains, and how the peasants immediately came to the rescue when one of the crew, barely conscious, weakly called out *'Frente Popular'*. And how the people hastily improvised stretchers – even using a newly-made coffin for one – to carry the wounded down the long, winding, tortuous mule-path past other villages, down, down all the way to where an ambulance waited below. And how all the peasants at each small village naturally fell in step as the relief march went by, men and boys walking silently alongside, the women crying but tending to the wounded, and the few airmen not hurt riding on the villagers' mules. Seen from below, this long line curving, swaying down the mountain, enduring as the very mountain itself, symbolized for him the eternal struggle of man, irreducible in his humanity and compassion.

Julie sits forward listening to every word as Malraux tells us about the International Brigade, a volunteer army of men coming from fifty-two countries to fight with the Loyalists. How they're smuggled in by boat through patrolled waters or by hiking over the Pyrenees because the French have closed the border. 'You can imagine,' he says, 'how difficult it is to whip men of such different temperaments, nationalities and backgrounds into a disciplined army. Many have never fought before. And yet their common cause welds them into an effective fighting force.'

Malraux's voice grows even more powerful. *'Why* are Hitler and Mussolini intervening in a civil war?' he demands.

'Because what we're witnessing – and *remember this* – is Spain being turned into a gigantic testing ground for modern warfare by the fascists. They're testing new equipment, experimenting to find out whether bombing, for example, civilian neighbourhoods, or a home for the aged or orphans – or a large hospital – may not ultimately be more effective than bombing only military sites as in the past. *They're revising the old rules of war, and modernizing warfare – and* we *must* be aware of this. *Beware.*

'The democracies, including your country, are giving them just what they need – time to get ready for the next war, a world war,' he predicts in a voice gone soft and ominous. He pauses to let his prophecy sink in. The audience is shifting uncomfortably in their seats and Julie looks at me meaningfully. Then Malraux bangs his fist on the lectern. 'The fascists *must* be defeated, they *can* be defeated in Spain. *We must keep the fire from spreading.*' With his hands outstretched, he appeals to us all.

The hall, as one, is on its feet. Banners are held high: LIFT THE EMBARGO, AID TO SPAIN, MAKE MADRID THE TOMB OF FASCISM, DEATH TO FASCISM. Furious handclapping, feet stamping. The audience starts chanting *'No pasaran! No pasaran! No pasaran!'*

Julie's quiet on the ride home. He's considering enlisting in the Abraham Lincoln Brigade. I know this because Lou, his closest friend, mentioned it to me last week. Not Julie, but Lou. He said that maybe both of them would do it together.

And me – I'm sad and confused. And frightened. In some ways, the world is so rotten, so meaningless. So chaotic. Seeing Tante Rosie die of cancer, suffering every day on the way to that final day ... and in Spain, one brother killing another, a country torn up, invaded ... Germany and Italy using it for their own evil ends ... and the democracies doing nothing to stop them ...

And I can't help feeling that our own salvation is tied up with theirs.

THIRTY-THREE

1937–8

A few months go by and still Julie says nothing. Though, knowing him as I do, I'm sure he's giving this whole business of enlisting in the Lincoln Brigade very serious thought.

It all comes to a head at Coney Island on a Sunday in July mobbed like you wouldn't believe. People swarming all over each other like a huge anthill. Kids throwing sand, getting it in strangers' eyes. A guy tosses a beach ball to his girl, she misses, and it bounces off the head of a weight-lifter type strutting by, and you should see his expression – surprise, then anger that his act is suddenly turned into a comedy routine. I start to giggle at the way things happen so unexpectedly.

'Why you laughin'?' this old Italian lady near me in a beach chair shouts. 'You thinka thatsa funny? People can't get a little rest, quiet, nobody disturb 'em, even on a Sunday. Look at 'em, like animals!'

'Thatsa one angry lady!' Julie says pulling me away fast.

Skywriting above. The mob's head, like one, follows the plane to the final message, 'BUY NATHAN'S HOT DOGS'. And we're still trying to find an empty spot when this guy comes by who looks like Fatty Arbuckle – from the old Mack Sennett comedies? He's in an undershirt and black pants with an apron tied around his waist like a grocer, and chanting in a minor key, 'Homemade candy – five cents a piece – best on the beach!' On his bald head, he's balancing a large aluminium tray with sesame seed candy bars and swaying like a native girl in the Caribbean carrying a basket of fruit.

'Let's get some, Julie.'

'Don't you want to wait until we sit down?' he asks.

'No, maybe he won't come by again.'

'Okay, hey fella, how much?' he calls out to the guy.

Finally we find a place to park in the shadow of the boardwalk and spread out our blanket. It's just as well – this way, Julie, who's very fair, won't get a burn, and I can get a tan.

It's so good to be here, I'm thinking, relaxed and away from politics and people. We both need it. Julie's not crazy about the water, so he settles down with a book, *An American Tragedy* by Theodore Dreiser. But I go in several times. I love the waves, playing with them, riding the breakers, feeling so alive and happy – and it brings back good memories of Sundays with Tante Rosie on Brighton Beach. I miss her so, even now.

As I start back, kids are running by me towards the water, grown-ups, too. Something's up! I start running, too. At the water's edge a crowd is watching a few men help the lifeguard launch his boat into the water. In seconds, he's off and rowing with another guy in the stern. Out beyond the ropes, quite a way, all you can see are two hands sticking up, then disappearing, coming up again, gone again. My heart's beating fast. Will he make it? 'There's a very strong current out there, you don't know it until it grabs you,' says this grizzled man near me with the broad chest and powerful arms of a swimmer. 'I had a hard time out there myself before.'

A shout goes up as the lifeguard tugs hard on the rope pulling someone into the boat! The tension oozes out of the crowd, people turn to each other, talking, lighting a cigarette, laughing again.

When the lifeguard comes rowing in with a kid, white as a sheet and shivering, someone throws a blanket around his shoulders. 'You all right, son?' the grizzled man asks him. He nods his head, a small frightened kid, maybe ten or eleven, head hanging, lips still blue, huddling in the blanket. Someone hands him a cup of coffee from a large thermos, and you can see the heat spread through his body, and his face takes on colour. 'He'll be all right now,' says the lifeguard. 'Okay, folks, break it up, give him room.' People drift away. I walk back to where we're sitting.

Julie's fallen asleep on his back with the book open by his side. The book has a drowning in it, I'm reminded. That's a funny coincidence. Something inside me keeps churning.

I watch him, how he's breathing so slow and even, his fingers still cradling some sand, his legs, the muscles smooth in sleep, stretched out, white, lean, hairy, and toeing out slightly. His belly is moving up and down rhythmically, and I fix that picture in my head for always. It's a Julie without his glasses, his large warm serious eyes closed – defenceless and endearing. I watch him this way for a while, then turn back to the sea pondering what's ahead for us and the world. Somehow for me, the two are always linked. And suddenly I'm aware how vulnerable that makes me feel. How the unexpected can knock you flat. I want Julie to hold me tight.

When he slowly opens his eyes a little later, he's ready for a dip. 'But not for long, I bet that water's cold!'

'It'll wake you up fast.' I don't mention the near-drowning.

'Yeah, that's what I'm afraid of,' he laughs and takes my hand and we splash into the water. It's great!

The beach is thinning out as we eat the picnic supper I brought – tuna sandwiches on rye, hardboiled eggs, pickles, honey cake with nuts from Ratner's, and some nice fruit – grapes, cherries and ripe peaches. While I'm setting out the food, Julie brings back some Cokes from the concession on the boardwalk, and we dig in.

'You really got some sun today – looks good, there's a golden sheen about you, even your eyes,' he says. 'Now you better cover up, it's enough for one day.'

'Don't worry, dear, I never burn.' Spoken too soon. A week later, my nose is still peeling.

Anyhow, when we're just resting quietly as the sun sinks

leaving the sky in flames, he says, 'Ethel, I have to talk to you.'

'Okay.'

'Look, I'm thinking of dropping out of school. What's the sense to it? Maybe I'm not cut out for it ... '

'That's sheer nonsense!' Fear always makes me angry. 'You're smarter than a lot of the guys in your class, I saw that.'

'Maybe, but a good deal of the time in these engineering courses, I'm plain bored. The professor's up there lecturing or writing formulae on the blackboard and my mind's elsewhere ... '

'Where?' I finally get the courage up to ask.

'Oh, for Godsakes, you understand! How can I forget the terrible things going on in the world today? In Spain ... Hitler, what he's doing to the Jews ... and all those other decent people ... terrible beyond our imagination even. Do you think he's re-arming just to play soldiers? What gets me is nobody is even trying to stop him ... Britain, France ... here in this country ... they're all playing Let's Pretend, let's pretend nothing's happening. It makes me sick! Only the Soviet Union understands and is doing something. How can I stay in school and concentrate on my narrow, selfish little personal ambitions when all these horrible things are happening! You know, I guess, that Lou and I have been talking ... '

I know already what he's going to say, that they've decided to enlist. And my heart stops. I can understand why he feels this way – I'd like to be in there, too – and yet I can't endure it, the terror that his words set up. Someone we both know personally, Maxie, a good kid from our neighbourhood, was killed. And Larry, from Julie's class, came back blind. And I can still see that one-legged vet at the CCNY rally urging those guys to join up ... Are you crazy, I thought, would I want Julie to go when all I have to do is look at you – with the trouser leg pinned up for the rest of your life!

Stubbornly he continues, 'And we've just about decided ... just haven't settled on when . . . problem is the

State Department makes it illegal.'

'Have you discussed it with your parents?' I ask, as calmly as I can. They'll stop him. To go fight? His mother'll never let it happen. Her *Yoynele*?

'Not yet, I wanted to tell you first.'

Inside, a sigh of relief. I don't want him to see, though, how it's affecting me, that wouldn't be fair. I'm still counting on his mother. I know she'll persuade him. It's her *Yoynele*, her baby!

'Let me think about it,' I tell him. 'That's some news you've given me.'

'You've probably seen it coming,' he points out.

After a few minutes of silence, I suggest a walk on the boardwalk.

By now we've dried off, so we brush off the sand, slip into our clothes, and start out. It's a beautiful night with one of those yellow full moons, like Wisconsin butter, that you only get in the summer. The air has cooled just enough so it's comfortable strolling along. And people, despite all the problems of the world, look content.

'Let's try it!' I suggest suddenly as we're walking by the Cyclone.

'You're sure?'

'Yeah, sure, c'mon, it'll be fun ... I've always wanted to.'

The noise of the car rattling uphill and the crowd ohing and aahing, the excitement and anticipation, it all goes to my head. I love it – just like the moment before the curtain goes up. That instant after going over the crest – just before the downward swoop – I love it, that sensation of going out of control, and at the same time, knowing it'll turn out all right, the people who run the roller coaster won't let anything bad happen. I know that when we buy the tickets.

A child's faith.

I look over at Julie to see how he's doing, and his face is twisted with fear, eyes closed tight, his hands bluish white as they fiercely grip the handlebar. A frightened child again. Is he recalling that time he went off to Bellevue in an ambulance all by himself with those horrible stomach pains, maybe ten at most, and they operate? Turns out to be appendicitis, almost ruptured.

All I want to do is to hold him close and protect him.

There's a moment of turning away from the truth of one's conviction that *is* a turning off the road, a slight veer that takes you in an altered direction; instead of due west, say, you're now headed north-west, instead of San Francisco, you arrive in Vancouver.

Suppose Julie had gone to Spain? What then? Would our lives have been different? Most likely. His friend, Lou, did go. And he came back, minus a hand, disillusioned, and went into the dairy store his father owned in Brooklyn. Maybe Julie would have escaped unharmed, come home safe – but changed; that *is* a certainty. Fighting in a war, such a war, *must* change a man, if not outside, then inside, and maybe I was more afraid of that change than the other, though I told myself I couldn't bear it if he were wounded or blinded or left helpless – or dead.

Maybe he'd have found out his own limits of courage, that he was a coward in battle – or that he didn't want to be an engineer; fighting with men might have turned him into a rabbi. A rabbi? Who knows? I know that sounds funny, but Julie loves people, he could give them courage and faith when their own is running out. Or perhaps a party official.

Whatever – he would have been a changed man, and I wanted him to stay the same and to continue on a sensible predictable course. 'Stay and finish up at City, and get your BS,' was what I would have said if I'd spoken up. Because my life was bound up with his and I didn't want the life we'd planned together changed in any way.

I've had time to think about all this – and to admit that in my own silent way, I was a collaborator; silently, without prearrangement or discussion, tacitly, I conspired with his family to talk him out of going to Spain. Silence speaks, oh, how silence can speak! And on my part, it meant no, don't go – and he knew it, for here was I, usually so enthusiastic, so outspoken, especially with him, suddenly I'm silent, I 'refuse' to express an opinion. 'I don't want to influence you,' I tell him – that's my out. It's what I keep repeating. 'I don't want to influence such an important decision for you.' Oh yeah! It's painful for me to admit this, but it's the truth.

In such small ways, debts begin, and the die is cast between two people.

THIRTY-FOUR

NOVEMBER 1938

Why did I join, I ask myself, looking back fifteen years.

Here was I silently opposing Julie's going off to fight for the Loyalists in Spain – and yet at the same time, I was making a decision, one that has changed my life irrevocably.

Why did I join?

Because the Party gave me a sense of belonging, a sense of belonging to something that has meaning, meaning for a world going out of control, and for me personally.

Because it becomes clear to me when I, finally, open my eyes, that in America, it *does* make a difference who you are – your sex and the colour of your skin – and when your family came here – and where from. Now that last one's very important.

England's better than Russia or Poland, I discover, also better than Ireland or China or Puerto Rico or Africa. Something I didn't know in the third grade. But in the Party, it makes no difference – that I'm the daughter of Jewish immigrants from Eastern Europe, with only a high-school degree, working as a shipping clerk. I find there are others like me who truly believe in working for a better life in America – for everyone. Sure there are sell-outs – people like Fannie and Robert. But one thing I do know, that when we all got together and organized, things improved for the shipping clerks, and all the other workers who joined the CIO.

Finally, I'm learning to decode the messages our society sends, to sort out the *real* messages from the ones that are only preached, not practised – it's like learning which traffic signals the police will enforce in a foreign country. Ethel Greenglass, the dreamer, the romantic, is still learning the natives' ways. And there's no book available in the library, that fully explains it to you with detailed diagrams. You have to find out for yourself.

For example, why is Christmas celebrated in our school when almost all of us are Jewish? Something's wrong with me, that's my immediate reaction in third grade when we put on the Nativity scene for the Christmas assembly programme and I play the Virgin Mary. Never really understanding what it's all about – except not to mention it at home. For me, it's pretending to be something I'm supposed to be – a Christian kid. Because it's their holiday – *an American holiday* – not ours. And afterwards, Mrs Gilhooley, who wears a gold cross around her neck, hands out Christmas candy canes and that, too, I know to finish before going home ...

And yet, something in me, even now, still wants to believe that all those words in the Declaration of Independence written over one hundred and fifty years ago still have meaning for all of us.

What swings the balance for me, though, is *Kristallnacht*. The worst pogrom since the Middle Ages, the papers said. The date – November 9, 1938. Fifteen years ago. Reading about it that night, seeing the photos – my skin crawls at the legalized sadism and cruelty and wreckage the Jews suffered all over Germany. I just want to get into bed and pull the covers over my head like I used to after I saw *Dracula* with Bela Lugosi. For a long time then, I was terrified the vampire would come into my room during the night and suck blood from some tiny cut ... But there's no release in sleep that November night ... I keep awakening and sinking back into a stupor ... Somewhere I'm on a hard-packed dirt road with half-buried rocks and stones under my feet, feeling the sharp edges poking through my soles ... and then I'm in a house, alone – a stranger's house – and outside the rain's beating down hard. Upstairs someone starts to play a piano – big crashing chords that shake the ceiling ... and suddenly it stops ... and in my head those thunderous chords crash on ...

I go to the window, the moon's a murky red ... like in my dreams the last few nights before Julie's arrested ... and the red spreads across the sky ... and yet the clouds, like a cold congealed film, don't screen out the moon's bloody aura from below ... Black swastikas, still wet, shimmer on Jewish shops and buildings. Huge red feathery flames leap up from an old synagogue as though from a live volcano. The firemen watch with folded arms as the beautiful dome caves in. And there's that big poster shown in the newspaper photo, only now it's as large as the Camel billboard in Times Square, showing an enormous dark oily Jew with a big hooked nose and thick leering lips wearing a black caftan, a *yarmulke*, and an armband with the Communist hammer and sickle. Smoke unfurls from his nostrils, and his eyes, the very eyes of the Devil himself, are fixed on YOU, as with one hand he tempts with gold coins while with the other, he wields a long curling snake whip. An evil macabre power twists out of that whip, and that image haunts me for days. A premonition?

Now the street below has gone curiously quiet, a significant quiet. And I feel like I'm holding my breath endlessly.

In the morning, I know what I have to do.

THIRTY-FIVE

AUGUST 1939

Although the World's Fair in New York, out in Flushing Meadows, opens in May 1939, suddenly it's late August and we still haven't been out there. Julie hates crowds and refuses to go on a weekend. So finally I say, 'Let's take a day off from work next week and we'll go.'

It turns out to be a grey day, one of those that keep threatening rain, and already there's a fine mist in the air.

As we pass through the gates, the smells of a hot summer's day and people pouring out of the subway and parking lots hit me. There's loud music blaring from invisible speakers and the noise all around. 'Let's get organized about this,' says Julie. 'There's so much to see. What do you want to do first?'

'I don't know – how about you?' And we both study the map of the Fair.

'Well, the Russian Pavilion, for one,' says Julie.

'Of course, what else?'

We both agree on the General Motors Futurama, and since it's the closest, we decide to start with that, see some others in the same area and then head to the International area. 'Also I'd like to see the Aquacade, I hear Johnny Weismuller and Eleanor Holm swim a duet.'

'You would?' He's surprised.

'Yes, I would.'

'Okay, what else?'

'Well, we'll have to watch our money ... it adds up ... how about going to the Merrie England Globe Theatre – they're doing Shakespeare and it's directed by Margaret Webster.'

'How much?'

'I don't know. Let's eat lightly, okay? But let's save that for tonight.'

Even if it's a Thursday, it turns out that all the big attractions are already mobbed with a long wait in line. Finally we get into the Futurama, which turns out to be a huge model depicting life in America in the Sixties. Which seems to be mostly complicated traffic circles and speedways with cars whizzing by. *Where are they all going?*

'There are the Trylon and Perisphere,' says Julie pointing to a huge pointed column and a large squat globe designed as symbols of the Fair.

'That Trylon looks like a huge penis,' I say.

'How about the Perisphere?' He winks and laughs just as a tractor train packed with people goes by playing 'The Sidewalks of New York', and almost runs us down. 'Let's get out of here,' he says, 'and head over to the Russian Pavilion.'

As we reach it, we're both excited. It's quite crowded and inside there's a replica of the Moscow subway, and it's beautiful – clean and spacious with gleaming tiles and murals. The guide explains how they've created the illusion of a long station and tracks disappearing down a tunnel with a mirror. They're so proud of it, and I can't help comparing it to our own dirty subway.

The other exhibits are packed with information about the important changes the Soviets have made in agriculture and manufacturing, how much better things are for the workers and the peasants. Huge paintings in bright colours show the peasants at work in the fields with strong happy faces and bodies, both men and women, and the same for workers in the factories.

Julie's a little disappointed in the art, though, because he likes the French Impressionists, and these are so realistic. But I find it all so exhilarating and full of promise and hope.

I buy a small round wooden plaque, hand carved and painted, which shows a peasant woman in a black kerchief swinging a scythe. Her face with those high cheekbones reminds me of Tante Rosie.

I'm getting tired and my feet hurt, though there's still so

much to see. 'Let's take a breather,' I suggest, looking around for a bench. As we sit down, I pick up the newspaper someone left behind and there's a big black headline.

'Oh Julie, look!'

GERMANY AND RUSSIA SIGN TEN-YEAR NON-AGGRESSION PACT
Moscow, Thursday, August 24, 1939.

I drop the paper and close my eyes. But then I pick it up again and read how Von Ribbentrop, the German Foreign Minister, flew to Moscow yesterday to sign this agreement, what a royal welcome he gets ...

'This can't be true, Julie!'

That's my first response. His, too, I suppose. We both sit there on the bench, dazed. I'm shaking my head, I simply can't believe it. I look around. Everything seems so normal, the crowd going by looks just the way they did a few minutes ago, people out for a good time. Surely, if anything like this had really happened, they couldn't look that way. For a moment that comforts me.

'Let's walk,' says Julie and his eyes won't meet mine.

We start walking, just walking, not saying anything. And then as we're passing the Polish Pavilion, a beautiful delicate building with openwork like lace, I start to sob.

'Oh for Godsakes!' he exclaims.

'How could they?' I ask him. I feel personally betrayed. 'The *Daily Worker* didn't say a word yesterday.'

'Hang on,' he says. 'I'm sure that there's a good reason, and we'll find out in time. Wait until we have all the facts. You know how the capitalist papers lie.'

'What facts?' I ask him. 'These are the facts!' I find myself pounding the paper. 'Here, read it for yourself.'

'Calm down,' he says calmly. At moments like this I could kill him, he's so in control. 'Wait and see,' he repeats.

'Oh Julie, it says right here, "Five swastika banners are

flying in the Moscow airport," ' and I slap the paper, 'here, and I'm not supposed to get upset? How can we close our eyes to this? I'm not a robot.'

'Wait and see,' is all he'll say.

Wait and see ... what?

That a week later Germany invades Poland ... and the Soviets attack from the east?

THIRTY-SIX

1952

'Dear Manny,' I wrote today.

'Please ask the warden to let me have the plant Michael sent with you last week for my birthday. You mentioned it, but since then, I haven't gotten it. And he'll be wondering what happened, why my silence. He's such a sensitive, perceptive child. Even if they'll just leave it outside my cell. Surely a philodendron can't be dangerous. But, at least, I can tell him I've received it – and what it looks like – and what it means to me.

'Please, Manny, do this for me?'

1945

My thoughts keep returning to 1945. Clearly now I see how it marked a turning point in our lives – Julie's and mine. But, at the time, we were more caught up with news of the war.

That January, people are optimistic again after a cold bleak December with long casualty lists from the Battle of the Bulge. The American troops are breaking through the German lines and pushing them back, so naturally our spirits are up, especially since the Russians have just swept into Warsaw, and the news from the Pacific is encouraging.

It must've been in February when Julie comes home earlier than usual. I'm not surprised. Once in a while he'll do that when he has some time coming to him. Looks washed out though.

'You're tired?' I ask him after he gives me a kiss absent-mindedly.

'I guess so. The damned elevator broke down again at the

fourth floor so I had to walk up seven flights.'

'That's the third time it's happened in the last two weeks. I'm going to bring it up at our Tenants' Council meeting next week. Did I tell you they asked me to write for the *Knickerbocker News*?'

But he's already in the living-room with Michael, who's pulling at him to play, 'Da-da, Da-da.' So he doesn't answer.

In a few minutes he calls out, 'Listen, Ethel, I think I'll lie down a little before dinner. I'm beat.'

'Good. Close the door so we won't disturb you.' And I pick up Michael and put him in the playpen and go back into the kitchen to start dinner. Broiled chicken again. Once in a while I can still get a good steak at the butcher's like when Dovey was in. But most of it is going on to the black market. I turn on the radio to catch the six o'clock news. The announcer comes on with an important news bulletin, 'From Yalta in the Crimea where the Big Three are meeting.' I turn up the volume. 'The textbooks will call this day – February 12, 1945 – a historic day,' he says. 'Stalin, Churchill and Roosevelt have just reached an agreement which will undoubtedly determine the fate of post-war Europe. The three major powers pledge themselves to continue the all-out fight to force Germany to an unconditional surrender. They have also drawn up plans for the post-war allied control of Germany so that a united Germany can never rise again.' And he goes on to report the rest – guarantees for free governments in Europe, and a meeting scheduled for April in San Francisco to set up the United Nations in order to build a world dedicated to peace, security and freedom.

Just wait till Julie hears this, I'm thinking. That should cheer him up!

Soon after, he comes in while I'm fixing the salad. He rinses his glasses, dries them carefully, and puts them on again. 'Need a hand?' he asks.

I shake my head. 'Up so soon? Couldn't you rest? Did I have it on too loud?'

'I rested enough,' he says, goes into the living-room, and picks up Michael. 'Anything on the news?'

'Yeah, hey, listen to this.' And I repeat the news.

'I only hope so,' he says grabbing a library book out of Michael's hands. That's his latest – tearing pages out.

'What dya mean?' I'm surprised at him, usually he's so optimistic.

During dinner Julie's unusually quiet, and after filling him in on my day – nothing special to report – I ask him, 'So how about you?' By now we're lingering over coffee and Michael's getting restless.

'Not so good.'

'What d'you mean, not so good?' My heartbeat picks up.

'Just that – they called me into the chief engineer's office this afternoon and told me they were suspending me.'

'Suspending you? For what?'

'For belonging to the Communist Party. US Government rules, no Nazi or Communist can work for the government. You know that.'

'Yeah, we went through this once before – and you were cleared. You've been working for the Signal Corps almost five years. So why are they bothering you now? Besides, only recently they promoted you.'

'Don't ask me! Except they've already pulled this on several other guys in our local.'

'They have? You didn't tell me.'

'I didn't want to worry you ... what with your back acting up again and those dizzy spells. How're you feeling today?'

'Better ... the heating pad helps ... also I forgot to tell you, I saw the doctor yesterday, and he says I'm definitely anaemic so he's starting me on iron shots ... also I should eat fresh liver.'

'None for me!'

'But Julie, you shouldn't keep anything from me, that really upsets me more than anything.'

'I was going to tell you ... that's why I've been so tied up

200

lately, we've been working on the union brief for these guys. Two of them have already been cleared, so I'm really not that worried. I know the union will go to bat for me. You know, the real reason they're after us? They're really out to bust the union, knock off the leaders one by one.' He pauses, notices my expression, and says, 'Don't get upset. I can always get another job. Gleason, the personnel manager over at Emerson Radio, told me several times he'd like to hire me. So it'll be okay.

'What bothers me,' he says, 'is how they're going about it. There's one guy who works with us – a real Nazi, loves baiting all of us "yids" – anyhow, he got drunk one night when he went out with us, and told us that he thinks Hitler's the greatest. So why haven't they fired him?'

Frankly, I'm more worried about us. 'But Julie, I still don't understand why they're starting this now. Here we just sign an agreement with the Russians. Let's be friends. Peacetime allies, and at the same time, they're ready to fire you? I don't like this, Julie, not one bit.'

Something's happening here I don't understand – and I have a queasy feeling this is only the beginning.

After Julie starts working at Emerson, our life settles down again, though someplace in me, there's still a flicker of anxiety. He's still very involved with his union, so between overtime and union activities, he's home even less. In April, he goes down to Washington on a weekend to see Congressman Dickstein about his discharge. I tell him he should forget the whole thing, but he's still upset. 'I don't want it on my record,' he insists. But he can't catch up with the Congressman, either in New York or Washington, so he comes home discouraged.

And Michael's even more of a handful than ever. I'm thinking of taking a course in guitar playing if Ruth will babysit with him. The truth is, I need some time out.

Just my luck, Ruth decides to go out to New Mexico to be

with Dovey. That's shortly before Roosevelt dies. Boy, is that a shock! What a loss — I sobbed like he's one of my own. Anyhow, about Ruth, she really misses Dovey and I think they want to start a family.

'David says he can find us an apartment in Albuquerque,' she tells us when I'm at Ma's, 'and he'll try to get in as much as possible. Maybe I can find a job out there, he thinks.'

So I drop the idea. I don't want to ask Ma. She's funny that way, you never know how she'll react. And Michael's been sick a lot lately with sore throats and swollen glands. The doctor says, if it continues, his tonsils will have to come out. God, I hope not.

Anyhow, the news from overseas continues to be good, and on May 8, we celebrate V-E Day. What a day!

Other memories . . . the day Eisenhower comes home to a hero's welcome in New York. In June, with huge crowds and police everywhere and ticker tape falling ... and Eisenhower's standing up in a limousine waving his garrison cap, smiling to beat the band, and the sun's glinting on his five stars. LaGuardia's right there alongside him, a big grin on his face, too.

Julie takes off two hours so we can go together to City Hall, where at noon the Mayor presents Eisenhower with a special medal cast in his honour. We can't really see the ceremony, the plaza's packed in tighter than sardines, not an inch of space to breathe, and little kids on their fathers' shoulders are waving American flags and everyone's cheering so hard I have to cover my ears.

I never thought that I'd find myself admiring a military man, but here I am cheering and waving like everyone else around us. It feels so good to be part of this happy crowd, all of us united in victory and for peace.

Julie hears the announcement about the atom bomb driving home from work with one of the guys. He comes in all excited. 'Did y'hear?' he wants to know.

'Hear what?'

'About the atom bomb dropped on Hiroshima?' And he fills me in on the announcement which Truman made this morning. That this new bomb, which is equal to 20,000 tons of TNT, was dropped on Hiroshima yesterday just about the time the Japs were sitting down to their Sunday breakfast. And that the War Department says that there's such an impenetrable cloud of dust and smoke that even the reconnaissance planes sent in afterwards can't begin to make an accurate report of the destruction. What's more, says Julie, Truman warned the Japs that if they don't surrender immediately, we will unleash such a rain of destruction the like of which has never been seen on this earth before.

We look at each other, not sure how to take all of this in. 'So that must be what Dovey's been working on!' he says. 'Whaddya know? Remember he mentioned high explosives? No wonder they didn't want word to get out. The announcer said it's been a race against time with the Germans. Wow! Unbelievable! Do you know what this means?'

I shake my head. Somehow my imagination can't come to grips with it yet, a bomb with so much power for destruction. And yet, I suppose, anything that can end the war sooner seems to make sense.

Two bombs like that – and the war with Japan is over. That's V-J Day, August 14. I don't know it yet, but our problems have just begun.

THIRTY-SEVEN

SEPTEMBER 1945

Then, there's that golden September day, a Saturday – just seven years ago today – and Julie's just walked in with Michael still in his stroller. They bring in autumn with their rosy cheeks and good spirits. I'd asked him to pick up some coffee cake, 'but they were all out of it,' he says, 'so I bought honey cake and *kichel* instead. Okay?'

'Sure, as long as I have something in the house to serve.' Dovey and Ruth got in last night, and he called to say he's stopping by this afternoon.

The doorbell rings and there's Dovey. He looks well, though he's put on some weight again. We've barely said hello, how are you, come in, when he blurts out, 'Well, now you know what we've been up to out there in Los Alamos. Big-time stuff, right?'

'Yeah, we were so excited,' Julie says, 'when we heard. We figured that's what you're in on, right?'

'Right,' he says.

This time, there's no holding him back. Now that the bomb's been dropped, he wants us to know that he's been right in there with all the big shots. The way he's talking you'd think men like Oppenheimer and Teller consulted him on everything.

Of course, we ask him questions. You don't know someone who's working that close to the atom bomb and not ask him questions.

Naturally, I'm curious about the whole set-up – *what's it like?* – and excitedly, he describes it to us. How they're on a mesa in a very isolated area with nothing around for miles and miles, except a few cottonwood trees. 'Like a hill,' he says, 'with very steep sides, and a level top with just these red cliffs around. And the air's very dry and sharp.' But it's very dusty so he always has grit in his hair and mouth, and his shoes are covered with sand. Though Dovey's not a great one for noticing beauty, he's obviously moved by the brilliant sunsets, 'all purples and golds and red', and he tells us how once he got up very early to see the sunrise, and it was spectacular. For Dovey, that's something.

Julie's curious, too, of course – about the scientists working there, what are they like, these men one only reads about. Are they nice guys to work for? Down to earth or absent-minded professor types? Probably all geniuses, Julie says, guys like Oppenheimer and Nils Bohr. He's so impressed that they've been able to do it, not let the Nazis beat us to it. 'What irony, though,' he says, 'the Japs caught what was intended for the Germans.'

But about the bomb itself – how it works, all that stuff? I'm not that interested, and besides, it's got to be much too complicated even to begin to explain it to us, I figure. Besides, Dovey wouldn't know, not on something as high-powered as this that only the most brilliant of the brilliant physicists could even begin to understand.

Mostly, we just want to get a first-hand report on the experience of working on something so momentous, so historic. They're saying this development is going to alter the world we live in, already they're calling it the Nuclear Age, almost the way you'd label some prehistoric era with its dinosaurs or glaciers, Pleistocene or whatever.

I ask about the other people there, what's the life like? Are there families, children on the grounds?

'Yeah,' Dovey says, 'but only the scientists can have their families there; the enlisted men live in temporary barracks, and boy, did they do a lousy job on them! The wind blows right through the cracks. Sure, you see kids around and signs saying Drive Slowly because a kid will run out on the road just as a truck's going by. And there's no diaper service, I heard one woman complain to another.' I'm trying to imagine what it would be like living there with a high fence all around and guards – and the excitement of being present at such a moment in history.

And he goes into a lot of detail describing the explosion when they first tested the bomb out there in the desert in July. Knowing him, I'm wondering if he was really there at the test site, which is the way he makes it sound, or read about it afterwards like the rest of us. After a while, listening to him go on and on, it strikes me that he's suddenly become the world's authority on everything – you should hear him spout off about international politics, atomic energy in the future, Soviet policy, even why Churchill got voted out of office.

He's still talking. 'Now I said to Ruth when they dropped it, if only Russia had the bomb,' he says, 'we'd be set for the next hundred years. No more wars. It figures, America's not going to start up with Russia, and she's not going to start up with us, if each one has it. Right?'

Of course, we agree. That it would be a good thing for everyone. All our friends feel that way. Lots of Americans, in fact. The way the Russians fought back against the Nazis has made them a lot of friends in this country.

'After all,' he continues, 'y'know the Allies wouldn't have lifted a finger to stop Hitler if he'd attacked only Russia and left them alone. That's what Chamberlain was angling for when he handed Czechoslovakia over to Hitler.'

'It's clear,' I say, trying to get a word in edgewise, 'he was giving Hitler a message, the go ahead sign. "Go east, young man." The trouble is Hitler just got too greedy for them. That was his big mistake.'

Julie laughs. 'D'ya know who said, "Go west, young man?"'

'Yes, of course. Horace Greeley from the *Herald Tribune*.' For a moment I'm annoyed with him. 'You don't have to explain my jokes. No kidding, Julie, sometimes you get under my skin.'

'C'mon now, whaddya making a fuss about?' he says.

I'm not sure whether it's Julie or Dovey I'm really getting annoyed with. Dovey's been talking non-stop. Like he can't give up being the centre of attention.

In his own way, my brother is now giving it to both of us. I can read him like a book. He's thinking, See, you always thought I was just a *schmendrik*, a know nothing, you were the big shots, and I was just the moron, the kid brother who flunked out of Brooklyn Polytech ... so what can you expect? That's what you were really thinking every time you looked at me. Both of you, especially Julie, the big shot with the degree in electrical engineering from City. So now I'm the one who knows the really important things. Not such a *schmendrik* after all.

Maybe he's not getting the strong reaction that he wants from us because he grabs a pad from the kitchen table and draws a sketch. 'Here,' he says, 'you wanta see something? *This* is the atom bomb that we dropped on Nagasaki. How d'ya like that!' And he steps back, puts down the pencil and looks at both of us expectantly.

Julie picks up the sketch, looks at it carefully, and says, 'That's a pretty crude sketch. Practically speaking, as an engineer, no one could really make anything out of this,' and he points to the sketch, 'if he had to work from this drawing to really build the bomb. You'd have to know the scale, the proportions, all the specifications.'

Dovey starts blustering, 'Whaddya mean ... '

Right away he's getting sore because he thinks Julie's putting him down. Julie, who's still caught up in what he's explaining, doesn't even notice Dovey's reaction; he continues in that same calm manner that's so natural to him. 'Someplace I read ... way back ... could be five years ago, an article, by the science reporter for the *New York Times* – Lawrence – that the big problem is stockpiling enough U-235, that's the essential material ... so that's where the important breakthrough must've been made   ...

technological advances are the real key.'

Anyhow, Dovey's standing there flushed with a funny expression on his face – like a little kid who brings home a drawing and expects his mother to make a big fuss and praise him, and instead she pats him on the head and says, 'Oh, that's nice, Junior – but why did you give the horse only two legs?'

Julie must notice Dovey's face because he does say, 'Listen Dave, it's all very interesting – fascinating, everything you've been telling us. I've been meaning to ask you – with all this good experience you're getting, maybe we can go into business together after you're out? I've been thinking about it, maybe start a machine shop – we'll manufacture custom-made parts for small companies. I'll help design them and get the business – and you'll make them. And maybe Bernie, your brother,' he turns to me, 'will come in with us, too. How's that sound to you, Dave?'

'We-ll, I'll have to think about it.' His tone is still huffy.

'No rush,' says Julie.

I'm surprised. Julie's already talked to me about going into business for himself after the war, and I'm all for it. 'I never want to go through that business again,' he says, meaning when he got fired. But with Dovey, that he never mentioned. Frankly, I have my doubts.

Dovey gets up. 'Anyhow, I gotta get going ... Ruthie's family is coming over to Ma's to see us, and I got orders to be home by five.'

'Here,' I crunch up the sketch and shove it at him, 'take it with you,' I say. 'I don't want it around.'

Julie laughs at me. 'What are you so afraid of?'

'Listen, if they can fire you, they can do anything.'

Julie makes a motion with his hand as though to say, Forget it! 'I don't want to live like that. This isn't Nazi Germany,' he says.

'Here, Dovey, take it with you ... don't leave it here.' His hand is curled up and I push it into his palm. He looks at his hand and the crumpled-up paper in it, shakes his head at me and says, 'Ettie, Ettie, what's happening to you?' and walks out.

But I'm nervous. Ever since Julie's been fired, this funny feeling hits me at times ... as though it's only the beginning of something more ominous. Why have they started in with this firing business? Julie isn't the only one ... even while the Soviets are our ally, why, I ask myself ... and I can see no good coming from it ... no, that much I know.

So later after he leaves, still all puffed up with himself, I say to Julie, 'Listen to me, don't get into anything with my brother. You know how he is – one minute he's here, the next minute he's there, you just can't count on him. He's still a *boychik*. And not too bright, let's face it, much as I love him.

'And he'll run to Ruth like a little boy, like he always did with Ma. And she'll end up telling him what to do. And she'll keep after him until he does it her way. And her way I don't trust, and I don't trust her. That's how he is – and if he doesn't listen to her, she runs to Ma and gets her to tell him what to do. Between those two, they've got him on strings dancing like a puppet. You think not? Let me tell you, I was there once when Ruth rushes in, crying and carrying on like they're out on the street already. I really got worried.

' "What'sa matter, what's going on?" She's got Ma upset, too.

'How that woman carries on. Finally she tells us what it's all about. "Dovey took two dollars out of the jar I'm saving for new kitchen curtains – and he bets it on a horse!"

'"On a horse?" Ma's aghast.

'"Yeah – not only that, but the horse lost!" More screams.

'"A bum! That's what he's become. How do you know this?" Ma recovers enough to ask her suspiciously. You can see she's not ready to believe anything bad about her *boychik*.

'"I finally got it out of him," says Ruth. So Ma absolutely promises her she'll get him straightened out, don't worry, and I'm sure Dovey caught it from her, but good. This is the guy you're thinking of taking in as a partner? Stay clear of him, Julie – even if he is my own brother.'

But that's how Julie is – once he makes up his mind.

Probably that one decision was the worst mistake we ever made.

Such innocents we were. So blind to the real historical forces at work. How all our dreams began to fall apart once the war's over. Roosevelt's dead and now there's Truman sworn in two hours after the President dies of a cerebral haemorrhage. And in 1946 Churchill comes here to make a speech in Fulton, Missouri – with Truman sitting there – about the Iron Curtain that now divides Europe, and all the propaganda starts about the Cold War. And Truman backs the Marshall Plan and aid to the dictators in Greece and Turkey ... and restoring prosperity to West Germany ... I remember studying about World War One and the aftermath – when Wilson dies (just like Roosevelt – never seeing his peacetime dream come true), and the Palmer Raids and the prosecution of Eugene Debs, and the IWW ... What made me think it would be any different this time?

What if Roosevelt had lived?

OCTOBER 13, 1952

The United States Supreme Court denies *certiorari*, refuses to review the case or to pass on the merits of the appeal. Justice Hugo Black dissents.

THIRTY-EIGHT

OCTOBER–NOVEMBER 1952

There comes a time when you can no longer pretend to yourself that it's all going to turn out all right. Like when you're a kid reading a scary story, knowing they'll never let anything really bad happen – so it's safe to read on to the end.

But in here suddenly, I realize my life has no such built-in guarantee even though Julie and I keep reassuring each other. When he's down, I say it to him, and when I'm down, he says it to me. Like an amulet that we pass back and forth between us as needed. Today when we saw each other, it was his turn.

'You'll see, sweetheart – it's happening slowly now, that's true, outrage followed by a popular outcry and then support from all over – but it'll come. Ever since the *National Guardian* published those articles about our case last fall, a National Committee *has* been formed to fight for us, isn't that so? You'll see, it'll pick up as soon as the people understand the importance of our case – give them a little time – they'll come to know what it means to them, to all of us. You'll see, don't give up hope, my darling, ever. It'll work out, you'll see.'

And I want to believe him – though sometimes I wish he wouldn't use so much Party rhetoric – just as he believes me when I say these same words to him. My spirits lift and when I go back to my cell, I lie there with my eyes closed and imagine in beautiful Technicolor the day that we're released from Sing Sing.

A sunny day, the sky as clear as that morning in 1944 when we arrived at Budd Lake in New Jersey with Michael for a week's vacation. Julie was still working for the Army Signal Corps then. I've never seen such a clear open sky – a blue that cleared the sky of any other colour.

And this beautiful dream, it's always the same. It always begins outside the prison gates. Julie is already there waiting for me – in that old tweed jacket I love and a blue shirt open at the neck, no tie, a few stray hairs dipping down on his forehead as always, with good colour in his cheeks – not the way he's become, so pale and washed out, sickly looking, his neck thin and stringy. And for a moment, as I come through the gates, we pause and look at each other, almost like strangers deciding to fall in love again and I feel so shy and young again in this dried-out body that's lived immured and alone for so many days and nights. Will he want this body and this woman again? As he takes my hand, we fall easily into step and walk away from that nightmare.

But today, when he murmurs those reassurances to me, they fly by my ears. Instead I'm listening to Ma months ago reciting facts. 'You'll die ... '

Why this crashing drastic change?

Yesterday, October 13, was our unlucky day. The Supreme Court refused to review our case. Only Justice Black dissented.

I think my hopes rested with the Supreme Court. Somehow I always saw them as removed and insulated from the daily hustle of politics. I figure, they're secure enough to follow their own true bent – and conscience. Funny I should say that, when I'm in prison precisely because of one man's lack of conscience. My own brother. Still, those Supreme Court judges are on the bench for life, so it seems to me they don't have to wheel and deal like Kaufman and all the other small fry judges fighting to move up. Of course, I'm thinking of Justices Marshall and Holmes – and Brandeis and Cardozo, men like that. And my hopes rest with Frankfurter – maybe a vote for us there, and William Douglas, who's a liberal and a fighter. And Hugo Black, a southerner who's certainly a changed man from the one who long ago admitted he once belonged to the Ku Klux Klan. And Robert

Jackson — after all, I figure, a man who's been one of the prosecutors at the Nuremberg Trials could be counted on in a case where anti-Semitism was clearly operating ... Julie told me he heard one of the FBI guys say to another while they were questioning him, 'Sooner or later, these kikes all break. No guts!'

So how come only Justice Black dissented?

November 29, 1952

I haven't written to Julie for weeks ... and I told Manny today not to come back next week. I'm sick and tired of his excuses, his reasoning, that pseudo-calm placating manner of his. Someplace along the line, Manny gave up and threw in the sponge — and has never admitted it to himself, or anyone else. The man flails, he's not in there fighting tooth and nail like Murray used to.

And Julie can't see it and won't face it — and when I broach it — maybe bring in someone else, another lawyer, *there must be another lawyer*, sharp, a born fighter not yet worn down, he grows pale and backs away from my words as though gasoline's been poured on them and I'm striking a match. Through his glasses, he looks at me and replies, oh so calmly, 'You're getting carried away by your feelings' — his standard argument always. How alike the two of them are. 'Don't get so worked up.' Why not? *It's our lives and our children's lives we're fighting for!*

But if and when I have to walk down that corridor, the long walk, that last time, I've made up my mind — it'll be for my own good reasons and not for anyone else's — or the Party's.

THIRTY-NINE

DECEMBER 1952

December 6, 1952

Recently, I've started a new list. This one deals with silence and silences . . . why not, I'm surrounded by it, a palpable silence that encloses me – like a noxious gas I have to fight off.

So far, I've listed the ones that have occurred to me, in the order in which they've occurred ... like this:

SILENCES

1 Silent accusations ... these came from my mother.

2 Silent assents ... there are things women have silently assented to that men will not abide hearing about, and this has been going on for centuries, unspoken, unacknowledged except between the women. It enrages men to learn they've been a party to this deception and injustice, so they deny it, and it will take women to talk about it.

3 Silent understandings ... the things Julie and I understand about our situation that we are not free to discuss.

December 11, 1952

I've been observing this woman I live with.

The hunger that's consuming her is with her when she awakens and stays with her until she passes out. The emptiness pursues her constantly, it never leaves her.

The nights are the worst. When the lights are lowered and she says good night to the matron, alone in the dark cave of her cell, she becomes a ravenous animal.

At first she nibbles on a potato chip or two as she reads by the dim light near her cot, but then the tempo picks up ... three ... four ... five ... six seven eight nine get it down get it down and she stuffs the chips into her mouth as fast as she can with no more pretence at reading. Strangely enough, each night starts out the same way, believing that she will only *nosh* a little, but once she starts, nothing in the world can stop her.

Finishing the chips, she rips open a bag of corn fritos and chomps her way through them. On and on until the prison floor is littered with empty bags and cartons.

Her favourite is Mallomars. Somehow that combination of dark chocolate with the spongy marshmallow inside appeals to her most, but often the commissary runs out of them, and she buys something else, anything else, maybe Oreos or Sunshine Sugar Wafers, it doesn't matter as long as it's sweet.

Gradually the sweetness coats her mouth, seeps into her veins, flows into her pelvis. Eating steadily on through the dark hours, her belly swells, nausea fills her throat, and finally, as the night sky fades into grey, she dozes off, only to be aroused by the early sun.

Washing, the mirror confronts her, her eyes smoky, her round face blurred. Only her lips grow tighter and smaller.

During the day, exhausted, eyes out of focus, she yearns for sleep. Yet secretly she makes preparations for this nightly seizure. For that's what it is. Every day she stocks up at the prison commissary as though for a long hard winter.

But it's never enough. She's first in line when the commissary opens. The cashier, a Sing Sing trusty and a kindly man, bluntly stares at her. For even if she's passing out treats to the matrons on all three shifts, she can't possibly use up all that food. One time he says to her, 'Ethel, are you trying to get bigger than the electric chair?'

Weakly she smiles.

She hides the food in her cell, under the hard mattress, behind books or a photo, wherever possible. Julie, after a few weeks, notices the change in her. 'Ethel,' he says mildly, 'aren't you putting on some weight?'

'So? So what if I am?'

'Look, I love you anyway.'

Thanks, she's thinking. Gee, thanks. 'I can't understand it,' she says, 'y'know, not on the garbage they feed us.'

'I know. Maybe a little exercise?'

'Yeah, I'm thinking about it ... I'll have to do something.'

During the day she pretends that nothing strange lies in wait for her at night. Yet more and more she waits for the night as a friend. When they bring in her tray she eats nicely, knowing the nights are hers. She's a good prisoner and gives them no trouble.

Like dreaming and making love, the eating has become a separate activity, disconnected from her daytime routine when she rigidly adheres to her schedule of meals, reading, writing, and walks in the prison yard. Lately she's refused to see Julie ... or Manny ... or her sons.

Tossing, on her cot, sometimes towards dawn, as she caresses her nipples, she wonders what would happen if they ever had the chance to be alone again. As she lovingly plays her hands over her swollen abdomen, she imagines what she desires most out there ... sex ... food ... surcease ...

As autumn reaches towards winter, memories encroach on her nights, gripping her with iron hands so that she can't elude them even as she tears open another wrapper with her teeth. Though she still eats savagely, the soothing sensation that's like mother's milk in her mouth no longer comes over her. Nor does the taste of the soft white inside of Mallomars lull her. Instead, in her ears ... Michael's scream over the phone as she tells him the verdict ... Kaufman ordering their murder ... worst of all, silence ... the dead silence of that moment when they throw the switch. Then the night's silence seizes her body and shakes it unmercifully.

Tonight as the cold December moon watches her through the small window high up, she gorges for several hours on Wise's Potato Chips, Utz's Bavarian Pretzels, Hershey bars with almonds, Goldenberg's Peanut Chews, Baby Ruth's, O'Henry's, Milky Ways, Tootsie Rolls, Jube Jubes, and Good and Plenty's, and boxes of Nabisco Chocolate Chip Cookies, Lemon Snaps, Pecan Chews and Animal Crackers. She never stops. Suddenly she shudders, then observes the trembling of her limbs. She can see it all so clearly now out there in the spotlight. *It's all happening in a play.*

December 31, 1952

Returning to my cell this afternoon after seeing Dr Singer, I felt the deepest wrench yet, a cry from so deep within that it could barely rupture the entwined tissues growing over it, as though it were buried in a forsaken garden riddled with browned old roots and dry stalks.

That cry? Eerie. Strangled. Felt, more than heard?

What is it that I have always known and never been able (or willing) to disclose to myself? That in my deepest recesses, I've always known that I was unwanted, that my coming was a burden to my mother, and that I've been trying to make it up to her ever since.

FEBRUARY 11, 1953

President Eisenhower denies the Rosenbergs' petition for clemency. Dr Singer's visits with Ethel are no longer permitted. A new execution date is set for the week of March 9.

FORTY

JANUARY 1953

Sing Sing Manor
January 1, 1953

More about SILENCES. Add this one.

4   Silent withholdings ... The words not spoken that cry out to be said.

Ma, did you know that when there's only silence between humans, close behind, breathing hard, is death?

You are my mother and I wish you could have shown me the way.

There are words I wish you had spoken to me that I needed to hear you say.

That you love me no matter what. There's such a hunger in me to hear you say those words to me, if only once.

And yet I know now that you never will, no matter what I do, or how hard I try.

I also know now that I deserve those words, even if you have never said them to me.

January 6, 1953

When Dr Singer came today, I handed him this:

> IF YOU ACT LIKE ALL YOU DESERVE IS
> CRUMBS, PEOPLE WILL END UP FEEDING
> THEM TO THE OTHER BIRDS.

He smiled.

Sometimes it's good for him, and for me, to know that he doesn't know everything about me.

Today I pretended to leave with him when he left, and we

drove back to New York together in his convertible with the top down, talking leisurely like old friends, and he drops me at the apartment. The boys are watching *Captain Video* and at first they don't look up even, and then they see me – and their excitement as they jump into my arms practically knocks me over, and we hug and laugh and cry.

And then I'm back in here again.

January 9, 1953

Lately I've become an observer of my own silence ... ah yes, an ongoing depression for months that makes it hard to get out of bed in the morning ... just want to pull the covers over my head, and stay in bed and cry ... and some days I do just that ... Dr Singer this last visit pointed out that it was really anger I'm feeling with Ma, and that I'm turning it on myself. And as soon as he said it, I knew he was right. An anger that's been hiding in me for years. I've been drunk with anger ... mostly misdirected against myself ... and also against those I care most about ... critical, dissecting them ... Julie, Manny ... of course, who else? ... I'll show them, all of them ... I don't need any of them, who needs them anyway?

January 11, 1953

More about SILENCES.

It's not my 'mother tongue' but my tongue that's becoming unlocked. By a free-flowing anger – most of all, with my mother, and with David and my whole family. To them, all I am is a sacrificial lamb. They have no feelings for me as a daughter and a sister.

The anger in me keeps soaring like Jack's beanstalk. Dough swelling with yeast! When I start to imagine that last walk – forcing me, a strong healthy woman with two small children – and my husband the same – to walk on my own two feet to the execution chamber to be electrocuted, I have to stop myself because my anger becomes impossible to contain. I feel as though I will physically splatter all over the walls. Only once before have I felt so explosive – during the strike. And if I need anything now, I know I need my sanity and that ability which Julie has always praised – to think clearly and rationally. And lately after feeling so depressed for months – thank God for Dr Singer! – that's become my goal, not to let the anxiety about the children and what'll happen to them, or anger, swallow me up so I'll become helpless and befuddled or go out of control.

My goal up to now has been simple – not to surrender to madness. For that's been my overwhelming fear. Yes, I see it now. Once I saw a woman, a neighbour of ours at Knickerbocker Village, go crazy after she got a telegram that her son had been killed in the Battle of the Bulge. Her family, they lived over our apartment and we could hear her shrieking and moaning all the time. It went on for weeks – even when the doctor came and gave her a shot, it didn't help for long. Finally, they called the ambulance from Bellevue and they came and took her away. When she came home several months later, she was a changed woman, so quiet I never heard her open her mouth again, shrunken and stooped, always with eyes on the ground. Her married daughter with whom she lived told me they gave her some kind of shock therapy. 'At least she quieted down,' she said. That's what I've feared more than anything. But not any more.

Words alien to the *Mamaloschen*, my mother tongue, come flocking in. Shibboleth, miasma, burdensome, parapet, even those beautiful words – incandescent, effulgent, revelation. What a freedom, to speak with my own tongue. I must ask Molly for a dictionary, surely there must be one in the prison library so I can look up these words, and so many others, that used to feel so foreign, not mine, even when I wrote them, and now they belong to me. My fingers are flying over the keys of this typewriter.

FORTY-ONE

JANUARY 1953

January 12, 1953

Today I said to Dr Singer, 'You know, I've never talked to you about Julie ... how I feel about him. You've probably wondered, haven't you?' I look at him. No expression. Yet I know he's just driven all the way from New York to keep our appointment and it's snowing, and I feel such a rush of gratitude for his kindness and devotion. 'Have I told you lately how much I appreciate your coming?' He smiles and brushes aside the thanks. So I continue, 'I bet other patients do, I mean, talk about their husbands ... their fights, money, kids, in-laws, how they can't stand them ... even their sex life. Honestly, at Knickerbocker Village, you'd hear just about everything! Nothing is sacred when women stand around outside with nothing to do except keep an eye on the kids and gab. The personal things they talk about, I couldn't believe! And gossiping about each other – that, too. So I never said much, whatever's going on between Julie and me is strictly between the two of us. I would have felt disloyal. Nor to my mother – not the way she felt about Julie from Day One. Never. But still sometimes I wished I had a best girlfriend, someone I really trusted, felt close to ... oh, I was friendly with all of them, sure – at least until Julie was arrested, after that you would've thought I was invisible – except to a few loyal friends. But even before, I was never close ... you see, basically Julie was a very good husband, totally devoted to us, and he worked so hard ... too hard, every night late, the business was eating him up alive. "Julie," I'd protest, "what kind of life is this ... you're never home ... "

'"But right now I have to put in such long hours," he'd

explain. "But once we make it, you'll see, Ethel, it'll give us the kind of life we want. A little more money. We'll move out to Long Island, like the Kaplans, and get out of this neighbourhood finally. I want to as much as you.'

'The truth is, though, that he was never a businessman. That becomes clear. He never charged his customers enough ... and just meeting bills! I used to dread the first of the month ... I know, Dr Singer, I still owe you ... '

'Don't worry about it,' he says, and dismisses it with a wave of his hand.

'But I do ... The truth is he never should've gone into business ... especially a partnership with David of all people. It was counter to his make-up, making a profit goes against his grain ... so he couldn't push customers to pay up because he felt sorry for them, imagine! "Give this one a little more time," he'd say to me when I'm helping him out with the bookkeeping. "The guy was practically crying over the phone to me the other day." Same thing, couldn't fire a guy who wasn't doing his job ... I remember this one particular guy, Sammy ... didn't know how to drive a nail in straight and still Julie doesn't want to fire him. "What'll happen to his family?" he asks me.

' "Julie," I could feel myself getting annoyed, "enough with the buts," I'd say, "how about feeling a little sorry for us?"

' "Ethel, we'll manage, we're not out on the street yet." And he'd get up and walk out. Discussion closed.

'So then it was up to me to manage somehow ... especially when things were going from bad to worse between him and David. I'm the one who has to face the guy in the grocery store down the street, and the butcher, and write the cheques for the rent, phone bill, the doctor, all that, and hold my breath the cheques wouldn't bounce. So when I heard them spinning those fairy-tales about how much money Julie was getting as head of a spy ring for the Russians, it's like they're talking about someone else. I tell you, Dr Singer,

227

there were lots of times when I was up to here with Julie being such a good guy in everyone's eyes. Because I'm the one who's catching it. At times I made up my mind to go back to work – anything to help out. But he wouldn't hear of it ... the same old story, *a mother should be home with the kids.*

' "Even when Michael's driving me up a wall?" I want to ask. I didn't because I knew his answer without asking. "He needs you." Those are fatal words to a woman, a mother, you know that, Dr Singer?'

This time he agrees with me.

FORTY-TWO

JANUARY 1953

January 13, 1953

Yesterday was to have been our execution day. The second one.

The first time, Judge Kaufman orders us killed on May 21 last year, only a few weeks after the trial ends. The guy's in a hurry. But the law intervenes on our behalf. So he yields, reluctantly, of course, and resets the date, this time for yesterday. And again it's postponed. So now it's for March 9. Less than two months away.

So I'm thinking, rightfully – no, that's the wrong word – 'wrongfully', I should be dead today. Interesting thought – to know with such certainty that is the day, the very day you are going to die. Now I ask you, how many people have such certainty about the most important fact of life – death. And, as the time approaches, even the exact hour. Think about all the despair – and hope – generated by this uncertainty. So Kaufman generously decides he'll spare us all that. He grants us foreknowledge. What power he commands! How good it must make him feel! Bigger! Stronger! More potent in bed! And how it must feed his ambition!

As I think about it, only suicides and inmates on Death House Row have such unrelenting certainty. And even suicides can't be sure. A morbid thought, still I wonder what the failure rate is, and what's considered 'success'. Depends, I suppose, whose point of view you're talking about. The suicide, or the family – or the Party, or the government. How would mine be viewed? – even if I were to consider such a possibility. Which I have, I have, who wouldn't? Saypol, Cohn, Kaufman and Co. wouldn't like it – they need a live body on the day of execution to wreak justice upon, to serve as a living example of what happens if you're poor and Jewish and a Communist in the US in 1953 AD. The Party wouldn't either – unless I'm portrayed as a victim of this infamous frame-up. Family? My mother? My beloved brother, David? Might save them some embarrassment. Vindicate David's sell-out. Friends? How many now that we're here? Julie, my kids ... I'd better stop right here ... tears blur these words ...

Back to what got me started on this ... that if Kaufman had his way, *I should be dead today. But I'm not.* I convince myself by holding my left wrist in my right hand and feel for the pulse.

Yup, by golly ... it's there ... and I cross my legs and tap my left knee with the back of my hairbrush and my leg jumps, just like in the doctor's office, so I know my reflexes are quote 'normal', unquote.

How normal can I be, though, under these abnormal circumstances? How 'normal' is it to hear Julie call out to someone from the adjoining corridor (the steel doors that seal us off from each other must be slightly ajar), and know that I won't see him for six days, and then only for one hour. He's calling someone named Harry, and it's his normal voice, the one he uses in Knickerbocker Village when he leans out the window and yells to the janitor outside, 'Hey, Harry, can you come up here a minute?' Funny coincidence, it's the same name.

That Harry, from Dachau, speaks only a broken English and Julie is trying to help him with the Immigration Service. That's my Julie. So who's this Harry he's calling to? That, I figure, is only the normal curiosity of a wife.

That's reassuring.

FORTY-THREE

FEBRUARY 1953

February 6, 1953

'Dear Manny,' I wrote him today.

'I'm worried about Robby, he was so stuffed up on his visit last Saturday. And also, I saw on his report card that he's been out a lot with sore throats and swollen glands. Maybe he needs a tonsillectomy? Please get him a check-up with a paediatrician, and let me know what he says.

'Also Michael's tenth birthday is coming up soon. Any way you can sound him out on what he'd like from us?

'I appreciate all this so much. And look forward to seeing you next week.

Your devoted admirer
Ethel

PS. Any word on our petition to Eisenhower?

February 10, 1953

Julie, my dearest Valentine (I wrote him today, though whether they'll pass it on to him I doubt),

I want you, I miss you, I crave you inside of me.

I want you here with me, both of us bathed in sunlight – remember how it streamed into the kitchen of our apartment? – you reading, totally absorbed in the print, or turning pages quickly, scanning, hearing, or maybe not hearing me as I moved around the kitchen talking to you, opening drawers, putting food away in the refrigerator, washing the dishes, calling to the kids outside, whatever. I want so much to be back there doing the very same housework I used to scorn, foolishly believing it took me away from doing the important things I was meant to do, though exactly what they were now, I can't remember any more. Right now I would gladly settle for a boring routine day back in Knickerbocker Village wiping snotty noses and fixing Michael his beloved ham sandwich every single day! Which used to drive me crazy. Other kids will, at least, try peanut butter and jelly. Not Michael. 'What do you want for lunch, Michael?' Maybe today he'd say American cheese or even salami. Tuna I'd given up on. 'Be reasonable, Michael,' I'd plead. 'Egg salad?' 'No!' 'Sliced chicken – from last night? It's delicious, here take a bite.' 'No, I want ham on white bread, no rye,' he'd order and stare back at me, tilting back in his chair, never yielding an inch. That's some *boychik* we've got, Julie!

I'll even take the day after your arrest, when nobody would get on the elevator with me, the time Michael and I came up from the laundry room in the basement to the ground floor and the doors opened, waited, and slowly closed as our neighbours (some neighbours!) stood there and turned their lily-livered faces away from me, pretending, I guess, I didn't exist or the elevator either – and we had to ride up alone, the elevator rattling its chains as a cold chill grabbed hold of my bones. Was it like that for the Jews in Hitlerland – neighbours, friends, turning blind faces away as the Gestapo dragged them away during the night?

Julie, what do I want from you at this moment? Sex, of course, and something else, too. I don't know what it is exactly, but let me try to say it – that it's the sense of fullness and completion – that sensation of total union that you bring to me, my lover, when we're together. Do you realize that it's twenty-nine months to the day today since we last made love? You must remember? (Warden, are you reading this? Getting a vicarious thrill, are you? Read on then, I refuse to be inhibited by your voyeuristic eyes.) It was the night before the FBI dragged you out of the apartment. The tall one with the sleepy dangerous eyes, and the other guy, the little puppy following on his heels, I wanted to maul them so they'd bleed like the pigs they were, daring to look with their piggish eyes on our few belongings, what they called the evidence ... of our poverty, our joy? My second-hand typewriter next to a children's story I'd written and had ready to submit to *Jack and Jill*. Big-time spies, right? Caught in their lair using fairy-tales to pass on information. Clever! What dangers there lie concealed in Little Red Riding Hood and the Wolf! Can't you see the Seven Little Dwarfs as a spy ring? I wanted to bite that viper's hand, how dare he put those burning steel handcuffs on your gentle wrists, those wrists I love to kiss so I can feel your heartbeat under my lips! Julie, why didn't I? What madness it drives one to when you're trying to behave in a civilized way under such extreme provocation! You should have seen me during that strike long ago at National – 1935? '36? – how I fought back when the police charged our picket line – you should have seen me! You would have been proud of me, I tell you, not this same craven woman who stood by quietly, biting her lips not to cry out – or to bite back like a rabid dog – as they took you away from us. Believe me, the taste of that cop's blood is still in my mouth and feeds the anger raging in me now for what they're doing to us and our children.

But this urge right now is so powerful, Julie, I could tear these bars apart and go to you like a bitch in heat. So why do I crouch here like a dumb senseless animal on this miserable cot, unable to budge, unable to do all the sensible things I must do to get through another poisonous day in this foul place?

Help me, Julie, help me with the sound and feel of you. I need to conjure you up in front of my eyes to slake my thirst, for at this moment I'm filled with such a wanting you, yet knowing it's impossible for today – and tomorrow – and the day after, too, and on and on so it feels like it'll go on for ever. And patience, my darling, who has often cautioned me about this, has *never* been one of my virtues. What's more, knowing it was *never* the whole answer. Ever. Remember, my beloved? That's what made it so delicious, so exciting, so tantalizing.

Just to be in the same room with you, to see you dressing in the morning, fresh from a shower, slow, deliberate, tying your shoelaces, stuffing the shirt tails into your pants and zipping up before a final look in the mirror on the closet door, or taking off your glasses and placing them carefully next to the bed before making love to me. And those luxurious languid Sunday afternoons when the boys were still little and napped? Even to imagine that now opens me up like a flower.

What am I saying, this woman whom the yellow press describes as stoical, a traitor with no feelings or regrets. Does it make any sense? Does it make our separation at 354 Hunter Street, Ossining, New York, on the Hudson, better or worse? If only they'd put us in the same cell, drape curtains over the bars and forget about us ... no, I don't really mean that, our boys are always there for me, my concern, our need to work out something for them for the present while we're stuck in here. *And the fight we must fight and win!*

But just for a few hours? My lover, always. I love you.

FORTY-FOUR

FEBRUARY 1953

February 12, 1953

Manny informs me that President Eisenhower has refused to grant us clemency.

The newspaper reports that at 4.30 p.m. yesterday, 'Mr Herbert Brownell, Jr, the Attorney General, brought the records of the case to the White House. At 5.07 p.m. a prepared statement was given out to reporters.'

Thirty-seven minutes it took him to review the records, which are voluminous, and to decide, after 'careful consideration', that justice has been done.

The President went on to say, 'It is the woman who is the strong and recalcitrant character, the man who is the weak one.'

They expected weakness from me, and instead I showed them strength. A good enough reason to condemn me to die.

The moral is, I presume, that as a woman, weak and submissive, I would be spared. Strong and resolute, I have to die.

One other bit of news Manny brought me today. That, in view of President Eisenhower's decision, the Warden informed him that Dr Singer's visits with me are terminated as of now.

Just like that! Sadists!

The only plus in this hellhole is that I can get mad as hell, yell, pound, scream out my lungs, and nobody stops me any more or cares.

Mr President,

Would you like to know what it's really been like for me? This woman, Ethel Rosenberg, whom you describe as 'strong and recalcitrant'?

I can still see it as though it's happening now, a scene I'm watching from the wings. It's a night like any other hot night in New York when it's too hot to breathe, and your thighs chafe from rubbing against each other so you keep applying talcum and thinking, I've got to lose some weight. I'm in the kitchen getting dinner ready. Our kitchen that's small, cramped and needs a good painting, apartment-house beige I call it. Over in the far corner on the right as you walk in, there's a white chipped sink with a drainingboard, and underneath, the pipes show. It's also where I keep the garbage can and the tin pail for mopping the floor. Next to it, a beige and black stove with space underneath for pots and pans, and the oven. Opposite the stove, right by the door, is a chipped white enamel table. We bought it from a private party in 1948 through an ad in the *Sunday Times*, along with four kitchen chairs for fifteen dollars; they came down from twenty-five. What a funny expression – private party! Do you suppose with all the headlines, I'm now a public party? Anyhow, they're a young couple in Brooklyn near the Brighton line station at Kings Highway and they're moving to a development in Syosset. Part of me envied them, moving out to Long Island. Nice for kids growing up. The chairs didn't match; it doesn't matter, I told myself, it's a lot of bourgeois crap.

In our kitchen the refrigerator's opposite the sink next to the wall, and for some crazy reason, the door opens from right to left, instead of from left to right like a normal refrigerator. You can't imagine how inconvenient that is,

Mr President – every time you open the refrigerator door, you're caught between the refrigerator, the wall and the door. Each time you take something out, you have to hold it in one hand, close the door with the other while getting out of the way of the door, put the package or jar down on the sink opposite and then go through the whole crazy business again for something else. Eight years we live in Knickerbocker Village? Well, for eight years I keep asking for another refrigerator, one that opens from left to right. And for eight years, I get promises … 'it's on order' … 'next week for sure' … 'soon' … and 'we'll check today why it hasn't come in' … and that night when the doorbell rings, I'm still boxed in by that damn refrigerator, can you believe it? At the very moment there's this long insistent ring.

It's loud enough so I hear it over the radio which Michael has turned up to listen to *The Lone Ranger*. 'Never mind, I'll get it!' I yell, grab the dishtowel, and wipe my hands. Julie came home very tired so he's resting in the bedroom, and I don't want him disturbed.

I go into the hall, turn on the light, straighten my housedress, and after a moment, I open the door.

Two men in gabardine trench coats like army officers, but wearing grey hats with dark bands and brims like in a gangster movie, step inside one after the other, and close the door behind them. It's my home and they're inside it, and I don't say a word because my heart is pumping so hard.

Both men speak simultaneously, quickly. 'Mrs Rosenberg? We're from the FBI,' and they both flash badges and quickly return them to the inside pockets of their matching jackets. Like a vaudeville team. One's tall, the other's short. 'We'd like to talk with your husband.'

What a crazy business. If you can believe it, my first thought when I see them? The apartment's a mess, what'll they think?

Even if David hadn't already been arrested in June, and Julie called in for questioning once, two official-looking men at our door would scare me. For that matter, any Jew. It's in our blood, that chilling fear. It always strikes out of nowhere. *What have I done?* Even when the police come around selling tickets for their Benevolent Association Dance, my heart used to leap ... I'm rambling ... I know it ... a fault of mine whenever the needle inside jumps and I have to go back to something I'd rather forget ... Part of me stays calm, though ... I can't let them see how frightened I am. They'll read it as guilt, and besides, for the children's sake ... So I say, 'Look, my husband's asleep ... I'll have to wake him up.'

The tall one who acts like he's in charge motions to me – *Go get him,* and then he barks at Michael, 'Hey kid, turn that damn thing off!'

Michael turns around, looks at him indifferently. 'Not yet ... it's not over.'

The FBI guy, without another word, walks over and flicks it off. Michael runs over and takes my hand. Robby's already clinging to my skirt, and holding them both so, I walk into the bedroom. Julie's out cold on Michael's bed, curled up like one of the kids. I shake him gently. He trembles ... and wakens. 'Wha ... What?' He automatically reaches for his glasses and sits up.

'Julie ... there are two men here from the FBI. They want to talk to you.'

Running fingers through his hair, still groggy, he stumbles into the living-room.

'You're coming with us,' says the tall guy. A clang of panic strikes within me.

Robby runs into the bedroom and comes back dragging his chewed-up security blanket with his thumb in his mouth. Michael asks the tall one, 'What's happening?' The guy ignores him and tells Julie to empty all his pockets. I'm standing there like a dummy.

Julie ignores him and squats down so he's eye to eye with

238

Michael. 'Look, Michael, they probably just want me to go downtown with them to answer some questions ... maybe I'll have to stay overnight.' Then he starts emptying his pockets, some change, keys, a scrap of paper with a customer's address, toothpicks, his wallet, soiled tissues.

'Okay, let's get moving,' says the tall one.

The two men surround him and whip handcuffs on his wrists. Handcuffs! In shock he stares at the cold steel.

I make an instant decision. 'Julie, I'm going with you ... I'll come back here later. I'll ask Terry Grossman if the boys can stay with them.'

The tall guy says, 'Okay, why don't you use the phone, just keep it short.'

As I go to use the phone, the short guy comes back from the bedroom with our Brownie reflex and my Timex.

'This is the only camera I could find,' he says, 'pushed back on the upper shelf in their closet. Behind some blankets, closet's a mess. And look at this room,' he exclaims with disgust, 'toys, pieces from jigsaw puzzles, blocks, crayons, potato chips, crumbs all over the floor. What slobs! That's a Commie for you ... and they think they can make a better world for people like us! Oh, the watch was in the kitchen, on the drainingboard ... no jewel box.'

As I'm dialling, the tall one's speaking. 'Two agents are coming in after we leave. They'll do the whole job.' Then he calls out to me, 'Listen, perhaps you better tell your neighbour you want the kids to stay there tonight.'

'Terry?' I say when she answers. 'No, no, I'm okay. Yes, really ... I just wanted to ask you a favour. Please tell me if it's okay, will you. Can Michael and Robby stay over with you tonight? Maybe you have a cot? I have one – it's in the hall closet ... Well, they're taking Julie ... to their ... uh, office ... yeah ... for some questioning ... I thought I'd go along ... yeah, I'll be back but I'm not sure what time. You will? How can I thank you enough! Look, Robby sleeps with a small light on. Would you have one? No? So take it from the top of our bureau – you'll see it – it's a Mickey Mouse figure holding up a small bulb in his hand. Oh sure, things will go okay. *Thanks, I know you wish us well.*'

FORTY-FIVE

MARCH 1951

To continue, Mr President.

The evening before the trial, I had this weird but exhilarating premonition that the case will be dismissed right off. That Manny's motion will be granted by Kaufman. Why not! The law of the land, the Constitution and the Bill of Rights will prevail. *I feel it, I just know it*. There I am, in my favourite chariot, delivered to the door of the House of Detention by a liveried chauffeur and royally I climb in and take off.

So I issue an open invitation. 'Hey everybody,' I call out, 'come by Rosenberg's deli!' That's what they call my cell. I'm always loaded up with food and I love to have company.

So we sing and tell jokes and laugh and I do imitations of a couple of the matrons who are off duty. There's one I swear must've worked in a concentration camp. I wind up reciting my final lines from *The Valiant* and even Jim's ... 'Cowards die many times before their deaths; the valiant never taste of death but once' ... Goose-pimples break out on my arms and I feel a sudden chill like an icebag's plunked down in my gut. The excitement drains out of me like an unplugged drain.

The rest of the night I'm shivering constantly. The next morning, getting dressed to go into court, I'm a wreck. My hands won't stop shaking. Finally I give up. Pauline, from the next cell, gently brushes my hair and even puts on some lipstick for me. 'It'll be okay, baby, you'll see,' she says. 'Just hang on, you'll do fine.' She keeps talking like that until I have to leave to get into the police van.

Outside, a tall thin woman in a worn winter coat and dark hat comes up to me, a loser in life – you can tell by the sour slump of her mouth – anyhow, she grabs my hand and gives it a hard squeeze. 'Listen,' she says, 'you know what I wish for you?' I look at her. 'They should send you right back to hell – that's where you dirty Commie traitors belong!' Already I'm public property.

Reporters and photographers are crowding around, asking questions, snapping pictures. That's the picture you've seen of me splashed across the front pages ... my eyes looking back at you with no expression, my lips tightly locked. *You won't get anything out of me*, that's what one person told me it was like. Others, even some of the matrons, said to me, 'That's a terrible picture of you, Ethel. It's not you, so unfriendly and cold, like a different woman.' Still that's the one that got printed in every newspaper all over the world, that people remember *as me*. My face frozen stiff. The whole time in court my hands are like ice, and my feet knock together under the table. I know that if I allow myself to feel anything, I'll go to pieces.

So what can I tell you about the trial? Don't believe the papers? But people do. Undoubtedly, Mr President – you did, too. A good part of the time I was in shock – I saw myself, Ethel Rosenberg, being transformed by the government and the press into a woman I didn't know, a woman whose steely lips wouldn't betray a word ... held back the story the whole world was waiting breathlessly to hear. They were waiting for me, Ethel Rosenberg, to speak. *Confess! Confess!* As if I had such a confession to make – about three slimy Jews ringing their oily hands in glee, two Judases and one Delilah, ready to do in the United States, ready to sell it out to the Russians for a few lousy dollars, a camera and a ladies' watch! They were pushing me, invent a story, coaching me, anything, but damn it, play your part! Don't run out on the show!

The trouble is, the script was being written for me, not by the one person who knew the real truth – namely, me! – but by those playwrights, those tremendous talents – you've heard of them? Clifford Odets? Maxwell Anderson? Lillian

Hellman? Arthur Miller? No, Saypol, Kaufman and Cohn. You ever heard of them before the trial? Not me either. Not till the day I was arrested – then I began to know all about them, believe me.

Yes, they were counting on me, all right, figuring they'd put the screws on me. Our two little sons left *ahf hefker*, lost, frightened, bewildered, no mother, no father, torn from us. And my own mother pleading with me, confess, Ettie, tell them the truth, whatever Dovey said, anything, *genug schein*. What truth, Ma, yours or mine? And my own kid brother's life at stake. David that I carried in my arms when he was a baby. And Julie – Julie, my star-crossed lover. Oh Julie, my beloved, from whence did this plague descend upon us? These locusts? I never really understood what was happening ... and where is our Moses? ... Manny Bloch? No, Manny can't do it. He isn't the man for the job though he means well. I love him like a father. So how can I tell him this?

I never could have imagined all this, not even in my wildest dreams, not even if I am one of the world's Great Dreamers. Not this, ever.

What a set-up for an onstage confession right there in the courtroom! In time for the five star extra. What real life drama! Can you imagine the applause when I would've finished? It would have been the longest, most dramatic scene in the history of the theatre and they wrote it just for me. Then they collect the royalties and I go to prison like a good girl with a fifteen-year sentence like David. Watch, he'll be out in a flash! And I turned it down. That they never expected.

I must admit our senior yearbook predicted it. I would have been America's leading actress – not in 1950, but in 1951. They missed by only one year. Not bad when you're forecasting twenty years in advance. Could Gallup have done better?

But I let them down. I told the truth – and they didn't want to believe me. What a letdown! All that tremendous preparation – and me, I walk off the stage. Nothing more to say than what I'd said before, over and over and over again. We hadn't done anything. Talk? Talk is cheap. It's the only thing left for poor people. What else do we have? Power? Money? Cars? An estate in the country? And for talk you go to the electric chair? Since when? In America? It says so in the Bill of Rights?

'She blew her lines!' says Roy Cohn to Saypol in the john afterwards. He's so mad he grabs his tie and rips it off. He's about to tear it up with his bare hands when he suddenly remembers he's got to go back into that courtroom and he doesn't have another one handy. 'Damn her! Didn't you make it clear to her that she had to learn her part before Opening Night? Didn't I make it clear to you?'

Wait a minute, why is Cohn talking to Saypol this way? Who's the boss here anyway? Who's taking orders from whom?

So Saypol flushes and comes out, and he washes his hands, slowly, methodically, letting the water wash over them. He's quiet and his skin is white like paper. For him I wouldn't object to a concentration camp. Maybe he's worried what his wife'll say when he gets home. 'Look, Cohn,' his voice quavers, but he tries to master it, 'don't talk to me that way.'

'I'll talk to you any way I like!' says Cohn, leering at his rat face in the mirror. With his manicured fingernail, he flicks a speck of egg off his tie, carefully knots it on again (would I like to pull it tight!) and stalks out letting the door slam on Saypol's foot. He slides his hand over his black slick hair and starts back into the courtroom.

'Let's go back in there,' says Kaufman, coming towards him grabbing his elbow. 'I have to talk to you.'

Inside he says, 'Well, let's get it over with, boys. I wanted to tell you, I went to synagogue last night.' That frog's mouth of his laughs self-consciously. 'To check it out with Him.' His aqueous eyes motion, Upstairs. 'It's okay.' He nods again to make sure they understand. Saypol and Cohn smile, a forced smile, granting him amnesty. Even they are offended by his arrogance. 'We can go the limit, see.' As he's saying this, he straightens his robes and pats his hair in place. With a satisfied smirk, he holds out his arm to Saypol. 'Let's go!' His voice carries the authority of the pretender to the throne.

The three henchmen link arms and march out.

That's a scene that never got reported in the papers, but I'll bet you my bottom dollar it happened.

FORTY-SIX

FEBRUARY 1950

How did it all get started? With David actually – if I look back to early in 1950.

One time – one of those grey days you get in February? – I remember he drops in when I'm home alone. 'Just passing by,' he says. So I offer him some tea and pound cake. 'With lemon?' I ask, knowing that's how he usually likes it.

'No, skip it,' he says. 'Gotta bad sore throat ... hurts when I swallow ... willya put some more sugar in ... or better yet, got some honey?'

'Sure. By the way, how's the new job going?' Ever since he got out of business with Julie last August, it's been a touchy subject between us.

'Okay,' he says, nothing more.

As I hand him the cup, I notice his hand's shaking. 'You worried about it? The sore throat, I mean? Maybe you should go see Dr Feinkuchen?'

'No, not necessary. Just a sore throat,' he snaps, and sits there like he's thinking. 'Yeah ... I don't know ... maybe I am ... could be ...'

Somehow he doesn't look right to me ... the troubled expression on his face. 'Dovey.' I go over to him, put my hand gently on his shoulder. 'What's with you? You haven't been yourself lately ... something on your mind?' I know my brother so well. 'Maybe I can help?' It's like the old days when he'd come to me with a problem. Maybe I've been missing that since he came back from service. Something between us has changed. Maybe it's just that he's married now and has Ruth to talk things over with. Who knows.

Anyhow, he doesn't say anything, just gets up and stands by the window looking out.

246

It's about five, almost dark. The street lights are on, and you can hear the children's voices in the courtyard below fading out as their mothers call them inside. Michael and Robby are downstairs at the Silvers' watching *Captain Video*. I switch on the lamp near him, and in the sudden glare, his eyes are small and agitated. Like a scared kid in a man's body, I'm thinking, and now that body's gone soft again since he got out of the Army – is it four years already? A real *Fresser* that David.

'C'mon Dovey, tell me,' I coax him. 'Y'know I want to help. Whatever differences you and Julie are having about the business, leave me out of it.'

'I know that, Ettie ... this time though I don' know ... Oh jeez ... ' and he takes a sip of tea and swallows hard, 'Well, it's like this ... now don' tell Julie, y'hear!'

'Okay,' I say, though I don't like promising something like that because Julie and I have no secrets from each other.

'Well, y'see, when I left Los Alamos, just as a souvenir ... I mean, the other guys were all doing it, too, y'know ... I took a capsule of uranium ... no big deal ... well, last week two guys from the FBI show up while we're eating dinner ... ask me all sorts of questions ... I dunno ... they kinda got me all tangled up ... I mean, oh well, they had me saying things ... I dunno.' And he stares down at his empty hands. He's got hands like a butcher I'm thinking, pudgy, reddish, with short fingers and no knuckles. Not like Julie's long sensitive fingers.

'Was it about this uranium?' By now something in me sounds like a gong and the whole feel of the day, a nice one up to now, changes. Something in me registers, don't ask me why ... intuition? This problem ain't going away ... like when Julie got fired from the government, I had the same reaction. You begin to learn that some things can affect your life for good ... and the seismograph inside me picks up on this one. Besides, I remember reading that two ex-sergeants from Los Alamos got sent to prison for helping themselves to some stuff. They, too, pleaded, 'Just souvenirs.' But one got six months, the other eighteen. At the time, I wondered if David knew them.

'So what did they want?' I ask him.

'At first, they wouldn't say ... almost like a social visit, if you can believe it ... friendly and all ... just checking out some information. They tell me that some of the guys who worked with me, enlisted men, are also being questioned about this missing uranium ... did I know anything about it? And they mention some names.'

'So what did you say?'

'*No, of course.* I didn't know if they had anything on me or what ... or were they just trying to trap me into incriminating myself? Then this FBI guy says one of the fellas told him I'd taken one, too. That's not true, I say. Who said it? Well, he wouldn't tell me. Anyhow, it goes on like this for a while ... and Ruth's sitting there trying to control herself, you know how edgy she gets ... even about little things. I just keep denying it ... maybe I shoulda asked to speak to a lawyer first.' He shrugs his shoulders. 'But I was afraid to say anything like that because I figured it's like admitting I've got something to hide. Oh Jesus! I don't know if I handled it right or blew it or what!'

'So what finally happened?'

'Well, maybe after an hour or so ... they even wander around the apartment looking around, pulling out books ... *The Communist Manifesto*, *Marx and Engels* ... Party literature.'

'Did you ask them if they had a search warrant?'

'No, I didn't think of it till afterwards ... anyhow, about the books ... also some you loaned me, like Lincoln Steffens' *Autobiography*, *Soviet Peace* by the Dean of Canterbury ... '

'You told them they were ours?'

'Yeah ... then one of them picks up the *Daily Worker* from yesterday lying on the kitchen table. "Read this regularly?" he asks.'

' "Yeah sure, why not? I read the *Daily News*, too," I tell him and smile.

' "What else?" the guy asks. *Smooth. Boy, are they smooth*.

' "Not much ... *Life* sometimes ... "

'So then he shows me a long list of subversive organizations, prepared by the Attorney-General. "Belong to any of these?"

'I shake my head. I decide to say no to everything. Flat out no. Maybe that's a mistake? I dunno. Y'think they'll get me on perjury? I mean, because I belonged to the Party? Anyhow, then he wants to know where I'm working.

'So I tell him about the business we started, Julie and me and Bernie, and how we're not getting along, so I decide to get out and now I'm working for another company. So he wants to know all about this partnership – who was in it, where we got the money, who's the boss, how come we didn't get along ... '

That's David, I'm thinking, always shooting his mouth off. 'So you told him?'

'Sure, why not? I got nothing to hide.'

'Did he ask anything about Julie?'

'No – just said that he knew he'd been fired from the government as a Commie. Oh yeah,' he says, like he's remembering something, 'he wanted to know if Julie still belonged. I told him I knew nothing about it. We're not talking much these days.'

I'm trying not to crack my knuckles. There's something in all this that frightens me. I don't understand why.

'Finally they get up to go after thanking us politely. At the door, one of them says, "Look, if you remember anything about that uranium, will you give us a ring? Day or night." And he writes down a number on a card and hands it to me. I put it in my wallet.'

I'm sitting there thinking, *It never fails*. The minute one problem in your life starts improving – like between Michael and me now that we're both getting therapy, some new problem socks in. Boy, that's life every time. You can practically count on it.

You're overreacting, I tell myself. Probably it's only a routine procedure; they'd question anyone who worked at Los Alamos on something like this, some missing uranium. *Of course that's it*, I reassure myself. Still I'm worried for him. He's such a big baby! At the same time, I'm sore as hell at him, for pulling something so stupid. That's David every time. Good judgement? – it's all in his *tochis*. But what good will it do if I bawl him out? So I say, 'Listen to me carefully, Dovey ... the first thing you gotta do is get rid of that capsule. That's number one. And right away ... like tonight.'

'But how? *How?*' he's demanding. 'Ruth and I been discussing it. They must have ways of tracing it. Maybe they're even checking our garbage. Who knows? They're bloodhounds, those guys! I can't just flush it down the toilet.'

'Calm down ... listen to me ... Take a walk down to the East River ... it's only a few blocks ... tonight ... check ... and if no one's following you, throw it in.'

'You think so?'

'Yeah, that's the way to do it ... and right away ... get rid of it.'

'Okay, I think you're right.' He sounds relieved and gets up. At the door, he turns to me. 'Do me a favour – don't mention that I've been here to Ruth.'

So that's how the whole thing started. A few days later when I see him at Ma's, I get him aside and ask, 'Did you do it?'

'Yeah, it's all taken care of.' But then he shuts up and from that time on never really opens up to me again. You see, knowing David, I had a sneaking suspicion that I hadn't heard the whole story, but only as much as he wanted me to know. That's always been his way. And as things turn out, I'm right. He'll tell you as much as he wants you to know so as to get you on his side and then, after a while, when you find out the whole story, it's too late to do anything about it. I remember once, he's in fourth grade, I'm already in high school – anyway, he's coming home all the time complaining about his teacher – a Mrs Callaghan – how she's always picking on him for nothing. After about a month Ma's had enough of it – and she goes barging up there to see the principal. It turns out that David's been cheating right and left, and they've tried everything – punished him, extra homework, kept him after school, all that, and are just about to send for Ma when she walks into it! Boy, did she spank him! Only time I ever saw her do it. But it didn't change him ...

Though, looking back, I can see that something in David had already changed when he returned from service – that's early in 1946. His guard was up and that's new. Before that, he was always like an open book ... too much so, in fact. When he was at Los Alamos, he and Ruth would write to each other about Party things, she told me so herself – what David said in his last letter – like there might be some potential members in his company and that he was subtly talking it up. And then she'd write back – about her own activities – moving from the YCL into the Party, things like that. Myself, I thought that was foolish ... indiscreet ... especially since he's working at a secret military project. Good judgement? ... not David, never ...

Anyhow, from that day on in February, it's clear that he's scared out of his wits. In fact, Julie and I wonder if the FBI will be around to question us about him, but in the next few months, no one shows up. I did tell Julie about the uranium, I had to, and he agreed I'd given David good advice.

I'd be lying though if I said I wasn't worried after that conversation. For David, of course. But also little flashes of worry like short bursts of electricity would cross my mind unexpectedly – maybe picturing the same FBI guys in David's apartment coming to ours. Always, I guess, anything to do with the government frightened me. A letter from the IRS, even with a refund cheque inside, I'd be anxious about before I opened it. I guess any Jew, the same – it's in our genes. I just didn't want anything to do with them. And somehow I knew from Julie's experience with the Signal Corps that once they start in on you, they won't let go – like a dog I once saw bite an old man on Sheriff Street right through his pants, he grabs hold of his leg – a skinny runt of a man, he's hobbling along on a cane – and this crazy dog comes up from behind him – I don't even know what kind, someone afterwards said it was a Spitz – anyhow, the dog won't let go. The poor guy is screaming bloody murder and Joe, the janitor, the *shiker* finally does something good – he runs up and grabs the dog's collar and twists so hard the dog starts to choke and lets go. The poor guy falls on his face, and someone calls an ambulance. I'm right there as these two big guys, the driver and the attendant, help him in. I still remember his tears – big ones running down the sides of his nose, past a large dark brown mole on one side, and catching in his beard.

And the way David's behaving does nothing to calm my fears. He's badgering Julie for money from his share of the business, and Julie explains over and over to him he just doesn't have it, but he keeps coming back and insisting he's got to have it. At least two thousand dollars.

'Look, Dave,' Julie says to him, 'you can't get money out of a stone. Why is it so urgent? You're working right now, aren't you? Give me a break. You know I'm good for the money.'

'Never mind,' he says, 'just get me the money. Now! Don't fool around with me, Julie,' he threatens.

Julie's getting very upset, so this time he starts to walk away from him, they shouldn't get into a real fistfight. Which has happened once already. David grabs his arm and says, 'I'll tell you what – will you ask your Dr Feinkuchen whether I can get a smallpox vaccination certificate from him without going there?'

Julie stares at him, he doesn't understand what he's

talking about. 'What's this all about, Dave? C'mon, for Godsakes, tell me – then maybe I can help you. Are you in some kind of trouble?'

But David just stands there, his eyes burning on Julie like he's his enemy. 'You'll be sorry,' he says, 'you'll see.'

FORTY-SEVEN

MARCH 1951

About the trial – I get so raving mad every time I think about it. How they painted us at the trial ... the lies ... the lies repeated and reinforced so often that after a while they smooth into a believable story. Like Hitler. You have to watch it. Lies, I mean, especially if you want to believe them, can have a hypnotic effect.

Frankly, the list of scientists, when Manny shows it to me on the first day, March 6, that the government's calling as witnesses, frightens me, that Oppenheimer and Kistiakowski, who was Eisenhower's scientific adviser, and others like that will be testifying against us. Somehow it lends an authority to the charges that I don't understand. I know we're innocent, and yet I don't know exactly what David's done, what he's hidden from us, what he's said to them about us. And the whole business with the atom bomb is a mystery to me. And terrifying. To the majority of people, I bet – a kind of twentieth-century witchcraft practised by the scientists. And how the Greenglasses managed to drag us into it still isn't at all clear to me.

Maybe David conspired with someone else in the Party and now he's covering up by dragging us in? Is he following Party orders? Ruth, when I asked her after they arrested him, insisted, 'No, he's innocent, we both are.'

But now, they've done a complete aboutface. Why? He's a defendant, and she's a co-conspirator by her own admission, but not on trial, notice, and instead she's testifying for the government. Why, I ask myself, why? Of course I know about the uranium he'd stolen, but now is there more to it than that?

Of course, it turns out that none of these scientists is

called. Instead two others who aren't even physicists – a John Derry, a construction engineer who worked for Major Leslie Groves, the military guy in charge of Los Alamos, and a chemist named Walter Koski, people I'd never heard of. And I keep wondering why not the others, and try afterwards to talk to Manny about it.

'Ethel,' he says in that reasonable voice that also tells me to stop this foolishness, 'that's not our problem. Keep your eye on the ball, willya? There's only one thing we have to do and that's to raise a reasonable doubt in the jury's mind. Just get one of them wondering maybe you're not guilty. That's our only chance.' Still I can't help wondering why Oppenheimer didn't testify with the others.

He also suggests I should work on the jury for their sympathy. 'Let them see how upset you are about the children, how worried. Play it up for all it's worth. Juries are human beings, y'know. And give them an appealing smile, a friendly look when you can.'

'I should smile! Are you kidding! You think I'm like my brother? And what's more, leave the children out of this,' I tell him, 'I won't have them dragged in.'

I guess I had to see for myself just how dirty they were going to play it, that David would take the witness stand and say the things he says, to believe this is happening. For real. And that we're going to have to use everything we've got. Which isn't much.

Just listen to how Judge Kaufman instructs the jury. 'The minds of the jurors should be the same as a white sheet of paper with nothing on it.' Can you believe it? This is March 1951. For almost a year American troops have been fighting the Communists in Korea, Alger Hiss is in jail for perjury – he's this big State Department guy who gets shot down by this ex-Communist, Whittaker Chambers, who strikes me as a psychopathic liar. And so are the eleven Communist Party leaders in jail for advocating the violent overthrow of the government. And Senator Joe McCarthy is running around

255

the country claiming the State Department is overrun with Communists! Where does Kaufman think the jury's been living? On another planet?

All the cards are stacked in their favour and Saypol, whom *Time* describes as the 'nation's number one legal hunter of Communists', is gunning for another notch on his belt.

This is strictly a Jewish show with Kaufman, Saypol and Cohn in on it – it's Jew against Jew. Like the Mafia, it's up to them to keep their own in line.

Liar! I scream inside as David tells the court that on his first furlough home in January '45, at Julie's urging, he draws a sketch for him of a high-explosive lens mould he's working on. What really gets me is when he says that Julie goes into the kitchen and comes back with an empty Jello box, asks me for a scissors, and then cuts the top into two pieces, like for a jigsaw puzzle. Then Julie gives him one of the pieces, and tells him that the contact who will come to him in Albuquerque this spring will have the matching piece. And he should give him more information about the bomb.

At first, I can't believe it, that this is going on in front of my eyes, not somebody telling me about it afterwards and I can say, this person's exaggerating. The funny thing is I hate Jello – that flabby tasteless rubbery goo! Every flavour tastes the same – raspberry, cherry, lemon, lime, makes no difference. I never even keep Jello in the house. So how come I suddenly have a box handy for Julie to use in setting up a whole spy operation? Lies – from beginning to end.

David had plenty of time to think them up – locked in the Tombs on the same floor with Harry Gold. A very strange fellow, that Gold, I tell you – a pudgy little man with heavy eyelids, his head and shoulders twitching, and he's smiling all at the same time. He even smiles over at me a couple of times. Can you imagine? Like we're all members of the same cast. Some play! Besides I never trusted guys whose pants are baggy. I always remember that bastard who beat up poor Lobelia.

So the two of them, with the help of the FBI, no doubt,

concoct this story how Gold goes to Albuquerque in June 1945, shows his half of the Jello box to David and, get this, says 'I come from Julius.' That's some spy! Using his own name as the code word. How dumb do they think we are? Even we'd know better! From the movies! And here the government's trying to prove that Julie's head of this super espionage ring for the Russians!

So David says he gives this Gold two more lens mould sketches and written data, that's in June, and then Gold testifies he takes it to his boss, this Russian, Yakelov, supposed to be high up in Soviet espionage (by this time, Yakelov has left the country so the prosecution doesn't have to produce him). And presto chango – they've got us tied in with the Russians! Like in a basketball game, David passes to Gold, Gold to Yakelov – and they score – with the jury. Just like that, the Russians get the secret. And we get the chair!

What's more, says David, in September that same year, when he's home on leave, he gives Julie a sketch of the atom bomb – the one they dropped on Nagasaki – and a report describing it. Julie reads it, likes it a lot, and gets me to type up the information right then and there! And Saypol produces a 'replica' of this so-called sketch as evidence.

Unbelievable! How he twists everything around – with the same mouth that I wiped for him when he's still in a high chair and I'm feeding him. The baby whose diapers I changed, the kid brother I took to the candy store, bought him penny candy – tootsie rolls were his favourite – sometimes a pinwheel, jacks, marbles. That he'd do this to me! To Julie now – a little of that I can understand, though not really. First of all, Julie isn't one of the family; secondly, he and Julie weren't getting along. I tried to tell them that when they put me on the stand. Not 'getting along' – that's putting it mildly. A lot of nasty things got said – yelling, calling each other names, came to blows once. Finally a crisis and Julie offers to buy him out. In 1949. Before that I keep hearing complaints from Julie – how sloppy David is, comes in late, leaves early, careless with the work. 'So what if something's off by a fraction?' he'd say to Julie. 'Or not ready on time?' Even I understand you can't do this in a machine shop just getting started. I try to stay out of it. But it's almost impossible. Julie comes home tired and furious after a day of handling such complaints from customers. A pounding headache, he has to take two aspirins and lie down for a while before eating. Later and later he's coming home. And the business just isn't coming in like we'd hoped.

And if I see David at Ma's, right away he starts making excuses — 'You know how it is,' and he shrugs his shoulders like since he doesn't mean it, he shouldn't be held responsible. How he managed in the Army I'll never know. But maybe he had problems there, too. I know Ruth at times looked worried after she'd get a letter from him, though to me she never said anything.

But once she did call Julie — that's before she went out to Albuquerque, in spring 1945 — and asked him to come over, something she had to talk to him about privately. He told me about it afterwards. She tells him David's got this idea to make some easy money while he's there.

'She's always nagging him about money,' I say. 'So what's the idea?'

'He didn't tell her what, just something to do with the project.'

Julie, of course, tells her to warn him, 'Drop it! Immediately! Don't fool around with the government.' Who should know better than Julie? Here he gets fired just for having been a member in the past of the Communist Party. Which is still a legal party in this country in 1945. 'Can you imagine doing something illegal on a secret wartime project!' he says to me. 'Your brother is a horse's ass.'

'I only hope he listens to you, Julie. Sometimes, I don't know what to make of him.'

'Don't worry,' Julie reassures me, 'he will. If Ruth tells him so.'

But with David, I'm thinking, you never know.

Anyhow, by 1948, '49, Julie's Adam's apple is getting bigger as though it's feeding on his aggravation. I've never seen him that way before. And the temper he's developing! And it all centres around David and my mother. 'When is she going to stop interfering in all of our affairs?' he bursts out. She's causing trouble between us because she's always putting in her two cents, telling Julie to make peace with him. 'So overlook a little ... he's still learning ... whaddya want from him? An Einstein?'

So Ma, I want to say, lay off, how about a little understanding for Julie? – what he's going through with the *kol-ye-keh*, David? Nothing David ever does comes out just right. Except at the trial. He turns out to be not only a good liar – but a great one!

Can't you all see that? I want to shout, listening to him testify. Look at him – smiling yet! About what? I want to ask – that you'll get off, you and your Ruth, and we'll pay the price for you? I didn't know you were *that* good. Where'd you learn to lie like that? You and Harry Gold practise together? – polishing your story? With the FBI's help? How long did it take you to learn your lines? You even got Ma to do your dirty work, like always, getting her to go to work on me to back up your story. You've convinced her – then we'll all get off together. Such betrayal exceeds anything I could've imagined ... it's so easy for you to whitewash your conscience, David, isn't it? By now, it's all our fault, right? If only we'd 'cooperate' the way you have, play ball, give out with some names – sure, people in our Party cell back when we belonged, even dead ones, do our little number like Max Elitcher and Elizabeth Bentley who've already testified for the prosecution. Suddenly we'd be heroes. Like Whittaker Chambers. Not accused spies fighting for our lives. For you, it's easy, my brother, the coward. For me – impossible. To drag in other innocent people with us!

Julie catches my eye. He shakes his head as if to say, Can

259

you believe this? Under the table, I show him my clenched fist ready to use on David. 'That fuckin' bastard!' Words I've never used before. Manny hears me and throws me a warning glance. That's one thing he's been telling us, 'You're going to have to stay calm in the face of a lot of provocation.' But how, Manny? I want to ask him, you didn't tell me how.

And the mock trial continues in front of our shocked eyes.

There are only four of us in that entire courtroom who know the real story, the *truth* – and I'm thinking, How is it possible for just the two of us, Julie and me, to convince all the others who are being taken in by that bastard – when he and Ruth are backed up by the entire government apparatus ... they've got the resources, the know-how, the money, the FBI ... even the newspapers on their side. And all we've got is Manny, not even an experienced criminal lawyer – civil rights cases are his line. And Alex, his 74-year-old father who writes contracts for bakeries in the Bronx. Manny's never even tried a capital offence.

I look up at Kaufman sitting there, disdainful and arrogant, a short guy with glasses and slicked black hair. Manny tells me he's only about forty – on the bench for less than two years when he volunteers to take our case. The grapevine has it that no other judge would touch it with a ten-foot pole. Who'd want such a case? Unless – aha! – unless it's being used as a step up the ladder. And guess what? Kaufman's wife's maiden name is Rosenberg!

And the jury – I'm trying to size them up. All white-collar workers – hardest to organize, too close to management. The foreman's young, only about thirty, with pale skin, sharp eyes, and hair carefully set into waves. Salesman, Catholic, the up and coming type like Kaufman and Saypol. These men understand each other – you don't fight the organization. The others? Several accountants, auditors, not the kind who'd go against the majority. Also one black guy who works for Con Ed demonstrating electrical appliances – about him, it's hard to say. Actually, there's only one man – older, who works for the bus company, said he was a member of Mike Quill's Transport Workers' Union – whose face I really like. Like he's in no hurry to get someplace. Not even the one woman, hardfaced – a Mrs Dammas, worked as a switchboard operator. If she's anything like Marie from National, she's right in there with the bosses. If only we had a Lobelia without the head injury, just one like her, that's all we need. And there are no Jews. How come in New York City there's not even one Jew on the jury?

Now Ruth takes the stand, backing up David, of course, supplying little details to make their story more convincing. Like she accuses Julie of throwing money around ... fifty, seventy-five dollars a night at nightclubs. When? I want to shout, tell me when! Here I'm counting every penny, buying a 25 cent Golden Book for Michael becomes a major decision ... and how he loves them ... I remember one, how the animals in the zoo escape and decide to go to Coney Island and become the animals on the merry-go-round. I'm a great believer in encouraging a child's imagination. Would you expect anything else from one of the World's Great Dreamers?

But coming back to what I'm talking about ... Mr and Mrs Julius Moneybags Rosenberg – that is, if you listen to David and Ruth. According to them, the Rosenbergs had a pretty big year in 1945, making money hand over fist – nightclubbing, leaving big tips for the waitress. They've become big-time operators in the spy business. So how come every month we still had to pay twenty-five cents to keep a checking account at People's Trust? We couldn't even maintain the minimum balance, a hundred dollars. Some spies! *Ahf meine sohnem gezugt!* It should only happen to my enemies.

Or that story David tells about Julie encouraging him to go to the University of Chicago – or MIT – to study physics so he could pick up more information about the bomb. This is my brother, David, remember? – who flunks out his first year at Brooklyn Polytech. Suddenly Julie is telling him to go to one of the best universities in the country!

Unbelievable! And yet, in that courtroom, filled with hatred and suspicion of anyone accused of being a Communist, they can sell it to the jury.

One good thing David's testimony does for me. Something in me hardens once and for all. There's this man up there on the stand, eager and smiling, ready to answer Saypol's every question (he doesn't have to take the Fifth, he's already been promised protection), *knowing* that every word he speaks is driving a nail into my coffin – and Julie's. He's strictly out to save his own neck – and Ruth's – by substituting mine – ours – on the chopping block. So I sit there and study him, as I've never studied him before. He's always been a composite for me, I realize, a collection of memories, so I've never seen him before without the baby face and rosy cheeks and sweet lips, the boy in knickers with the line under his chin where the soap and water stopped.

All of these images ran together in my head, they must've, but not today. Today I sit there and observe this man like he's a total stranger on the stand – everything about him is sharp, like my vision is suddenly 20/20 with no astigmatism – and I dislike everything about this man, this stranger.

There's a kind of run-over, blurry quality about him like he'd be a hard man to pin down, a sloppiness in the way his socks drape around his ankles and stop short of his trouser legs so the chubby white flesh with dark hair shows, the way his pudgy hands rest on his over-stuffed thighs that shape into a broad V as he sits there slouching in the dark-brown witness chair, smiling, maybe enjoying all the attention. And maybe he doesn't have the money to buy a new suit that'll fit more loosely than his old grey pinstripe, but all the weight he's put on bulges out of his collar, strains at the arm holes of his jacket, and makes his rosebud mouth in that big round white face look silly and childish as he shapes those bullet words that will send us to the electric chair. Sit up! I want to say, pay attention for once – and do the right thing – which is to tell the truth for once! – instead of having to make excuses for something you didn't do right in the first place.

David, how come two of us from the same family can end up so differently? I can't lie to save my skin, and you don't know how to do anything else ... Never again, David – and I feel such a sadness saying it – will I feel the same about you. And I hate giving up that feeling of love and tenderness that I've always felt towards you – it's almost like asking me to stop loving Michael or Robby. But then I think, if it weren't for you, I'd be home with my two sons, living the love and tenderness that I always want to feel inside – and the magic of my old feelings for you vanishes. I don't give up easily, David, I thought, I really don't, I've hung on to this love for you through all that's happened up to now, but now it's truly over and finished, and you've done it, not I. For me to stop loving – is almost impossible. Almost, but not quite.

FORTY-EIGHT

MARCH 1951

I have to come back to something that happens when David is testifying that really worries me throughout the trial. At the time I know Manny's making a terrible mistake, but there's nothing I can do to stop it.

It all centres about Exhibit 8 – which Saypol introduces when David's testifying about the information he says he passed to Julie in September 1945. This Exhibit 8 is the 'replica', Saypol says, of the sketch David drew of the implosion bomb dropped in Nagasaki – and gave to Julie. He's about to hand it to the clerk for marking when Manny dramatically stands up and in a loud voice, requests the court 'to impound this exhibit so that it remains a secret to the court, the jury, and the counsel'. There's a shocked silence. My heart thuds, and I feel sick to my stomach. Julie looks at me, I look at him. How could he do such a stupid thing!

Even Saypol is startled into saying that this is indeed a strange request to be coming from the defendants. He knows that Manny is cutting the legs right out from under us, by conceding right off to the prosecution that this sketch is indeed the secret of the atom bomb. Rather than fighting them all the way. Because this is the heart of the case – proof that an act of treason was committed – and in this charged courtroom, the jury is prepared to believe that two Communists, like Julie and me, indicted for conspiring to commit espionage, would commit treason with no pang of guilt – especially if her brother says so. Manny, for Godsakes, fight its admission as evidence! Challenge him, what proof is a 'replica' without the original? And what proof is there that David drew this or did it without a lot of help from the FBI? Oh yes, there are lots of questions Manny could have asked,

264

good probing questions. After all, our defence position right along has been, aside from insisting on our own innocence, that David – a machinist assigned to one small specialized phase of this gigantic project – isn't sufficiently bright, knowledgeable, or at a high enough level in the Los Alamos operation to have access to such valuable secret information, and therefore could not have passed such information to anyone. Which would also raise questions about Gold's testimony. Whether he wasn't perjuring himself. Which he'd already done in another case a few months before. And yet Manny never cross-examines him.

Manny, I'm thinking, you've just handed them a present. Because it's just what the prosecution would have had to prove – if you hadn't done it for them with that one impulsive remark.

Kaufman, of course, is delighted with this unexpected turn, and immediately agrees that the sketch will be sealed after it has been shown to the jury. At which point, Manny, as if he hadn't done enough damage already, asks to speak to the judge out of earshot of the jury. And says to Kaufman – get this! – that even at this late stage this information may be of advantage to a foreign power, so he's satisfied that it should be kept a secret by clearing the courtroom.

So Kaufman clears the courtroom of all spectators, but allows the press to remain. You can just imagine the impression all this makes on the jury. I can see it in their eyes, that relieved look that says, 'Yeah, they did it!' It's been settled.

Later Manny apologizes to Julie for his mistake. 'I wanted to make the point that the defence was as patriotic as the prosecution in defending America's military secrets.'

'Don't worry about it,' says Julie.

What else can he say?

FORTY-NINE

MARCH 1951

Even though at the time I got sore at Manny for bringing up the sympathy angle, as the trial gets underway, I'm seriously considering it. All I have to do is think about Michael who turns eight today, March 10. With us on trial, and he and Robby in a children's shelter in the Bronx! There's such a hunger in me to see him, those intelligent eyes that used to trust the world. But no more, I bet. It's seven months almost to the day – will I be home for Robby's birthday in May? His fourth. *Oh God, please let it happen.*

Besides, the actress in me is responding. I've done it before. So why not now? I start working on it in my cell after the lights are out – the brave little woman, all those June Allyson movies, innocent, unjustly accused ... not self-pity, but the pain of a mother ... poor, but proud, needing help so badly ... what gestures, expression ... facing towards the jury slightly when I testify ... very respectable, try to look nice, hair soft and curling, a little make-up, but not too much ... my hands in my lap clutching a white handkerchief ready to dab at the tears, but fighting them back ... imagining myself back to those days when we were rehearsing *The Valiant*, how I could summon all these feelings and project them to the audience ... that poor, poor young woman, how I played it to the hilt ... and even Jim, the convicted murderer – her brother – had the audience feeling sorry for him. And for a brief while, I'm back there, reliving all that emotion ... and the applause ... though now it strikes me as all so phoney and contrived in the face of the real drama that's my life. Tomorrow, I decide, I'll wear the beige hat to court that Pauline in the next cell crocheted for me. And she offered to do my hair ... and the white gloves that Tante Rosie gave me ...

The trial goes on ... It's March 22, two weeks already, and I want it to be over. And today Julie's on the stand. And, much as I feel for him, I'm somewhat relieved that he's called on first, not me. Anything to put it off.

Day after day of testimony, cross-examination, motions, objections, rulings – first the prosecution, and now the defence. And all these mixed emotions churning in me – tension, fear, anger, worry about the children – and just plain exhaustion – and yet I absolutely have to concentrate on what's going on right this minute in the court. I don't dare let my mind wander off or miss a thing. I try a few friendly glances toward the jury. Not one of them will look me in the eye. It's been that way right along. I shrivel and feel like some kind of monster in captivity up there on display.

And I'm watching Saypol, how ruthless he is, how he's circling Julie, trying to corner him, like the leader of a wolf pack with a lamb. Recalling a wildlife movie we once saw that was filmed on a sheep farm out West. And all Julie can do is to deny David's story, tell what happened – about the money David demanded, how he threatens Julie if he doesn't get it to him, also about the vaccination certificate David asks for – all this, and that we're innocent. Unfortunately, compared to polished lies, the truth is much less dramatic.

This guy, Saypol, with the square jaw and tight lips of a Dick Tracy – is out for blood, going after Julie, not only with David's flimsy story and the so-called evidence, but with one thing – and one thing only – *This man is a Communist, a real live Communist you see before you*. A member of the YCL in college. Discharged from the Signal Corps for being a Communist. Right away the jury sees red horns and a pitchfork in Julie's hand. That's what Saypol's using for all it's worth – and it's working. You should see their faces, the jury – how they sit there, stony faced, and stare at this evil man. Like there's a bad smell in the room!

By the time it's my turn, I know we're in deep deep trouble. But I'm ready for him, the bastard! This isn't going to be that naïve kid, Ethel, pleading with her boss, 'Please, Mr Kantrowitz, please don't fire me.'

Our lawyer in questioning me tries to bring out the facts that will favourably influence the jury – how young the children are, that I've been a devoted mother who's stayed home, taken courses in child psychology and such. I'm answering in a soft voice as though these memories are very special to me. And they are.

But as soon as Saypol starts his cross-examination he tries to rattle me by firing one question after another about a stupid wristwatch that Julie lost on a train way back in 1948 when we were returning from the country. And I'm supposed to remember every detail, can you imagine! – which train, where were we coming from, when did he discover it, where did he report it? – as though that's all I've had to remember in the last few years. Then he warms up to the real hatchet job. 'Have I been truthful in my answers here?' 'Yes,' I say. 'And before the Grand Jury?' 'Yes.' The old 'are you still beating your wife' technique. I'm very nervous, what's all this leading up to? And he's got me so tied up defending myself, there's no time to shed a few tears, show a mother's grief ... just this rapidfire rat-tat-tat-tat exchange between us.

What he's doing is using my answers before the Grand Jury against me, twisting the whole thing around, and making it sound as though I've been inconsistent in my answers – and therefore untruthful. How come I pleaded the Fifth before the Grand Jury, and now I'm willing to answer the same question? He asks me a question, I start to answer fully with an explanation, and he cuts me off, won't let me finish, and instead reads the answer I gave to the same question before the Grand Jury. '*I refuse to answer on the grounds*

268

that it might incriminate me.' Which is what Manny advised me
to say at the time. 'As Julie's wife,' he told me, 'you cannot be
made to testify against your husband. So just take the Fifth
Amendment on every question, and play it safe.'

Now Saypol, who knows very well why I pleaded the Fifth
before the Grand Jury, has the *chutzpah* to ask me, 'How come
you're giving a different answer now? *Here you tell us you're a
truthful person, and yet you're giving two different answers to the same
question.*'

God, is he clever! Creating suspicion that I have something to hide (don't all Communists?) and am therefore
guilty as charged.

Over and over, all the jury is hearing is the repetition of
that single sentence which I used before the Grand Jury, 'I
refuse to answer ... ' He's deliberately trying to confuse
them, create a smokescreen, drown out everything I'm now
trying to answer voluntarily, in detail on the stand. Each time
Manny objects to these tactics, Kaufman overrules him. It
feels as though I'm in front of a one man firing squad that's
using this loaded machine gun to mow me down. And when
he pauses for breath, Kaufman jumps in with the same
tactics. One look at the jury, their closed faces (and closed
minds), and I know with a dead certainty (some pun!) that
Saypol's strategy is working. We figured he'd go after me with
the same tactics he used on Julie. But he needed something
more because the evidence connecting me to the supposed
crime is so flimsy. David says I typed two of his reports! That's
all they have against me! And now it's clear what he's up to.

It's taking everything I've got to stay in there with him and
hold my own. Forgotten is any idea about playing a role.
What comes to my rescue is anger – and I've got lots of fuel to
keep it going – first David, then Ruth, and now Saypol ...
Don't lose your head, baby, I keep saying to myself, just stay calm.

As he's hammering away at me, I'm reminded of Ma and
Sam that night I came home from Amateur Night – and how
already I was guilty in their eyes. This time, though, I'm

fighting back, not taking it lying down. I'm innocent and you're not going to make me feel guilty. It's as though I've become two strong headlights directed at the target. I'm speaking coolly, concisely. I'm wary, cautious, and using everything I've ever learned, every bit of me, intuition, and most of all, the awareness of an animal that it's being stalked.

Each time, it's the same thing – 'But how would that have incriminated you, if you're innocent?'

And each time I answer, 'It wouldn't necessarily incriminate me, but it might tend to.' That's where he interrupts me each time. But finally I break through that intimidating voice and finish what I started to say, ' ... and as long as I had any idea that there might be some chance for me to be incriminated, I had the right to use that privilege.' Finally, finally, I finish what I have to say.

But he won't give up with this line of questioning. And, at this point, I decide to reply with one thing and one thing only. *'I have already answered that.'* Even Kaufman knows he's going too far and finally cuts him off. I will not let him beat me down or make me lose my head.

Later, when I step down, Manny congratulates me. 'You were wonderful. Right on your toes. The guy tried to crucify you!' he says, and gives me a big fatherly hug. Which feels good, and I've earned it. So I don't tell him that it's anger, anger hard as steel, that protects me. It's as though every instinct in me for survival took over. Only later, back in my cell, do I remember that day in Central Park Zoo with the giraffe and the lion. I was determined to stand my ground and win in that life and death struggle. That's why I couldn't play for sympathy. It was one or the other – either the poor helpless little woman begging for sympathy and mercy from the jury. Or the fighter, taking on Saypol, cool and calculating. Staying in control because I knew that if I ever let the anger in me erupt, I'd lose my head, and then I didn't trust myself in that courtroom.

The papers reported I was emotionless, that I came across,

some said, as a fanatical Communist spy ready to die for the cause. If only they knew what a seething volcano I was inside!

We lost, it's true, but I don't regret it that my anger took over that day. The best of me was on that witness stand. After years of trying to please, I learned, once and for all, it never works.

FIFTY

FEBRUARY 1953

February 25, 1953

Dear Dr Singer (I decided I could write to him, even if I can't see him),

It took a few days before I could finally calm my heart, and my head – then I said to myself, Ethel, you and I've got to have a talk together. When they can pull something like this – stop me from seeing Dr Singer – they mean business, and unless you fight back with everything you've got – you and Julie are finished. And then where'll the kids be?

So stop worrying about Play-dough and *tsatkes* and the psychological wear and tear on them (something you've been saying to me) – and use everything you've got to beat this rap. Just as you did during the strike.

Then I really started to use my head.

I'm thinking we have to fight them tooth and nail, not yield an inch. Manny was trying too hard to be a nice guy with Kaufman and his henchmen at the trial. And it won't work. I learned that a long time ago with the bosses at National. People like that? They love nice guys. They eat them for breakfast. Though I love the guy – like a father he's been to me – still I think we have to bring in another lawyer – or two. People with experience in such cases.

'Manny,' I asked him straight-out yesterday, 'why'd you take so much crap from Kaufman and Saypol?'

'You wanna know the truth?'

'What else is there time for?'

'Because I could tell the bastards had their hearts set on a death sentence. Right from Day One. And I was willing to do anything, take anything from them – whatever I had to do – to avert that.'

'You didn't tell us that.' What can I say to such a man?

'What was there to tell you? Would it have helped if I did?'

'Honestly speaking, Manny?' I look him straight in the eye. 'No, it wouldn't have.'

'So.' He spreads his hands helplessly. 'You were right, of course. I should never have asked the court to impound David's sketches. Made them sound super important. I lost the case for you right there, you knew that at the time, I could see it from your expression, you were biting your lips not to say something.'

He sits quiet for a few minutes. But not me, I got *schpilkes* in my whole body like someone injected Mexican jumping beans in my nervous system.

'Ettie, I never told you how alone I felt ... the whole time ... before the trial, during the trial ... after ... none of the scientists who knew anything about the bomb, who could have advised me, would come near me ... everyone's so afraid for his own skin ... I even tried writing to some of the big ones in Europe ... Bohr, Meitner ... no one answered. No other lawyers to talk it over with, only my father ... just the two of us ... Recently I talked with one of the big scientists, I can't even tell you his name, he made me promise ... anyhow, he's been wising me up ... that the government's perpetrating a fake on us and the public. He says there's nothing David could have known that would amount to the "secret of the atom bomb" ... and yet I still can't get any of them to testify to that. He explained to me, that once we dropped the bomb, every scientist in the world working in the field knew it was now possible to solve that problem – and if there was any "secret" – we gave it away ourselves when we dropped the bomb on Japan. Go to the *Smyth Report*, this guy tells me, use it, it's all in there – the government's given away for free a lot more information on the bomb than David ever could have known and it was published shortly after the war. If the Russians wanted information, it's right in there ... There's a lot I've messed up on, Ethel, I'm sorry ... '

273

I'm thinking how lonely it's been for him ... and all the time he's been trying, in his own way, to protect us from knowing the worst. Not possible, Manny, I'm thinking, it never is ... just like we can't protect our kids no matter how hard we try. The world will still treat them as the Rosenberg sons. So will they have to pay the price, too? God, I don't want that to happen. Bad enough us. The only way we can help them is to give them pride in us, in who they are, not shame.

'The situation is changing though, isn't it? I mean, here are people like Einstein and Urey – and even the Pope – who are appealing to Eisenhower for clemency. Even if he won't listen. And Julie tells me he heard on the radio that thousands of letters are pouring into the White House ... ministers, rabbis, people from all over the world ... wouldn't it be possible now to get a lawyer who specializes in these cases?'

He hesitates, then says, 'Well, there's a man by the name of John Finerty, I think, who helped Tom Mooney ... I could try ... also there's a law professor at the University of Chicago, Malcolm Sharp, who wrote to me recently. He's interested ... '

'Let's do it, Manny. Get in touch with them right away.'

I'm like a different person when I go back to my cell. There's hope.

FEBRUARY 17, 1953

The US Court of Appeals stays the executions so the Supreme Court can consider a new petition for review.

FIFTY-ONE

MARCH–APRIL 1953

Today Ma sent a delegation of one to do her dirty work. Bernie, my dearly beloved brother, shows up with a present for me, a box of stationery from Woolworth's. The funny thing is he looks so much like Pa – with the same straw hair that's faded into grey, but without Pa's smile and gentle eyes. And seeing him makes me sad. I miss Pa. Five years he's gone. I know he would have stood behind me, even if he wouldn't have openly opposed Ma. I guess he didn't have enough strength for that, but still he always managed to let me know he understood and was behind me, and *not* behind *her*. I think a lot about him these days. *I miss you, Pa.*

And what's dear Bernie supposed to tell me? He's been coached by her, I can tell, and he's not a very good actor; he hems and haws like he's trying to remember his lines.

'Listen, Ethel,' he says, 'you're coming down to the finish line, so you better do something quick. Don't forget – June 18th!' Our fourteenth anniversary. As if I *could*! 'Why won't you tell the government what you know? Ma said to tell you, "Why won't you listen to us, your family? Who else cares as much about what happens to you. You think, *his* family?"'

My heart's on fire! 'So you're at it again! My loving devoted family, interested only in what's good for me, right?'

I must be screaming, though it doesn't seem that way to me, because Bernie starts shushing me and trying to out talk me.

'You want,' he says, 'they should make me leave? That's what you want? Then why don't you stop yelling?'

'Why don't you stop getting me so upset?'

'Who's trying to upset you? Such foolishness. We're only begging you to save your own life. Forget about Julie. He

277

wants to die in the electric chair? That's his business! So let him. Who says you have to walk that last mile with him, too. Him? Or the Party?'

That's all he has to say. 'Goddamit! That's one thing none of you is even willing to try to understand. Julie and I are telling the truth, and we're not lying, and we're not following Party orders. Can't you understand that! Once and for all?'

'But how about your children? Can't you give one thought to them? Do you remember how when Ma came to see you that first time, she asked you what to tell Michael, how that poor kid keeps asking her, "Grandma, when is my mother coming home?" Not once, mind you, but over and over again. And you said to her, "Tell him I'll be home in two years." Yes, that's what you told her to tell him, don't say different. And Ma's never repeated to you what Michael said when she gave him your answer, because she didn't want to hurt your feelings. But as soon as he heard those words, "in two years", he started to cry and carry on. You know how Michael gets and you know what he said? "I hope she dies because of the harm she's causing me." Those are your son's very words. So God help me! That's what you want? He should be hurt because of you? Left an orphan, him and Robby – mind you, not because you're hit by a car, die from double pneumonia. No, because you're more loyal to the Commies, those friends of yours, than to your own children. Dovey's smart, he knew enough to look out for himself and his family.

'Tell me, so what are *they* doing for you now that you're in here? They're raising money, getting you the best lawyers? No. Two years already here you sit, and here you'll die if you don't think of yourself and your children first. But still they mean more to you than your own kids!'

'Get out of here! Get him out of here!' I'm roaring.

I'm still shaking.

FIFTY-TWO

APRIL 1953

The minute Celia walks in with a box of Whitman's candy, I know she's changed, big changes, but not until we've talked for a little while, can I pin them down.

In appearance, she's still a tall handsome woman in a black suit with a long skirt and a lace-trimmed white blouse that's less severe than she used to wear. But it's eight to ten years since we've seen each other – somehow we lost touch after Michael was born and I was all taken up with him – and for a woman, that's a long time. So I'm prepared for some change – how the little corners of her square jaw sag so that her face is even squarer, the skin with larger pores, a few more blemishes, and that beautiful brownish-gold hair bleached into a shade only she and her hairdresser could describe. Also her figure's heavier, less graceful, the dancer's calves more like a working woman's who's been standing on her feet all day.

Why her appearance matters so much to me, I can't tell you, except that she was the first woman I admired in all ways, someone I wished I was like – and part of me still wants to believe that certain people don't change. My life may have changed irreversibly, but someone else has found the right answers. Right answers for me involve not having to accept changes for the worse. Outwitting life, I'm beginning to think. Has anyone really done that?

Maybe it's her manner, that she no longer acts like she's Somebody, and expects to be treated that way.

When she tells me, 'You're looking well,' and hesitates, I'm embarrassed. I know it's not true and that the Celia of the old days wouldn't have said it. First off, she'd have demanded, 'What are the bastards doing to you?' and next,

'And what are you doing about it?' I want her to get angry, feel that furious energy she used to have. Face it, I tell myself, we've both changed, after all, I was a wide-eyed kid in those days believing whatever I was told, especially by people I admired.

To forestall a lot of questions, I ask about her.

She answers with a question. 'Do you remember Murray?'

'Oh sure.' His name brings back such good memories, even if those were difficult times. 'How is he? What a swell guy!'

'That's the guy I married.'

'Murray!' I simply can't believe it.

'You sound surprised.'

'I guess I am ... wasn't he married?' I hesitate to ask, but still ...

'Yeah sure – but you know how these things are, people outgrow their marriages.'

'How long are you married?'

'Officially eight years, but actually we've been together much longer, you musta known that.' You can see she's honestly surprised that I didn't know they were lovers back then.

Little Miss Naïveté, that's me.

'So what are you doing in South Carolina? I know the Garment Workers have organized shops down there ... '

'No, Murray's not with them any more.' She's playing with her leather gloves, straightening each finger carefully, first the right hand, then the left.

I don't know what to say, it's clear my questions are making her uncomfortable. But something in me has to know. 'So what's he doing?'

It's like pulling teeth. 'Well, he's personnel director for a large textile company in Spartansburg.'

'And you?'

'I work for them, too, in the office ... in charge of production records and piece rates.' She nods several times along with a funny wiggle of her lips and looks me in the eye, *so now you know it all*.

'After the divorce,' she goes on, 'Murray had to earn more money, his wife took him to the cleaners for child support. Bitch! She could've gone to work like the rest of us. Not that one!'

'Do you have a union in the shop?' I can't resist asking.

'No – but the Textile Workers are calling for an NLRB election,' she answers in a level voice, 'and they'll probably get it.'

'And Fannie?'

'She married some *schnook* she put through dental school, and then he walked out on her for another woman, just like that. The story of her life. And you?' she asks. 'Are they kind to you here?'

Obviously we're running out of conversation. 'What can I tell you, Celia, that you can't imagine for yourself? In the daytime, I struggle to be hopeful, nights I give in. Julie's doing okay, and somehow we're still in there fighting, and there are others out there now ... you know, there's been a committee set up?'

'Yes, I gave.' She brushes aside my thanks. 'Has the Party helped you?'

'No.' Answering that one honestly hurts, I realize it for the first time.

'Bastards! I hear the same about the Smith Act defendants. The men sit in jail and their wives get no support either. First you use people, then you throw them away.'

'You sound bitter.'

'Yes, I am – none of them will speak to me any more. Can you believe that?'

'Sure.'

'But it's no good this way either, believe me,' she says. Her voice is like a piano that's gone out of tune. She sits there, a bigger woman, yet somehow blurrier, lost in her own thoughts. I realize what's changed – the lustre of belief in the

281

future, and therefore in herself, is gone.

I'm wondering why she came when she reaches into her purse and pulls out a white index card with some words typed on it. 'Here, I brought you something. I remembered a long time ago, maybe the last time I saw you, you asked me to make a copy of this for you – and I forgot to do it.' She hands it to me quickly, gets up and leaves with just a jerky backward wave of her hand.

The words Albert Camus wrote:

> It is now nine years that men of my generation have had Spain within their hearts. Nine years that they have carried it with them like an evil wound. It was in Spain that men learned that one can be right and yet be beaten, that force can vanquish spirit, that there are times when courage is not its recompense. It is this, doubtless, which explains why so many men, the world over, feel the Spanish drama as a personal tragedy.

Reading it, I recall just when it was she showed it to me – right after Julie got fired from his government job.

Back here now in my cell, pondering her visit, the distance she came, I'm thinking, sorrowfully, *Celia, it's not up to me. Can you forgive yourself?*

April 19, 1953

Today a new addition to my list of SILENCES. This one ...

5   Silent Betrayals ... Worst of all, I've decided, is to betray oneself.

MAY 25, 1953

The Supreme Court again refuses *certiorari*, Justices Hugo
Black and William Douglas dissenting.

MAY 29

Judge Kaufman sets a new execution date for the week of
June 15.

FIFTY-THREE

MAY 1953

Poverty fades people, I'm thinking today. Look at Ma – the dragon's getting toothless. Since she was last here, three front teeth gone, two uppers and a lower.

'It's been two years, Ma, hasn't it? And for me, lots of time in between to think.'

Immediately she reacts like I'm swinging at her with a baseball bat. 'Why ya talkin' to me like that? It's right there, the poison in your voice.'

So I relent. 'Thanks for the sponge cake ... looks great ... I can't wait ... ' What's the use! But I catch myself, you're at it again, out to please her.

So before she can start in on me, I look her straight in the eye. 'I want to ask you something. I'm not going to change my mind, so don't get your hopes up, and don't ask me to – it's just that I have to know, so for once be honest with me, don't try to gloss over it like it isn't there between us. I'm past all that now. What I need is to see a clear light and to know it's a clear light I'm seeing, and that my eyes are telling me the truth. So I'm asking you, *Why do you want me to back up David's story?* You know he's a liar, we both know it like we both know today is Tuesday. For him, it's always been easier to lie than to tell the truth. And I never, you know that, too, neither Julie nor me, it just doesn't come to us naturally. To him, it does, the minute he gets frightened or makes a mistake.

'Do you know what Manny told me? That when Julie and David were in jail already – before I was arrested? – that though they kept them on separate floors purposely, one day on the stairs, David passes him going down as Julie's going up, and he snarls at Julie, "Listen you s.o.b., I told you I'd get you, but one thing I want you to know, I'll never get Ethel mixed up in this. I told them that she never had a hand in this and that's a fact! And I'm gonna stick by my guns on this ... no matter what, but as for you ... "'

'That boy don't know what he's saying ... they got him so *verdreht*, so mixed up with all that questioning ... '

'Yeah, Ma, he was so confused that he told the truth at first. Only later he remembered to lie, right?

'Remember when he was maybe six or seven, you said to me once, "What is it with him – you ask that boy a simple question – Where were you? Did you do your homework – and you get a bunch of lies." Remember? You were very upset with him. And don't brush it away with your hand like it never happened.

'*Don't do that – it's too late for that!* That's what you'd like to do, I know, pretend that things you don't want to be, never happened, right? But they did, dammit! And I'm paying the price! So tell me now – why do you keep insisting we should lie along with him and that *verbissene kaatz*, Ruth?'

She sits there opening and closing the clasp of her pocketbook like it's the most important thing in her life, and the corners of her eyes fill up. Typical!

And then the age-old cry. 'Why do you want to keep torturing me?'

'Stop it, Ma, this minute!' I'm shaking like the motor inside me is rocking the whole damn prison. 'Me torturing you? Who's gonna die, me or you? Don't give me that, you've been doing that to me all my life – *What I'm doing to you!* Where do you get off with that!'

I'm doing it to her! How dya like that! For the first time I really understand what's gone on all my life. I want to hit her, even my fingers are agitated, and she must see it because her face goes white like white crêpe paper left hanging in the rain.

'I'm leavin' – you talk to me that way.' And she starts to get up.

'You walk out, Ma – and I'll curse you every step of the way to the electric chair.' My voice sounds dangerous even to me. 'I'll sit down in that chair and every second there's still life in me I'll curse you and God'll be on my side, you'll see.'

Someone else has taken over my body and I've got no control over what's coming out. She sits down like a policeman ordered.

'*Veyez mir, veyez mir,*' she moans, rocking back and forth clawing at her cheek with those broken fingernails. A drop of blood stains her blouse and spreads. Her eyes, the whites yellowed and bloodshot, fix on the stain and a shudder goes through her. Then like a gypsy reading tea leaves, very solemnly she prophesies, 'The blood of this family will be on your hands.'

She's just trying to frighten me, I quiet myself, but no, there's that wild look of tragedy in her eyes. I saw it once before when Julie and I went to see *Medea* with Judith Anderson, and I'll never forget that look. Within me there's a gush of sorrow, but I remind myself, stay in your skin, don't climb into hers.

'Stop it! And stop with that goddam pocketbook!'

The rocking and moaning stop. Her hands she ties down by interlacing her fingers in her lap tight as can be.

This is a scene I never could've imagined, even in my wildest dreams. We're in a Greek play and the immensity of what's involved here sounds in me like a gong. Each word is moving us towards something I hadn't anticipated, and I don't know where it'll end, but everything else is silenced by the piling up of words towards some deep profound truth, hidden, maybe, from both of us.

Her fingers, like worms trapped under a rock, keep wiggling. Finally, in a beaten voice, a voice I heard only once before, many years ago, in my room after that big fight she had with Sam when she whimpered, "Stay with me, Etteleh," and clung to my hand, and hers was like ice, finally she speaks. 'What do you want me to say?'

Her question hangs between us. I won't look at her face. I don't want to see that face. I don't dare. Not this time. A pump inside me keeps the adrenaline going.

'*Why do you want me to lie?*' I put it to her straight.

'*What do you want me to say?*' she repeats.

'Just answer what I asked you. Why do you want me to lie when you know and I know that *he's the liar*, not me? You know in your heart that I'm telling the truth! You know I never did anything wrong and I don't deserve to die.'

The hands of the clock on the wall jerk forward. We both look up, startled by the sharp tock. *She'll have to live with her own pain for a long time, I'm thinking. I won't.*

Now that I've started, I have to keep going. 'You keep telling me I'm a mother, that I should live for my kids ... Oh how can you be this way?' Everywhere I see circles revolving around us, in her face, the face of the clock, and in me the same spinning motion. If only I could smash my fist into that big round familiar face that I long to trust and that's always withheld the one thing I wanted from her, keep punching that big soft mother's body that's never held me close ... 'and all the time you know it's David and his lies against us that are keeping me from my sons. *How can you be this way?* You're their grandmother! Don't you have any feeling for them yourself? What kind of a grandmother are you?' This voice of mine, when has it ever spoken with such honest strength? I feel the power generating in me, unleashing my tongue. 'Why don't you go to David and tell *him* to tell the truth. Tell him what he is – a sell-out! A fink! A dirty coward! No brother of mine! Order him! "For once tell the truth and nothing but the truth!" Then we'll all be saved.'

'Do you know what you're doing? You're tearing out my *neshomeh! Rebeynu shel oylem!*'

And she gives a good performance tearing at her blouse as though I had plunged a dagger deep in her breast, baring those breasts that I remember from long ago, full of milk and life. Exposed they hang empty like stretched-out doughy

288

pancakes under the greying peach-coloured bra she forgot to hook up.

The clock can't match the racing of my heart. Minus those front teeth, the mouth bent and bitter, the shoulders hopeless, suddenly she's an old woman in front of my eyes – like all those forgotten old women on the East Side I never wanted to end up being – *schlepping* along with the shopping bags filled with a bunch of nothings from the pushcarts and alleys, even garbage cans – used up by life, a life over which they had no say. Even the black tufts that used to sprout from her jaw are now a few lonely white hairs stiff like her. The anger drains out of me.

What's the use, let it go, you'll never change her.

She adjusts her bridge which never fit right and mumbles on, 'I'm only trying to do what's best for everyone. Why are you so stubborn? You know, if Dovey talks like you, you'll all die. So you'll be innocent, but dead. That's what you want? This way you'll live. That's the way I see it.'

The arthritis in her fingers is worse, how hard it is for her to button up her blouse. But her voice is Mama back in the old days. 'Believe me, Ettie, I know these *goyim* like I know my own face.'

'We're not dealing with *goyim*!' Can she fire me up! In one second flat. 'We're dealing with a Jewish *momser*, Judge Irving Kaufman and his Jewish henchmen, Saypol and Cohn. *Goyim* they are? Since when?

'And where was that great Jewish liberal, Judge Felix Frankfurter, when the Supreme Court turned us down? Only one judge, Justice Black, a Southerner, a former member of the Ku Klux Klan and *a goy*, voted for us!'

'Listen, they understand and you don't,' she says. 'America, Schmerica – forget it! – the *goyim* are still running this country – just like in Hitler's Germany and in Russia with the pogroms. They still hate us – and there's only one way for Jews to live – *you got to learn how to live with them!* Did you ever hear that *shiker* janitor next door what comes out of his mouth when he's drunk? That's the way it's always been and that's the way it's always gonna be!'

'Ma, listen to me. When are the Jews ever gonna have the freedom to tell the truth – like us – if they keep giving in? Acting like they didn't deserve better? Like they have it coming to them? Did it help the Jews in Germany? Did it keep Hitler from burning six million of them – even those who had themselves baptized – in those concentration camp ovens? This I'm making up? Why did you come to this country if in some way it wasn't going to be better?'

'Because it *is* better. We live better here, believe me, I know, as long as we play by the rules. And they make the rules, believe me.'

Okay Ma, I'm thinking, *you really believe all that. I'm finally convinced.* 'Let's let it go.' I'm making her an offer. 'But you still haven't answered my real question. You're avoiding. Don't get off on a sidetrack. Why have you always favoured David? And Sam and Bernie? Because they're boys? But, most of all, him. Given him his way. Always. That's what we're really talking about, whatever he wanted – toys, money for the movies, whatever he asked for, he got – and me, you got mad if I asked for the slightest thing. A nickel and I'd get an argument. For me, you never had time. Why, Ma?' I'm pleading with her, and at the same time, there's a fire raging in me out of control. 'Once and for all, tell me the truth – and don't drag in the Nazis.'

Her face is touched with maggots. Perhaps it's the cold blue light overhead. 'All right, you wanna know – so I'll tell you.'

Waiting, the same cold buries itself in my fingertips.

'Because you're strong, you always were, even as a little girl, smart and capable, with a head on your shoulders. Like me. Fourteen when I came here by myself with a sign pinned on my coat, NEW YORK ... ' I wait ... she drifts off ... and comes back. 'And that one ... no.' I almost can't hear that last no. Now she's talking. I can tell the difference right away,

290

now we're two women talking about the pain that comes with one's children. What you dream for them – and what happens for real. Even with Michael I felt it already when the social worker said he had serious problems, that I'd been too permissive.

'You saw yourself how Dovey was – from little on, it was in him different than you or Bernie – everything was harder for him right from the start – and I knew then, I swear on my mother's grave – may she rest in peace – that for the rest of my life, I'd have to be by his side to protect him – and you see ... I was right. Something inside told me that, I swear to God, right back then.'

'I don't believe that.' I'm so furious I don't want to be swayed by her pain. 'So I'm to pay the price for David? That's fair? That's what you want?' I'm having a hard time breathing. 'How can you choose between us? *I couldn't!* Between Michael and Robby? *Never!*' I want to die. An ocean of pain is swallowing me up alive.

'That's why you must change your story. And live! ... Talk to Julie ... He'll listen to you,' she's beseeching me. 'They told me so themselves ... '

'What d'ya mean *They? You ... talked ... to the FBI?*'

That's when her fingers part, slide out of each other's grasp and turn blue-white.

'Molly!' I let out a yell they must've heard in Kalamazoo.

'What's the matter, Ethel?' She comes running from the other side of the room where she's been sitting and crocheting.

'I'm through here.' I can barely whisper. 'Take me back.' Gently she leads me by the elbow.

Every cell in my body is exploding.

I never look back.

FIFTY-FOUR

JUNE 1953

I'm in that icy region of fear. Like a spinal block working on me. That huge freezer in the old Breyer's ice-cream plant that Julie and I, in our innocence, walked into on a boiling summer's day, I dressed in thin cotton, Julie in shorts, and all those enormous cartons, boxes, round, square and oblong, stuffed with ice-cream, the frozen air misting everything, crystals of ice like dainty piping on the edges. 'Julie,' I cried out, 'let's get out of here.'

Only the hot shower brings me alive – and the thought of what's ahead today sends me to the shower. I know their emissary will try to buy me off. What will I do?

I want Julie. 'Hold me. Hold me and let me hold you,' I cry out.

I want to be held and cuddled and stroked like a baby, but there's no one here to do it. Hold me, hold me, I'm screaming inside, but no one hears me. If I were to yell, Anna Marie, the German *hausfrau* who's on duty, would come, but her hands smell like my mother's – of Lysol and oily rags and strong brown laundry soap – and my mother's hands never comforted me or even tried to do so. I remember the slap on my behind, never her hand around my shoulder even when I was little.

I'm weak with fear and with the pain that won't stop.

Yet I know that what I'm struggling with is to have the courage of my convictions. Please give me the strength not to submit, sustain me, oh God, please sustain me.

Help me to walk out of there with my shoulders thrown back!

This James V. Bennett, Director of the Bureau of Prisons, he looks like a kindly grandfather – a *goyische* one, though, not like our *Zayde* Barnett. Or a thin Santa Claus, if there is such a thing. He's just pulling out his gold pocket watch when Anna Marie brings me in. I check my own watch and it's just noon. We're left alone. That's unusual. For him it's just a business trip and probably he wants to get back home in time for dinner – maybe a drink or two before – to relax him after such a strenuous day.

'Here, put your feet up,' says his wife placing a hassock under his legs. She's already mixed the martinis – ice cold and waiting in the refrigerator.

'What a day!' He makes a face, loosens his dark foulard tie, opens the top button of his shirt and settles back with a sigh in his favourite leather chair. 'The Hudson River had this strong fishy smell today,' he says, 'the smell is still in my nostrils.' And he swallows as though fighting back nausea. After a few minutes, he picks up the iced martini, eyes the play of colour as the thick liquid sways in the expensive crystal and takes a sip. 'Just right!' he compliments her and sighs again, this time more contentedly.

She moves quietly around the room, straightening a rose in a silver bud vase, checking the cigarette box, plumping a pillow. They've been together now for so long – thirty-eight years – that they know each other's habits better than their own. She knows he'll unwind gradually and tell her about the day. He hadn't said much before, though he tossed restlessly all night, mumbling something about Sing Sing, and was out the door first thing this morning.

'I'll never understand these Jews!' he suddenly explodes. 'You offer them their lives – and that's not good enough for them. What the hell do they want? A full pardon? An apology from Eisenhower?'

Sympathetically, she murmurs, his good dutiful wife, 'Tell me what happened. You're upset!'

'Goddam right I am!' He downs the martini and signals for another.

She obliges.

He picks up the glass and begins speaking. 'I thought, too, there was a chance ... otherwise, Brownell would never have sent me. Julius, when I talked with him today, before I saw her – I could understand, his refusal to change his story – a man has his principles, and right or wrong, he has to stand by them. But Ethel – a mother with two small kids? – that we never expected, her obstinacy! I tell you she's worse than he is, that one, absolutely insisting on their innocence, refusing to consider the chance to live. You'd think she'd grab at it!

' "Listen," I said to her, "just hear me out. If you'll cooperate with us."

'But it's difficult just getting her to sit still in that chair while I tell her about our offer. Every time I say, "Just cooperate with us ... consider it, at least," she interrupts me, "Mr Bennett, if you think for a minute ... " and stands up to leave.

'"Just be quiet and listen!" I finally shouted and she sank down in her chair watching me out of those sharp brown eyes like I'm trying to put something over on her.

'"All I'm proposing is that you just go over the case with someone who's very familiar with all the details – maybe you'll remember something you've forgotten."

'"Yeah," she interrupts, "just like you coached David and Harry Gold when you put them together on the same floor? You know, of course, Mr Bennett, that David lied. Out and out lied. And Ruth backed him up – to save her skin, and his.

'"And I've finally figured it out, Mr Bennett – what happened, what I think – David was mixed up in some way, maybe stealing and selling stuff – I'm not sure, all I know is he had more money than usual when he came home on furlough in September – bought Ma a new expensive radio – I don't know where that money came from. But he had it."

'"That's not the point, what we're discussing, what I'm asking you to do," I reply trying to stay with the strategy we'd worked out. "After all, people's memories play tricks on them."

'"Not mine, not about something that makes the difference between life and death! C'mon now, Mr Bennett!" The look she gives me I'll never forget.

'There's something about that woman I've never seen before ... in all the years I've worked in the prison system ... ' he shakes his head, 'I don't understand it ... a resistance to reason, just being sensible about the whole thing ... you'd think a mother with two kids! ... that are being tossed around all over the place, what is it with her? ... as though she's wearing an armour plate in her brain.

'"If you'd only agree to cooperate, something could be worked out," I repeat.

'"How about a new trial?" she answers. "Let us live so we can prove our innocence."

'"That's impossible, but if you cooperate ... "

'"No deal," she says. "That's for Hitler's Germany, not here in America."

'We keep going in circles like this. There's no budging her.

'"Mr Bennett," she says, "my husband and I are who we are ... Our strength comes from that ... something you can't understand, but we do. To dishonour ourselves and to go on living would be impossible for us. What's more, for me to make a separate deal with you, as you're suggesting, is absolutely unthinkable. For me to live on knowing my life cost me my husband's life. We're both innocent and either we'll live together or die together.

'"And if that's all you've come to discuss with me – then I'm ready to go back to my cell." '

He shakes his head in disbelief. 'And she motions to me with her head, get the matron. The woman who is waiting outside down the corridor comes in and tries to take her by the elbow, she shakes her off, and the two of them walk out. You could never tell, watching them leave, that both of them aren't free to leave the prison when the daytime shift is over.'

He shakes his head again and sighs. 'Never saw anything like it ... I'll never understand these people. What is it about them?' he asks his wife plaintively.

'Maybe the ability to endure pain and grief … comes down to them through the genes … so many centuries … ' says his wife, and empties the pitcher into his glass.

Walking back with Anna Marie, I hear Ma speaking. 'Listen to me,' she's saying, 'you are going to die in here. You'll burn in the electric chair, Ettie, unless you tell them, "You're right, whatever you say I did, I did. David is telling the truth." Lie, anything,' she demands of me, '*rebeynu shel oylem*, but live for your children.'

It was tempting. I won't deny it. There we are, just the two of us. That, in itself, is most unusual. And Bennett's like a silver-tongued adder – coaxing me to take one bite of the apple. The poisoned apple? Or am I mixing up Snow White and the Garden of Eden. A 'nice' man, he makes it all sound so easy. 'Cooperate,' he urges me – a pleasant word that conceals the dagger they've hidden inside.

And I think of Ruth Greenglass – who's out there with her kids, while I'm in here, and she's managing somehow with my mother's help (another dagger, this one in my heart) to get along while David is in prison. He'll be out in a few years – and it'll be over – and they'll be together again. A family united.

Like I want ours to be – more than anything – and that could be me, out there, waiting for Julie to get out.

Two words from me. That's all it would take. I'll talk. So what would I say. The truth is …

But you see, the truth is … you don't want the truth … you'd twist it around and use it against me … because the truth won't satisfy you. You want me to lie. A simple request. Is it worth my life?

What you really want, Mr Bennett, is I should say anything you want me to – and that I can't do. Because when I look at you, Mr Bennett – I see my old bosses, and the policeman who clobbered me, the Pinkerton thug who fixed Lobelia's head for life ... all the bad guys I've ever known.

And I think of the good people in my life – in and out of the Party – who fought hard for the decent things in life, and I know in my heart, I belong with them. These are my people.

So you see, the only question that really matters is – could I live with myself? And the answer is no.

And could we live with each other? Could we live with each other knowing we'd bought our lives too dearly?

The shame we'd feel, always, the self-hatred reflected and magnified in the other's eyes each time we looked at each other.

Our home would be a home with a silver vase on the table holding the ashes of the two people we once were.

Is this a way in which to raise two young children?

Anna Marie unlocks the steel door. Slowly I walk inside. I hear the fierce metallic clang behind me. I'm looking straight at Michael and Robby, their dear photos pinned up near my cot, and I answer her, 'I can't do it, Ma ... not now any more ... not here in America. That's how it is ... ' I'm crying and saying farewell to something buried deep inside me.

FIFTY-FIVE

JUNE 1953

Later, I'm still seething, and yet her voice won't leave me alone.

Ma, I'm answering, I don't have to listen to you any more. I'll do what I have to do. What *are* my choices? To lie as the whole bunch of you are trying to coerce me into doing, with a knife at my throat, just repeat David's story, maybe throw in a few names, dead or alive?

Or stick to the truth?

Believe it or not, there's even a time before the trial, when I consider trying to tell in court exactly what happened. Manny says I'm crazy. That he's told Julie the same thing and Julie agrees. And Julie and I have never had the opportunity to talk it over alone, privately, I mean, because we knew our conversations were being monitored and taped. But I'm thinking about it myself ...

How we talked and how innocent it all was ... suppose I were to tell about those furloughs, how David bragged and boasted and carried on – hinting, hinting at such important things he personally was involved in, egging us on so we'd ask more questions – and the names he drops, names I don't know, but Julie recognizes, so, of course, we're curious. Who wouldn't be! Everyone wants to be let in on secrets, gives them a feeling of importance. Even with gossip, you're dying to know the inside story. Look at someone like Walter Winchell. Or Leonard Lyons. What are their careers built on? You think we're any different? Or that you would have done differently? Especially when it involved the Soviet Union. Sure we had a special feeling for the Soviets. We believed in socialism and that it could work. And was there anything during the war that would make us feel otherwise?

But that doesn't make us spies – or traitors, Mr Saypol, I wanted to say.

Remember in 1945, the Nazis were our common enemy, not the Russians. Right there you're already turning history around. Think back to Yalta, and that photo of the three of them – Roosevelt with the black cape, Stalin in uniform smiling, and Churchill with the big cigar. So what's the big deal if I said, and that's all I said, 'I wonder if the Russians know about this?' and Julie says, 'I hope so. They should.'

But see now what you'd do with that, Mr Saypol. If you can slyly change 'might tend to incriminate me' to 'would incriminate me', then you'd change 'should share' with the Russians to 'must share' until the jury is hypnotized into believing that 'should' equals 'must' equals 'must give' – and, of course, then it follows that a Communist not only would think that way, but behave that way, too. And with one wave of your magic wand, you've got us giving information to the Russians – as though the thought is equal to the action. Let me ask you, Mr Saypol, have you ever considered adultery? Aha, you're blushing! Does that make you guilty of it? You do understand what I'm getting at, don't you? And so with that one magical leap, you've cleared the path to our conviction of roadblocks, boulders, any reminders that once this was not a connecting road, but just a blueprint in your mind – for how to brand us TRAITORS!

Back then in 1945, our own government offered to share the information with them, did you know that? And again in 1946, Bernard Baruch gets up before the UN with such a proposal. So even our government saw the wisdom of it, provided, of course, it could be under international control. I had so much hope then, that it could be worked out. And I'll tell you something else, it bothered me, bothered me plenty that the Russians didn't go along with that offer to try to work out a compromise. A big mistake. But as time passes, I'm so busy with our own problems that I really don't discuss it with any of our friends who've been in the Party. People are drifting apart – and part of it, in a subtle way, is happening because of the changing mood in America. Much as you fight it, it still exerts a silent clamp on what you say to each other. First, Julie gets fired, then Truman starts the loyalty oath business in 1947, and the House Un-American Activities Committee goes after so many decent people in Hollywood and entertainment, including my old classmate, Zero Mostel. This whole Cold War mentality affects all of us, even if we've never been in the Party. People are changing, even some who've been Communists are becoming very anti-Communist. You'd think twice before saying something – am I talking to someone who's sympathetic? – or is it someone who'll run and tattle? Look what's happening right now with McCarthy?

Suppose I told them, we talked, yes, we talked – up in the air, just suppose the Russians had this bomb, and that it was the furthest thing from my mind to do anything about it. *That's how we talked* – and then we dropped it. Period. Period, I tell you.

Daydreaming ... of a better world ... and not the way we're headed ... war in Korea ... building the hydrogen bomb ... the Communist witchhunt ...

And from that one conversation with no serious thought or intention behind it, David made up that whole story about us – with the help of the FBI. And lots of rehearsing with Harry Gold. With the Jello box and all.

Watching Saypol in action, I know it's no use. It'll only make it worse for us. He'll twist and turn what I say to their advantage, making it sound like proof of our guilt. 'Aha! So you admit you talked about it, that David drew a sketch for you!' That's all I have to say! 'Now tell us the rest, *tell us*!' Like the night I came in from Loew's Amateur Night. This time I won't be made to feel guilty. I'm not guilty, and I know it like I know my own name. And I will not let them force those words from my lips. I am innocent.

The truth didn't stand a chance in that courtroom. That's

not the reason we're there – or that Kaufman sentences us to die – after a long speech about how many casualties we're responsible for in Korea – over 50,000 – 'And millions more,' he says, 'may pay the price of your treason.'

Treason? Let me stop you there. *But we haven't been convicted of treason, Judge Kaufman*, let's keep things straight for the record. The jury found us guilty of conspiracy, a much less serious charge, so how come you're conveniently switching words around again. You and Saypol. To justify the death sentence? Because we're the first Americans ever to be sentenced to death in peacetime for conspiracy!

I suppose the dreamer in me believed that the man with the nice face, the one from the Transport Workers' Union, would go home and talk it over with his wife. And she'd say, 'Don't do it.' So we'd live.

But it didn't happen that way.

FIFTY-SIX

JUNE 1953

'Julie,' I said to him today, 'do you remember that day in court after Kaufman pronounced sentence?'

He nods. But his eyes drop. Doesn't he want me to see the pain?

'And afterwards they took us both downstairs to the bullpen? Marty Sobell, too. Poor guy! Thirty years he got. And before I could say another word to you, the matron takes me away and locks me up. And I see they've taken you way down to the other end. And when she slams the door on me – I've never told you this before – it feels like you've been wrenched physically apart from my own body. I look down, slide my fingers over my hips to see if I'm bleeding, so bad is the pain. And then I think, how awful it must be for Julie, even worse than for me, because you expected they'd give you the death sentence, but you never believed they'd do it to me. You told me that!'

'Yeah,' Julie says, 'I really thought they'd spare you for the children's sake. That even Kaufman would know that's going too far.'

'But Julie, I never believed that, so in a crazy way I'm prepared. But for you! Oh God, I thought, how can he bear it! That I have to die – and then there'll be no one to take care of Michael and Robby. They're our very lives. What else is there? And I want to go to you and comfort you, say somehow it'll work out yet, you'll see. And there I am locked into that cage. If I were a gorilla, I'm thinking, I'd seize those bars and rattle them until the whole goddam building shook and the bars gave way. Oh give me the strength!'

'Was that when you started to sing?' he asks.

I nod.

'My favourite aria, "One Fine Day He Shall Return ... " '
he says, 'from my favourite opera, *Madame Butterfly* ... in
Italian yet.' And he hums a few bars. 'Do you know what that
meant to me?' And he covers his face with his hands.

'Sweetheart, you don't have to hide the tears from me. I
hoped you'd understand ... because y'know, Julie, you were
always there for me ... all the way from the first moment we
met ... on my side. I never had that before. From anyone
except maybe Tante Rosie and Pa sometimes. And for you, I
wanted to sing better than I ever had before. To sing what's in
my heart. And to say I'm with you one hundred per cent,
don't give up hope.'

'You know,' he says, 'everyone there, the prisoners, the
guards around me, they were all taken by surprise, this they
never expected. Such singing! They drank it in, and when
you finished, one of the deputy marshals came over to me
and said, "Y'know Rosenberg, you're a lowdown son-of-
a-bitch. They have you pegged upstairs. But down here,
you're the luckiest man in the world, because no man ever
had a woman who loved him that much!"

'"Thanks," I said to him, "thanks, but think of it this way,
buddy. With all the money I'm supposed to have made from
running a spy ring, I never had a cent to train that voice. Even
if they don't believe me upstairs, I never had the money to do
anything for her."'

The bitter expression on his face I hate to see, but then his
face softens. 'You know, Ethel, that very first night I heard
you sing – at that NMU benefit – it was as though you were
singing only to me ... I knew then that you were the one for
me ... for always.'

Oh, to be back there. When everything looked new and
green.

'When I finished,' I said, 'I could hear the applause ...
yours ... the others didn't matter. And it was as though you
were holding me close. And then you called out, "Ethel, sing
the other one, too."

'So I sang "Ah Dolce Notte". And then you sang to me. Remember? We really had something going, didn't we? "Irene", "The Peatbog Soldiers", "Ballad for Americans" ... and nobody even tried to stop us. Remember the last one you sang?'

'Oh sure. Such beautiful lines. "The Battle Hymn of the Republic".

'Will you sing it for me again ... now?'

He's startled. But only for a moment. Then very softly he begins,

'He hath loosed the fateful lightning of
　　His terrible swift sword,
　His truth is marching on ...'

FIFTY-SEVEN

JUNE 1953

June 7, 1953

I've been thinking about *The Valiant*. What a lot of phoney baloney! All that family loyalty! That sweet simpering sister, my role – there she is – in the Warden's office, pleading with him, sticking by him, her brother, to the end, and he, noble to the end (not so with my brother!), quotes Shakespeare, a great exit line: 'The valiant never taste of death but once.'

Not true, Mr Playwright! You had it all wrong. What's more, I've died over and over again in here, pictured that electric chair with the leather straps and wires in my mind so many, countless times and shivering all the while. But – but the one thing I could never imagine or truly believe – was that my own mother would betray me! That *is* unimaginable. Unforgivable. That's Queen Gertrude in *Hamlet*. That's Medea, preparing to murder her children. But that it should happen to Ethel Rosenberg?

June 9, 1953

I woke up crying during the night and the pain around my heart was so bad. It wasn't the dream that made me cry. It was the waking up and finding that the dream was just a dream.

In it, David and me, we're both wearing dark robes like Judge Kaufman – and we come towards each other with hands outstretched. Performers in the night. As though we no longer belonged in the daylight, only in the night. 'I'm sorry,' he says, 'I'm really sorry, Ettie, I know I shouldn't have done it. It was the wrong thing to do. And yet I couldn't help myself. It happened in spite of me.' And he sits down on some kind of embankment and starts to cry – the way a man will cry who hasn't cried in a very long time ... wrenching cries that twist his gut ... head in hands, crying, crying ...

I sit down next to him, close enough to feel his shoulders heaving, and listen. He's doing the crying for both of us. What makes me saddest of all is that I know he's telling the truth. That he couldn't help himself, that this is the man he is.

I can't console him, I just sit there listening to his crying, feeling like it's my own ...

JUNE 15, 1953

The Supreme Court refuses a stay of execution. The vote is 5 to 4, Justices Black, Douglas, Frankfurter and Jackson dissenting.

JUNE 16

Application for a stay of execution is made to Justice Douglas, based on the view that the Atomic Energy Act of 1946 should have been applied to the case.

FIFTY-EIGHT

JUNE 1953

June 16, 1953

The children have just left. I'm numb. Michael screaming, 'I'll never see you again.' I kissed them goodbye. I didn't cry.

I write these words and stop. Not because there's nothing to say, but because there's too much to say. Ever. And time is so short, so pitifully thin.

Maybe tomorrow ...

During the night, the pain welled up in me, moist, fiery red ... like some strange underwater creature bathed in cyanide.

June 17, 1953

I've been writing letters furiously these last few days – just in case – though there is this last-minute attempt to win us a new trial. It's based on a new appeal filed by two new lawyers who've entered the case and contend we were tried and convicted under the wrong law. And Justice Douglas has granted us a stay of execution until the lower courts can consider this new appeal. So there's still a fighting chance – nevertheless, I must write my letters – just in case.

June 17, 1953

'Dear Judge Kaufman,' I wrote today. I don't know if he'll ever see this letter, whether Manny will pass it along, but I had to write it.

'Ever since that horrible day in court, when you sentenced us to die, your words have been eating at the lining of my stomach like lye. "Lye." Interesting what a word will suggest. Yes, lies eat at us, our own, but also others'. And you spoke an untruth about me. Is that said delicately enough, so that I won't offend your magisterial presence?

'To be blunt, Judge Kaufman, you said – and the words are etched in lye within me – "Indeed the defendants, Julius and Ethel Rosenberg ... were conscious that they were sacrificing their own children ... their cause dominated their lives – it was even greater than their love for their children."

'Not so! Never in a million years!

'You see, you speak of a cause.

'I speak of beliefs – the very same God-given, delivered to Moses on the Mount, beliefs and human values that you and I share as Jews. The Ten Commandments. Those make it impossible for me to lie now and save my life. I love my children with all my heart, but I don't intend to try to prove it by "living" for them – as you would have me do. By lying (again that word). In time, they will come to understand, even if there are those who will want to believe otherwise.

'My memory is a strange storehouse, and in these last few weeks I seem to be able to pluck at will the words I've heard or read – and experiences – that must have, without my knowing it, shaped my beliefs, and yes, I now see it, my life. Permit me to ramble for a moment ... Some time in the late 1940s, Julie and I went to see *Joan of Lorraine* by Maxwell Anderson. It was some years after I'd had some disillusioning experiences with people – and after Julie'd been fired – and I was feeling somewhat cynical and lost. It was a Saturday matinée performance, and Ingrid Bergman played Joan – she was so beautiful up there on the stage. And in the third act, Joan is summoned to appear before her accusers, and speaking to them quietly, as much to herself as to them, she says, "But to surrender what you are, and live without belief – that's more terrible than dying – more terrible than dying young."

'It's in this voice I appeal to you, hoping that you'll hear me.

Dear Manny,

My whole life feels like it's been a bunch of lies. Promises, promises – and I believed them, bought them, lived for them, waited for them to come true. And what is true today? What *is* – is that I'm here in solitary with a death sentence hanging over my head, instead of celebrating our fourteenth wedding anniversary at home tonight with our sons and a cake.

And also that I've been 'asked' once again, this time by Mr Bennett, to join in the Ultimate Lie, that the only way those dull-witted Russians could've figured out the secret of the atom bomb – the bomb with the power to destroy the whole world – was for two little inconsequential Jews, children of immigrants fleeing from persecution, to slip it to them on the sly. Only a crazy dreamer like J. Edgar Hoover could dream up that one. What hidden power in these deceitful dark-complexioned strangers, he's saying, who tell us they want only to live peacefully among us, to join us as citizens of this great land – and all the while, their only intent is to betray us to the enemy! The anti-Christ Communists!

He's the crazy dreamer. Thank God, it's not I. Yes, I am proud to be one of the World's Great Dreamers. Yes, I dream that some day we'll all love, instead of hate, that we'll live peacefully without arms, that sons won't die on battlefields as mothers and fathers weep, that there won't be hunger and sickness and ghettoes that breed the sickness, and people will work side by side and share the fruits of their labour.

If I agree to lie, i.e. pay the price they're demanding for my life, then we'll be remembered as *those* Rosenbergs, Julius and Ethel, those dirty Jews who betrayed our country. And all the other Rosenbergs, and Cohens, and Shapiros, and Levines, and those with 'assimilated' names will be suspect, too; no, not just suspect, but *guilty* by association. Isn't that what Joe McCarthy and company are diabolically teaching this country? Benedict Arnold? Bad enough for a *goy* to be accused of treason. But a Jew!

But if I refuse until the life is burned out of me, and my tongue (not my mother's tongue) will no longer speak, then there will always be an uneasiness abroad in this land. Like Hamlet stalking the parapets of Elsinore at midnight, unable to rest. Murder will out, I say. If we are killed, the conscience of this country will never again rest easy.

PS. Just got your message late this afternoon that Chief Justice Vinson has hastily reconvened the Supreme Court in an extraordinary, unprecedented action calling them back to Washington from their vacations to act on the Douglas stay of execution. Bastard! No, make that plural. Because it's not just Vinson, but also Brownell and Kaufman and Hoover and company. I just can't believe the lengths to which they'll go to get it over with. To have us dead and buried. Are they afraid of all the large demonstrations here and abroad at the US embassies? And the direct appeals from the President of France and others in high office? What's their big hurry? How dangerous can we be? They've got the atom bomb – and the electric chair. And we? Only the truth.

JUNE 1953

June 19, 1953

It's all clear to me now, finally at this late hour. They had their script, I had mine.

Theirs: 'Confess, lie, and you'll live.'

Mine: The surprise ending, snatched from under the oncoming train at the last moment by Hairbreadth Harry. Bess stops Harry in the upstairs hall of the White House. 'Listen,' she says, 'I dreamt about the Rosenbergs last night, they're innocent.'

'Do me a favour,' says Harry. 'Take a sleeping pill tonight.'

No, not Truman any more, now it's not even Dwight or Justice Douglas or the People ... or God, the Number One Dreamer of them all.

This morning, hearing the news about the Supreme Court 6 to 3 vote to vacate the stay of execution, I no longer believe in O'Henry, in Hollywood movies and happy endings. Only my own integrity tossed in the teeth of Life, and the good people I love, so many, after all ... Julie and Michael and Robby – and Dr Singer, and Manny, and all you good people who've stuck by us and will remember us, and perhaps let that memory guide you to your own decisions – and your own destinies.

June 19, 1953

My darlings,

Always remember we love you more than life itself.

And remember us, your parents, as two people who lived through difficult times – but the times *are* always difficult – who lived honestly and courageously and lovingly – and through all these bitter hours and days and months, we never gave up hope – for ourselves and for a better world.

Love always,
Mother

June 19, 1953

Dear Dr Singer,

My *dear* Dr Singer, to whom I owe so much – this final truth you, most of all, will understand.

Perhaps with all the tears I've cried lately and my eyes continually watering, I am opening the door of my prison. The prison that has held me inside this long ... too long.

A prison from which I waited to be released – waited for the custodian to come with all the keys on a heavy metal ring – not brass, but steel – hitched to a heavy leather belt, who would say, 'Well, it's time for you to be let out, your term is up.' I've waited for all these years, but no one has come with the keys. Not my mother, not my brothers, not my father, his thoughts were elsewhere – not my husband, how could he? Not my children. How could they?

So one day recently I felt around in my pockets, in all of them, and the one closest to my heart felt the most weighed down, the heaviest, and there were all these keys, brass and steel, even a graceful handwrought iron one that fitted an old trunk we bought long ago at Goodwill.

In my frantic desire to be freed, I tried them all and none of them worked. The knob would not turn. In anger and despair I pushed on the door, and to my surprise, it swung wide open at my touch.

That totally surprised me. But it also frightened me. Terribly. That the door had never been locked. How could that be?

But it was so.

My heart was beating like a hummingbird's wings. I closed the door again, just to see, I told myself, if it could be opened again. Or was it that I would find it more reassuring to be back inside – in a comfortable familiar place?

But no more – the shadows loomed darker, more ominously. I wanted to be out of there.

I pushed on the door and again it swung open. I felt the sun on my back and it followed me as I walked out past the cell block, past the desk where the custodian usually sat. The chair was empty.

I just kept walking until I was on the outside, and there was no one around to stop me ... any more. Just sun and distant mountains, blue against the sky ...

JUNE 19, 1953

It's almost six now. But still the golden light warms the small window high above our heads. Our last moments together. I'm glad it's June. Not December or January. Then it really would be like dying.

I look into Julie's eyes – they're clear and the light that's always in them is there. Nothing's hidden. He touches the tips of his fingers to mine reaching through the wire screen, barely making it. We stand there like that, touching, yet separated, and the charge is still there between us ... like always. I never knew how much the eyes could say.

'Y'know,' he says, 'the grapevine has it that the FBI is housed someplace around Sing Sing – still hoping for a last-minute confession, that one of us will crack.'

We look at each other.

He shakes his head. 'They never give up.'

And that's that.

'The children. Will they understand?' he asks me. He's asking only to hear me say it again.

'Someday they will. I'm sure. What d'ya want most right now?' I ask him, kidding.

'A good thick corned-beef sandwich with a half-sour pickle, and potato salad. And you?'

I have to think about that. 'How about a chocolate éclair with whipped cream.'

He smiles.

'Why are you smiling?'

'Because I'm thinking about that little girl, Ettie, who used to buy one coming home from school, or was it a charlotte russe? Remember you told me?'

'Yeah – she was quite a dreamer, that kid, seven or eight, skinny legs, skinny arms, and already a great actress in her head ... like Lillian Gish ... Mary Pickford ... '

We're both silent. In my head, so many memories ... mostly the good ones, the joyous ones ... I'm choosing carefully ... opening night with *The Valiant* ... the couple of summers at Budd Lake in New Jersey with the kids ... Michael learning to swim while Julie plays lifeguard ... going to a farm nearby to see the cows milked ... their excitement. 'Ud-dah ... ud-dah' Robby kept repeating when Julie explained to him where the milk was coming from. 'Ud-dah, ud-dah, Mud-dah!' he said and clapped his hands in glee. How we all laughed at that ... how pleased he was ...

Meditatively, Julie says, 'You know what Rashi wrote? "As for the wise, their body alone perishes."'

I hear their heavy footsteps coming ... Our fingers still touch ...

Justice Hugo L. Black's dissent:

' ... this Court has never reviewed this record and has never affirmed the fairness of the trial below. Without an affirmation of the fairness of the trial by the highest court of the land there may always be questions as to whether those executions were legally and rightfully carried out.'

Justice Felix Frankfurter's dissent:

'To be writing an opinion in a case affecting two lives after the curtain has been rung down on them, has the appearance of pathetic futility. But history also has its claims. This case is an incident in the long and unending effort to develop and enforce justice according to law. The progress in that struggle surely depends on searching analysis of the past though the past cannot be recalled, as illumination for the future. For only by sturdy self-examination and self-criticism can the necessary habits for detached and wise judgement be established and fortified so as to become effective when the judicial process is again subjected to stress and strain.'

Acknowledgements

I am deeply grateful to several institutions and libraries, and numerous individuals for their generous support and assistance, as well as to those people, including Ethel's son, Michael, her psychiatrist, Dr Singer (pseudonym), and Julius's sister, who spoke with me about her, and to Professor Henry Linschitz, physicist, who worked in the Explosives Division at Los Alamos during the war. And to the many others who gave me encouragement and sustenance throughout.

To the Bunting Institute, Radcliffe, Cambridge, Mass., the Sociology Department, Brandeis University, Waltham, MA, the Fund for Open Information and Accountability, New York, NY, and the Virginia Center for Creative Arts, Sweet Briar, VA.

To the New York Public Library, Boston Public Library, Goldfarb Library, Brandeis University, Widener Library, Harvard University, and the Archives of the International Ladies Garment Workers.

To Ethel Alper, Joyce Antler, Rabbi Albert Axelrad, Beatrice Chorover, Anne Edelstein, Gordon Fellman, Ellis Freedman, Virginia Gardner, Sarah Gelb, Rose and Philip Grant, Carol Green, Maurice Greenbaum, Barbara Haber, Sonya Hess, Constance Hunting, Marian Kilson, Anita Landa, Carl Marzani, Michael Meeropol, Sonya Michel, Rob Okun, Tillie Olsen, Marshall Perlin, Tracy Paget, Shula Reinharz, Maurice Schwartz, Phyllis and Maurice Stein, Tobias and Esther Stein, Bertha Stein, Judith and Howard Vogel, Joseph Wershba and Irving Zola.

To my gifted editor, Jane Hill, and my literary agent, Shelley Power.

To my children, Deborah, Steffi, Jean, Gerson and Ben, who taught me about love.

Most of all, to my dearly beloved late husband, Alvin Nason.

Fontana Paperbacks: Fiction

Fontana is a leading paperback publisher of fiction.
Below are some recent titles.

- [ ] ULTIMATE PRIZES Susan Howarth £3.99
- [ ] THE CLONING OF JOANNA MAY Fay Weldon £3.50
- [ ] HOME RUN Gerald Seymour £3.99
- [ ] HOT TYPE Kristy Daniels £3.99
- [ ] BLACK RAIN Masuji Ibuse £3.99
- [ ] HOSTAGE TOWER John Denis £2.99
- [ ] PHOTO FINISH Ngaio Marsh £2.99

You can buy Fontana paperbacks at your local bookshop or newsagent. Or you can order them from Fontana Paperbacks, Cash Sales Department, Box 29, Douglas, Isle of Man. Please send a cheque, postal or money order (not currency) worth the purchase price plus 22p per book for postage (maximum postage required is £3.00 for orders within the UK).

NAME (Block letters)_____

ADDRESS_____

_____